D0585472

THE CERTIFICATE LIBRARY

* * *

MATHEMATICS

BOOK 2

THE CERTIFICATE LIBRARY

THIS SERIES of books has been designed to cover the various syllabuses of the Ordinary Level Examination for the General Certificate of Education. The books are equally suitable for all students who wish to improve their standards of learning in the subjects of the various volumes, and together they form an invaluable reference library.

The Editor of each book is an experienced Examiner for one or more of the various Examination Boards. The writers are all specialist teachers who have taught in the classroom the subject about which they write; many of them have also had experience as Examiners.

Each volume is comprehensive and self-contained and therefore has far more than an ordinary class textbook: each has a full treatment of the subject; numerous illustrations; questions on the chapters with answers at the end of the book; and a revision summary for each section of the book.

These summaries give the information in a concise and compact way so that examination candidates may easily revise the whole contents of the book—they can soon see how much they readily know, and how much they have forgotten and need to study again. The facts in these summaries serve, therefore, as a series of major pegs upon which the whole fabric of the book hangs.

Advice is given on answering the examination paper and there are questions of examination standard together with suggested answers.

Series Executive Editor
B. E. COPPING, B.A.HONS.

THE CERTIFICATE LIBRARY

★ ★ ★

MATHEMATICS

BOOK 2

Edited by
H. R. CHILLINGWORTH, M.Sc., Ph.D.
Principal Lecturer in Mathematics,
College of St. Mark and St. John, Chelsea.

Contributors:
G. S. BARNARD, B.Sc.
Furzedown College of Education, London.

E. W. BURN, M.A.
Formerly Senior Mathematics Master, Derby School.

P. B. CHAPMAN, M.A.
King Edward's School, Birmingham.

C. A. R. BAILEY, M.A.
Principal Lecturer in Mathematics, Newton Park College, Bath.

R. A. JEFFERY
Formerly of St Dunstan's College, Catford.

THE GROLIER SOCIETY LIMITED
LONDON

First published 1965
Reprinted 1968

© *The Grolier Society Limited, London*, 1965

*Made and printed in Great Britain by
Odhams (Watford) Ltd., Watford, Herts*

PREFACE

YOU ARE now half-way through this course and probably will know which type of examination paper you are taking. The G.C.E. O-level examinations are mainly of two kinds, known as "Syllabus A" and "Syllabus B," respectively. The former comprises separate papers in Arithmetic, Algebra and Geometry; the latter combined papers having rather less Geometry, a little more Trigonometry and some Calculus.

This book covers both types of syllabus and the Revision Summary sections, on tinted paper, indicate which aspects are applicable to "A", "B", or both. Of course, the wider your knowledge of Mathematics, the greater your proficiency becomes, and the greater the resources at your disposal. If, eventually, you intend to go on to Advanced Level studies, you should certainly master it all.

Here, as in Book 1, the subjects are arranged in separate sections for ease of reference, and in order to avoid any confusing multiplicity of cross-references from one section to another certain material is included in more than one section. When you meet the same idea in both Arithmetic and Algebra, or in both Geometry and Trigonometry, it frequently provides a better understanding of the topic concerned.

If you are able to choose between taking Syllabus A or Syllabus B, you will want to know which one is likely to suit you better. If you are particularly fond of, or skilful at, Geometry you will perhaps find more scope for your talents in Syllabus A. If you find Calculus interesting and easy, Syllabus B is the one for you. Nowadays, the number who take each examination and the proportion of those who pass are roughly equal, so don't just try to find the "softer" one! If in this book you thoroughly understand the material concerned with the syllabus you select, you will have no difficulty in passing the examination—whichever your choice!

Finally, the purpose of learning Mathematics is not necessarily to pass an examination in that subject. Equally important is your ability to use it intelligently and thereby gain a greater understanding of the scientific and technological developments that play such an important part in life today.

H. R. CHILLINGWORTH

CONTENTS

ARITHMETIC AND TRIGONOMETRY

BY C. A. R. BAILEY AND R. A. JEFFERY

BY P. B. CHAPMAN

ALGEBRA AND THE CALCULUS

BY C. A. R. BAILEY AND R. A. JEFFERY

BY G. S. BARNARD

CONTENTS

Mathematics is essential in most trades and professions.

ARITHMETIC AND TRIGONOMETRY

CHAPTER 1

AVERAGES

THE STAR batsman of the local team was having a bad month. On four consecutive Saturdays he had scored only 2, 7, 1 and 6 runs respectively. A total of 16 runs in 4 innings. If he had scored exactly 4 on each occasion, the result would have been the same—16 runs in 4 innings. No wonder that he complained that his average for the month was only 4 runs per innings.

This example illustrates what is meant by an average: 4 runs per innings is his average, because if he had made that same score of 4 *every time* the final result would have been the same—16 runs altogether. Notice that in fact he did not score exactly 4 in any of his innings.

Indeed, if he had made the same sort of calculation after only 3 innings, by which time he had scored 10 runs altogether, he would have said that his average was *then* $3\frac{1}{3}$ runs per innings, since that score on each occasion would have produced the same final result of 10 runs in 3 innings: this in spite of the fact that a score of $3\frac{1}{3}$ is not possible. The average result may not have occurred or even be possible.

Example:

With her savings a girl bought 3 records costing 6s. 9d. each and one long-player at 21s. 9d. What average price did she pay for the records?

She spent in all $3 \times$ 6s. 9d. = 20s. 3d.
+ 21s. 9d.
42s. 0d.

If each record had been the same price, that price would have been $\frac{42\text{s.}}{4}$ = 10s. 6d. Thus the average price was 10s. 6d.

Notice that it would have been wrong to take the average of 6s. 9d. and 21s. 9d., which is 14s. 3d.: 4 records at 14s. 3d. cost 57s., not 42s. To find the average price, we had first to find the total amount spent, and then divide by the number of records bought.

Example:

In a history test, the average mark of the 18 boys in the class was 52, and the average mark of the 12 girls was 57. What was the average mark of the whole class?

We must remember that the statement that the average mark of the boys was 52 means that the total number of marks obtained by the boys was the same as if each boy had scored 52. Some may have scored 80, some only 20: possibly none scored 52 exactly. But the total was

$$18 \times 52 = 936$$

Similarly, the girls' total was $12 \times 57 = 684$

Thus the grand total of all the marks was

$$936 + 684 = 1620$$

This total was achieved by the combined marks of 30 children, so the average mark was

$$\frac{1620}{30} = 54$$

Notice again that the average was not half-way between 52 and 57.

EXERCISE 1A

1. During a certain week a housewife kept a careful check on her spending, with the following result: Monday, 16s. 4d.; Tuesday, 22s. 6d.; Wednesday, 19s. 2d.; Thursday, 17s. 5d.; Friday, 8s. 11d.; Saturday, 42s. 8d.; Sunday, 5s. 5d. What was her average expenditure each day?

2. A shooting team of eight people had an average score of 83 out of 100. What was their total score?

3. A batsman had an average of 26 runs per innings after 8 innings. What was his total? What must he score on the next occasion to make his average 30 runs per innings after 9 innings?

4. The average height of the boys in a class of 30 is 5 ft. 3 in. The five tallest boys have an average height of 5 ft. 8 in. What is the average height of the remaining 25?

Figures having only Fractional Variations

In many situations where we deal with averages the figures involved are all fairly close to one another. For example, when conducting a scientific experiment involving accurate measurement it is usual to make several readings and take their average. Such a set of, say, eight readings might look like this:

37·2, 37·2, 37·4, 37·1, 37·5, 37·3, 37·4, 37·3.

Since all the readings come to a little over 37, it is only necessary to find the average of the decimal parts: taking these as 2, 2, 4, 1, 5, 3, 4, 3, which total 24, and dividing by 8, we find that the average decimal part is ·3, so that the average reading is 37·3. This setting aside of the 37 makes for a great easing of labour.

EXERCISE 1B

1. Use the above method to find the average of 782, 751, 765, 756, 764, 779, 758. (Set aside 750.)

2. Find the average of 27·4, 27·1, 27·2, 27·1, 26·7. (Set aside 27, and treat 26·7 as − 0·3.)

3. The average age of a class of 25 boys is 13 years 4 months and the average age of a parallel class of 30 boys is 13 years 7 months. Find the average age of the two classes taken together, giving your answer to the nearest $\frac{1}{10}$ of a month.

Speed-Time-Distance Problems

The idea of average speed is one which often leads to muddled thinking. A well-known catch question goes something like this:

> A man has 1 hour to catch a train at a station 4 miles away. Clearly he must cover the distance at an average speed of 4 m.p.h. Since the first half of the journey is up a rather steep hill, he only walks at 2 m.p.h. for this stretch. At what speed must he cover the rest in order to catch the train?

At first glance, most people reason like this: he must average 4 m.p.h. altogether, and since he averaged 2 m.p.h. on the first half, he must average 6 m.p.h. on the second half, since the average of 2 and 6 is 4.

But this is quite wrong: on the first half of the journey he walks 2 miles at 2 m.p.h., so he takes 1 hour to get to the top of the hill. By now the train is just on the point of leaving: he will never catch it.

This example should warn you to be careful with average speeds. The average speed for a journey is found by taking the distance involved and dividing it by the time taken. You cannot combine average speeds: you can only combine distances and times, so that in such questions it is essential to calculate the distances and times involved.

Example:

A motorist travels for 2 hours at 30 m.p.h. and then for a further 3 hours at 40 m.p.h. What is his average speed for the whole journey?

In 2 hours at 30 m.p.h. he travels 60 miles.
In 3 hours at 40 m.p.h. he travels 120 miles.
Thus in 5 hours he travels 180 miles altogether.
His average speed is $\frac{180}{5} = 36$ m.p.h.

Example:

A boy cycles to a friend's house at 10 m.p.h. and returns home at 12 m.p.h. If his friend lives 30 miles away, what is his average speed for the double journey?

30 miles at 10 m.p.h. takes 3 hours.
30 miles at 12 m.p.h. takes $2\frac{1}{2}$ hours.
Hence the 60 miles are covered in $5\frac{1}{2}$ hours altogether.

Thus the average speed is $\frac{60}{5\frac{1}{2}}$ m.p.h.

$= 60 \times \frac{2}{11}$ m.p.h.

$= 10\frac{10}{11}$ m.p.h.

EXERCISE 1C

1. To travel from London to Wick you can take a train to Edinburgh, a distance of 360 miles, and then a plane from Edinburgh to Wick, which is a further 180 miles. If the train averages 45 m.p.h. and the plane averages 180 m.p.h., what is the average speed for the whole journey?

2. A driver has 4 hours to keep an appointment at a town 180 miles away. Twenty miles of the journey is through city streets where he can only average 25 m.p.h. The rest of the journey is on the motorway, what speed must he average there?

3. A man goes out for a joyride on his new motor-cycle. For the first hour he averages 25 m.p.h., but for the next two hours he averages 34 m.p.h. What speed did he average for the whole ride?

Density Problems

The same technique that we have used for finding average speeds can be used to find the average density of a mixture of two or more substances. The density of a substance is the weight of some standard volume of the substance.

Example:

The weight of 2 cu. ft. of water is about 125 lb., so that 1 cu. ft. will weigh about $62\frac{1}{2}$ lb. We say that the density of water is about $62\frac{1}{2}$ lb. per cu. ft. Of course, if we work in different units, we shall not arrive at the same number, $62\frac{1}{2}$.

If we work in the metric system, we find that the density of water is 1 gm. per c.c. (Remember this is not a lucky accident: 1 gram is defined as the weight of 1 c.c. of water.)

Now suppose we take 2 litres of a liquid whose density is 0·8 gm. per c.c. and mix them with 3 litres of another liquid of density 1·05 gm. per c.c.

1000 c.c. of a liquid of density 0·8 gm. per c.c. will weigh 800 gm.

So 2 litres of the first liquid will weigh 1600 gm.

Similarly 3 litres of the second liquid will weigh 3150 gm.

Thus the mixture consists of 5000 c.c. of liquid weighing 4750 gm. altogether. Hence the density of the mixture is

$$\tfrac{4750}{5000} \text{ gm. per c.c.}$$
$$= 0{\cdot}95 \text{ gm. per c.c.}$$

Example:

Two metals whose densities are 420 lb. per cu. ft. and 560 lb. per cu. ft., respectively, are alloyed in the ratio 60 per cent to 40 per cent by weight. What is the density of the alloy?

Since the mixture is described by percentage of weight, we can choose any two convenient weights (provided that they are in the correct ratio) and work with them. Suppose we take 6 lb. of the first substance and 4 lb. of the second

6 lb. of metal of density 420 lb. per cu. ft. requires $\frac{6}{420} = \frac{1}{70}$ cu. ft.

4 lb. of metal of density 560 lb. per cu. ft. requires $\frac{4}{560} = \frac{1}{140}$ cu. ft.

The total volume will be

$$\tfrac{1}{70} + \tfrac{1}{140} \text{ cu. ft.} = \tfrac{3}{140} \text{ cu. ft.}$$

and this will weigh 10 lb. altogether: thus the density of the alloy will be

$$10 \div \tfrac{3}{140} = \tfrac{1400}{3} = 466\tfrac{2}{3} \text{ lb. per cu. ft.}$$

EXERCISE 1D

1. An 8 cu. ft. block of wood weighs 360 lb. What is its density?

2. If the density of a substance is 144 lb. per cu. ft., what will 1 cu. in. weigh?

3. If the density of a substance is 120 lb. per cu. ft., what volume will weigh 10 lb.?

4. An alloy consists of a mixture of lead (density 11·4 gm. per c.c.) and tin (density 7·2 gm. per c.c.) in the ratio 70 per cent to 30 per cent by volume. Find the density of the alloy.

5. 30 gm. of silver (density 10·5 gm. per c.c.) are mixed with 8 gm. of copper (density 8·8 gm. per c.c.). Find the density of the mixture.

Mixed or Blended Commodities

Many commodities sold nowadays are mixtures or blends. For instance, a firm may sell a brand of coffee which is a mixture of two different qualities.

The cheaper would sell at 1s. 9d. per lb. and the better quality would sell at 2s. 6d. per lb. If the firm want to sell the blend at 2s. per lb., they would argue like this:

Each lb. of cheaper coffee sold at 2s. would give a profit of 3d.
Each lb. of dearer coffee sold at 2s. would give a loss of 6d.

Thus 2 lb. of the cheaper coffee must be sold for every 1 lb. of the more expensive one, in order to balance the loss: so the coffee must be blended in the ratio 2 : 1. Let us check this:

2 lb. at 1s. 9d. per lb. costs 3s. 6d.
1 lb. at 2s. 6d. per lb. costs 2s. 6d.
so 3 lb. of the mixture costs 6s.

and the average price of the mixture is 2s. per lb., as required.

EXERCISE 1E

1. Sugar worth 1s. per lb. is mixed with sugar worth 1s. 2d. per lb., and the mixture is to be sold at 1s. $1\frac{1}{2}$d. per lb. In what ratio must the two qualities be mixed?

2. Coal costing 6s. per cwt. is to be mixed with coal costing 7s. 6d. per cwt. and the mixture is to be sold at a profit of 20 per cent for 8s. 6d. per cwt. In what ratio must the two types be mixed?

3. Lead and tin (for densities see Exercise 1D, No. 4) are to be mixed to produce an alloy of density 8·4 gm. per c.c. In what ratio by volume must they be mixed? What will be the ratio by weight?

Average Speeds and Densities

You will have seen from many examples in this chapter that quantities such as average speed and average density cannot be found by simply taking the average of the speeds or densities given in the problem. Let us examine the facts a little more closely.

Example:

Suppose first that a car travels at different speeds for *equal times*, say 1 hour at 20 m.p.h. and 1 hour at 30 m.p.h. Then he will clearly cover 50 miles in 2 hours, which gives an average speed of 25 m.p.h. Thus for *equal times* the average speed *is* the same as the average of the different speeds.

Now take the same speeds over equal distances: say 1 mile at each speed. The total time taken is

$$\tfrac{1}{20} + \tfrac{1}{30} \text{ hour} = \tfrac{1}{12} \text{ hour}$$

Since he covers 2 miles in this time, his average speed is 24 m.p.h.

Notice that 24 is *not* the average of 20 and 30, but the fraction $\frac{1}{24}$ *is* the average of the two fractions $\frac{1}{20}$ and $\frac{1}{30}$.

The number 24 is called the *harmonic mean* of 20 and 30, whilst the more technical name for the ordinary "average" (i.e. 25 in this case) is the *arithmetic mean.*

The harmonic mean is found by first inverting the two numbers, that is, "turning them upside down," then finding the ordinary average of the resulting fractions, and finally inverting the result.

Thus for the numbers 3 and 6, if we first invert we get the fractions $\frac{1}{3}$ and $\frac{1}{6}$: the average of these two fractions is

$$\frac{\frac{1}{3}+\frac{1}{6}}{2}=\frac{1}{4}$$

and if we invert the fraction $\frac{1}{4}$ we get 4: thus 4 is the harmonic mean of 3 and 6.

The original example suggests that if a vehicle travels at different speeds for equal *times*, the average speed is the arithmetic mean of the different speeds, whereas if it travels at different speeds for equal distances, the average speed is the harmonic mean of the different speeds.

EXERCISE 1F

1. Find both the arithmetic mean and the harmonic mean of the following pairs of numbers:

(a) 30 and 70; (b) 6 and 10; (c) 12 and 18.

(Notice that in each case the arithmetic mean is larger than the harmonic mean.)

2. If a cyclist travels at speeds of 12 m.p.h. and 18 m.p.h. for equal times of 2 hours show that his average speed is the arithmetic mean of 12 and 18.

3. If the cyclist in No. 2 travels at the given speeds for equal distances of 3 miles show that his average speed is the harmonic mean of 12 and 18.

4. If two substances of densities 3 gm. per c.c. and 6 gm. per c.c. are mixed in equal *volumes* of 5 c.c. each, show that the density of the mixture is the arithmetic mean of the two given densities. If now they are mixed in equal *weights* of 30 gm. each, show that the average density is the harmonic mean of the original densities.

The Geometric Mean

Yet a third type of mean is illustrated by the following well-known problem:

If a water-lily doubles its size every day, and takes 20 days to fill the pond, how long will it take to fill half the pond?

The answer, of course, is not 10 days, but 19 days, because if it has reached the stage of filling half the pond, it will double its size the next day and fill the whole pond.

Let us look at some intermediate stage of this process: suppose that on a certain day the area of the lily was 2 sq. ft. then on the next two days the area will be 4 sq. ft. and 8 sq. ft. respectively. The numbers 2, 4 and 8 are said to

form a geometric progression, and the number 4 is called the *geometric mean* of 2 and 8. Notice that $2 \times 8 = 16$, and $4^2 = 16$ also. In other words, the geometric mean of 2 and 8 is the square root of 2×8.

If we take three other numbers in the sequence we shall find the same thing: try 8, 16 and 32.

$8 \times 32 = 256$, and $\sqrt{256} = 16$, so 16 is the geometric mean of 8 and 32.

There is nothing special about the doubling process: the numbers 4, 12, 36 are such that each is *three* times the previous one:

$4 \times 36 = 144$, and $\sqrt{144} = 12$, so 12 is the geometric mean of 4 and 36.

An example of such processes in nature is that of radioactive decay. A radioactive substance changes into another substance in such a way that only half of it is left after a certain time (called the half-life). For instance, if the half-life is 2 years, and we start with 24 gm. of the substance, then after 2 years we will have 12 gm. left: after 4 years only 6 gm. left: after 6 years only 3 gm. left, and so on. If we take three of these numbers in succession, such as 12, 6 and 3, we see that 6 is the geometric mean of 12 and 3, since $12 \times 3 = 36 = 6^2$.

EXERCISE 1G

1. Find the geometric mean of 12 and 27.

2. The number of flies in a house, if they are left unchecked, grows in geometric progression. If there were 5 flies in the house on Tuesday, and 125 flies on Thursday, how many were there on Wednesday, and how many will there be on Friday?

3. A scientist produced 25 gm. of a radioactive substance, and discovered that after two weeks he had only 4 gm. left. How much had been left after one week?

CHAPTER 2

MENSURATION III

THE FIRST Book of Kings, Chapter 7, describes the building of Solomon's Temple, which was ornamented with a molten sea, described in verse 23 as follows:

> **23 ¶ And he made a molten sea, ten cubits from the one brim to the other: *it was* round all about, and his height *was* five cubits: and a line of thirty cubits did compass it round about.**

Clearly the writer is describing a circular object, whose diameter was 10 cubits and whose circumference (perimeter) was 30 cubits. It implies that the circumference is three times as long as the diameter. This is only very roughly true: for any circle the circumference is slightly more than three times the diameter. Two thousand years ago Archimedes, the famous Greek mathematician and engineer, showed that the actual ratio was somewhere between $3\frac{1}{7}$ and $3\frac{10}{71}$.

As a matter of fact, it is not possible to express this number as an exact fraction, though we can calculate its value to as many decimal places as we wish, by a method which is unfortunately too difficult to discuss here. We take as many decimal places as we require for the accuracy of the problem in hand.

Here are the first few:

$$3{\cdot}141592653589793 \ldots$$

Even for very accurate work it is usually sufficient to call it

$$3{\cdot}1416$$

and for everyday calculations we only use

$$3{\cdot}14 \text{ or the fraction } 3\tfrac{1}{7} \left(= \tfrac{22}{7}\right).$$

This curious number is always referred to by the Greek letter π (pronounced pi): thus we can say that the circumference of a circle is π times the diameter, or more shortly still,

$$C = \pi d$$

Remembering that C stands for the circumference and d for the diameter.

Since π is not exactly expressible either as a fraction or as a decimal, any calculation in which we use π can only give us an approximate answer; answers which do not come out to round numbers are usually expressed in decimals.

Example:

If the diameter of a circle is 7 in., and we take π as $\frac{22}{7}$, we find that the circumference is

$$\tfrac{22}{7} \times 7 \text{ in.} = 22 \text{ in. approx.}$$

but if the diameter is 8 in., the circumference is

$$\tfrac{22}{7} \times 8 \text{ in.} = 25\tfrac{1}{7} \text{ in.} = 25 \text{ in. approx.}$$

It is unwise to give more than 2 significant figures in the answer if we have taken $\pi = \frac{22}{7}$, which we shall do throughout this chapter.

EXERCISE 2A

Find the circumference of the following circles:

1. Diameter 21 cm.

2. Diameter 10 yd.

3. Radius $3\frac{1}{2}$ in. (Remember that radius is *half* the diameter.)

4. Radius 6 ft.

5. The circumference of a circle is 44 in. Find its diameter.

6. The circumference of a bicycle wheel is 88 in. Find its radius.

7. The circumference of a circular clock-face is 18 cm. Find its radius.

Area of a Circle

Since the radius of a circle is half the diameter, the formula $C = \pi d$ can also be written $C = 2\pi r$ where r stands for the radius.

To find the area of a circle, let us cut it up into very thin wedge-shaped slices, and then put them together again in a different way, like this:

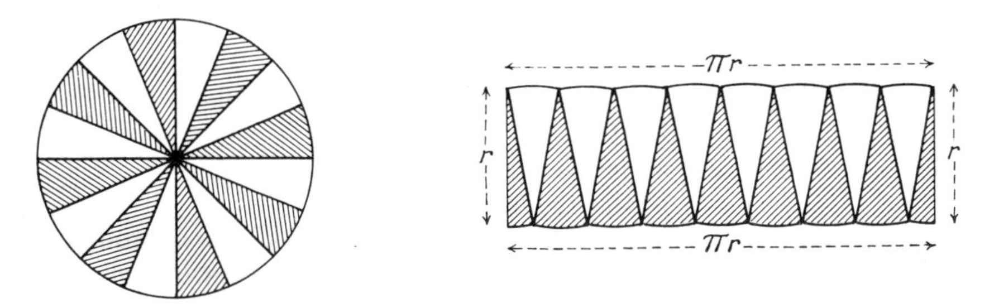

We have turned the circle into a rather mis-shapen rectangle. The two longer sides between them account for the whole circumference of the circle, which we know to be $2\pi r$ units long. Thus the approximate length of our approximate rectangle is πr units long. The breadth is clearly the radius of the circle, r, so that the area must be approximately

$$\pi r \times r \text{ sq. in.} = \pi r^2 \text{ sq. in.}$$

All this calculation cannot claim to be accurate, of course, since a figure with curved sides cannot be called a rectangle, but if we take enough thin slices, it will resemble a rectangle very closely. In fact, it can be proved that the formula just found is accurate, even though the argument we have used to find it is rather doubtful.

If we use the letter A to represent the area of a circle, we have the formula

$$A = \pi r^2$$

It is important to remember the order of operations in this formula: first the radius is squared, and then the result is multiplied by π. It would be *wrong* to multiply the radius by π first, and then to square the result.

Example:

For a circle of radius 7 in. the area is

$$\pi \times 7^2 \text{ sq. in.} = \tfrac{22}{7} \times 49 \text{ sq. in.}$$
$$= 154 \text{ sq. in.}$$

EXERCISE 2B

Find the areas of the circles given in Exercise 2A, No. 1 to 4.

5. If the area of a circle is 616 sq. in., find its radius. (Divide the area by π, thus finding r^2, and then take the square root of your result.)

6. Find the radius of a circle whose area is $9\frac{5}{8}$ sq. cm.

Problems Concerning Area and Circumference

To avoid confusing the two formulae for the circumference and area of a circle, remember that an area is always given in *square* inches, etc., and the formula for the area contains *r squared.* The next exercise contains questions, some of which require one formula and some the other: but first here are some examples of how to tackle the more complicated questions.

Example:

Two concentric circles have radii 20 in., 27 in. Find the area of the ring enclosed between them.

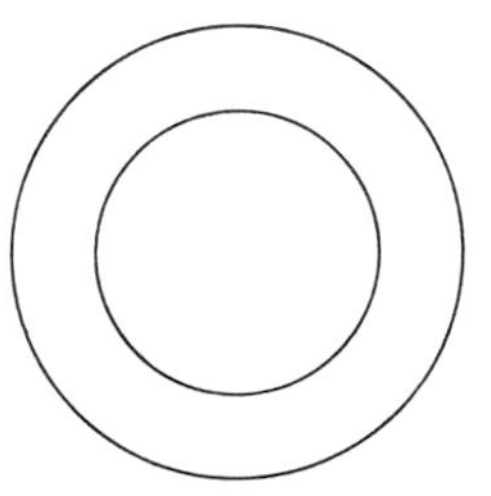

Concentric circles are circles having the same centre, as shown in the diagram. Clearly we have to find the area of each circle and subtract one from the other.

An important saving of labour will be achieved by finding each area as a multiple of π, and not substituting the value $\pi = \frac{22}{7}$ until *after* subtracting the areas.

$$
\begin{aligned}
\text{Area of outer circle} &= \pi \times 27^2 \text{ sq. in.}\\
&= 729\pi \text{ sq. in.}\\
\text{Area of inner circle} &= \pi \times 20^2 \text{ sq. in.}\\
&= 400\pi \text{ sq. in.}\\
\text{Area of ring} &= 729\pi - 400\pi \text{ sq. in.}\\
&= 329\pi \text{ sq. in.}\\
&= 329 \times \tfrac{22}{7} \text{ sq. in.}\\
&= 47 \times 22 \text{ sq. in.}\\
&= 1034 \text{ sq. in.}
\end{aligned}
$$

Answer: 1000 sq. in. (to 2 significant figures).

Example:

A bicycle wheel of radius 14 in. is performing 24 revolutions in 10 seconds. Find the speed of the bicycle in m.p.h.

We must first find the circumference of the wheel, which will be the distance travelled in one revolution, and then find the distance covered in 10 seconds.

From this we can go on to find the distance travelled in an hour, which, when expressed in miles, will be the speed.

$$
\begin{aligned}
\text{Circumference of wheel} &= 2\pi r\\
&= 2 \times \pi \times 14 \text{ in.}\\
&= 88 \text{ in.}\\
\text{Distance travelled in 10 seconds} &= 88 \times 24 \text{ in.}\\
\text{Distance travelled in 1 minute} &= 88 \times 24 \times 6 \text{ in.}\\
\text{Distance travelled in 1 hour} &= 88 \times 24 \times 6 \times 60 \text{ in.}\\
&= \frac{88 \times 24 \times 6 \times 60}{36 \times 1760} \text{ miles}\\
&= 12 \text{ miles}
\end{aligned}
$$

Answer: 12 m.p.h.

EXERCISE 2C

1. A running track is in the form of a rectangle 110 yd. long and 70 yd. wide, with a semi-circular stretch on each of the shorter sides. Find the total perimeter of the track. If the interior of the track is to be sown with grass at 2d. per sq. ft., find the total cost of this operation.

2. A flywheel of diameter 14 in. rotates at 750 revolutions per minute. Calculate the distance travelled in one revolution by a point on the circumference. Calculate also the speed of this point in miles per hour.

3. The wheel of a motor-car makes 960 revolutions in travelling a mile. Find the radius of the wheel in inches. If the wheels are revolving at 12 revolutions per second, what is the speed of the car in miles-per-hour? If the wheels were 1 in. greater in radius and revolved at the same rate, what would be the percentage increase in the speed of the car?

4. The circumference of a circular lake is 2420 yd. Find its area in acres.

Measurement of Cylinders

If we take an ordinary rectangular piece of paper and fold it as shown in the diagram we shall form a circular cylinder. The area of the curved surface of this cylinder is the same as the area of the piece of paper with which we made it. Now the *breadth* of the paper has become the *height* of the cylinder, and the *length* of the paper has become the *circumference* of the cylinder.

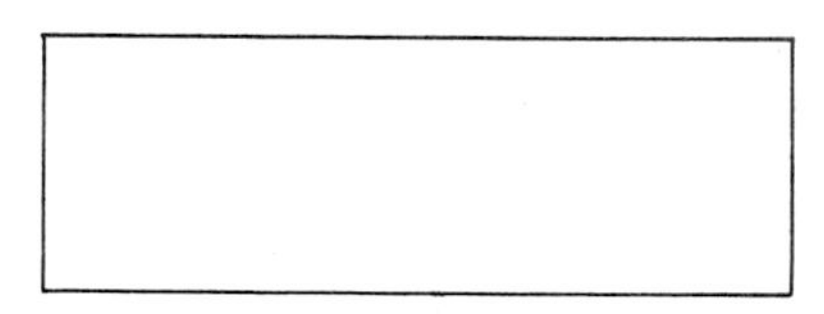

Since the area of the paper is

$$\text{length} \times \text{breadth}$$

it follows that the area of the cylinder is

$$\text{circumference} \times \text{height}$$

Now the circumference of the cylinder can be found from the formula

$$C = 2\pi r$$

so if we use h to represent the height, then the area is given by

$$A = 2\pi rh$$

Although we have spoken of the height of a cylinder, and have used the letter h for it in the formula, it must be remembered that, for example, in the case of a pencil, we would speak of its length rather than its height, whereas in the case of a penny we would speak of its thickness.

Nevertheless the letter h in the formula will represent both of these. Also, if the cylinder is closed at one or both ends, then the *total* area will be found by adding to the area of the curved surface the circular area(s) at the end(s). Thus if we have a closed tin can of radius 2 in. and height 5 in., the total area is

$$\begin{aligned} \text{area of curved surface} &= 2 \times \pi \times 2 \times 5 \text{ sq. in.} \\ + \text{ area of two circles} &= 2 \times \pi \times 2^2 \text{ sq. in.} \\ \text{Total area} &= 20\pi + 8\pi \text{ sq. in.} \\ &= 28\pi \text{ sq. in.} = 88 \text{ sq. in.} \end{aligned}$$

Notice how here we have again delayed substituting a value for π until the end of the calculation.

EXERCISE 2D

1. Find the area of the curved surface of a cylinder of radius 3 cm. and height 7 cm.

2. Find the area of the wetted surface of a cylindrical water-butt of radius 1 ft. containing water to a depth of 6 in.

3. A gasholder is in the form of a cylinder with a circular top. The radius is 36 ft. and the height is 52 ft. Find the area of the metal surface.

4. The curved surface of a cylinder has an area of 110 sq. cm. and it is 5 cm. high. Find its radius.

5. A man rolls a cricket ground of 3 acres with a roller 8 ft. wide. How many miles does the roller travel? If the diameter of the roller is 33 in., how many revolutions does it make?

6. The diagram represents a tea-caddy consisting of a cylinder with a circular base of radius 3 in. and height 4 in., surmounted by an open funnel of radius 2 in. and height $1\frac{1}{2}$ in. Find the total area of metal sheeting used to make it.

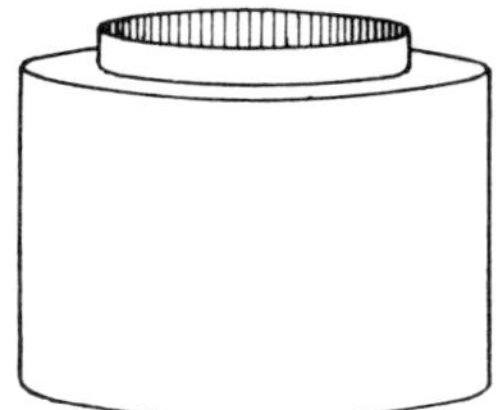

Volume of a Cylinder

A cylinder is a solid of uniform cross-section, and so we can find its volume from the formula

$$\text{volume} = \text{area of base} \times \text{height}$$

Since the base is a circle of area πr^2, we can express this formula as

$$V = \pi r^2 h$$

As many liquids and other substances are kept in cylindrical containers, this formula is in frequent use. Here are some examples:

Example:

A cylinder of height 6 cm. contains 231 cu. cm. of household cleaner. Find its radius.

From the formula, the volume is $\pi \times r^2 \times 6$ cu. cm.; that is, r^2 multiplied by 6π gives us the volume. So to find r^2 we must divide the volume by 6π.

$$r^2 = \frac{231}{6\pi}$$

$$= \frac{231 \times 7}{6 \times 22}$$

$$= \frac{49}{4}$$

$$\text{so } r = \frac{7}{2}$$

Answer: $3\frac{1}{2}$ cm.

Example:

A rain gauge is a cylindrical jar of diameter 3 in. Rain is collected in it by means of a conical funnel whose diameter is 8 in. If $\frac{5}{8}$ in. depth of rain is collected in the funnel, what is the rainfall at that place?

We must first find the volume of water collected in the gauge. This is the volume of rain that has fallen on a circle of 8 in. diameter. If we divide this volume by the area of this circle, we shall find the depth of rainfall.

You will see that by postponing the substitution of a value for π, it will appear that π will cancel, and so no substitution is necessary.

$$\begin{aligned}
\text{Volume of water} &= \pi \times (1\tfrac{1}{2})^2 \times \tfrac{5}{8} \text{ cu. in.} \\
&= \pi \times \tfrac{45}{32} \text{ cu. in.} \\
\text{Area of circle} &= \pi \times 4^2 \text{ sq. in.} \\
&= 16\pi \text{ sq. in.} \\
\text{Rainfall} &= \pi \times \frac{45}{32} \times \frac{1}{16\pi} \text{ in.} = \tfrac{45}{512} \text{ in.}
\end{aligned}$$

EXERCISE 2E

1. A cylinder's volume is 44 cu. cm. and its height is $3\frac{1}{2}$ cm. Find its radius.

2. A cylindrical water tank has a radius of 4 ft. and contains water to a depth of $3\frac{1}{2}$ ft. Find the quantity of water in gallons.

3. A circular disc of metal 1 ft. in diameter and 2 in. thick is melted down and stamped into coins of diameter 1 in. and thickness $\frac{1}{10}$ in. How many coins can be made thus?

4. A cable consists of a copper core 1 in. in radius, surrounded by a rubber sheath 0·7 in. thick. Find the volume of rubber required for 1 mile of cable. Give your answer in cu. ft.

5. Water flows at the rate of 50 gal. per minute into a circular lake of radius 21 ft. How long will it take to raise the water level by 1 ft.?

Finding Volume by Immersion

When an object is put into a container with water in it, the water level will rise. Provided that the water does not overflow the rim of the vessel, the volume above the original level of the water will be equal to the volume of the object in the water: this diagram shows the sort of thing that happens.

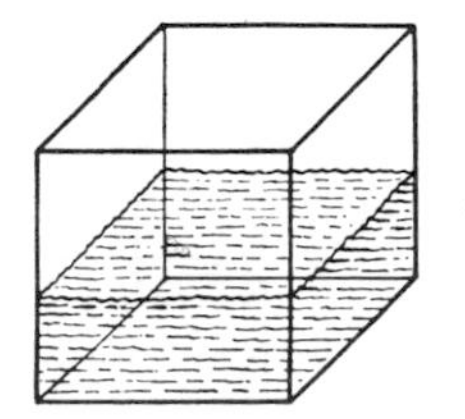

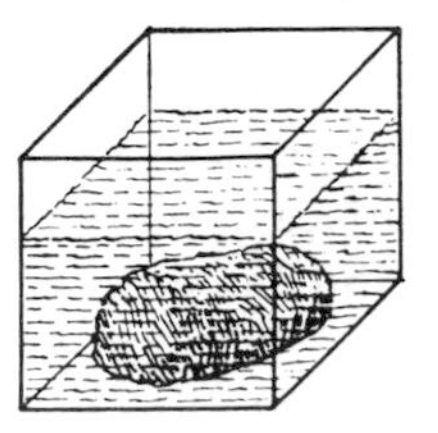

If the sides of the vessel are vertical, so that it has a constant cross-section, the volume of the water above the original level will be the product of the area of the base of the vessel and the rise in the water level. Put another way, this means that the rise in level is found by taking the volume of the object and dividing it by the area of the base.

Obviously if we now take the object out again the water will return to its original level, so the same calculation will find the fall in level when an object is removed from water in such a vessel.

Thus we can express the process in words by saying

$$\text{rise or fall} = \frac{\text{volume of object immersed}}{\text{area of base of vessel}}$$

It must be remembered that this formula will only apply if the vessel has a constant cross-section, and if we know exactly how much of the object is under water.

Example:

A tank with a square base of side 3 ft. contains water to a depth of 2 ft.

A cube of side 18 in. is placed in the tank. How much does the level rise?

The depth of the water (2 ft.) is sufficient to cover the cube, so we may apply the formula.

$$\begin{aligned} \text{Volume of cube} &= (1\tfrac{1}{2})^3 \text{ cu. ft.} \\ \text{Area of base} &= 3 \times 3 \text{ sq. ft.} \\ \text{Rise} &= \frac{3}{2} \times \frac{3}{2} \times \frac{3}{2} \times \frac{1}{3 \times 3} \text{ ft.} \\ &= \tfrac{3}{8} \text{ ft.} \\ &= 4\tfrac{1}{2} \text{ in.} \end{aligned}$$

Now suppose in the same problem there had been only 1 ft. of water in the tank to start with. When the cube is placed in the tank the water will not rise enough to cover it, and since we don't know how much it has risen, we cannot tell how much of the cube is under water, so the formula is useless.

We must approach the problem in a different way.

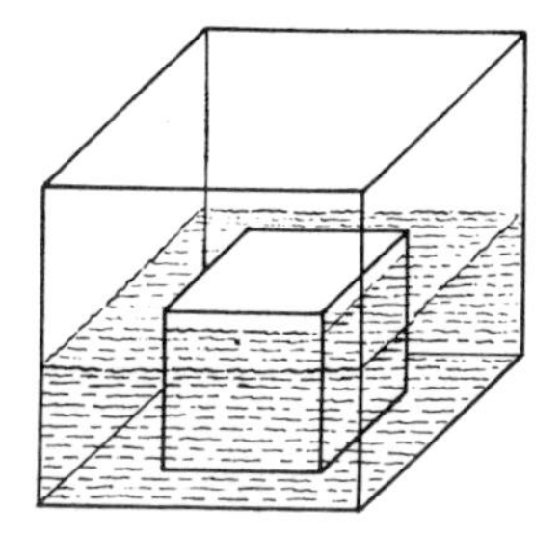

The original volume of water was $3 \times 3 \times 1$ cu. ft., i.e. 9 cu. ft. This is unchanged, but since the cube is now resting on the bottom of the tank, the wet surface of the base has been reduced by $(1\frac{1}{2})^2$ sq. ft. So the area on which the water is now resting is:

$$9 - 2\tfrac{1}{4} \text{ sq. ft.} = 6\tfrac{3}{4} \text{ sq. ft.}$$

We can now find the depth of water by division; it is

$$9 \div 6\tfrac{3}{4} \text{ ft.} = 1\tfrac{1}{3} \text{ ft.}$$

Thus the water has risen $\frac{1}{3}$ ft., or 4 in.

EXERCISE 2F

1. A cylindrical jug whose internal radius is 4 cm. is placed on a table, and inside it is placed, on end, a solid metal cylinder of radius 3 cm. and height 4 cm. Water is poured in until the metal cylinder is half submerged. The metal cylinder is then removed.

Find by how much the water level falls.

(Do not substitute for π: it will cancel out.)

2. A solid cylinder of radius 3 in. and length 14 in. is placed, with its axis horizontal, in a tank whose base is 2 ft. square and which contains water to a depth of 8 in. How much does the water level rise?

3. A tank with a rectangular base whose sides are 3 ft. and 2 ft. 6 in. contains water to a depth of 1 ft. A rectangular metal bar 1 ft. long and of cross-sectional area 32 sq. in. is placed in the tank. How much does the water level rise?

Rate of Flow of Liquids

Most water pipes have a circular cross-section. Suppose that water is flowing along a pipe at 6 ft. per second and then is being discharged from a tap.

This means that in every second a 6-ft. length of pipe is emptied.

If we know the area of the cross-section of the pipe (assuming the pipe is full), then the volume of water discharged in 1 second will be

(area of cross section) $\times$ 6 cu. ft.

We shall refer to the volume of water discharged in a second as the *rate of discharge*, and the speed of the water in the pipe as the *speed of flow*. Our reasoning above leads us to the conclusion that:

rate of discharge = area of cross-section $\times$ speed of flow

We must take great care to be consistent with our units when using this formula: it is only too easy to get lost in a muddle of feet, inches, gallons, minutes and seconds. Settle on a sensible selection of units at the beginning and stick to it.

Example:

A pipe in which the water flows at 7 ft. per second delivers water at a rate of 13,750 gal. per hour. Find the diameter of the pipe.

We must first find the area of the cross-section of the pipe, by division of the rate of discharge by the speed of flow. We shall work in feet and seconds.

$$13{,}750 \text{ gal.} = 13{,}750 \div 6\tfrac{1}{4} \text{ cu. ft.}$$

$$\text{Rate of discharge} = 13{,}750 \times \tfrac{4}{25} \times \tfrac{1}{60} \times \tfrac{1}{60} \text{ cu. ft. per sec.}$$

$$\text{Area of cross-section} = (\text{rate of discharge}) \times \tfrac{1}{7} \text{ sq. ft.}$$

$$= (\text{rate of discharge}) \times \tfrac{1}{7} \times 144 \text{ sq. in.}$$

$$(\text{radius})^2 = \frac{(\text{area of cross-section})}{\pi}$$

$$= 13{,}750 \times \tfrac{4}{25} \times \tfrac{1}{60} \times \tfrac{1}{60} \times \tfrac{1}{7} \times 144 \times \tfrac{7}{22}$$

$$= 4$$

$$\text{radius} = 2 \text{ in.}$$

Answer: 4 in. diameter

Notice how we avoided working out the intermediate steps, but built up instead an enormous fraction, which then cancelled down to 4. (You should check for yourself that this is so.)

EXERCISE 2G

1. Water is flowing at 6 ft. per second through a pipe of diameter 7 in. and is being discharged into a rectangular swimming bath 110 ft. long and 70 ft. wide. How long will it take for the water level to rise 1 in.?

2. Water is being discharged at the rate of 110 cu. ft. per minute through a pipe of diameter 8 in. Find the speed of flow in ft. per second.

3. A pipe is discharging water at 7,700 cu. ft. per hour. The water flows at 8 ft. per second. Find the diameter of the pipe.

CHAPTER 3

SQUARES, SQUARE ROOTS AND THE USE OF TABLES

YOU SHOULD know already how to find the square root of a number which is a perfect square. You remember that we factorize it into its prime factors and each of these must occur an even number of times. Thus $49 = 7^2$, $16 = 2^4$ and $144 = 2^4 \times 3^2$. If we know that a very large number, like 1,334,025 for example, is a perfect square we can factorize it:

$$
\begin{array}{r|r}
3 & 1{,}334{,}025 \\ \hline
3 & 444{,}675 \\ \hline
5 & 148{,}225 \\ \hline
5 & 29{,}645 \\ \hline
7 & 5{,}929 \\ \hline
7 & 847 \\ \hline
11 & 121 \\ \hline
11 & 11 \\ \hline
 & 1
\end{array}
$$

Therefore the factors are $3^2 \times 5^2 \times 7^2 \times 11^2$
and the square root is $3 \times 5 \times 7 \times 11$, or 1155

But there are many numbers whose square roots are not whole numbers, and tables of squares and square roots are used in arithmetic to save time and trouble. The tables in common use are four-figure tables—that is to say the values in them are given to 4 significant figures and are correct only to 3 significant figures, although the error in the fourth figure is usually small. Here is an extract from a page of four-figure tables of *squares* of numbers.

SQUARES

	0	1	2	3	4	5	6	7	8	9	1	2	3	4	5	6	7	8	9
10	1000	1020	1040	1061	1082	1103	1124	1145	1166	1188	2	4	6	8	10	13	15	17	19
11	1210	1232	1254	1277	1300	1323	1346	1369	1392	1416	2	5	7	9	11	14	16	18	21
12	1440	1464	1488	1513	1538	1563	1588	1613	1638	1664	2	5	7	10	12	15	17	20	22
13	1690	1716	1742	1769	1796	1823	1850	1877	1904	1932	3	5	8	11	13	16	19	22	24
14	1960	1988	2016	2045	2074	2103	2132	2161	2190	2220	3	6	9	12	14	17	20	23	26
15	2250	2280	2310	2341	2372	2403	2434	2465	2496	2528	3	6	9	12	15	19	22	25	28
16	2560	2592	2624	2657	2690	2723	2756	2789	2822	2856	3	7	10	13	16	20	23	26	30
17	2890	2924	2958	2993	3028	3063	3098	3133	3168	3204	3	7	10	14	17	21	24	28	31
18	3240	3276	3312	3349	3386	3423	3460	3497	3534	3572	4	7	11	15	18	22	26	30	33
19	3610	3648	3686	3725	3764	3803	3842	3881	3920	3960	4	8	12	16	19	23	27	31	35

The first column on the left is numbered from 10 to 99, and the next ten, headed 0-9, are called the *main columns*. On the right are 9 *difference columns*. Notice that there are no decimal points in the tables and we must make a rough approximation to decide where a decimal point, if needed, should go.

Example:

Using the tables, find the square of 1·728.

Rough check: $1^2 = 1$, $2^2 = 4$.
So the answer lies between 1 and 4.

Read down the left-hand column until you come to 17 (the first two figures of the number). Then read *across that line* until you come to the main column headed 2 (the third figure of the number). This reads 2958. Continue across the same line until you get to the difference column headed 8 (which is the fourth figure in the number 1·728). This says 28. *Add* this to 2958:

$$2958 + 28 = 2986$$

From our rough check we know the number must be between 1 and 4, so that the decimal point must be inserted after the figure 2.

$$\text{So } 1{\cdot}728^2 = 2{\cdot}986 \text{ (approx.)}$$

If we were to multiply $1{\cdot}728 \times 1{\cdot}728$ in the normal way, the answer would contain 6 places of decimals. Notice that the answer in this case contains only 3.

But such approximate answers are often quite accurate enough.

The square of 17·28, 172·8 and 1728 all contain the same significant figures, the answers differ only in the position of the decimal point.

In the case of $17{\cdot}28^2$ for example, the answer lies between 10^2 (100) and 20^2 (400).

Therefore using the same figures in the tables,

$17{\cdot}28^2 = 298{\cdot}6$ (approx.);
$172{\cdot}8^2$ lies between $100 = 10{,}000$
and $200^2 = 40{,}000$.
$\therefore\ 172{\cdot}8^2 = 29{,}860$ (approx.)

You might like to work out what $172{\cdot}8^2$ is more exactly by multiplication. The same significant figures apply if we wish to find the answer to $0{\cdot}1728^2$, only here it is necessary to remember that the square of a number less than 1 is *less* than the number.

A rough check would show us that since 0·1728 lies between 0·1 and 0·2, the answer to $0{\cdot}1728^2$ must be between $0{\cdot}1^2$ ($\frac{1}{10} \times \frac{1}{10} = \frac{1}{100} = 0{\cdot}01$) and $0{\cdot}2^2$ (0·04).

$$\therefore\ 0{\cdot}1728^2 = 0{\cdot}02986 \text{ (approx.)}$$

When looking up a number which has more than 4 significant figures, it must be corrected first:

Example:

Work out $1{\cdot}3257^2$.

$$1{\cdot}3257 = 1{\cdot}326 \text{ (correct to 4 figures)}$$

Rough check: The value must lie between 1^2 and 2^2 (1 and 4).

Looking up the numbers 1326 in the tables gives us the significant figures 1758.

$$\therefore\ 1{\cdot}326^2 = 1{\cdot}758 \text{ (approx.)}$$

EXERCISE 13A

Use the extract from the tables to look up:

1. $10{\cdot}52^2$
2. $105{\cdot}2^2$
3. $0{\cdot}1052^2$
4. $14{\cdot}63^2$
5. $1{\cdot}291^2$
6. $100{\cdot}9^2$
7. $16{\cdot}97^2$
8. $1{\cdot}111^2$
9. $1{\cdot}204^2$
10. 1600^2

Square Roots

You remember that if $x^2 = 25$

$$x = 5,$$

but that the sign $\sqrt{\ }$ means the positive square root only, so that $\sqrt{25} = +5$. Square roots can also be looked up in tables, but there is a striking difference between tables of square roots and those of squares, because with square root tables there are two possibilities for each number you look up. Why this should be so can best be seen if we look at some square roots:

$$\sqrt{4} = 2,$$

but $\sqrt{40}$ is not 20!

We know that $\sqrt{36} = 6$ and $\sqrt{49} = 7$ and so we would expect $\sqrt{40}$ to be between 6 and 7. It is, in fact, 6·325 (approx.).

Again, the square root of $\sqrt{400}$ is 20, and $\sqrt{4000}$ is somewhere between 60 ($\sqrt{3600}$) and 70 ($\sqrt{4900}$). It is, in fact, 63·25 (approx.).

If we set these out in table form:

$$\sqrt{4} = 2$$
$$\sqrt{40} = 6{\cdot}325$$
$$\sqrt{400} = 20$$
$$\sqrt{4000} = 63{\cdot}25$$

You will see that the answers alternate between 2 (or 20, or 200) and 6·325 (or 63·25 or 632·5). There are two possible answers when we look up the square root of the significant figures 4000. Square root tables, therefore, either have two entries against each line, or are split up into two separate pages. When we want to look up the square root of an awkward number, how are we to decide which entry is the right one?

Example:

Find the square root of 63450.

1. Mark off the number in pairs from the decimal point:

   6 | 34 | 50

2. Write above the left-hand figure (or figures if there are two) the biggest number whose square is less than the number there. In this case the biggest number whose square is less than 6 is 2 ($2^2 = 4$). 3 would be too big because $3^2 = 9$, which is greater than 6. Above each other pair of letters put a dot or cross to show how big the answer must be. The decimal point goes above that in the original number:

   2 x x
   6 | 34 | 50

   Therefore, we have as the rough *estimate* 200.

Now look up the number 6345 in the square root tables:

SQUARE ROOTS

	0	1	2	3	4	5	6	7	8	9	1	2	3	4	5	6	7	8	9
55	2345 7416	2347 7423	2349 7430	2352 7436	2354 7443	2356 7450	2358 7457	2360 7463	2362 7470	2364 7477	0 1	0 1	1 2	1 3	1 3	1 4	1 5	2 5	2 6
56	2366 7483	2369 7490	2371 7497	2373 7503	2375 7510	2377 7517	2379 7523	2381 7530	2383 7537	2385 7543	0 1	0 1	1 2	1 3	1 3	1 4	1 5	2 5	2 6
57	2387 7550	2390 7556	2392 7563	2394 7570	2396 7576	2398 7583	2400 7589	2402 7596	2404 7603	2406 7609	0 1	0 1	1 2	1 3	1 3	1 4	1 5	2 5	2 6
58	2408 7616	2410 7622	2412 7629	2415 7635	2417 7642	2419 7649	2421 7655	2423 7662	2425 7668	2427 7675	0 1	0 1	1 2	1 3	1 3	1 4	1 5	2 5	2 6
59	2429 7681	2431 7688	2433 7694	2435 7701	2437 7707	2439 7714	2441 7720	2443 7727	2445 7733	2447 7740	0 1	0 1	1 2	1 3	1 3	1 4	1 5	2 5	2 6
60	2449 7746	2452 7752	2454 7759	2456 7765	2458 7772	2460 7778	2462 7785	2464 7791	2466 7797	2468 7804	0 1	0 1	1 2	1 3	1 3	1 4	1 4	2 5	2 6
61	2470 7810	2472 7817	2474 7823	2476 7829	2478 7836	2480 7842	2482 7849	2484 7855	2486 7861	2488 7868	0 1	0 1	1 2	1 3	1 3	1 4	1 4	2 5	2 6
62	2490 7874	2492 7880	2494 7887	2496 7893	2498 7899	2500 7906	2502 7912	2504 7918	2506 7925	2508 7931	0 1	0 1	1 2	1 3	1 3	1 4	1 4	2 5	2 6
63	2510 7937	2512 7944	2514 7950	2516 7956	2518 7962	2520 7969	2522 7975	2524 7981	2526 7987	2528 7994	0 1	0 1	1 2	1 3	1 3	1 4	1 4	2 5	2 6
64	2530 8000	2532 8006	2534 8012	2536 8019	2538 8025	2540 8031	2542 8037	2544 8044	2546 8050	2548 8056	0 1	0 1	1 2	1 2	1 3	1 4	1 4	2 5	2 6
65	2550 8062	2551 8068	2553 8075	2555 8081	2557 8087	2559 8093	2561 8099	2563 8106	2565 8112	2567 8118	0 1	0 1	1 2	1 2	1 3	1 4	1 4	2 5	2 5
66	2569 8124	2571 8130	2573 8136	2575 8142	2577 8149	2579 8155	2581 8161	2583 8167	2585 8173	2587 8179	0 1	0 1	1 2	1 2	1 3	1 4	1 4	2 5	2 5
67	2588 8185	2590 8191	2592 8198	2594 8204	2596 8210	2598 8216	2600 8222	2602 8228	2604 8234	2606 8240	0 1	0 1	1 2	1 2	1 3	1 4	1 4	2 5	2 5

The tables are used exactly the same way as were the tables of squares. We read across the line 63 until we reach the main column headed 4. There we find 2518 and 7962. Our rough estimate begins with 2 and so we take the first, 2518. We read along *that* line until we reach the heading 5 in the difference column, and there we find 1, which we *add*, making 2519. Our approximation has also told us how big the number is (approximately 200), and so

$$\sqrt{63450} = 251{\cdot}9 \text{ (approx.)}$$

Example:

Evaluate $\sqrt{5942}$.

$$\begin{array}{c|c} 7 & x \\ 59 & 42 \end{array}$$

∴ *Rough check* is 70

From the tables, $\sqrt{5942} = 77{\cdot}08$ (approx.)

Example:

Evaluate $\sqrt{0{\cdot}006425}$.

Mark off the number in pairs from the decimal point:

$$\begin{array}{c|c|c} 0 & 8 & x \\ {\cdot}00 & 64 & 25 \end{array}$$

∴ *Rough check:* 0·080

From the tables, $\sqrt{0{\cdot}006425} = 0{\cdot}08015$ (approx.)

(Notice that the square root of numbers less than 1 is *bigger* than the number.)

EXERCISE 3B

From the extract from the tables printed above, find the value of the following. Make a rough estimate first.

1. $\sqrt{5{\cdot}932}$
2. $\sqrt{59{\cdot}32}$
3. $\sqrt{593{\cdot}2}$
4. $\sqrt{66{\cdot}07}$
5. $\sqrt{0{\cdot}6607}$
6. $\sqrt{6{\cdot}398}$
7. $\sqrt{0{\cdot}06004}$
8. $\sqrt{0{\cdot}005987}$
9. $\sqrt{65920}$
10. $\sqrt{6{\cdot}201}$

CHAPTER 4

STOCKS AND SHARES

A YOUNG man wanted to buy a small garage and repair business which was for sale for £6,000. He had no money himself, but luckily he had two quite wealthy uncles who had a high opinion of him: Uncle Bert was willing to lend £2,000, and Uncle Charlie could lend another £1,000. Between them they persuaded the bank to lend him the rest at 6% interest.

The young man bought the business, and after a year's hard work found that, having paid himself and his assistant a living wage, he could pay back £300 of the bank loan as well as the interest, and still have £350 over. He discussed the matter with his uncles, who would be called shareholders in the business, and it was agreed to spend £200 on buying more modern equipment for the garage and to divide the rest between the two shareholders.

This £150 divided between the shareholders is called the *dividend*. Since Uncle Bert had lent twice as much as Uncle Charlie, he received £100 and Uncle Charlie received £50. You will see that each of them received 5 per cent of what he *invested*, or lent. We say that the business paid a dividend of 5% to the shareholders.

The next year the young man found that the modern equipment he had bought improved business, and eventually he had £240 to distribute to the shareholders: since this represents 8% of the £3,000 his uncles had lent him, he paid a dividend of 8%, so that Uncle Bert got 8% of £2,000, that is £160, and Uncle Charlie got £80. They were very pleased with their investment.

What happened with this small business is repeated on a much bigger scale with large firms. If a new company is formed, or an old company wants to borrow some extra money, they don't have to approach Uncle Bert, but simply issue shares to anyone who wants to buy them.

Suppose the Tiger Bicycle Company want to raise £500,000 to extend their factory: they may decide to issue 2 million shares at 5s. each, and anyone may buy as many as he wishes. If you decide to buy 400 of them you will pay 400 × 5s. (= £100).

At the next Annual General Meeting of the company the Chairman announces that the company is paying a dividend of 10%: that means that for each 5s. share you hold you will get 10% of 5s., which is 6d. Since you hold 400 such shares, you will receive 400 × 6d. = £10.

This is obviously also 10% of the £100 which your share certificate tells you the shares are worth: this is called the *nominal value* of your holding. The dividend is always expressed as a percentage of this nominal value.

EXERCISE 4A

How much will you receive if you hold the following shares and the dividends are as indicated?

1. 200 (£1) shares: 8%. **2.** 300 (10s.) shares: 6%. **3.** 60 (£5) shares: 12%.

Cash Value and Nominal Value

After a few years in which the company has flourished and the dividends have gone up and up, you decide to sell your shares because you need the money to buy a car. Since the company are paying such good dividends, there is a considerable demand for the shares, and you find that people are prepared to pay 7s. 6d. for each share, which cost you 5s.

So when you hand over your share certificate stating that you own 400 shares, you receive 400 × 7s. 6d. (= £150) for it. You have made a capital gain of £50 on your shares, quite apart from the money you have received in dividends over the years.

Of course, you might have been unlucky and have found that people were only willing to pay 4s. for each share, in which case you would only have got 400 × 4s. (= £80) for your shares.

The point is that, except when the company issues the shares at the very beginning, the amount the shares are worth, that is what people are prepared to pay for them (called the *cash value*) is hardly ever the same as the *nominal value* printed on the share certificate. The prices of shares are printed each day in the financial columns of the newspapers. In the case we have just discussed we would say that

Tiger Bicycles' (5s.) shares stand at 7s. 6d.

When the cash value of the shares is higher than the nominal value, the shares are said to *stand at a premium*: if the cash value is lower than the nominal value, they are said to *stand at a discount*. In the rare cases in which the two values are the same, the shares are said to *stand at par*.

INDUSTRIAL	STORES	SHIPPING	TEXTILES
Af Clnr ..6/4½—0/1½	A Edwrds 2/10½	A Noress 42/3— 1/-	Alre 19/10½
Agar C 9/-	Am Nv ....24/6+ 0/3	Aviat 2/10½	Ambir J 14/4½
Airbrne ..14/4½	Aqua A 4/7½	Britn 5/7½	Aristoo ..19/-
Airfix A ..24/3— 0/3	Aus Rd 39/-	B Com ..18/3	Bear Bd ..8/3
Albrt W ..24/6+ 1/-	Bntals ....12/-—0/1½	Calrn 6/1½	Bellami ..7/6
Am Anth 19/1½	Brne H 7/4½	Coast ....37/3— 0/3	Bt Cot 6/4½
Am Dent ..51/6	B Home ..20/1½	Court 7/6	Bulmer ..11/1½—0/1½
Am Met ..33/6	Burtn A ..19/1½	Cunrd ....16/3— 0/3	Calico ..10/10½—0/1½
Aspro ..14/10½	Chiesmn ..17/9	Dene 18/-	Carr Dw ..15/-— 0/3
As Chem ..18/3+ 0/6	Civ Ser ....9/7½+0/1½	Dnldsn ..25/6	Coats ....44/-+6/4½

It must be remembered, however, that whatever price is paid for the shares, the dividend paid is a percentage of the *nominal value*.

The man who paid £150 for your Tiger Bicycles' shares holds a certificate to show that he holds 400 (5s.) shares of nominal value £100, and if the company pay a dividend of 15% he will receive 15% of £100, i.e. £15; the company is not concerned with what he paid for them, but only with the value shown on the share certificate.

EXERCISE 4B

1. Bigwood's (10s.) shares stand at 8s. How much will 50 shares cost? What will be their nominal value? If the company pay a dividend of 4% how much will the owner of these 50 shares get?

2. A man spends £360 on Newson's (5s.) shares when they stand at 6s. How many shares does he buy? What is their nominal value? What does he receive from a 6% dividend?

3. A man sells 200 (10s.) shares for £90. What is the price of one share? Do these shares stand at a premium or at a discount?

Let us return to the man who bought your 400 (5s.) shares for £150, and suppose that the next dividend the company paid was 15%. Since the nominal value of the shares was £100 he actually received a dividend of £15, so that on the £150 he paid for the shares he receives 10%.

This percentage is called the *yield*. We say that the investment yields 10%. Obviously this figure is of great interest to anyone buying shares as an investment. He will want to know what sort of return he is going to get on the money he actually spends in buying the shares.

Example:

A man invests £200 in Barton's (£1) shares when they stand at 16s. If they pay a dividend of 8% what is the yield on his investment?

The number of shares bought is £200 divided by 16s., i.e. 250 shares.
The nominal value of 250 (£1) shares is £250.
A dividend of 8% on £250 gives £20.
£20 income from an investment of £200 is a yield of 10%.

Dividend and Yield

Notice that the ratio of the nominal value to the cash value of the shares was £1 : 16s., that is 5 : 4. If we alter the dividend of 8% in the ratio 5 : 4 we get 10%, which is the yield. This is a quick way of finding the yield without considering the money actually spent on the shares, but must be used carefully in case the figures are used the wrong way round.

A check should be applied to the answer: if the shares are at a discount, you are buying them cheap, and your yield will be greater than the figure of the percentage dividend. If they are at a premium, the reverse applies.

Shares cannot be bought and sold in a shop, like shoes or soap. All share (and stock) transactions are done through a stockbroker, who naturally charges a small commission for his work. The amount he charges, however, is small compared with the amount of money involved in the buying and selling of the shares, so that we shall not take this into account in this book.

This is how to set out the calculations involved in this type of problem.

Example:

A man sold 400 Orpington (£5) shares at £4 2s. which were paying a dividend of $3\frac{1}{2}\%$, and invested the money in Popperton (£1) shares at 41s. which were paying a dividend of 9%. By how much did he improve his income?

The nominal value of the Orpington shares was $400 \times £5 = £2{,}000$, and the dividend paid would be $3\frac{1}{2}\%$ of this, i.e. £70.

400 Orpington shares sold at £4 2s. each would fetch 400×82s.

This money spent on Popperton shares at 41s. would buy

$$\frac{400 \times 82\text{s.}}{41\text{s.}} = 800 \text{ shares}$$

The nominal value of 800 Popperton (£1) shares is £800.

The dividend will be 9% of this, i.e. £72.

Thus he would improve his income by £2.

EXERCISE 4C

1. If (5s.) shares standing at 7s. 6d. pay a dividend of 9%, what is the yield?

2. If (£1) shares standing at 16s. pay 4% what is the yield?

3. A man sells 250 Waxford (10s.) shares at 13s. and invests the money in Greville's (5s.) shares at par. How many Greville's shares did he buy?

4. A man bought 600 (£1) shares at 22s. 6d. and sold them at 23s. 9d. How much did he gain?

5. A man paid £320 to buy 480 Newbolt (10s.) shares and after receiving a dividend of 12%, sold the shares again at 12s. What was his total loss?

6. A man invested £600 in (£1) shares at 25s. paying $7\frac{1}{2}\%$. He sold the shares at 28s. and invested the proceeds in (5s.) shares at 3s. 6d., paying 4%. How many (5s.) shares did he buy, and what was the change in his income?

Dealings in Stock

The basic purpose of buying shares is, as the name implies, in order to receive a share in the profits of a company. You may, of course, sell the shares to anyone who will buy them, but the company does not undertake to pay back the money originally invested.

Stock, on the other hand, represents a loan of money to a government, a City Corporation or other large official body, who undertake to pay back the money to the stockholder (that is, to *redeem* the loan) at a certain fixed date. In the meantime they will pay a certain fixed rate of interest on the *nominal* value of the stock.

Thus, the Government of Ruritania may wish to borrow £5 million to modernize the country's railway system: to do this they will issue £5 million stock, to be sold in units of £100, on which they will pay 4% interest until they redeem the stock in 1999. To encourage the sale of the stock, they will sell each £100 unit for £97 cash only. This will be quoted in the papers as

Ruritania 4% Stock, 1999 at 97.

Of course, since they are selling 50,000 units of £100 stock at only £97 per unit, they will only receive

$$50{,}000 \times £97 = £4{,}850{,}000$$

but this should be sufficient for their purpose. They will have to pay back the full £5 million when they redeem the loan, however, as well as the 4% interest each year on £5 million, which amounts to £200,000 annually.

Just as with shares, you may sell your holding of stock at the current market price, which will always be quoted as the cash price for £100 stock. Thus if the Ruritania stock mentioned above is quoted at 93, this means that

(a) £93 cash will buy £100 stock;
(b) the interest on this will be 4% of £100, i.e. £4.

Unlike shares, stock can be bought in any fractional amount. If you decide to invest £500 in a stock standing at 80, you will be able to buy $\frac{500}{80}$ units of stock, that is, $6\frac{1}{4}$ units of £100, and you will receive a certificate to show that you hold £625 stock.

If the stock pays 4%, your income on your £500 investment will be 4% of £625, or £25.

Since the symbols £ s. d. appear in these problems both to define the quantity of stock involved and the cash paid, it is important to use the words "stock" and "cash" when writing out calculations based on this sort of problem. This is how to set out the work:

Example:

A man invests £700 in Barchester $4\frac{1}{2}$% Stock at 120. What is his income?

£120 cash buys £100 stock
£700 cash buys £100 × $\frac{700}{120}$ stock
= £583 6s. 8d. stock
Income = $4\frac{1}{2}$% of £583 6s. 8d.
= $\frac{9}{200} \times £583\frac{1}{3}$
= £26 5s.

As with shares, if we express the income as a percentage of the *cash* investment, the result is called the *yield.* In the case above, the yield is

$$\frac{26\frac{1}{4}}{700} \times 100\% = 3\tfrac{3}{4}\%$$

This could also have been found by changing the $4\frac{1}{2}\%$ interest rate in the ratio of the nominal value to the cash value of the stock, i.e. 100 : 120, thus

$$4\tfrac{1}{2}\% \times \tfrac{100}{120} = \tfrac{9}{2} \times \tfrac{5}{6}\% = 3\tfrac{3}{4}\%$$

When discussing stocks, the yield is often expressed as the money received on £100 cash invested. In this case, $3\frac{3}{4}\%$ of £100 is £3 15s., and we would say that the yield is £3 15s. *per cent.*

EXERCISE 4D

1. If you wish to buy £400 3% stock at 75 how much will it cost? What will be your income?

2. If you invest £500 cash in 6% stock at 125, how much stock will you receive, and what will be your income?

3. A man invests £800 in 3% stock at 90. What will his income be? What will be the yield in £ s. d. per cent?

4. If a 6% stock stands at 120, what is the yield?

The Importance of Setting-out Problems Correctly

More complicated problems on the buying and selling of stocks are essentially the same as similar problems on shares. The important thing is to set out the work clearly so as to be quite certain what stage you have reached and what you are about.

Example:

A man holds 150 (£5) shares which are paying an annual dividend of 8%. He sells the shares at £6 4s. and invests the money received in $4\frac{1}{2}\%$ stock at 62. How much stock does he buy and what is his change in income?

150 (£5) shares have a nominal value of £750

The income on this at 8% is $\frac{8}{100} \times$ £750 = £60

For 150 shares sold at £6 4s. he receives £6·2 × 150 cash

= £930 cash

£62 cash buys £100 stock

£930 cash buys £100 × $\frac{930}{62}$ stock

= £1500 stock

The income on £1500 $4\frac{1}{2}\%$ stock is $\frac{9}{200}$ × £1500

= £67 10s.

Thus he buys £1500 stock and increases his income by £7 10s.

EXERCISE 4E

1. A man sells £400 stock at 70 and with the money buys another stock at 80. How much of the second stock does he buy?

2. A man invests £350 in a stock at 105 and sells out again when it has fallen to 90. How much has he lost?

3. A man withdraws £450 from his bank, where he has been receiving $3\frac{1}{2}\%$ interest, and invests the money in a 3% stock at 75. What is his change in income?

4. A man sold £2000 of a 5% stock at 90 and invested the money in a 7% stock at 108. What was his change in income?

5. A man invested £620 in a 4% stock at 80. When it had risen to 85, he sold out and reinvested the money in a 3% stock at 68. What was his change in income?

CHAPTER 5

LOGARITHMS

WE HAVE met in algebra the index notation for powers of numbers: using for instance a^3 to mean $a \times a \times a$: and we have discovered rules for multiplication and division with indices, as follows:

(i) $a^m \times a^n = a^{m+n}$
(ii) $a^m \div a^n = a^{m-n}$

These rules can be explained in words: "To multiply powers (of the same number) you add the indices; to divide you subtract."

Now addition and subtraction are usually shorter and easier tasks than multiplication and division, a fact which we often make use of in simple calculations.

For example, to multiply 100 by 100,000 we add the numbers of noughts ($2 + 5 = 7$) and immediately write 10,000,000 as our answer because, in index notation,

$$10^2 \times 10^5 = 10^7.$$

Or again, to divide 100,000 by 100 we obtain the answer 1,000 by subtracting two noughts from five noughts, because $10^5 \div 10^2 = 10^3$.

When one number is expressed as a power of another, e.g.

$$1{,}000 = 10^3$$

it is useful to have names for the various parts of the equation. We say that 3 is the *logarithm* of 1,000 to the *base* 10, meaning the power to which 10 must be raised to give 1,000: and we say that 1,000 is the *antilogarithm* of 3 to the base 10, meaning the value of 10 raised to this power. It is assumed here that 10 is being used as the base, and we write for short:

$$\textit{log}\ 1{,}000 = 3 \text{ and } \textit{antilog}\ 3 = 1{,}000.$$

How do the index rules apply to logarithms? The logarithm is itself an index, so we can explain the rules like this:

(1) To multiply numbers, add their logarithms and write down the antilogarithm of the result.
(2) To divide a number P by a number Q, subtract the logarithm of Q from that of P and write down the antilogarithm of the result.

To illustrate these rules, we will work out the two examples given above by using logarithms.

Logarithms

A list must first be made showing the logarithms of various numbers which are exact powers of 10:

Number	10	100	1,000	10,000	100,000	1,000,000	10,000,000
Logarithm	1	2	3	4	5	6	7

Notice that each number in the upper line is the antilogarithm of the number immediately below it.

(a) To multiply 100 by 100,000: add 2 (the log of 100) to 5 (the log of 100,000): result 7, the antilog of which is 10,000,000.

This can be set out more neatly like this:

	No.	*Log.*
	100	2
	100,000	5
Answer:	10,000,000	7

(b) To divide 100,000 by 100 set out the working as in the example above:

	No.	*Log.*
	100,000	5
	100	2
Answer:	1,000	3

Obviously if we knew the logarithm and antilogarithm of every number, we could carry out any multiplication or division by this method. So far we have only considered whole-number powers of 10; we first extend our list of logarithms by repeatedly dividing the first entry by 10:

$1 = \frac{10}{10}$ so the log of 1 is found by subtracting the log of 10 from the log of 10: i.e. log 1 = (1 − 1) = 0.

0·1 = $\frac{1}{10}$ so log 0·1 = (log 1 − log 10) = (0 − 1) = − 1.

Each division by 10 reduces the logarithm by 1, and the extended list looks something like this:

Number	0·0001	0·001	0·01	0·1	1	10	100	1,000
Log.	− 4	− 3	− 2	− 1	0	1	2	3

continuing in both directions.

Try using this table to divide 0·1 by 100: subtract 2 (the log of 100) from − 1 (the log of 0·1): result − 3, the antilog of which is 0·001.

Our list is still only a skeleton table of logarithms, but it is only necessary to fill in the numbers between 1 and 10, for a reason which will be explained presently. We shall only outline the method of calculating logarithms, for the tables in use today are the outcome of years of patient work, particularly by seventeenth-century mathematicians John Napier and

Henry Briggs who, of course, were without the benefit of modern electronic computers!

Suppose we require the logarithm of 2, correct to one decimal place. Now $2^{10} = 1{,}024$, which is near enough 1,000 for the accuracy we want. So if we write down the log of 2 ten times and add, the sum should be approximately the log of 1,000, which is 3. Thus the log of 2 is a tenth of 3 which is 0·3; in a four-figure table you will find log 2 given more accurately as 0·3010. When we realize that a table of logarithms contains more than a thousand entries, each correct to four decimal places, we should be grateful to the pioneers.

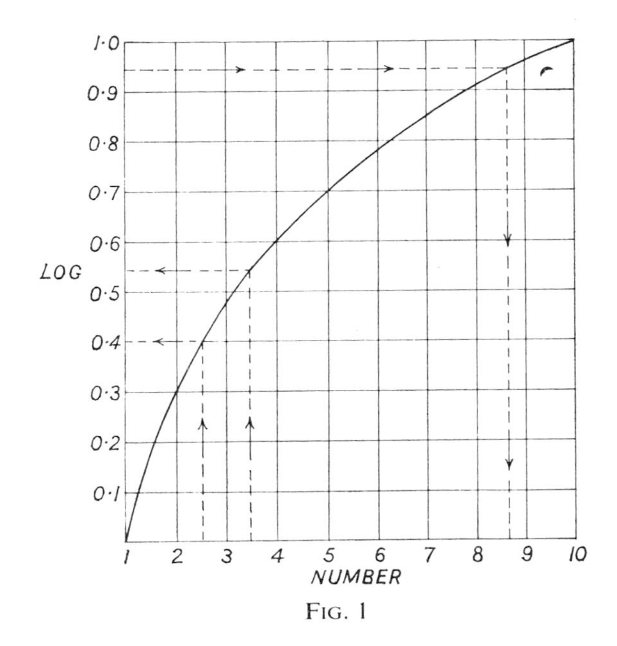

FIG. 1

Four-figure tables are the most accurate way of using logarithms (apart from such huge compilations as 7-figure tables), but they are not the most simple. Fig. 1 shows a graph of the logarithms of numbers from 1 to 10: they can be read off correct to about 2 decimal places.

Try using this graph to multiply 2·5 by 3·5: read from 2·5 on the horizontal scale up to the graph and across to the vertical scale, giving a log of 0·4; again with 3·5, giving a log of 0·54; add these logs—result 0·94; read from 0·94 on the vertical scale across to the graph and down to the horizontal scale, giving an antilog of 8·7, which is your answer correct to 2 significant figures. These readings are shown by the dotted lines on Fig. 1.

Fig. 2 illustrates the principle of the slide-rule. On each of two straight edges, numbers are marked at distances from one end in proportion to their logarithms.

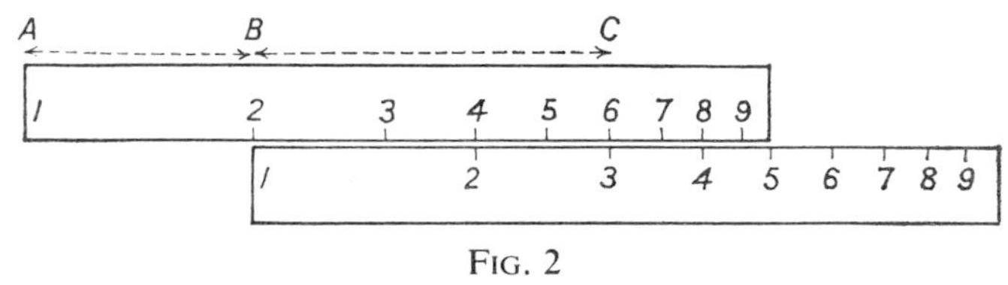

FIG. 2

To multiply, say, 2 by 3, set the figure 1 on the lower scale against the figure 2 on the upper scale, then read the answer (6) on the upper scale against the figure 3 on the lower scale. This method works because distance *AB* (Fig. 2) is proportional to log 2, distance *BC* is proportional to log 3, and therefore distance *AC* is proportional to (log 2 + log 3) which is equal to log 6. A modern slide-rule is marked in tenths or even hundredths, and has a number of additional scales.

Look now at the table of four-figure logarithms which you will find on page 466. This gives the logarithms of numbers from 1·000 to 9·999, and is used in the same way as square and square root tables. Notice, however, that all decimal points are omitted to save space: thus to find the log of, say, 2·345 we first follow the row marked 23 across to the column marked 4, finding the figure 3692; then continue across to the difference column marked 5, finding the figure 9; adding this to 3692 gives 3701, but remember that these figures are decimals, so that the log of 2·345 is actually 0·3701. Notice also that the answers given in an antilogarithm table are all numbers between 1 and 10, so the antilog of 0·5786 appears in the table as 3789 but is actually 3·789.

We will use the tables for working two examples, giving the explanation first and the short tabular form below. The answers, of course, are as accurate as the tables allow but are still only approximate. We shall keep to numbers between 1 and 10 first.

Example:

Multiply 2·345 by 3·178:

log 2·345 = 0·3701, log 3·178 = 0·5022.

So the log of their product is 0·3701 plus 0·5022 which is 0·8723.

Their product is the antilog of 0·8723 which is 7·452.

No.	*Log.*
2·345	0·3701
3·178	0·5022
7·452 ←	0·8723

Answer: 2·345 × 3·178 = 7·452 approximately.

Example:

Divide 6·563 by 1·732:

log 6·563 = 0·8171, log 1·732 = 0·2385

0·8171 − 0·2385 = 0·5786

The quotient is the antilog of 0·5786 which is 3·789.

No.	*Log.*
6·563	0·8171
1·732	0·2385
3·789 ←	− 0·5786

Answer: 6·563 ÷ 1·732 = 3·789 approximately.

EXERCISE 5A

1. Use tables to find the logarithms of:
(i) 3·142 (ii) 1·037 (iii) 7·949 (iv) 4·750

2. Use tables to find the antilogarithms of:
(i) 0·1735 (ii) 0·9087 (iii) 0·3248 (iv) 0·5000

3. Write down the values of:
(i) log 10,000 (ii) log 0·001 (iii) antilog 5

4. Use logarithms to multiply:
(i) 1·547 × 4·703 (ii) 3·142 × 2·143 (iii) 6·336 × 1·248

5. Use logarithms to divide:
(i) 7·949 ÷ 4·166 (ii) 9·372 ÷ 3·279 (iii) 6·336 ÷ 1·248

6. Consider the multiplication 5 × 8. Look up the logarithms of 5 and 8 and add them. What is the result? This number is clearly the logarithm of 40; how does it compare with the logarithm of 4? What do you think is the logarithm of 400?

Numbers Greater Than 10

The last question of the previous exercise introduced the logarithm of a number greater than 10, and we shall now see why these numbers need not be included in the tables.

Suppose that we wish to find the log of 234·5: we can write 234·5 = 100 × 2·345; but to multiply two numbers we add their logarithms, so the log of 234·5 will be 2 (the log of 100) plus 0·3701 (the log of 2·345), that is, 2·3701.

If we multiply 2·345 by different powers of 10 and calculate logs in this way, we obtain the following table:

Number ..	2·345	23·45	234·5	2,345	23,450	234,500
Logarithm ..	0·3701	1·3701	2·3701	3·3701	4·3701	5·3701

As in the tables on page 40 each multiplication by 10 increases the logarithm by one. A number between 1 and 10, such as 2·345, is said to be in *standard form*; and the rule for finding the log of a larger number can be stated as follows:

(i) The whole number part of the logarithm (which should be written down first) is the power of 10 by which the standard form has been multiplied—it can be seen most easily as the number of places the decimal point has moved.

(ii) The decimal part of the logarithm is simply the logarithm of the standard form.

Example: What is the log of 1,765? (3 places)

Standard form = 1·765. Shift of decimal point = 3 (1·765)

Log. of 1·765 = 0·2467 ∴ Log of 1,765 = 3·2467

Example: What is the antilog of 4·8432?

N.B. Find the antilog of the decimal part first, then multiply by the appropriate power of 10 by moving the decimal point.

Antilog of 0·8432 = 6·969. Shift of decimal point = 4

∴ Antilog of 4·8432 = 69,690 (6·9690)

Notice that when we are asked to "express a number in standard form," it is customary to state both the number between 1 and 10 *and* the power of 10 by which this must be multiplied, i.e. we write it in the most suitable form for finding its logarithm easily. So that, for example, 234·5 is expressed "in standard form" as $2{\cdot}345 \times 10^2$.

EXERCISE 5B

1. Find the logarithms of:

(i) 63·25 (ii) 19,610 (iii) 243,000 (iv) 981·8

2. Find the antilogarithms of:

(i) 3·5786 (ii) 1·0167 (iii) 6·9345 (iv) 2·4149

3. Use logarithms to calculate:

(i) $213{\cdot}7 \times 17{\cdot}32$

(ii) $3{\cdot}142 \times 11{\cdot}59 \times 2{,}240$

(iii) $\dfrac{764{\cdot}5}{83{\cdot}7}$

(iv) $\dfrac{45{\cdot}88 \times 31{\cdot}2}{285{\cdot}7}$

(v) $326{,}500 \div 547{\cdot}3$

(vi) $\dfrac{623{\cdot}4}{19{\cdot}1 \times 8{\cdot}571}$

We can also think of the whole number part of a logarithm as showing whether the number (i.e. the antilogarithm of the logarithm) is in the units, tens, hundreds, thousands, etc. For example, a logarithm of the form 2·—— immediately indicates a number in the hundreds, for it lies in the range between 2 (the log of 100) and 3 (the log of 1,000).

What, then, is the whole number part of the logarithm of a number in the tenths, or in the hundredths?

To find the answer to this question, we will try to extend our table on page 43 to the left, by dividing the first number by 10. Now $2{\cdot}345 \div 10 = 0{\cdot}2345$, so the log of 0·2345 will be the log of 2·345 minus the log of 10.

$$\therefore \text{Log } 0{\cdot}2345 = (0{\cdot}3701 - 1) = -0{\cdot}6299$$

To leave it like this would be rather a nuisance, because it would mean that every "standard form" would need two entries in the table; so we keep the 0·3701 and the -1 separate, and say that the whole number part is -1 and the decimal part ·3701, writing the logarithm as $\bar{1}{\cdot}3701$ to indicate that the minus sign refers only to the whole number. This is usually spoken of as: "*Bar one*" point three seven nought one. Let us divide again:

$$2{\cdot}345 \div 100 = 0{\cdot}02345$$

so that the log of 0·02345 is found by subtracting 2 (the log of 100) from 0·3701; the result this time appears as $\bar{2}{\cdot}3701$, the whole number part is called "*Bar two*."

If we divide a few more times, our extended table will be like this:

Number	0·0002345	0·002345	0·02345	0·2345	2·345	23·45
Logarithm	$\bar{4}{\cdot}3701$	$\bar{3}{\cdot}3701$	$\bar{2}{\cdot}3701$	$\bar{1}{\cdot}3701$	0·3701	1·3701

Compare this with the extended table on page 43. A "bar" number obviously indicates that standard form has been *divided* by this number of powers of 10, or that the decimal point has moved the same number of places to the *left*.

Example: What is the log of 0·005476?

Standard form = 5·476. Shift of decimal point = $\bar{3}$ (0005·476)

Log of 5·476 = 0·7385 $\therefore$ Log of 0·005476 = $\bar{3}{\cdot}7385$

Example: What is the antilog of $\bar{2}{\cdot}2982$?

Antilog of 0·2982 = 1·987. Shift of decimal point = $\bar{2}$ (i.e. 2 to left)

$\therefore$ Antilog of $\bar{2}{\cdot}2982$ = 0·01987 (001·987)

When a multiplication or division involves adding or subtracting whole number parts of logarithms, some of which may be "bar numbers," the usual algebraic rule of signs must be remembered: look carefully at the following examples:

$3 + \bar{1} = 2$	$\bar{2} + 1 = \bar{1}$	$\bar{2} + \bar{1} = \bar{3}$	$1 - \bar{2} = 3$	$2 - 5 = \bar{3}$
$\bar{1} - \bar{4} = 3$	$\bar{2} - 5 = \bar{7}$	$\bar{4} - \bar{1} = \bar{3}$	$3 + \bar{3} = 0$	$3 - \bar{3} = 6$

Example: Multiply 38·26 by 0·0007251.

$$38{\cdot}26 = 3{\cdot}826 \times 10^1 \text{ and}$$
$$0{\cdot}0007251 = 7{\cdot}251 \div 10^4$$

so the whole number parts are 1 and $\bar{4}$ respectively. There is 1 to carry from the tenths column, and $(1 + \bar{4} + 1) = \bar{2}$.

No.	*Log.*
38·26	1·5828
0·0007251	$\bar{4}$·8604
0·02774	$\bar{2}$·4432

Answer: 38·26 × 0·0007251 = 0·02774 approximately.

Example: Divide 0·4359 by 0·006705.

04·359 [1 place to left ($\bar{1}$)]

0006·705 [3 places to left ($\bar{3}$)]

1 has to be borrowed from the units column, and

$(\bar{1} - \bar{3} - 1) = (-1 + 3 - 1) = 1$

No.	*Log.*
0·4359	$\bar{1}$·6394
0·006705	$\bar{3}$·8264
65·01	1·8130

Answer: 0·4359 ÷ 0·006705 = 65·01 approximately.

EXERCISE 5C

1. Find the logarithms of:
(i) 0·003345 (ii) 0·8167 (iii) 0·01414 (iv) 0·0000273

2. Find the antilogarithms of:
(i) $\bar{2}$·3629 (ii) $\bar{4}$·9345 (iii) $\bar{1}$·5786 (iv) $\bar{6}$·6021

3. Simplify the following:
(i) $\bar{3} + 2$
(ii) $\bar{2} - 3$
(iii) $\bar{4} - \bar{1}$
(iv) $\bar{2} + 5$
(v) $\bar{1} + 1$
(vi) $\bar{3}$·9250 + 1·6465
(vii) 2·7387 − $\bar{1}$·9843
(viii) $\bar{1} - 4 - \bar{2}$

4. Use logarithms to calculate:
(i) 0·2494 × 47·85
(ii) 3·162 ÷ 0·02236
(iii) $(0·4139)^2$
(iv) 0·005062 ÷ 0·193
(v) 173·2 × 0·2857 × 0·08571
(vi) 7 ÷ 246·8

Basic Rules in the Use of Logarithms

Before we use logarithms to work out various problems in arithmetic, it is worth noting a few rules which will make things easier and mistakes less likely:

1. Cancel or simplify before using logs only when this can be done easily and will leave you fewer logarithms to look up:

e.g. (a) $\frac{1}{3} \times \frac{62·7}{0·429}$ We can quickly divide 3 into 62·7 leaving the division $\frac{20·9}{0·429}$ with two figures to look up instead of three.

but (b) $\frac{13·7 \times 19·45}{186·5}$ There is no point in cancelling by 5, for (apart from possible mistakes in division!) nothing is gained and there would still be three logarithms to find.

2. When evaluating a fraction like $\dfrac{28{\cdot}57 \times 0{\cdot}683}{4{\cdot}211 \times 13{\cdot}09}$ the numerator and denominator should first be calculated separately, but can be left as logarithms (without finding antilogs) because it is only their logarithms which will be needed to carry out the final division of one by the other.

3. Do not forget that, although numbers are multiplied by adding logarithms, we cannot use logarithms to add numbers: so in an expression like $(7{\cdot}823 \times 28{\cdot}7) + (192{\cdot}6 \times 0{\cdot}774)$ don't start adding together the logarithms of the two brackets.

4. In one special case, however, one multiplication can take the place of two multiplications and a subtraction. When we have an expression like $(27{\cdot}17)^2 - (15{\cdot}03)^2$ to calculate, we remember the rule of algebra:

$$a^2 - b^2 = (a + b)(a - b)$$

and write it as:

$$(27{\cdot}17 + 15{\cdot}03)(27{\cdot}17 - 15{\cdot}03) \text{ i.e. } 42{\cdot}20 \times 12{\cdot}14$$

5. It is a good habit to make a rough estimate of the answer to a problem before starting the actual working. Consider, for example, Question 3 (vi) in Exercise 1B:

$$\frac{623{\cdot}4}{19{\cdot}1 \times 8{\cdot}571}$$

A rough estimate of this is $\dfrac{600}{20 \times 8}$ i.e. $\dfrac{600}{160}$ or nearly 4. If our calculated answer turns out to be 0·3808 we must suspect a mistake in the working, probably in this case in the position of the decimal point.

6. It is worth trying to remember the logarithm of π, a number which occurs very often in problems about circles and cylinders. Taking 3·1416 as a more accurate value than 3·142, we have:

$$\text{Log } \pi = 0{\cdot}4971$$

Example: A bicycle wheel has a diameter of 26 in. How many times does it revolve while the bicycle travels a distance of 435 yd.?

	No.	*Log.*
	435	2·6385
Distance travelled $= 435 \times 36$ in.	36	1·5563
Circumference of wheel $= \pi \times 26$ in.	Numerator	4·1948
$\therefore$ No. of revolutions $= \dfrac{435 \times 36}{\pi \times 26}$	π	0·4971
	26	1·4150
Rough estimate $= \dfrac{400 \times 30}{3 \times 20}$	Denominator	1·9121
	Numerator	4·1948
$= 200$	Denominator	1·9121
	191·7	2·2827

Answer: The wheel revolves approximately 192 times.

Example: A rectangular sheet of copper measuring 11·3 in. by 13·7 in. weighs 3 lb. 2 oz. Calculate its thickness, given that copper weighs 557 lb. per cubic foot.

Weight of sheet $= 3\frac{1}{8}$ lb.

$= 3{\cdot}125$ lb.

$\therefore$ Volume of sheet $= \dfrac{3{\cdot}125}{557}$ cu. ft.

$= \dfrac{3{\cdot}125 \times 1728}{557}$ cu. in.

Area of sheet $= 11{\cdot}3 \times 13{\cdot}7$ sq. in.

$\therefore$ Thickness $= \dfrac{\text{Volume}}{\text{Area}}$

$= \dfrac{3{\cdot}125 \times 1728}{557 \times 11{\cdot}3 \times 13{\cdot}7}$ in.

Rough estimate $= \dfrac{3 \times 1800}{600 \times 10 \times 15}$

$= \dfrac{3}{50} = 0{\cdot}06$

No.	*Log.*
3·125	0·4949
1728	3·2375
Numerator	3·7324
557	2·7459
11·3	1·0531
13·7	1·1367
Denominator	4·9357
Numerator	3·7324
Denominator	4·9357
0·06262	$\bar{2}{\cdot}7967$

Answer: The thickness of the sheet is approximately 0·0626 in.

EXERCISE 5D

1. An aircraft flew over a measured course of 31·5 miles in a time of 2 minutes 41·7 seconds. Calculate its speed in m.p.h.

2. It is planned to build a motorway for 87·1 miles with an average width of 71·4 ft. How many acres will it cover?

3. A town with a population of 7,230 consumes 376,500 gallons of milk every year. How many pints a day does the average inhabitant drink?

4. Smith works a 41-hour week and is paid £12 16s. per week. His union asks for an increase of $7\frac{1}{2}$d. per hour. By how much per cent would this increase Smith's earnings?

5. A computing machine can do 195 additions per minute or 37 multiplications per minute. How long, to the nearest tenth of a second, would it take to do 36 additions followed by 24 multiplications?

6. Calculate the volume of a circular coin of diameter 4·16 cm. and thickness 0·235 cm.

Powers and Roots

Suppose we have to calculate $(17{\cdot}63)^3$: this involves writing down the logarithm of 17·63 three times and adding: obviously the process can be shortened by writing down the logarithm and multiplying it by three.

Thus instead of:

No.	*Log.*
17·63	1·2462
17·63	1·2462
17·63	1·2462
	3·7386

we can write

No.	*Log.*
17·63	1·2462
	× 3
	3·7386

This method should be used whenever a number is to be raised to a power; the general rule is:

$$\text{Log}\,(a^n) = n \times \text{Log}\,a$$

A little care must be taken if "bar" numbers occur, as in the following:
Example: Calculate $(0{\cdot}7195)^5$.

Five times bar one is bar five.

There are four to carry from the tenths column, and $\bar{5} + 4 = \bar{1}$.

No.	*Log.*
0·7195	$\bar{1}{\cdot}8570$
	× 5
0·1928	$\bar{1}{\cdot}2850$

Answer: $(0{\cdot}7195)^5 = 0{\cdot}1928$ approximately.

Now consider an expression like $\sqrt[3]{17{\cdot}63}$. This expression, when cubed, gives the answer 17·63 (for this is what we mean by cube root), so its logarithm multiplied by 3 must give the logarithm of 17·63 (by the rule set out above for powers); and so:

$$\begin{aligned} \text{Log}\sqrt[3]{17{\cdot}63} &= \tfrac{1}{3}\,(\log 17{\cdot}63) \\ &= \tfrac{1}{3}\,(1{\cdot}2462) \\ &= 0{\cdot}4154 \\ \therefore \sqrt[3]{17{\cdot}63} &= \text{antilog}\,(0{\cdot}4154) \\ &= 2{\cdot}602 \end{aligned}$$

This is set out in tabular form below:

No.	*Log.*
17·63	1·2462
	3)1·2462
2·602	0·4154

The general rule for finding roots is: $\text{Log}\sqrt[n]{a} = \dfrac{1}{n} \times \text{Log}\,a$

At first sight there is a slight difficulty with bar numbers. For suppose that we have to divide, say $\bar{2}{\cdot}4627$ by 5; if we carry $\bar{2}$ into the tenths our next division is 5 into "bar-twenty" four! The answer is that we must always carry a positive remainder, if any, so we must look for the nearest number *below* $\bar{2}$ into which 5 divides exactly:

$\overline{10}\ \ \bar{9}\ \ \bar{8}\ \ \bar{7}\ \ \bar{6}\ \ \bar{5}\ \ \bar{4}\ \ \bar{3}\ \ \bar{2}\ \ \bar{1}\ \ 0\ \ 1\ \ 2\ \ 3\ \ 4\ \ 5$

←——→

A glance at the scale shows that this number is $\bar{5}$, into which 5 divides $\bar{1}$ times. We therefore rewrite $\bar{2}\cdot4627$ as $\bar{5} + 3\cdot4627$, the division now proceeds normally (5 into 34 etc.) with the result:

$$5)\overline{\bar{2}\cdot4627}$$
$$\bar{1}\cdot6925 \text{ correct to 4 decimal places}$$

Notice that if a number is less than one, any power or root of this number will also be less than one, but the power will be less than the original number while the root will be greater. In the example above, the fifth root of 0·02902 (whose log is $\bar{2}\cdot4627$) turns out to be 0·4926 (the antilog of $\bar{1}\cdot6925$).

EXERCISE 5E

1. Use logarithms to calculate:
(i) $(9\cdot631)^3$ (ii) $(13\cdot08)^4$ (iii) $\sqrt[5]{257\cdot3}$ (iv) $\sqrt[4]{18\cdot22}$

2. Simplify the following:
(i) $\bar{1}\cdot7219 \times 4$ (ii) $\bar{2}\cdot4577 \div 3$ (iii) $\bar{5}\cdot6336 \div 4$

3. Use logarithms to calculate:
(i) $(0\cdot6543)^5$ (ii) $(0\cdot0852)^3$ (iii) $\sqrt[3]{0\cdot3456}$ (iv) $\sqrt[4]{0\cdot00419}$

4. The volume of a sphere is given by the formula $V = \frac{4}{3}\pi r^3$. Find the radius of a sphere whose volume is 1 cubic inch.

Things We Have Learned

Let us summarize, in the form of a table, some of the main rules we have learned in this chapter:

Numbers	*Logarithms*
In standard form (between 1 and 10)	In form 0·xxxx (between 0 and 1)
Each multiplication by 10 ..	Add 1
Each division by 10..	Subtract 1 (i.e. add bar-one)
To multiply .. To divide ..	Add Subtract
For *N*th power .. For *N*th root ..	Multiply by *N* Divide by *N*

Finally, some questions and suggestions:

(i) Use 4-figure tables to draw an accurate graph of $y = 10^x$.

(ii) How would you use log tables to calculate reciprocals?

(iii) Construct a slide-rule from two pieces of cardboard, using a scale log 10 : 10 in. (log 2 : 3·01 in. etc.). Can you see how to use it for division sums?

(iv) The law of compound interest is $A = P\left(1 + \frac{r}{100}\right)^t$. Could this be calculated with logarithms? If so, with what accuracy?

(v) Assuming $\log 2 = 0{\cdot}3$, use the approximation $3^4 \simeq 2^3 \times 10$ to obtain an approximate value for log 3.

(vi) In some equations in physics, it is necessary to work out expressions like $(24{\cdot}63)^{1{\cdot}483}$. How would a table of the logarithms of logarithms of numbers help? Notice that many slide-rules have scales marked "LogLog."

(vii) Try to find out something about the early calculating device known as "Napier's Bones."

(viii) Is it always sensible to use logarithms? Notice that $3^4 = 81$, but what answer do you get for 3^4 using logs?

(ix) What is the log of 32 to the base 2? Why does 10 make the most convenient base for logarithms?

(x) Can you discover the origin of the word "logarithm"?

CHAPTER 6

TRIGONOMETRY

WE HAVE used the method of scale-drawing to solve problems such as the following:

Port A is 3 miles due west of Port B, and the bearing of a ship is N. 50° E. from A and N. 30° W. from B; how far is the ship from Port A? (Fig. 1.)

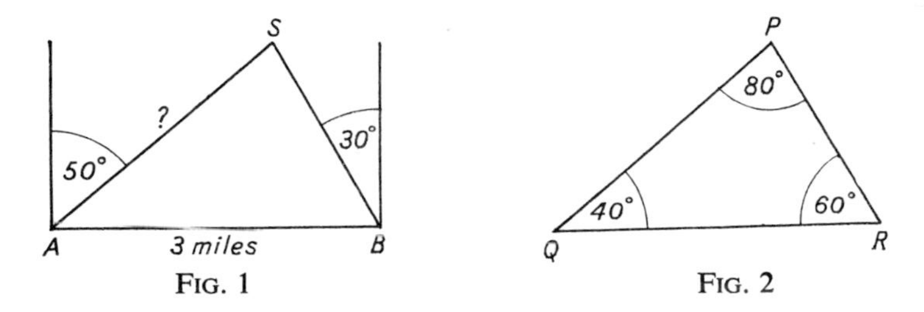

FIG. 1

FIG. 2

The method is to construct a triangle *similar* to the actual figure (Fig. 2) and use the fact that the two triangles will then have their sides in the same proportions. In practice we shall probably make QR equal to 3 inches, so that the length of PQ in inches will give the distance SA in miles; but in fact any scale will do, and the ratio $\frac{SA}{AB}$ will always equal the ratio $\frac{PQ}{QR}$.

Now this ratio is obviously the same for all 40°, 60°, 80° triangles and if we could look it up in a table we should not need to make the scale drawing. Unfortunately, a table listing all shapes of triangles with angles given in degrees and minutes would need a book of more than 1,000 pages; so for the present we shall consider the ratios of sides in right-angled triangles only: other kinds of triangle will be dealt with in the next chapter, but remember that by dropping a perpendicular any triangle can be divided into two right-angled ones.

The Tangent of an Angle

In a right-angled triangle, one other angle must be given to determine its shape; it is useful to name the three sides by their position in relation to this given angle and the right-angle.

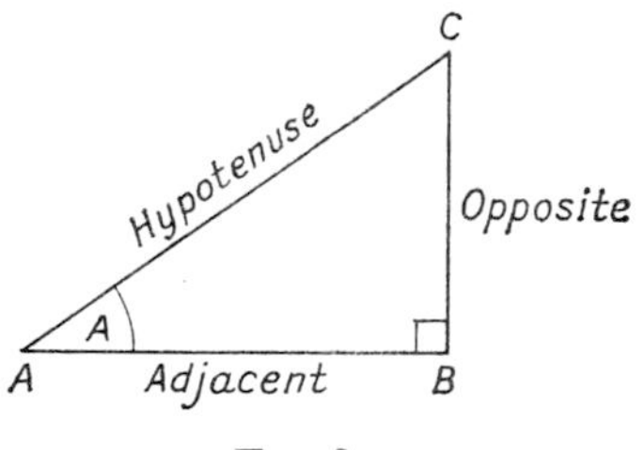

FIG. 3

In Fig. 3, A is the given angle and B the right-angle. Side AC is thus the *hypotenuse*, and of the sides containing the right-angle BC is *opposite* the angle A while side AB is *adjacent* to angle A. The ratio $\frac{BC}{AB}$ is called the TANGENT of the angle A, or for short tan $\hat{A}$, and we must remember that:

$$\text{Tangent} = \frac{\text{Opposite}}{\text{Adjacent}}$$

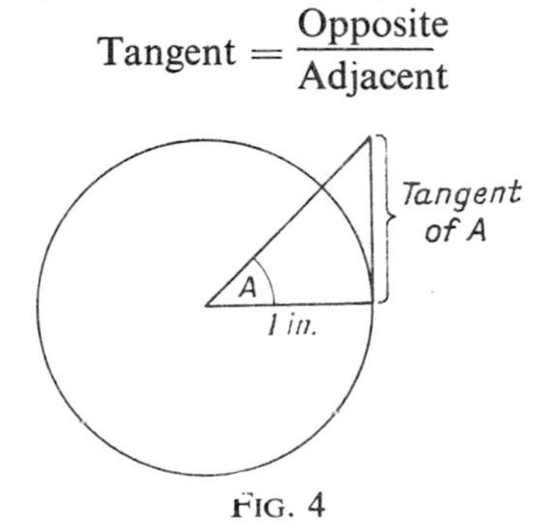

FIG. 4

The reason for this name can be seen from Fig. 4: to a circle of radius 1 in. draw a tangent to subtend an angle A at the centre; its length in inches will be tan $\hat{A}$. This would be a simple, though not very accurate, way of making a table of the tangents of angles.

On the next page is given a table of tangents correct to 3 significant figures for angles at intervals of one degree. We shall later use 4-figure tables with angles in degrees and minutes.

Note:

(i) For small angles the *opposite* side is approaching zero length, and so tan $0° = 0$.

(ii) For an angle of 45° the triangle is isosceles, so tan $45° = 1$.

(iii) As the angle approaches 90° the *adjacent* side approaches zero length, so that tan 90° is infinitely large.

(iv) Tan $\hat{A}$ is enough to fix the shape of a triangle, for if we know two sides we can calculate the third by Pythagoras' theorem; this however would be rather tedious, and we shall later use other ratios involving the hypotenuse.

Tangents, correct to 3 significant figures:

$\hat{A}$	tan $\hat{A}$	$\hat{A}$	tan $\hat{A}$	$\hat{A}$	tan $\hat{A}$	$\hat{A}$	tan $\hat{A}$	$\hat{A}$	tan $\hat{A}$
0°	0	19°	0·344	37°	0·754	55°	1·43	73°	3·27
1°	0·0175	20°	0·364	38°	0·781	56°	1·48	74°	3·49
2°	0·0349	21°	0·384	39°	0·810	57°	1·54	75°	3·73
3°	0·0524	22°	0·404	40°	0·839	58°	1·60	76°	4·01
4°	0·0699	23°	0·424	41°	0·869	59°	1·66	77°	4·33
5°	0·0875	24°	0·445	42°	0·900	60°	1·73	78°	4·70
6°	0·105	25°	0·466	43°	0·933	61°	1·80	79°	5·14
7°	0·123	26°	0·488	44°	0·966	62°	1·88	80°	5·67
8°	0·141	27°	0·510	45°	1·00	63°	1·96	81°	6·31
9°	0·158	28°	0·532	46°	1·04	64°	2·05	82°	7·12
10°	0·176	29°	0·554	47°	1·07	65°	2·14	83°	8·14
11°	0·194	30°	0·577	48°	1·11	66°	2·25	84°	9·51
12°	0·213	31°	0·601	49°	1·15	67°	2·36	85°	11·4
13°	0·231	32°	0·625	50°	1·19	68°	2·48	86°	14·3
14°	0·249	33°	0·649	51°	1·23	69°	2·61	87°	19·1
15°	0·268	34°	0·675	52°	1·28	70°	2·75	88°	28·6
16°	0·287	35°	0·700	53°	1·33	71°	2·90	89°	57·3
17°	0·306	36°	0·727	54°	1·38	72°	3·08	90°	∞
18°	0·325								

Some of the problems for which we shall use this table will contain the terms "angle of elevation," "angle of depression" and "altitude" (of the sun). The first two are measured, respectively, upwards and downwards from the horizontal, as shown in Fig. 5. The sun's altitude at any time is its angle of elevation (see Fig. 6).

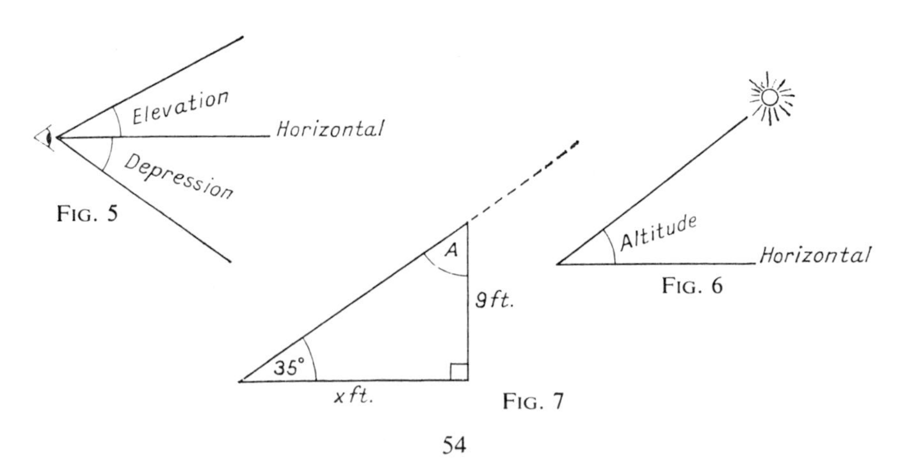

FIG. 5

FIG. 6

FIG. 7

Example 1. How long will be the shadow cast by a post 9 ft. high when the altitude of the sun is 35° (Fig. 7)?

Let the length be x feet.

$$\hat{A} = 90° - 35° = 55°$$

$$\text{Then } \frac{x}{9} = \tan 55° = 1{\cdot}43$$

$$\therefore x = 9 \times 1{\cdot}43$$

$$= 12{\cdot}87$$

Answer: The shadow will be approximately 12·9 feet long.

Note:

(i) We could also write $\frac{9}{x} = \tan 35°$

but this leads to the equation

$x = 9 \div \tan 35°$, a division which may require logarithms. It is generally more convenient to use the angle *opposite* the side we are trying to calculate.

(ii) The answer must be corrected to 3 significant figures: the fourth figure cannot be certain when we use 3-figure tables.

Example 2. A ship sails 7 miles due north, then 13 miles due west. What is her bearing then from the starting point (Fig. 8)?

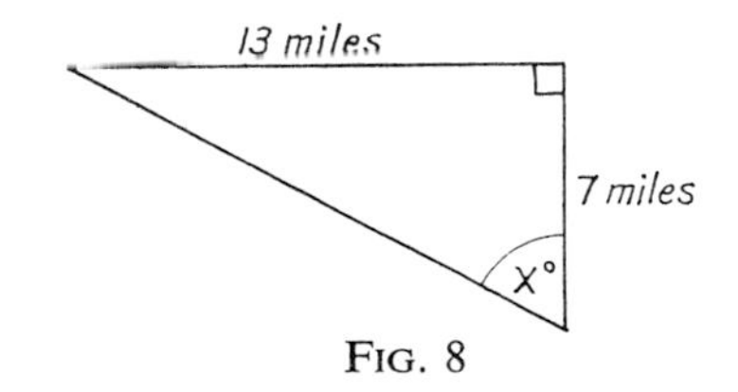

FIG. 8

Let the bearing be N. $x°$ W.

Then $\tan x° = \frac{13}{7} = 1{\cdot}86$ approx.

$\therefore x = 62$ to the nearest whole number.

Answer: The bearing is approximately N. 62° W.

Note: With 3-figure tables it is usually necessary to give the angle to the nearest degree; though if the tangent were, say, 1·84 then it would be reasonable to estimate the angle as $61\frac{1}{2}$ degrees.

EXERCISE 6A

1. From a point 100 yd. (horizontally) from the foot of a television mast, the angle of elevation of its top is 23°. Find the height of the mast in feet.

2. An aircraft takes off and climbs at an angle of 13° to the horizontal. How far does it travel horizontally in reaching a height of 1,500 ft.?

3. A man of height 5 ft. 8 in. casts a shadow 7 ft. 8 in. long. Find the sun's altitude.

4. In the triangle shown in Fig. 9, $AP = 5$ cm. Find the length of BP and use this result to find the length of CP.

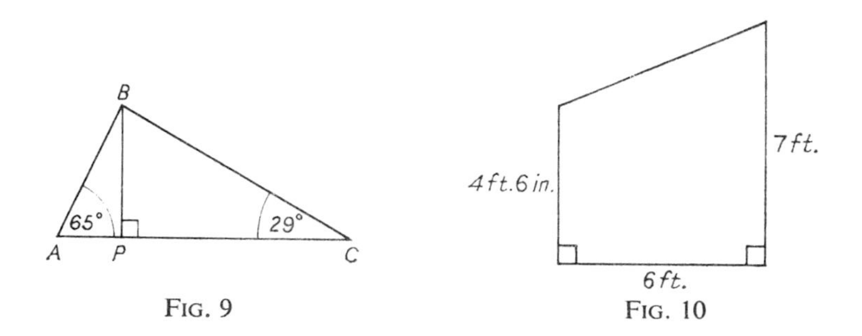

FIG. 9

FIG. 10

5. Fig. 10 shows the end view of a lean-to shed. Find the angle which the sloping roof makes with the vertical.

Four-figure Tables

You will find on page 480 a four-figure table of tangents. Angles are given at intervals of 6 minutes, and differences in minutes. The whole number part of the tangent is shown only in the first entry in each row: heavy type is used to indicate that the whole number is one more than in this first entry.

Suppose we wish to find the tangent of 71° 43′.

At 71° 42′ the entry, in heavy type, is 0237: at 71° the tangent is 2·9042, so this entry shows a tangent of 3·0237. The difference given under 1′ is 29, so tan 71° 43′ = 3·0237 + 0·0029 = 3·0266.

Example 3. From the top of a vertical cliff, 137 ft. above sea-level, the angle of depression of a boat is 24° 32′. Find its distance from the foot of the cliff.

Let the distance be d feet (Fig. 11).

$$\text{Then } \frac{d}{137} = \tan \hat{A} = \tan 65^\circ 28'$$

$$= 2{\cdot}1910$$

$$\therefore d = 137 \times 2{\cdot}191$$

$$= 300{\cdot}1$$

No.	*Log.*
137	2·1367
2·191	0·3406
300·1	2·4773

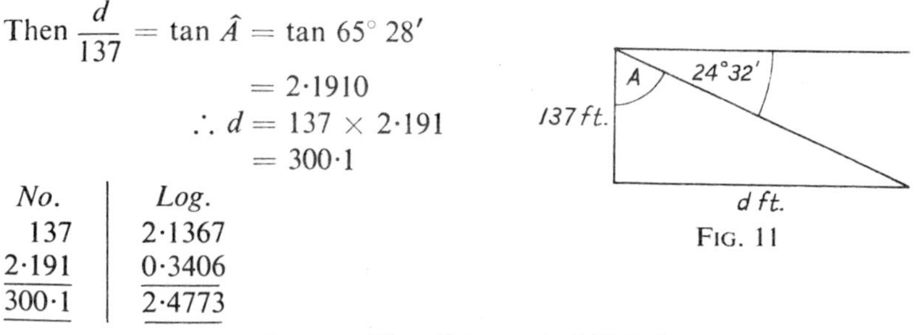

FIG. 11

Answer: The distance is 300·1 ft.

Logarithmic Tangents: In the example above we first found tan 65° 28′ in a table of tangents, and later looked up the logarithm of this number in a table of logarithms. The result, 0·3406, is called the logarithmic tangent (log tan for short) of this angle, and could have been found directly from the table headed "Log Tangents" on page 474.

The working would then have been:

$$d = 137 \times \tan 65^\circ 28'$$
$$= 300{\cdot}1$$

No.	*Log.*
137	2·1367
tan 65° 28′	0·3406
300·1	2·4773

EXERCISE 6B

(Use four-figure tables)

1. Find the tangents of:
(i) 13° 31′ (ii) 28° 23′ (iii) 59° 11′ (iv) 82° 42′

2. Find the angles whose tangents are:
(i) 0·0811 (ii) 0·4827 (iii) 1·4523 (iv) 3·431

3. A diagonal of a rectangle makes an angle of 61° 27′ with the shorter sides, whose length is 9·145 cm. Find the length of the longer sides.

4. From a point at sea level the elevation of a mountain peak whose height is known to be 3,461 ft. is 6° 36′. Calculate, in miles, how far away it is horizontally.

5. ABC is a triangle right-angled at B. $AB = 1{\cdot}732$ in. and $BC = 1{\cdot}237$ in. Calculate, to the nearest minute, $\hat{A}$ and $\hat{C}$.

Sine and Cosine

Returning to the right-angled triangle in Fig. 3, we see that the tangent does not involve the length of the hypotenuse: two ratios which do so are the sine and the cosine. The ratio $\frac{BC}{AC}$ is called the SINE of the angle A (Fig. 12), in other words: Sine $= \frac{\text{Opposite}}{\text{Hypotenuse}}$

Now consider the ratio $\frac{AB}{AC}$; AB is the side opposite to angle C, so this ratio is the sine of C. As C is the complement of A, we call this ratio the COSINE of $\hat{A}$.

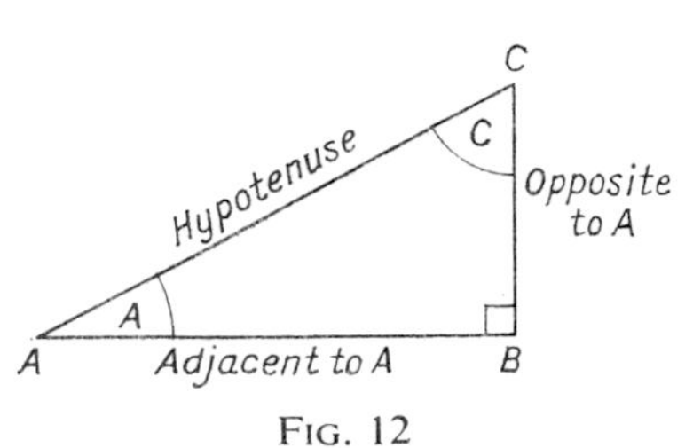

FIG. 12

But AB is adjacent to $\hat{A}$, thus:

$$\text{Cosine} = \frac{\text{Adjacent}}{\text{Hypotenuse}}$$

These ratios are written for short as "sin $\hat{A}$" and "cos $\hat{A}$" respectively. It is not often necessary to use the cosine, because for cos $\hat{A}$ we can always write sin $(90° — \hat{A})$.

("Cosine = Sine of Complement.")

The sine and cosine are the ratios of the opposite and adjacent sides respectively to the hypotenuse: they are thus the fractions by which the hypotenuse must be multiplied to find these two sides:

Opposite = Hypotenuse × Sine; Adjacent = Hypotenuse × Cosine

In the examples which follow we shall use four-figure tables of sines and cosines, which can be found on pages 476 and 478.

Note:

(i) Since the hypotenuse is the longest side in a right-angled triangle neither sine nor cosine can have a value greater than 1. Thus, apart from the special cases sin 90° = cos 0° = 1, the whole number part of each entry in these tables is to be taken as 0.

(ii) As $\hat{A}$ increases, cos $\hat{A}$ decreases; and therefore in the table of cosines the figures under the difference columns are amounts to be *subtracted* from the original value.

Example 4. A ship sails 19·3 miles in a direction N. 34°, 34′ E. How many miles is she then to the north of her starting point?

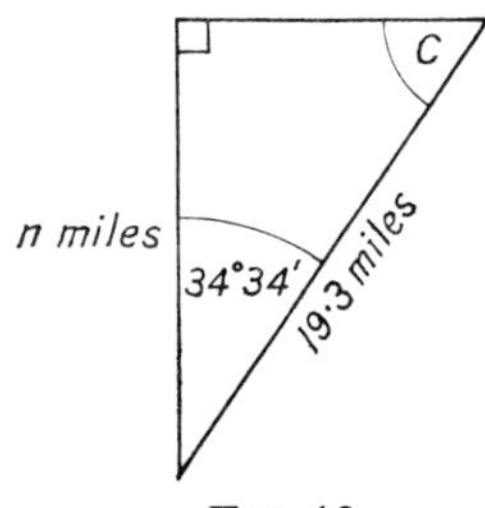

FIG. 13

Let the distance be n miles (Fig. 13)

$$\text{Then } \frac{n}{19{\cdot}3} = \cos 34°\,34'$$

$$= 0{\cdot}8234$$

(Subtract the difference, 0·0007 from 0·8241, the cosine of 34° 30′.)

$$\therefore n = 19{\cdot}3 \times 0{\cdot}8234$$

$$= 15{\cdot}90$$

No.	*Log.*
19·3	1·2856
0·8234	$\bar{1}$·9156
15·90	1·2012

Answer: She is 15·90 miles north of her starting point.

Note: We could also have written $\frac{n}{19{\cdot}3} = \sin 55^\circ\, 26'$, using $\hat{C}$ which is the complement of 34° 34′. Look at the table of sines and you will find that $\sin 55^\circ\, 26' = 0{\cdot}8231 + 0{\cdot}0003 = 0{\cdot}8234$ also. The logarithm of this number, which is $\bar{1}{\cdot}9156$, could be found directly under the angle 55° 26′ in a Log Sine table, or under 34° 34′ in a Log Cosine table.

Example 5. A ladder, which reaches 31 ft. 6 in. up a vertical wall, makes an angle of $68\frac{1}{2}^\circ$ with the ground.

How long is the ladder?

Let its length be l feet (Fig. 14)

Now Opposite = Hypotenuse × Sine

$$\text{i.e. } 31{\cdot}5 = l \times \text{Sin } 68^\circ\, 30'$$
$$= l \times 0{\cdot}9304$$
$$\therefore l = \frac{31{\cdot}5}{0{\cdot}9304}$$
$$= 33{\cdot}86$$

No.	*Log.*
31·5	2·4983
0·9304	$\bar{1}{\cdot}9687$
33·86	2·5296

Answer: The ladder is approximately 33 ft. 10 in. long.

Fig. 14

Example 6. A straight road rises 485 ft. in a distance of $\frac{3}{4}$ mile (measured along the road). At what angle is it inclined to the horizontal? (Fig. 15)

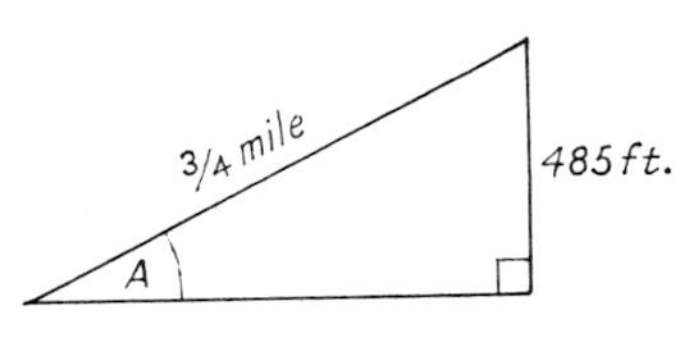

Fig. 15

Let the angle be A.

$$\text{Then } \sin \hat{A} = \frac{485}{\frac{3}{4} \times 5280}$$
$$= \frac{485}{3960}$$
$$= 0{\cdot}1225$$
$$\therefore \hat{A} = 7^\circ\, 2'$$

No.	*Log.*
485	2·6857
3960	3·5977
0·1225	$\bar{1}{\cdot}0880$

Answer: It is inclined at 7° 2′ to the horizontal.

EXERCISE 6C

1. A ladder 38 ft. long rests against a vertical wall, making an angle of 25° with the wall. How far from the wall is the foot of the ladder?

2. In crossing a road 32 ft. wide, a man walks 43 ft. in a straight line. Find the angle between this line and the direction of the road.

3. A car is driven at 30 m.p.h. up a hill inclined at 15° to the horizontal. At what rate, in feet-per-second, does it gain height?

4. How far must a ship sail in a direction N. 47° W. before she is $4\frac{1}{2}$ miles north of her starting point?

5. Find from four-figure tables the values of:

(i) $17{\cdot}67 \times \cos 61^\circ 37'$

(ii) $\dfrac{1{,}760}{\sin 35^\circ 29'}$ (iii) The angle whose sine is $\dfrac{119{\cdot}5}{257{\cdot}3}$

6. In the triangle shown in Fig. 16 $AB =$ 5·36 in., $BP \perp AC$, $\hat{A} = 29^\circ 17'$, $\hat{C} = 64^\circ$. Calculate: (i) the length of BP; (ii) the length of BC.

7. The diagonal of a rectangle is of length 11·9 cm. and is inclined at 39° 45′ to the longer side. Calculate the area of the rectangle.

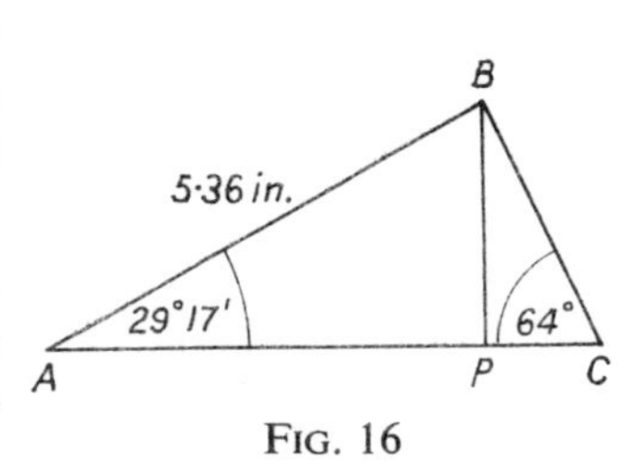

FIG. 16

Triangles Other Than Right-angled Ones

Question No. 6 in the last exercise illustrates the method of dropping a perpendicular in a triangle which is not right-angled. Here are two further examples of this method.

Example 7. (The problem stated at the beginning of this chapter).

Port A is 3 miles due west of Port B, and the bearing of a ship is N. 50° E. from A and N. 30° W. from B. How far is the ship from Port A?

Drop a perpendicular AP from A on to SB.

Let distance $AP = p$ miles, and

let distance $AS = s$ miles.

Then $p = 3 \times \sin 60^\circ$

Also $p = s \times \sin 80^\circ$

$$\therefore s = \frac{p}{\sin 80^\circ} = \frac{3.\sin 60^\circ}{\sin 80^\circ} = \frac{3 \times 0{\cdot}8660}{0{\cdot}9848} = 2{\cdot}637$$

FIG. 17

No.	*Log.*
3	0·4771
0·8660	$\bar{1}$·9375
	0·4146
0·9848	$\bar{1}$·9934
2·637	0·4212

Answer: The ship is 2·637 miles from A.

Example 8. (An isosceles triangle, for which the method is very suitable.)

The diagram (Fig. 18) represents the legs of a step-ladder when fully opened. Calculate $A\hat{T}B$ and the height of T above the ground.

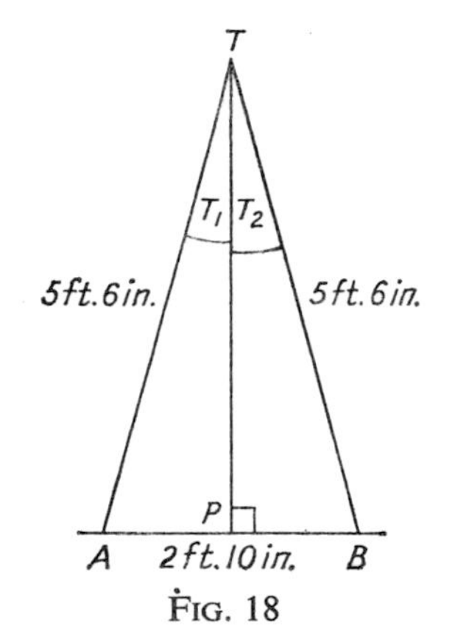

FIG. 18

Drop a perpendicular TP from T on to AB as shown.

Since $\triangle\ ATB$ is isosceles, $AP = PB = 1'\ 5''$.

Then $\sin \hat{T}_1 = \sin \hat{T}_2 = \dfrac{17}{66} = 0{\cdot}2575$

$\therefore\ \hat{T}_1 = \hat{T}_2 = 14°\ 55'$

$\therefore\ A\hat{T}B = \hat{T}_1 + \hat{T}_2 = 29°\ 50'$

No.	Log.
17	1·2304
66	1·8195
0·2575	$\bar{1}$·4109

Let height $TP = h$ in.

Then $\dfrac{h}{66} = \cos 14°\ 55' = 0{\cdot}9663$

$\therefore\ h = 66 \times 0{\cdot}9663$

$= 63{\cdot}77$

No.	Log.
66	1·8195
0·9663	$\bar{1}$·9851
63·77	1·8046

Answers: The angle is 29° 50′

The height is 5 ft. $3\frac{3}{4}$ in.

The following exercise contains further miscellaneous examples involving tangent, sine and cosine. Use the four-figure tables at the back of this book.

EXERCISE 6D

1. Calculate the area of $\triangle\ ABC$ given that $AB = 7{\cdot}31$ in., $BC = 5{\cdot}95$ in. and $\hat{B} = 61°\ 29'$.

2. On a map whose scale is 6 in. to the mile, the 300 ft. and 400 ft. contours on a hillside are 1·47 in. apart. Calculate the average inclination of the hillside to the horizontal over this region.

3. From a point 35 yd. from the foot of a vertical tower, the angle of elevation of the top of the tower is $36° 30'$, while that of the top of a flagstaff surmounting the tower is $41° 24'$. Find the length of the flagstaff in feet.

4. PQ is a chord of length 18·8 cm. in a circle of radius 12·5 cm. Find the angle which PQ subtends at the centre of the circle.

5. A crane of length 15 ft. is mounted, 4 ft. above the ground, on a breakdown lorry. What is its maximum permissible inclination to the horizontal if the lorry is to pass under a bridge whose maximum headroom is only 15 ft.?

6. A rhombus has angles of 47° and 133° and a longer diagonal of 16·7 cm. Find the lengths of (i) the shorter diagonal; (ii) the sides.

7. The width of a railway cutting is 140 ft. at the top and 35 ft. at the bottom. Its vertical depth is 30 ft. and one side slopes at 35° to the horizontal. What is the slope of the other side?

8. $ABCDE$ is a regular pentagon inscribed in a circle of radius $4\frac{1}{2}$ in. Calculate the lengths of (i) side AB; (ii) diagonal AC.

9. From an aircraft flying at a height of 4,000 ft. a target is directly ahead with an angle of depression of 12°. Twenty seconds later it is still directly ahead but the angle of depression is 16°. Find the speed of the aircraft to the nearest mile-per-hour.

10. A and B are two towns on a straight road running from N.E. to S.W. and B is 2·9 miles N.E. from A. The bearings of a third town, C, from A and B are respectively N. $5° 45'$ E. and N. $12° 24'$ W. Find the perpendicular distance from C to the road through A and B.

Reciprocal Ratios

We have used so far three ratios in the right-angled triangle: the tangent, sine and cosine. There are altogether six possible ratios of three given lengths; the other three are the reciprocals of these three. They are not often used in calculations but are listed below for completeness:

$$\text{Tangent} = \frac{\text{Opposite}}{\text{Adjacent}} \qquad \text{Cotangent} = \frac{\text{Adjacent}}{\text{Opposite}} = \frac{1}{\text{Tangent}}$$

$$\text{Sine} = \frac{\text{Opposite}}{\text{Hypotenuse}} \qquad \text{Cosecant} = \frac{\text{Hypotenuse}}{\text{Opposite}} = \frac{1}{\text{Sine}}$$

$$\text{Cosine} = \frac{\text{Adjacent}}{\text{Hypotenuse}} \qquad \text{Secant} = \frac{\text{Hypotenuse}}{\text{Adjacent}} = \frac{1}{\text{Cosine}}$$

These last three are usually abbreviated to cot, cosec and sec.

Notice that by taking $(90° - \hat{A})$ in place of $\hat{A}$, we exchange the positions of the opposite and adjacent sides, because $(90° - \hat{A})$ is the angle at the vertex opposite to $\hat{A}$.

We thus obtain the results:

$$\tan(90^\circ - \hat{A}) = \frac{\text{Adjacent}}{\text{Opposite}} = \cot \hat{A}$$

$$\sin(90^\circ - \hat{A}) = \frac{\text{Adjacent}}{\text{Hypotenuse}} = \cos \hat{A}$$

$$\cos(90^\circ - \hat{A}) = \frac{\text{Opposite}}{\text{Hypotenuse}} = \sin \hat{A}$$

Example 9. Prove the relations (i) $\dfrac{\sin \hat{A}}{\cos \hat{A}} = \tan \hat{A}$; (ii) $(\sin \hat{A})^2 + (\cos \hat{A})^2 = 1$.

Denote the sides as in Fig. 19:

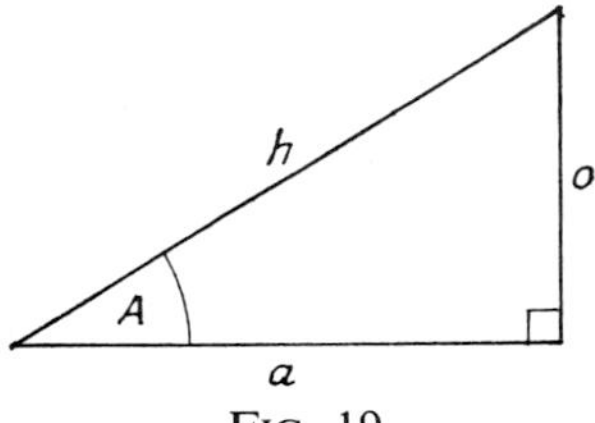

FIG. 19

$$\text{(i)}\quad \frac{\sin \hat{A}}{\cos \hat{A}} = \frac{o}{h} \div \frac{a}{h} = \frac{o}{h} \times \frac{h}{a}$$

$$= \frac{o}{a}$$

$$= \tan \hat{A}.$$

$$\text{(ii)}\quad (\sin \hat{A})^2 + (\cos \hat{A})^2 = \frac{o^2}{h^2} + \frac{a^2}{h^2} = \frac{o^2 + a^2}{h^2}$$

$$= \frac{h^2}{h^2} \text{ (by Pythagoras)} = 1$$

Example 10. Given that $\cos \hat{A} = 0{\cdot}8$, find without using tables the values of $\sin \hat{A}$ and $\tan \hat{A}$.

(i) Let $\sin \hat{A} = s$

Then $s^2 + (0{\cdot}8)^2 = 1$

$\therefore s^2 = 1 - 0{\cdot}64 = 0{\cdot}36$

$\therefore s = \sqrt{0{\cdot}36} = 0{\cdot}6$

(ii) $\tan \hat{A} = \dfrac{\sin \hat{A}}{\cos \hat{A}}$

$= \dfrac{0{\cdot}6}{0{\cdot}8}$

$= 0{\cdot}75$

Answer: $\sin \hat{A} = 0{\cdot}6$ and $\tan \hat{A} = 0{\cdot}75$.

Note: It is sometimes easier to consider a suitable triangle and apply Pythagoras' theorem directly. In the example above, $\cos \hat{A} = 0{\cdot}8 = \frac{4}{5}$, so consider a triangle with hypotenuse 5 in. and side adjacent to A, 4 in.; (these lengths give the value $0{\cdot}8$ to $\cos \hat{A}$). The opposite side is found from Pythagoras' theorem to be 3 in., so that

$$\sin \hat{A} = \tfrac{3}{5} = 0{\cdot}6 \text{ and } \tan \hat{A} = \tfrac{3}{4} = 0{\cdot}75.$$

The last two results are examples of trigonometrical formulae. In the next chapter we shall look at the trigonometry of the triangle in more general terms, and prove some formulae connecting trigonometrical ratios of the angles with the lengths of the sides and the area. These formulae will be true for any triangle, not only right-angled ones. As a triangle can contain one obtuse angle, we must also consider what is meant by the tangent, sine and cosine of an obtuse angle: remember that we have explained these ratios only in a right-angled triangle, where the other two angles must necessarily be acute.

The trigonometry of the triangle is important because:

(i) The triangle is the simplest figure to which trigonometry can be applied, and the formulae derived from it are the basis of most trigonometrical calculations.

(ii) Any other straight-line figure can be dealt with if necessary by dissecting it into a number of triangles. In particular, the problem of surveying and mapping any large area of country is most easily solved by the method of "triangulation."

CHAPTER 7

TRIANGLES

THE LAST chapter showed a way of dealing with triangles which are not right-angled, by drawing a perpendicular from one vertex to the opposite side. For ease of calculation, however, it is generally more convenient to use one of a number of *formulae* connecting the sides and angles of any triangle: we shall begin this chapter by proving some of these formulae.

Since we need to know to which sides and angles the letters in a formula refer, we must first decide on a standard way of labelling these dimensions. Suppose we are considering a triangle ABC, then we shall use capital letters $\hat{A}$, $\hat{B}$, $\hat{C}$ for the three angles. We shall use small letters a, b, c for the three sides, with the understanding that the side opposite any angle carries the same letter, for example a is the length of the side opposite $\hat{A}$ (Fig. 1).

Similarly in triangle PQR we would write:

$$PQ = r$$
$$QR = p$$
$$RP = q$$

to denote these lengths.

What properties of triangles do we know already? Here are two, written as formulae, to illustrate the use of letters shown above:

FIG. 1

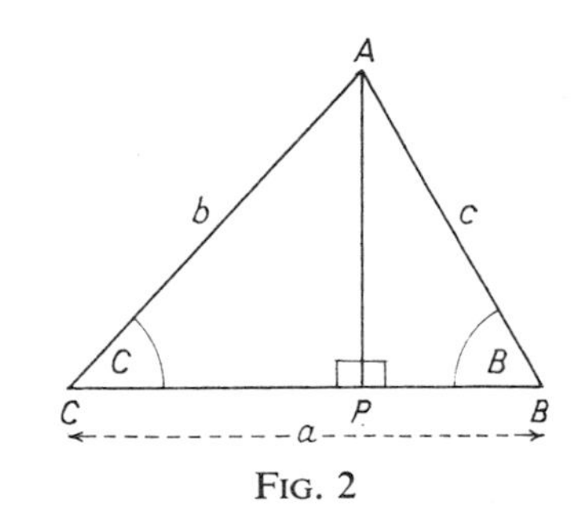

FIG. 2

Property	*Formula*
1. Interior-angle sum	$\hat{A} + \hat{B} + \hat{C} = 180°$
2. Pythagoras' Theorem	If $\hat{A} = 90°$, $a^2 = b^2 + c^2$

In order to obtain further formulae, we divide our basic triangle into two right-angled triangles by drawing a perpendicular, AP, from A on to BC (Fig. 2): we then apply simple sine and cosine ratios to the triangles APC and APB. It is assumed for the present that $\hat{B}$ and $\hat{C}$ are both acute, so that P will lie between them.

Formula 1: $a = b.\cos\hat{C} + c.\cos\hat{B}$

Proof: $\dfrac{CP}{AC} = \cos\hat{C}$ $\therefore CP = b.\cos\hat{C}$. Similarly $PB = c.\cos\hat{B}$.

But $a = CP + PB = b.\cos\hat{C} + c.\cos\hat{B}$.

Note: By drawing perpendiculars from B or C we obtain also

$$b = a.\cos\hat{C} + c.\cos\hat{A} \text{ and } c = a.\cos\hat{B} + b.\cos\hat{A}$$

Formula 2: $AP = b.\sin\hat{C} = c.\sin\hat{B}$

Proof: $\dfrac{AP}{AC} = \sin\hat{C}$ $\therefore AP = b.\sin\hat{C}$. Similarly $AP = c.\sin\hat{B}$.

Note: The lengths of perpendiculars from B and C are

$$BQ = a.\sin\hat{C} = c.\sin\hat{A} \text{ and } CR = a.\sin\hat{B} = b.\sin\hat{A}$$

The triangle in Fig. 2 has all its angles acute, but it is hoped that these formulae will be true also for obtuse-angled triangles. Since not more than one angle could be obtuse, let us now see what happens if our triangle has $\hat{A}$ and $\hat{C}$ acute, $\hat{B}$ obtuse. The foot of the perpendicular AP will now lie on CB produced (Fig. 3).

The Sine of an Obtuse Angle.

In Fig. 3 we have $AP = b.\sin C = c.\sin A\hat{B}P$, while Formula 2 is

$$AP = b.\sin C = c.\sin B$$

We therefore assume that:

$$\sin B = \sin A\hat{B}P = \sin(180° - B)$$

i.e. we take the sine of an obtuse angle to be the sine of its supplement.

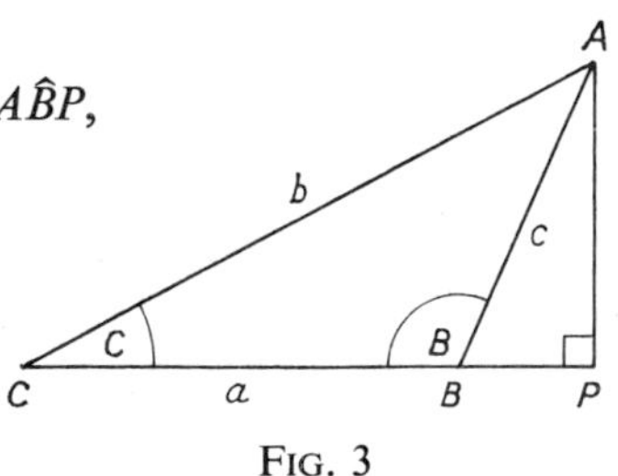

FIG. 3

Example: Use tables to find the value of sin 137° 49′.

$$\sin 137° 49' = \sin(180° - 137° 49') = \sin 42° 11' = 0{\cdot}6715$$

The Cosine of an Obtuse Angle.

In Fig. 3 we have $BP = c.\cos A\hat{B}P$ and $CB = CP - BP$

so that $a = b.\cos\hat{C} - c.\cos A\hat{B}P$

while Formula 1 is $a = b.\cos\hat{C} + c.\cos\hat{B}$

This time the formula will be correct if we assume that

$$\cos\hat{B} = -\cos A\hat{B}P = -\cos(180° - \hat{B})$$

i.e., the cosine of an obtuse is *minus* the cosine of its supplement.

Example: $\cos 120° = -\cos 60° = -0{\cdot}5$

The Tangent of an Obtuse Angle.

In the last chapter the formula $\tan \hat{A} = \dfrac{\sin \hat{A}}{\cos \hat{A}}$ was proved. If this is to hold for obtuse angles, then in the case above $\tan \hat{B}$ is given by:

$$\tan \hat{B} = \frac{\sin \hat{B}}{\cos \hat{B}}$$
$$= \frac{\sin (180^\circ - \hat{B})}{- \cos (180^\circ - \hat{B})} = - \tan (180^\circ - \hat{B})$$

i.e., the tangent of an obtuse angle is minus the tangent of its supplement.

Example: Find the angle whose tangent is $-0{\cdot}5486$.

From a four-figure table we find that $\tan 28^\circ 45' = 0{\cdot}5486$. Thus the supplement of this angle, $151^\circ 15'$, has a tangent of $-0{\cdot}5486$.

The definitions above have been chosen to make Formula 1 and Formula 2 true for obtuse-angled triangles; later in this chapter their use will be justified in a rather more algebraic way. Before we go any further, here is a summary of the results obtained so far, followed by a short exercise.

Triangle formulae	*Obtuse-angle formulae*
$a = b.\cos \hat{C} + c.\cos \hat{B}$	$\sin \hat{A} = \sin (180^\circ - \hat{A})$
$AP = b.\sin \hat{C} = c.\sin \hat{B}$	$\cos \hat{A} = - \cos (180^\circ - \hat{A})$
	$\tan \hat{A} = - \tan (180^\circ - \hat{A})$

EXERCISE 7A

1. Given $\triangle LMN$ with sides l, m, n:

(i) To which side does the letter m refer?

(ii) Write down a formula for m in terms of other sides and angles.

(iii) What is the formula for the length of the perpendicular from L on to MN?

2. Use tables to evaluate:

(i) $\sin 163^\circ 18'$; (ii) $\cos 129^\circ 47'$;

(iii) $\tan 99^\circ$;

(iv) the obtuse angle whose sine is $0{\cdot}3726$;

(v) the angle whose cosine is $-0{\cdot}5923$.

3. In Fig. 4, calculate the lengths of:

(i) AP;

(ii) AB; (iii) CB.

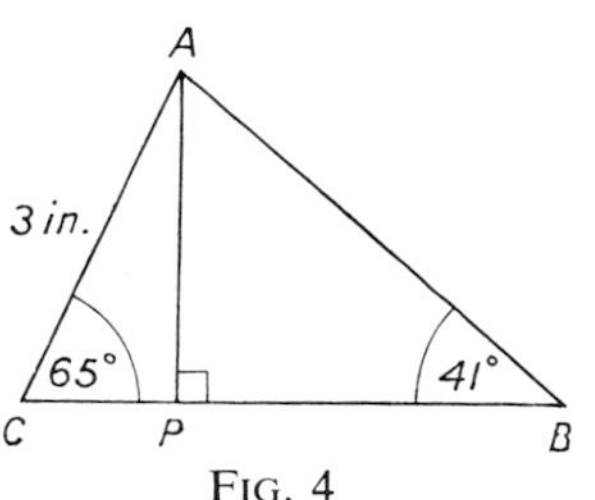

FIG. 4

4. Prove that the area of the triangle in Fig. 2 is given by the formula

$$\tfrac{1}{2}a.b.\sin \hat{C}$$

The two most important triangle formulae, both frequently used in practical calculation, are known as the "sine rule" and the "cosine rule." Each can be proved from one of the two formulae already given.

The Cosine Rule

(i) $b = c.\cos \hat{A} + a.\cos \hat{C} \quad \therefore \quad b^2 = bc.\cos \hat{A} + ba.\cos \hat{C}$
(ii) $c = b.\cos \hat{A} + a.\cos \hat{B} \quad \therefore \quad c^2 = cb.\cos \hat{A} + ca.\cos \hat{B}$
(iii) $a = b.\cos \hat{C} + c.\cos \hat{B} \quad \therefore \quad a^2 = ab.\cos \hat{C} + ac.\cos \hat{B}$

Comparing these three expressions for the squares on the sides of a triangle, we see that the sum $(b^2 + c^2)$ of the first two exceeds the third (a^2) by an amount equal to twice $bc.\cos \hat{A}$.

$$\therefore a^2 = b^2 + c^2 - 2bc.\cos \hat{A}$$

This result, known as the cosine rule, is an improvement on Formula 1 because it enables one to calculate the third side of a triangle from the other two sides and the angle between them (Formula 1 gave a in terms of the other sides and *two* angles) and also because, given the three sides of a triangle, it enables one to find any angle. For this purpose it is convenient to rewrite the equation making $\cos \hat{A}$ the subject:

$$\cos \hat{A} = \frac{b^2 + c^2 - a^2}{2bc}$$

Example 1. In $\triangle ABC$, $AB = 4{\cdot}25$ cm., $BC = 6{\cdot}7$ cm. and $B = 53°$. Use the cosine rule to calculate the length AC.

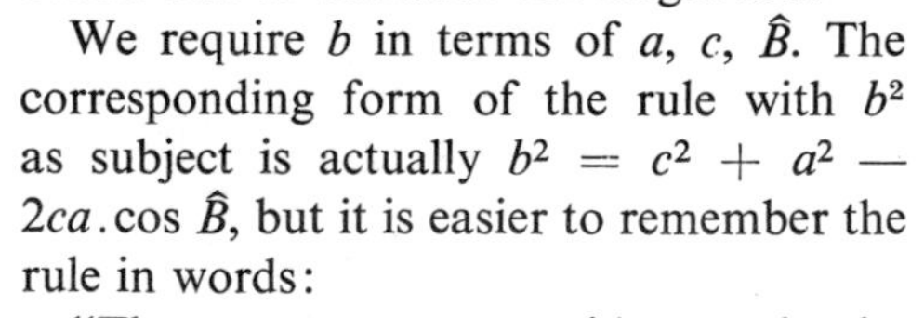

FIG. 5

We require b in terms of a, c, $\hat{B}$. The corresponding form of the rule with b^2 as subject is actually $b^2 = c^2 + a^2 - 2ca.\cos \hat{B}$, but it is easier to remember the rule in words:

"The square on any side equals the sum of the squares on the other two sides minus twice the product of the other two sides and the cosine of the angle between them."

Here (Fig. 5) we have

$$\begin{aligned} b^2 &= 4{\cdot}25^2 + 6{\cdot}7^2 - 2\,(4{\cdot}25)\,(6{\cdot}7)\cos 53° \\ &= 18{\cdot}06 + 44{\cdot}89 - 8{\cdot}5\,(6{\cdot}7)\cos 53° \\ &= 62{\cdot}95 - 34{\cdot}28 \\ &= 28{\cdot}67 \\ \therefore b &= 5{\cdot}355 \end{aligned}$$

No.	*Log.*
8·5	0·9294
6·7	0·8261
cos 53°	$\bar{1}$·7795
34·28	1·5350

No.	*Square*
4·25	18·06
6·7	44·89
5·355	28·67

Answer: The length AC is approximately 5·355 cm.

***Example* 2.** A triangular field has sides of length 47 yd., 73 yd. and 105 yd. Calculate the angle opposite the longest side.

Letter the triangle as in Fig. 6.

$$\text{Then } \cos \hat{A} = \frac{b^2 + c^2 - a^2}{2bc}$$

$$= \frac{47^2 + 73^2 - 105^2}{2\,(47)\,(73)}$$

$$= \frac{2{,}209 + 5{,}329 - 11{,}025}{94 \times 73}$$

$$= \frac{-\,3{,}487}{6{,}862}$$

$$= -\cos 59^\circ\, 27'$$

$$\therefore \hat{A} = 180^\circ - 59^\circ\, 27'$$

$$= 120^\circ\, 33'$$

No.	*Log.*
3,487	3·5425
6,862	3·8364
cos 59° 27′	$\bar{1}$·7061

Answer: The angle is approximately 120° 33′.

Notes:

(i) $\bar{1}$·7061 is looked up directly in a log cosine table.

(ii) Since cos $\hat{A}$ is negative, $\hat{A}$ is an obtuse angle: the supplement of the acute angle whose cosine is $+\dfrac{3{,}487}{6{,}862}$

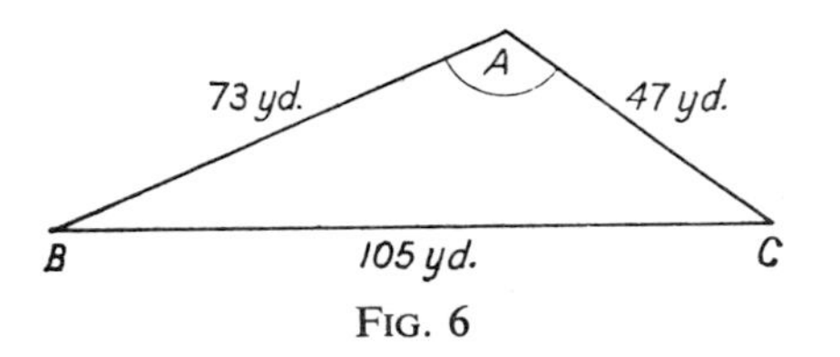

FIG. 6

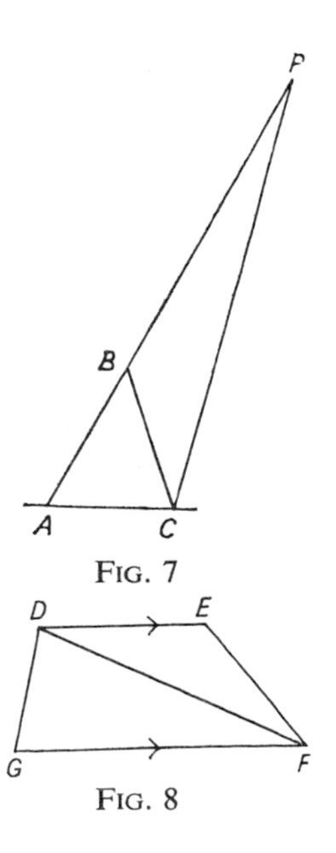

FIG. 7

FIG. 8

EXERCISE 7B

1. Use the cosine rule to find the angles of a triangle whose sides are 5 in., 7 in. and 8 in.

2. A ship sails N.E. for 9 miles and N. 30° W. for another $6\frac{1}{2}$ miles. How far is she then from her starting point?

3. PQR is an isosceles triangle with $PQ = PR = 14$ cm. and $\hat{P} = 29°$. Calculate the length RM, where M is the mid-point of PQ.

4. Fig. 7 shows the framework of a crane. $AB = 12$ ft., $BP = 25$ ft., $BC = 11$ ft. and $AC = 9$ ft. 6 in. AC is horizontal.

(i) At what angle is arm ABP inclined to the vertical?

(ii) What is the length of the strut PC?

5. Fig. 8 shows a trapezium in which DE is parallel to GF. $DG = 3$ in., $DE = 4$ in. and $FD = FG = 7$ in.

(i) Calculate angle DGF. (ii) Calculate length EG.

The Sine Rule

From Formula 2, $b.\sin \hat{C} = c.\sin \hat{B}$.
Divide each side of this equation by $(\sin \hat{B})(\sin \hat{C})$:

$$\frac{b}{\sin \hat{B}} = \frac{c}{\sin \hat{C}}$$

Similarly from $c.\sin \hat{A} = a.\sin \hat{C}$ it follows that

$$\frac{c}{\sin \hat{C}} = \frac{a}{\sin \hat{A}}$$

$$\therefore \frac{a}{\sin \hat{A}} = \frac{b}{\sin \hat{B}} = \frac{c}{\sin \hat{C}}$$

Thus the sides of a triangle are in proportion to the sines of the angles opposite to them. This result is known as the sine rule. Each of these fractions is actually equal to the diameter of the circumcircle of $\triangle ABC$, as can be discovered from Fig. 9:

CD is a diameter of this circle.
$D\hat{B}C = 90°$ (angle in a semicircle)
$B\hat{D}C = \hat{A}$ (angles in same segment)

$$\therefore a = CD \sin \hat{A}$$

$$\therefore \frac{a}{\sin A} = CD$$

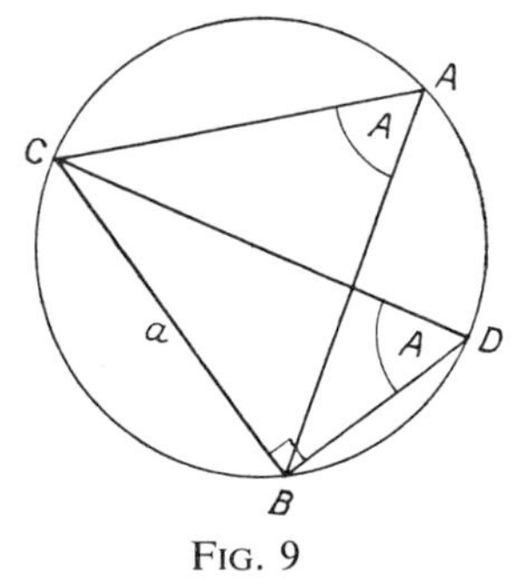

FIG. 9

The sine rule has two main uses:

(i) Knowing the angles of a triangle and one side, one can use it to calculate either of the remaining sides.

(ii) Knowing two sides and a non-included angle, one can use it to calculate the *sine* of the other non-included angle.

Since, however, an acute angle and its supplement have the same sine, *it may not be possible to determine the actual angle*: this should not be surprising for two sides and a non-included angle is the "ambiguous case." It is sometimes possible to rule out the obtuse-angle solution on the grounds that it and the given angle would have a sum exceeding 180°.

This will be seen in the second of the following examples.

Notice the ease of calculation with the sine rule (no squaring and adding): it should always be preferred to the cosine rule if there is any choice, and full use should be made of log sines.

Example 3. $\triangle ABC$ has $\hat{A} = 39°$, $\hat{B} = 73°$ and $AB = 6·1$ in. Calculate BC (Fig. 10).

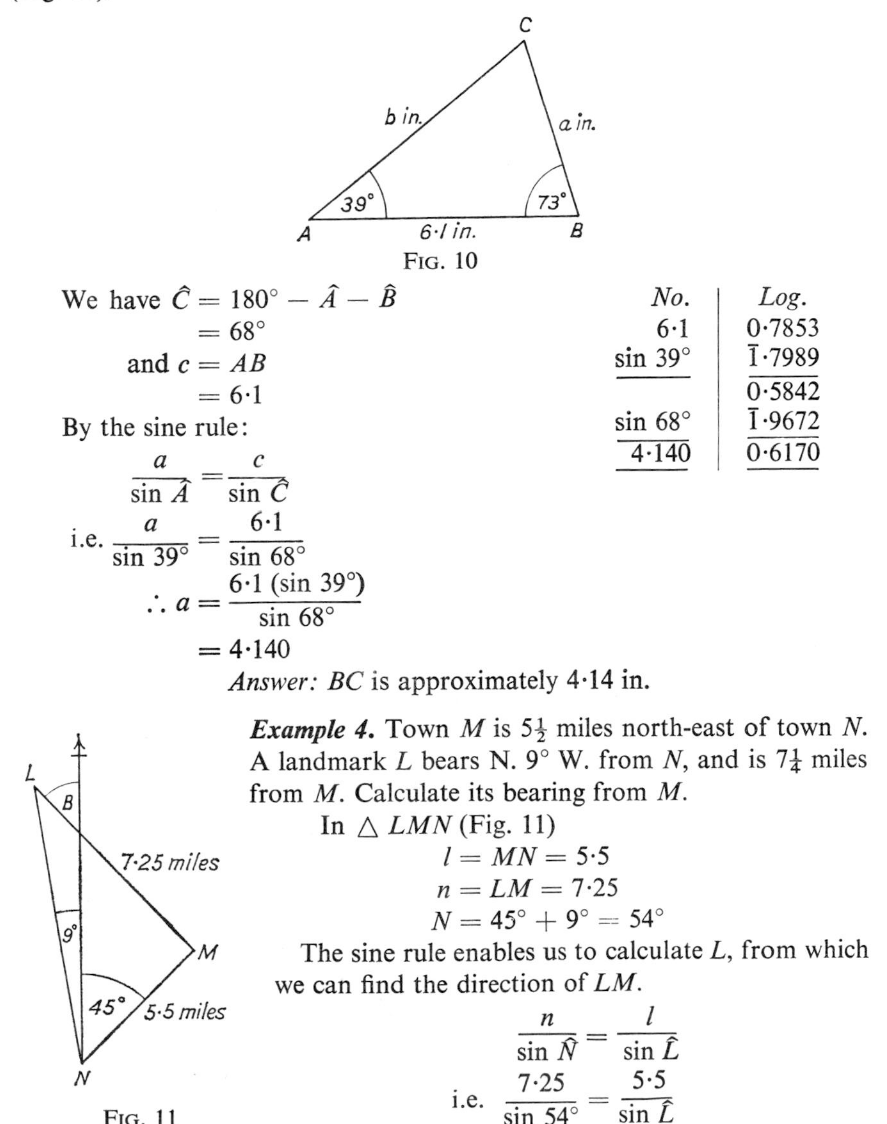

FIG. 10

We have $\hat{C} = 180° - \hat{A} - \hat{B}$

$= 68°$

and $c = AB$

$= 6·1$

By the sine rule:

$$\frac{a}{\sin \hat{A}} = \frac{c}{\sin \hat{C}}$$

$$\text{i.e. } \frac{a}{\sin 39°} = \frac{6·1}{\sin 68°}$$

$$\therefore a = \frac{6·1 (\sin 39°)}{\sin 68°}$$

$$= 4·140$$

Answer: BC is approximately 4·14 in.

No.	*Log.*
6·1	0·7853
sin 39°	$\bar{1}$·7989
	0·5842
sin 68°	$\bar{1}$·9672
4·140	0·6170

Example 4. Town M is $5\frac{1}{2}$ miles north-east of town N. A landmark L bears N. 9° W. from N, and is $7\frac{1}{4}$ miles from M. Calculate its bearing from M.

FIG. 11

In $\triangle LMN$ (Fig. 11)

$$l = MN = 5·5$$
$$n = LM = 7·25$$
$$N = 45° + 9° = 54°$$

The sine rule enables us to calculate L, from which we can find the direction of LM.

$$\frac{n}{\sin \hat{N}} = \frac{l}{\sin \hat{L}}$$

$$\text{i.e. } \frac{7·25}{\sin 54°} = \frac{5·5}{\sin \hat{L}}$$

$$\therefore \sin \hat{L} = \frac{5\cdot5 (\sin 54^\circ)}{7\cdot25}$$
$$= \sin 37^\circ 52'$$

(This answer is obtained directly from log sine tables.)

No.	Log.
5·5	0·7404
sin 54°	$\bar{1}$·9080
	0·6484
7·25	0·8603
sin 37° 52′	$\bar{1}$·7881

Now if L has the same sine as 37° 52′, L is either 37° 52′ or its supplement, 142° 8′.

But we already have $N = 54^\circ$, and 142° 8′ + 54° exceeds the angle sum of a triangle.

So $L = 37^\circ 52'$.

The bearing of L from M is given by the angle marked B (Fig. 11), which is 9° + 37° 52′ (exterior angle of triangle).

Answer: The bearing is approximately N. 46° 52′ W.

EXERCISE 7C

1. The legs of a step-ladder are inclined at 73° and 77° respectively to the horizontal when their feet are placed a yard apart on level ground. Calculate the lengths of the two legs, which are unequal.

2. Calculate angle A in each of the following triangles, giving both possible answers if the solution is ambiguous:

(i) $AB = 9\cdot8$ cm., $BC = 7\cdot9$ cm., $\hat{C} = 123^\circ$

(ii) $AC = 1$ ft. 11 in., $BC = 2$ ft. 5 in., $\hat{B} = 43^\circ 10'$.

(iii) $AB = 11\cdot7$ in., $AC = 8\cdot31$ in., $\hat{C} = 60^\circ$

3. A ship, S, bears N. 63° E. from a port P and N. 47° E. from a lighthouse L. If the port is 2·9 miles due W. of the lighthouse, calculate the distance from the port to the ship.

4. Five miles S.E. of a jetty a buoy is moored. A boat sails from the jetty in a direction S. 39° 35′ E. When the boat is first exactly 1 mile from the buoy, what will be the bearing of the buoy from the boat?

The Area of a Triangle

We have seen the equation $AP = b.\sin \hat{C} = c.\sin \hat{B}$ where AP is the perpendicular from $\hat{A}$ on to BC. But the area of a triangle is given by

Area $= \frac{1}{2}$.base × perpendicular height.

In this case the base is a (the side BC) and the height is $b.\sin \hat{C}$, so that the area is equal to $\frac{1}{2}ab.\sin \hat{C}$ or $\frac{1}{2}ac.\sin \hat{B}$ or, since $a.\sin \hat{B} = b.\sin \hat{A}$, it is also equal to $\frac{1}{2}bc.\sin \hat{A}$.

In each case the formula can be expressed in the form:

Area = half the product of two sides by the sine of the included angle.

Example 5. Fig. 12 is the plan of a plot of land which has been surveyed with a view to finding its area. The lengths are shown in yards. Calculate the area as a decimal part of an acre.

The area in square yards is:

$$\tfrac{1}{2}(15{\cdot}2)(20{\cdot}5)\sin 107^\circ 45' + \tfrac{1}{2}(22{\cdot}3)(22{\cdot}6)\sin 80^\circ 30'$$

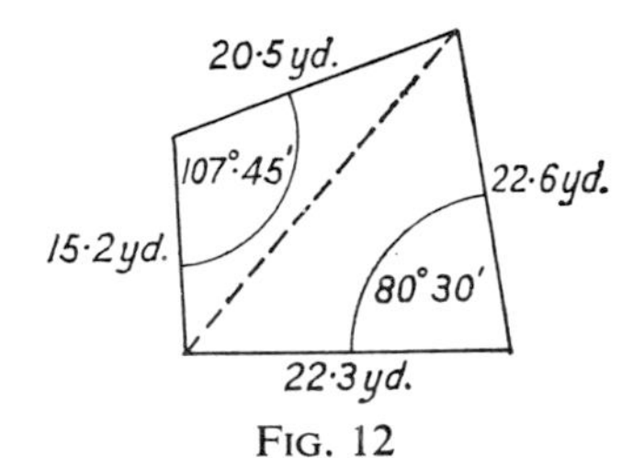

FIG. 12

	No.	*Log.*
	7·6	0·8808
	20·5	1·3118
sin 107° 45' =	sin 72° 15'	$\bar{1}$·9788
	148·4	2·1714

No.	*Log.*
11·15	1·0472
22·6	1·3541
sin 80° 30'	$\bar{1}$·9940
248·5	2·3953

$$\therefore \text{area} = (148{\cdot}4 + 248{\cdot}5) \text{ sq. yd.}$$
$$= \frac{396{\cdot}9}{4{,}840} \text{ acre}$$
$$= 0{\cdot}08202 \text{ acre}$$

No.	*Log.*
396·9	2·5987
4840	3·6848
0·08202	$\bar{2}$·9139

The Solution of Triangles

When three dimensions (e.g. three sides or two sides and the included angle) of a triangle are given, the process of finding the remaining three is known as the solution of the triangle. The method to be adopted depends on the kind of data given, as follows:

(i) *Three sides given*
Use the cosine rule to find one angle. Use the sine rule to find another angle.* The last angle is found by subtraction from 180°.

(ii) *Two sides and the included angle given*
Use the cosine rule to find the third side. Use the sine rule to find another angle.* Find the last angle by subtraction from 180°.

(iii) *Two sides and a non-included angle*
Use the sine rule to find the sine of the other non-included angle. If the angle can be decided without ambiguity, find the third angle by subtraction and the third side by the sine rule.

(iv) *Two angles and a side given*

Find the third angle by subtraction, then use the sine rule to find each of the other sides.

These methods make use of the sine rule wherever possible. In the two steps marked with an asterisk, there will apparently be uncertainty as to whether the angle is acute or obtuse. In each case, however, all three sides are known, and it is a property of the triangle that the largest angle is opposite the longest side. The remedy, then, is to choose an angle *not* opposite the longest side: such an angle will always be acute (because an obtuse angle must be the largest). This will be seen in the following example.

Example 6. Solve the triangle ABC given $a = 6{\cdot}7$ cm., $\hat{B} = 53°$, $c = 4{\cdot}25$ cm.

Step 1: Use the cosine rule to find b. (This has been worked out in Example 1, page 68, where a diagram of this triangle is also given.)

The answer obtained is $b = 5{\cdot}355$ cm.

Step 2: Use the sine rule to find $\hat{C}$ (which cannot be obtuse because it is not opposite the longest side).

$$\sin \hat{C} = \frac{c.\sin \hat{B}}{b} = \frac{4{\cdot}25 \sin 53°}{5{\cdot}355}$$

$$\therefore \hat{C} = 39° \ 19'$$

No.	*Log.*
4·25	0·6284
sin 53°	$\bar{1}$·9023
	0·5307
5·355	0·7288
sin 39° 19′	$\bar{1}$·8019

Step 3: Find $\hat{A}$ by subtraction.

$$\hat{A} + 53° + 39° \ 19' = 180°$$

$$\therefore \hat{A} = 87° \ 41'$$

EXERCISE 7D

1. Triangle DEF has $DE = 17{\cdot}3''$, $\hat{E} = 59° \ 36'$, $EF = 13{\cdot}7''$. Find its area.

2. An isosceles triangle of area 12 sq. cm. has equal sides of 5·76 cm. Calculate two possible values of the angle between them.

3. Solve the following triangles:

(i) $\triangle ABC$, given $a = 135$ yd., $\hat{B} = 107° \ 10'$, $\hat{C} = 41° \ 27'$.

(ii) $\triangle PQR$, given $p = 8{\cdot}1$ in., $q = 10{\cdot}9$ in., $\hat{Q} = 60°$.

(iii) $\triangle X\hat{Y}Z$, given $x = 1\frac{1}{2}$ miles, $y = 2\frac{1}{2}$ miles, $z = 3\frac{1}{2}$ miles.

Algebraic Treatment

So far, the sine, cosine and tangent of an angle have all been defined in terms of ratios of sides of a triangle, with special meanings in the case of an obtuse angle to fit certain triangle formulae. We now consider the subject in an algebraic way.

Fig. 13 shows the axes used in drawing graphs, in which x is considered positive to the right, negative to the left; y is considered positive when measured upwards, negative downwards. A line OP has been drawn, of length r, making an angle θ with the x-axis (measured anti-clockwise).

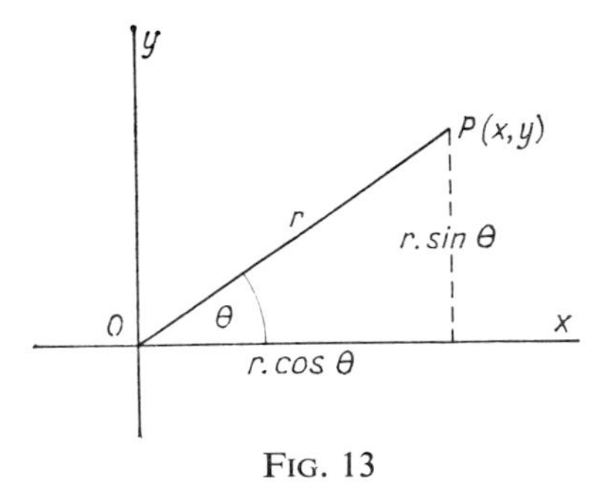

FIG. 13

When θ is acute, as in this diagram, we have:

(i) The x co-ordinate of P = the projection of OP on the x-axis $= r.\cos\theta$

(ii) The y co-ordinate of P = the projection of OP on the y-axis $= r.\sin\theta$

(iii) The gradient of $OP = \dfrac{y}{x} = \tan\theta$

We take these relations as definitions of sin, cos, tan for *any* angle, in other words we assume that for any direction of OP:

$$\cos\theta = \frac{x}{r} \qquad \sin\theta = \frac{y}{r} \qquad \tan\theta = \frac{y}{x}$$

where x and y can be positive or negative according to the directions in which they are measured. We shall now see what happens if θ is obtuse.

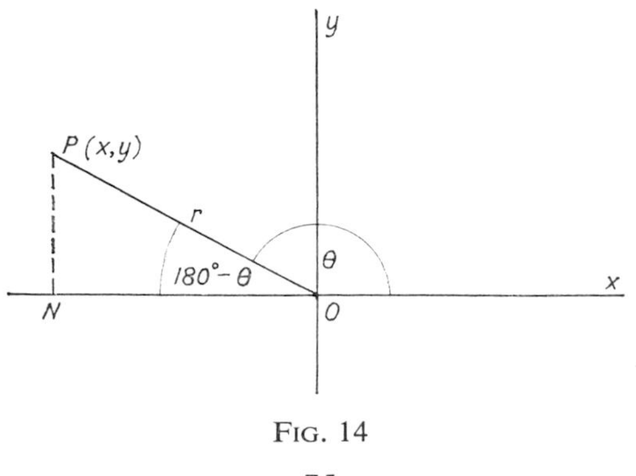

FIG. 14

Fig. 14 shows the case when θ is obtuse. Here $y = PN = r.\sin(180^\circ - \theta)$ but x is negative, so that $x = -ON = -r.\cos(180^\circ - \theta)$.

$$\therefore \left\{ \begin{aligned} \sin\theta &= \frac{y}{r} = \sin(180^\circ - \theta) \\ \cos\theta &= \frac{x}{r} = -\cos(180^\circ - \theta) \\ \tan\theta &= \frac{y}{x} = -\tan(180^\circ - \theta) \end{aligned} \right\}$$

which agree with the results summarized on page 67.

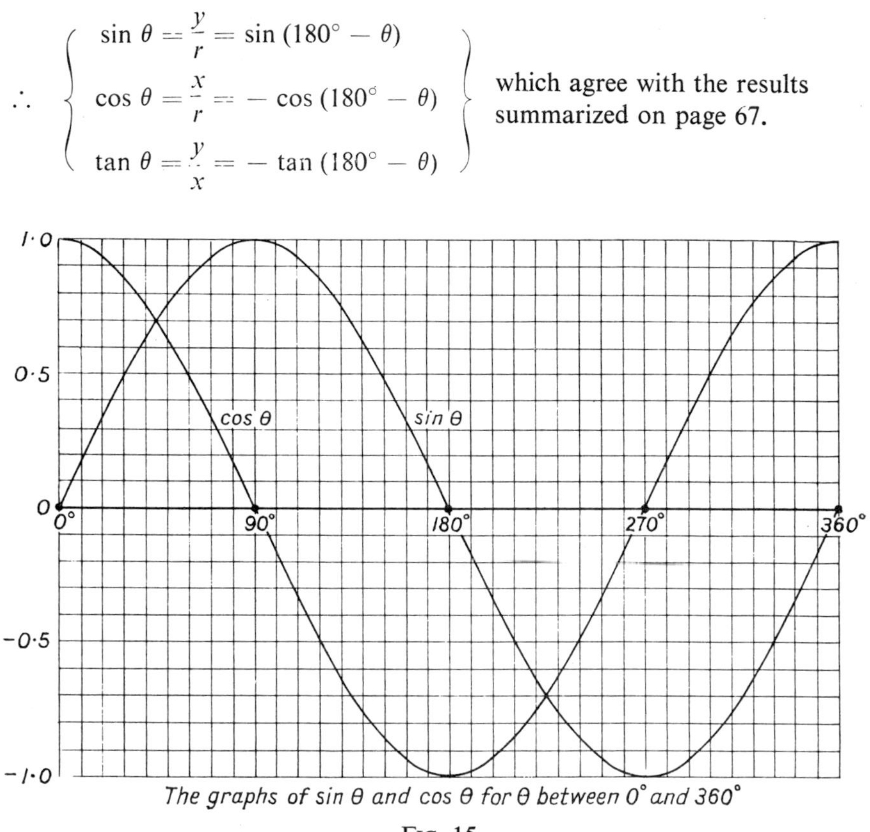

The graphs of sin θ and cos θ for θ between 0° and 360°

FIG. 15

This process could be extended to include angles greater than 180°: for example, if θ lies between 180° and 270°, x and y are both negative; so $\cos\theta$ and $\sin\theta$ are negative while $\tan\theta$ $\left(= \frac{y}{x}\right)$ is positive.

In this way the values of $\sin\theta$, $\cos\theta$ and $\tan\theta$ can be calculated for any angle. It is interesting to compare the graphs of $\sin\theta$ and $\cos\theta$ and in Fig. 15 you will find each plotted on the same diagram, for any angle from 0° to 360°. Notice these features:

(i) Sin θ and $\cos\theta$ always lie between -1 and 1 (a continuous graph of $\tan\theta$ cannot be drawn because at 90° its value becomes infinite).

(ii) The shapes of the two graphs are basically the same, but that of $\cos\theta$ is "staggered" forward 90° relative to that of $\sin\theta$.

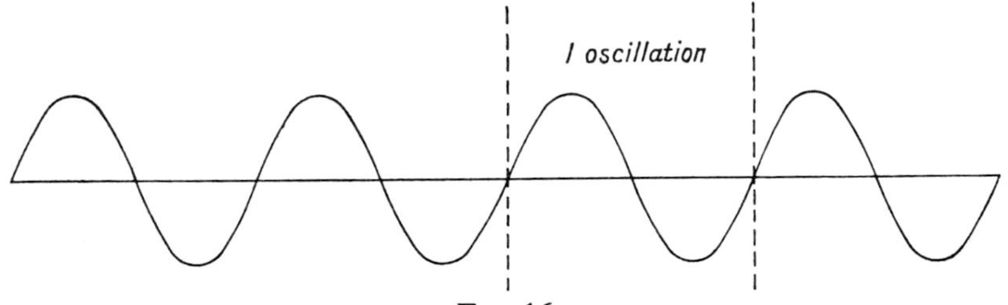

FIG. 16

(iii) This shape is known in physics, where it occurs frequently, as a sine wave: the two waves in Fig. 15 are said to be "out of phase" by 90°. A range of 360° along the θ-axis represents one complete oscillation of the wave motion (Fig. 16).

The Trigonometry of Plane Figures

We return now to problems involving trigonometry. In the next chapter we shall look at three-dimensional problems: here we consider plane (two-dimensional) figures requiring several applications of the various rules, which are summarized again for quick reference.

The Cosine Rule ..	$a^2 = b^2 + c^2 - 2bc.\cos \hat{A}$
The Sine Rule ..	$\frac{a}{\sin \hat{A}} = \frac{b}{\sin \hat{B}} = \frac{c}{\sin \hat{C}}$
The Area Formula ..	area $= \frac{1}{2}bc.\sin \hat{A}$

A worked example is followed by an exercise containing some further problems of this kind. In any step of a solution, the reasoning is set out on the left of the page and the working on the right. Where there is a choice of methods, use in order of preference:

(i) Simple ratios if a triangle is right-angled or isosceles.
(ii) Sine rule whenever an angle and the opposite side are known.
(iii) Cosine rule in other cases (three sides, or two sides and the included angle).

Example: A house stands 90 ft. from the foot of a railway embankment. Calculate the height of the embankment from the following observations (Fig. 17):

Elevation of embankment from top of house: 8° 12′
Elevation of embankment from base of house: 17°
Elevation of house from foot of embankment: 10° 30′

We shall proceed as follows: find TB by tangent ratio, then TE by sine rule, then EH by sine ratio, and add EH to TB.

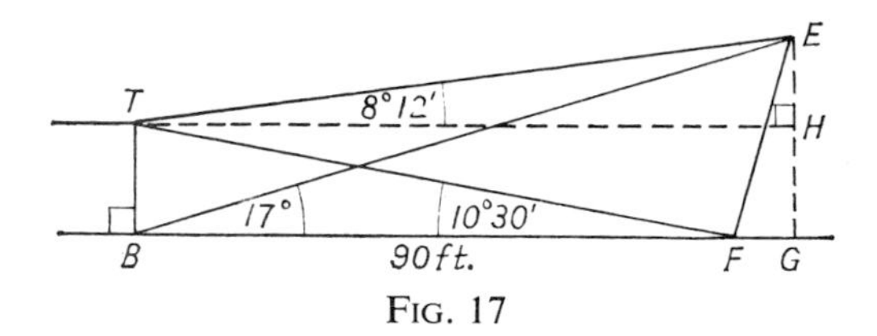

FIG. 17

(i) $TB = 90.\tan 10°\ 30'$
$= 16{\cdot}68$

(ii) $T\hat{B}E = (90° - 17°) = 73°$
$T\hat{E}B = (17° - 8°\ 12') = 8°\ 48'$

$$\frac{TE}{\sin 73°} = \frac{16{\cdot}68}{\sin 8°\ 48'}$$

$$\therefore\ TE = \frac{16{\cdot}68 \sin 73°}{\sin 8°\ 48'}$$
$= 104{\cdot}2$

(iii) $EH = TE.\sin 8°\ 12'$
$= 14{\cdot}87$

(iv) $EG = EH + HG$
$= EH + TB$
$= 14{\cdot}87 + 16{\cdot}68$
$= 31{\cdot}55$

No.	Log.
90	1·9542
tan 10° 30′	$\bar{1}$·2680
16·68	1·2222

No.	Log.
16·68	1·2222
sin 73°	$\bar{1}$·9806
	1·2028
sin 8° 48′	$\bar{1}$·1847
104·2	2·0181
sin 8° 12′	$\bar{1}$·1542
14·87	1·1723

Answer: The height of the embankment is approximately 31·55 ft.

Note: Suppose we wished also to find the angle of slope of the bank. One way would be to proceed:

(i) $BG = TH = 104{\cdot}2 \times \cos 8°\ 12'$
$= 103{\cdot}1$ (working is not shown here);

(ii) $FG = 103{\cdot}1 - 90$
$= 13{\cdot}1$;

(iii) $\tan E\hat{F}G = \dfrac{31{\cdot}55}{13{\cdot}1}$ giving $E\hat{F}G = 67°\ 27'$.

EXERCISE 7E

All of the questions are based on the work done in this and the previous chapter, but Nos. 7, 8, 9, 11 and 15 are slightly harder than the rest—either longer or of the "problem" type. These questions might be left until after a second reading.

1. ABC is a triangle in which $AB = 3$ in., $BC = 4$ in., $CA = 5$ in. and P is the mid-point of BC. Calculate the angles of $\triangle\ APC$.

2. A building stands at the foot of a hill which slopes at 9° to the horizontal. From a point 75 ft. up the hillside the elevation of the top of the building is 25°. Calculate its height.

3. Fig. 18 shows the dimensions of a window catch. When the window is closed, holes A and B engage with fixed pegs at P and Q respectively. At what angle is the window held open when hole A engages peg Q?

4. A triangular field has sides of lengths 95 yd., 110 yd. and 143 yd. By how many square yards does its area exceed 1 acre?

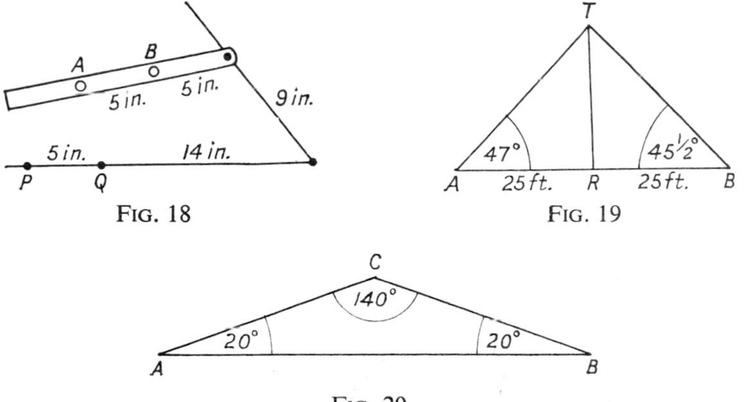

FIG. 18

FIG. 19

FIG. 20

5. Driving due north along a straight road at 25 m.p.h., a motorist first spotted a certain church in a direction N. 29° E. Eight minutes later its bearing was N. 61° E. Find the distance he was from the church when he first saw it.

6. AB is a chord of a circle, centre O, of radius 12 cm. $A\hat{O}B = 119°$. Find the length of the perpendicular from A to the tangent at B.

7. Fig. 19 shows two measurements of the elevation of a leaning tower. ARB is horizontal. At what angle is the tower TR inclined to the vertical? What is the vertical height of T above the ground?

8. A cruiser, C, is steaming due east at 20 knots. At noon a destroyer, D, is sighted 3 nautical miles away in a direction N. 30° E. At 12.10 the destroyer is 2 nautical miles away and still bears N. 30° E. Assuming that the destroyer is on a steady course, find its speed and direction, and show that if neither vessel alters course or speed they will collide at 12.30.

9. In the isosceles $\triangle ABC$ (Fig. 20) obtain an expression for the ratio $\frac{AB}{AC}$

(i) by applying the sine rule to $\triangle ABC$;

(ii) by drawing a perpendicular from C on to AB

and hence prove that $\sin 140° = 2.\sin 70°.\sin 20°$.

10. $\triangle$ PQR has $PQ = 7$ in., $P = 29° 30'$, $R = 90°$. On the side QR an equilateral $\triangle$ QRS is drawn outside PQR. Find the length PS.

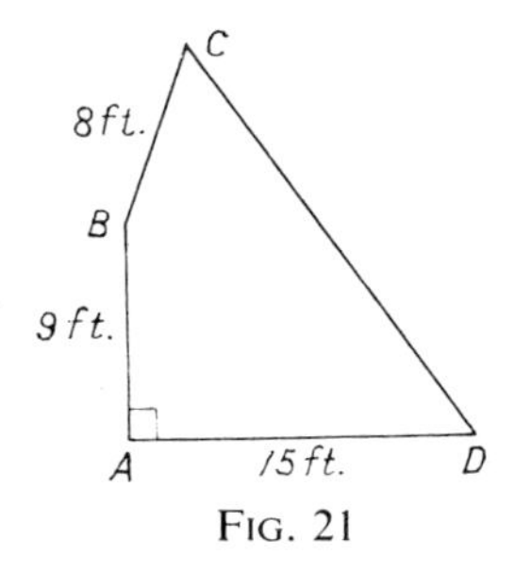

FIG. 21

11. Quadrilateral $ABCD$ in Fig. 21 represents the sail of a yacht. $A\hat{B}C$ is 160°. Calculate:

(i) the length CD;

(ii) the area of sail.

12. When the sun's altitude decreased from 28° to 25°, the shadow of a vertical post lengthened by 11 in. Find the height of the post.

13. $\triangle$ ABC has $AB = 25{\cdot}2$ cm., $A = 90°$, $AC = 18{\cdot}9$ cm. The bisector of $B\hat{A}C$ meets BC at X. Calculate lengths BX and CX.

14. From a coastguard station a ship is observed 800 yd. away at a bearing of 147°. If there is a lighthouse 650 yd. from the coastguard station at a bearing of $116\frac{1}{2}°$, what is the distance and bearing of the ship as seen from the lighthouse?

15. An aircraft which has an airspeed of 380 m.p.h. is to proceed to a station 125 miles away to the north-east. There is a steady 70 m.p.h. gale blowing from due east. In what direction should the pilot steer so as to allow for the wind, and how long will the flight take?

CHAPTER 8

THREE DIMENSIONS

THIS CHAPTER will deal, in various ways, with simple three-dimensional figures and problems; let us first consider some of their features which do not occur in plane figures:

1. The presence of planes as well as lines and points.
2. The idea of the angle, (a) between a line and a plane, or (b) between two planes.
3. The possession of volume.
4. The difficulty of representing a three-dimensional figure by a plane diagram.

1. *Planes in Addition to Lines and Points*

Because of the existence of distinct planes, two lines may not meet even though they are not parallel: they are then said to be skew. The various possibilities of intersection of lines and planes are seen by looking at the drawing of a cube (Fig. 1).

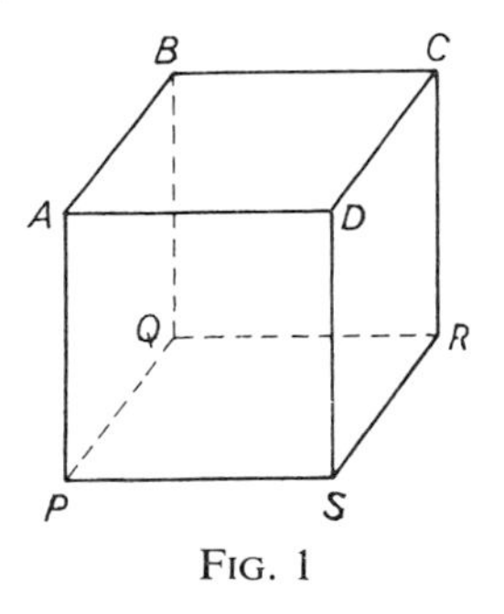

FIG. 1

Two lines may be *skew*, e.g. the edges AB and PS,
or *parallel*, e.g. edges AD and PS,
or they may *intersect*, e.g. edges AP and PS.

A line and plane, unless they are parallel (e.g. AB and $PQRS$), or the line lies in the plane (e.g. AB lies in $ABCD$), will *intersect in a point* (e.g. edge AP meets the plane $PQRS$ at P).

Two planes, unless they are parallel (e.g. $ABCD$ and $PQRS$), will *intersect in a line* (e.g. $ABCD$ and $APSD$ intersect in AD).

Because we have chosen the faces and edges of a cube, all of these intersections are at right-angles. We next consider the more general case of oblique intersection and the definition of angle.

2 (a). *The Angle between a Line and a Plane*

A line is said to be perpendicular to a plane if it is perpendicular to any line in that plane: look again at Fig. 1 and notice that the edge AP is perpendicular to each of the lines PQ, PR and PS which lie in the plane $PQRS$.

We can thus speak of the perpendicular from a point on to a plane. In Fig. 2 PN is the perpendicular from the point P on to the plane shown, the length of PN is called the distance from P to the plane, and the point N, the foot of the perpendicular, is also called the *projection* of P on this plane.

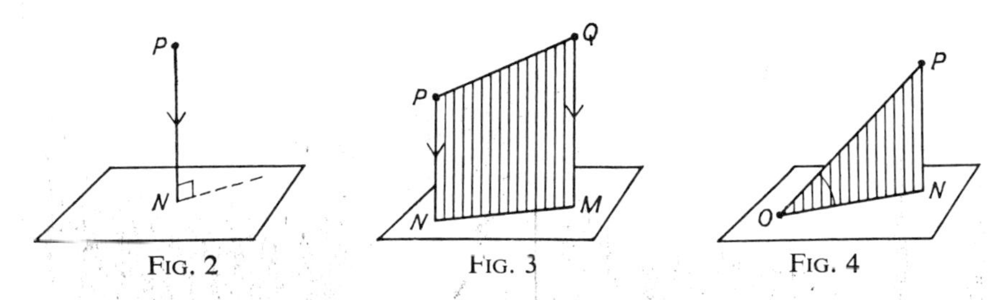

FIG. 2 FIG. 3 FIG. 4

The idea of projection is important and Fig. 3 shows the effect of projecting all the points of a straight line: the line NM is called the projection of line PQ on the plane shown.

Now PQ and NM are not skew (because they both lie in the plane $PQMN$) so they are either parallel or intersecting: *the angle between a line and a plane is taken to be the angle between the line and its projection in that plane.*

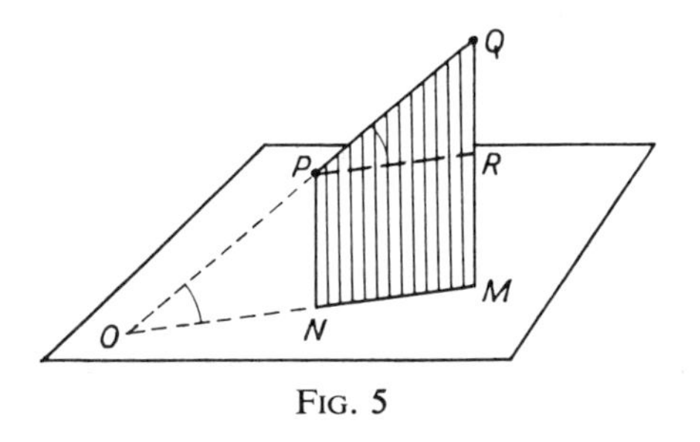

FIG. 5

Fig. 4 shows the case when the line meets the plane: ON is the projection of OP, and $P\hat{O}N$ is the angle which OP makes with the plane. But in a case like Fig. 3 it is not necessary to produce OP and MN to meet: instead we construct PR parallel to NM (see Fig. 5). $Q\hat{P}R$ and $Q\hat{O}M$ are corresponding angles and so QPR is also the angle between PQ and the plane.

Notice a useful trigonometrical relation here: since $NM = PR$ and $\frac{PR}{PQ} = \cos Q\hat{P}R$ it follows that the angle between a line and a plane is given by the rule:

$$\cos\theta = \frac{\text{length of projection}}{\text{length of line}}$$

Example: In the cube shown in Fig. 1, find the angle between the diagonal PC and the face $PQRS$.

Since CR is perpendicular to $PQRS$, the line PR is the projection of PC on the plane $PQRS$. Thus $C\hat{P}R$ is the required angle (Fig. 6).

Suppose each edge of the cube is of length x. Then as PR is the diagonal of a square face:

$$PR^2 = PS^2 + SR^2 = 2x^2$$

$$\therefore PR = \sqrt{2x^2}$$

$$= x\sqrt{2}$$

$$\therefore \tan CPR = \frac{CR}{PR} = \frac{x}{x\sqrt{2}}$$

$$= \frac{1}{\sqrt{2}}$$

$$= 0{\cdot}7071$$

$$\therefore C\hat{P}R = 35^\circ\ 16'$$

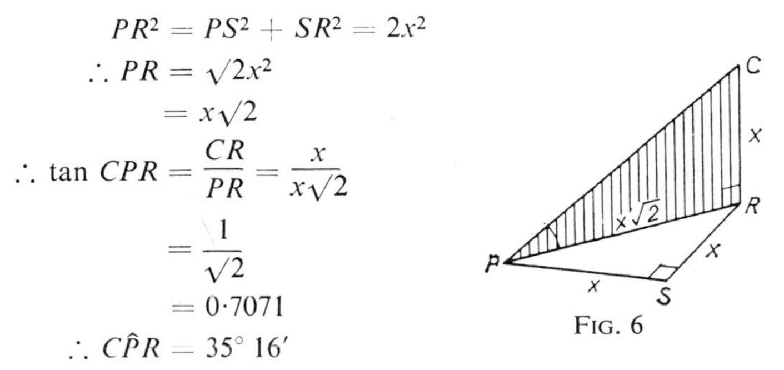

FIG. 6

This result could have been obtained, with rather less accuracy, by means of scale drawings of the face $PQRS$ and $\triangle$ CPR.

2 (b). *The Angle Between Two Planes*

This is defined as follows: take any point P in their line of intersection and let PA, PB be lines, one in each plane, each at right-angles to the line of intersection. Then $A\hat{P}B$ is the angle between the two planes. This is illustrated in Fig. 7.

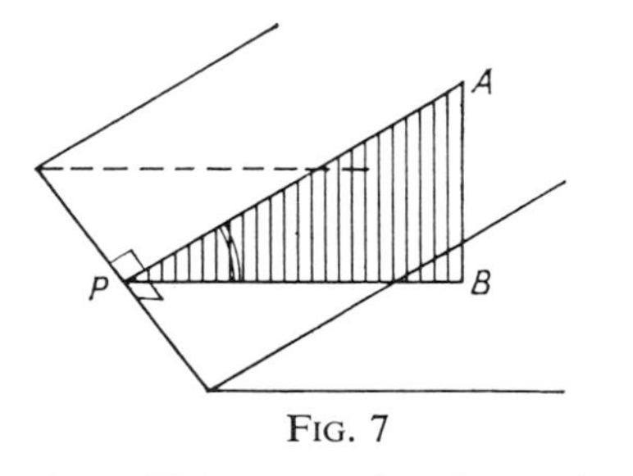

FIG. 7

These lines at right-angles to the edge lie in a plane (shown shaded) which is at right-angles to each of the given planes. Thus the projection of PA on to the other plane lies along PB (produced if necessary) and vice versa. Also each forms the greatest possible angle with the other plane: if one of the planes is horizontal, such a line in the other plane is called a *line of greatest slope*. This expression is particularly used in relation to paths going up a hillside.

Example: Find the angle between two faces of a regular tetrahedron.

Let $TABC$ be the tetrahedron and M the midpoint of the edge AB. Then since all faces are equilateral TM and CM are perpendicular to AB, and $T\hat{M}C$ is the angle between faces TAB and CAB (Fig. 8). Let each edge of the figure be 2 in., then $AM = 1$ in., and by Pythagoras' theorem $TM = \sqrt{4 - 1} = 1{\cdot}732$ in. (alternatively $TM = TA.\sin 60°$). Similarly $CM = 1{\cdot}732$ in.

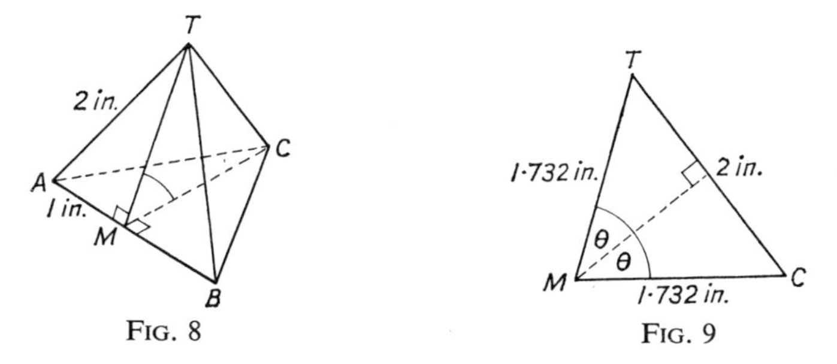

FIG. 8

FIG. 9

It now remains to find $\hat{M}$ in $\triangle\ TMC$ (Fig. 9). As three sides are known, we could use the cosine rule, but noticing that the triangle is isosceles we drop a perpendicular from M on to TC, and let $M = 2\theta$:

$$\sin\theta = \frac{1}{1{\cdot}732} = 0{\cdot}5773$$
$$\therefore \theta = 35°\ 16'$$
$$\therefore T\hat{M}C = 2\theta = 70°\ 32'$$

Because the figure is regular, the angle between any two faces would be 70° 32′. The angle between two adjacent faces of a solid is known as the dihedral angle (polyhedron = many faces; dihedral = of two faces); the cube, for example, has dihedral angles of 90°. The term is also applied to the wings of an aircraft, to denote their inclination to the horizontal.

3. *The Possession of Volume*

We are already familiar with the idea of a volume, and with the method of calculating the volume of a *prism*, i.e. a solid of uniform cross-section:

Volume = Area of cross-section × Perpendicular height

This formula gives the volume of a cylinder as $V = \pi r^2 h$, the cross-section in this case being a circle.

For a *pyramid*, i.e. a solid of uniformly tapering cross-section, the corresponding result is:

Volume = $\frac{1}{3}$ × Area of base × Perpendicular height

and, as a special case of a pyramid, volume of cone $= \frac{1}{3}\pi r^2 h$.

The only other important volume formula is that for the sphere:

$V = \frac{4}{3}\pi r^3$ where r is the radius.

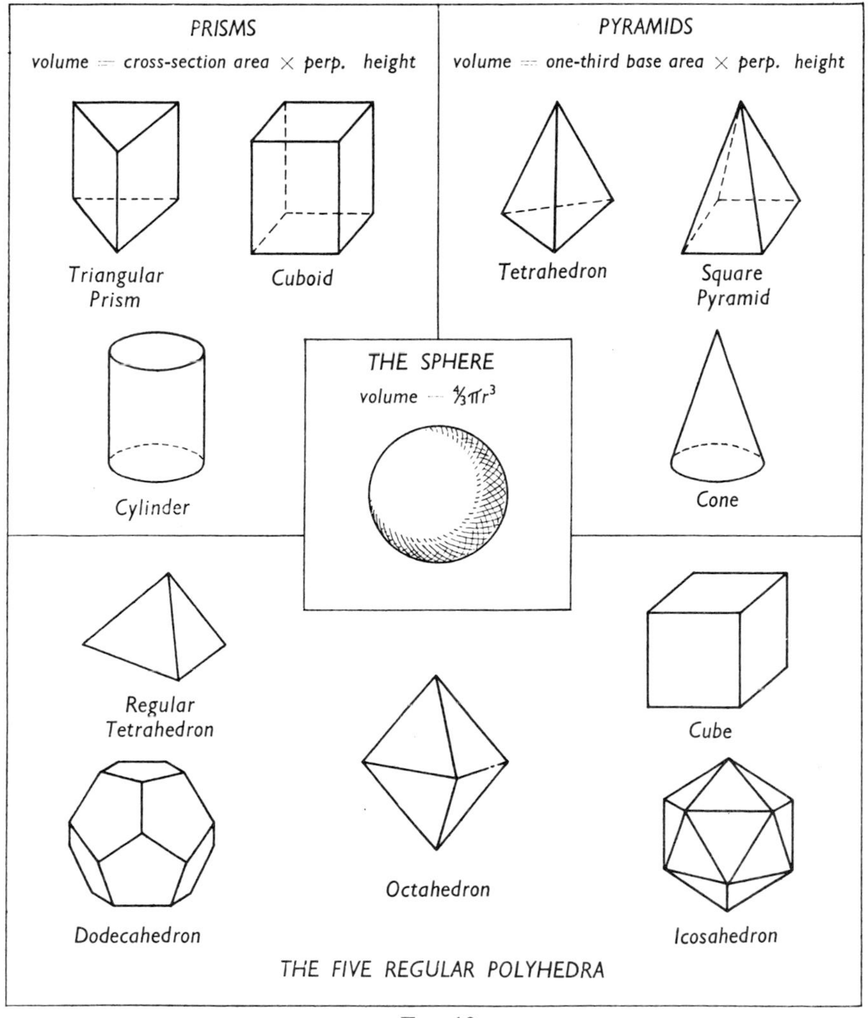

FIG. 10

These facts are summarized, with diagrams, as part of the chart of solid figures (Fig. 10). We shall not be much concerned with the calculation of volumes in this chapter, but a few examples where trigonometry is involved in the calculation of distances and areas are given in the Exercises.

4. *Diagrams of Three-dimensional Figures*

A diagram on a sheet of paper, must itself be a plane figure; this can be obtained from a three-dimensional figure either by drawing a plane part of it or by projecting the whole of it on to a plane and drawing the projection.

A plane part may be external: a *face* of the figure
or internal: a *cross-section*.

A projection is usually made on to either a horizontal plane, when it is known as a *plan*, or on to a vertical plane, as an *elevation*.

The drawing of a face needs no comment, and Figs. 8 and 9 show the way of drawing a suitably chosen cross-section.

The next two diagrams illustrate the use of projection. Fig. 11 shows a solid figure (a roof-shaped wedge) placed in the angle between two planes, one horizontal and one vertical. Dotted lines represent the perpendiculars from each point of the solid on to the two planes, and the feet of these perpendiculars make up the projections.

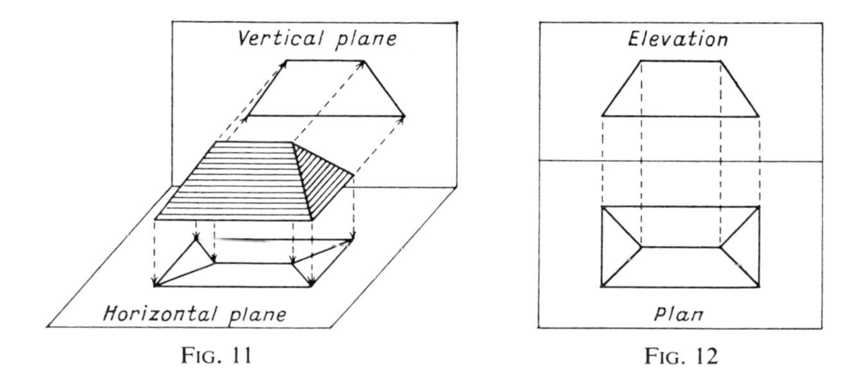

FIG. 11

FIG. 12

If you now imagine the two planes to be a single sheet of paper folded along the line of intersection, then unfolding this sheet of paper would show the plan and elevation of the solid in their usual position one above the other as in Fig. 12. In this position the two projections of any point are in a line at right-angles to the "fold": this fact, which is illustrated by the dotted lines of Fig. 12, is the basis of the practical method of drawing projections. We shall discuss it further at the end of this chapter.

Trigonometrical Problems

We shall now look at some typical problems involving simple figures in three dimensions.

Example 1. A hillside slopes uniformly at 12° to the horizontal, and a straight path in the hillside makes an angle of 25° with the line of greatest slope (Fig. 13). Find the angle at which the path is inclined to the horizontal.

Let PH be the path, PZ a line of greatest slope through P, HZ a horizontal line through H in the plane of the hillside. Let P, Q, R be the projections of P, Z, H respectively on a horizontal plane through P (Fig. 13).

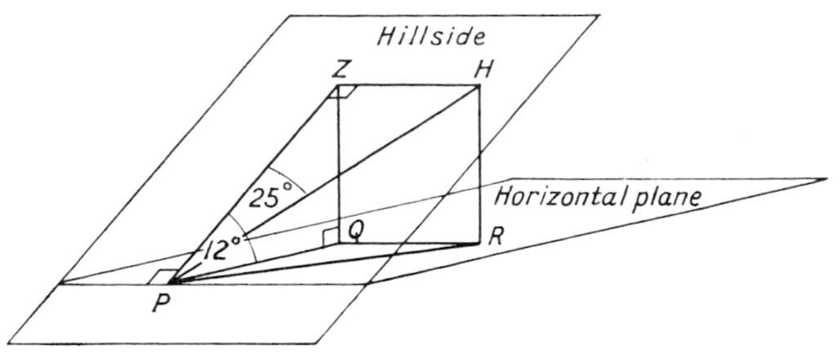

FIG. 13

Since PR is the projection of PH on a horizontal plane, the required angle is $H\hat{P}R$. It is known that ZPQ is 12° and HPZ is 25°.

Now $HR = ZQ$ ($HRQZ$ is a rectangle)

$$= PZ.\sin 12^\circ$$

$$= (PH.\cos 25^\circ) \sin 12^\circ$$

$$\therefore \sin H\hat{P}R = \frac{HR}{PH}$$

$$= \cos 25^\circ.\sin 12^\circ$$

$$= \sin 10^\circ\ 52'$$

No.	*Log.*
cos 25°	$\bar{1}$·9573
sin 12°	$\bar{1}$·3179
sin 10° 52′	$\bar{1}$·2752

Answer: The path slopes at approximately 10° 52′ to the horizontal.

***Example* 2.** $VABCD$ is a pyramid on a square base $ABCD$ of side 6 in. $VA = VB = 5$ in. and the face VAB is inclined at 60° to the base (Fig. 14). Calculate (i) the volume of the pyramid; (ii) the angle between planes VBC and $ABCD$.

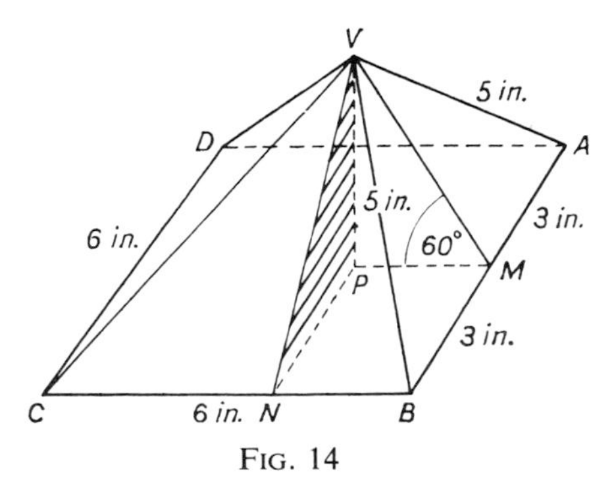

FIG. 14

Let M be the mid-point of AB: then since $\triangle\ VAB$ is isosceles VM is perpendicular to AB and is a line of greatest slope in the face. Thus if P is the projection of V on $ABCD$, $V\hat{M}P$ is the inclination of 60°.

$VM = 4$ in. (by Pythagoras) and $VP = VM.\sin 60^\circ = 4\,(0{\cdot}8660) = 3{\cdot}464$ in.

(i) Volume of pyramid $= \frac{1}{3} \times (6 \times 6) \times 3{\cdot}464 = 41{\cdot}57$ cu. in.

(ii) Let VN be the perpendicular from V on to BC, then PN is also perpendicular to BC.* Thus $V\hat{N}P$ is the required angle.

$$VP = 3{\cdot}464 \text{ in. and } PN = MB = 3 \text{ in.}\dagger$$

$$\therefore \tan V\hat{N}P = \frac{VP}{PN} = \frac{3{\cdot}464}{3} = 1{\cdot}155$$

$$\therefore V\hat{N}P = 49^\circ\ 7'$$

Notes: *A proof of this fact runs as follows:

$VP \perp$ plane $ABCD$ (constr.)

$\therefore VP \perp BC$ (a line in $ABCD$)

$VN \perp BC$ (constr.)

$\therefore BC \perp$ plane VPN (it is $\perp$ to two lines in VPN)

$\therefore BC \perp PN$ (a line in VPN)

†A similar proof shows that PM is perpendicular to AB, and it follows that $PMBN$ is a rectangle.

Example 3. Two roofs, whose ridges meet at right-angles 8 ft. above the eaves, are inclined respectively at 30° and 45° to the horizontal (Fig. 15). At what angle is their line of intersection inclined to the horizontal?

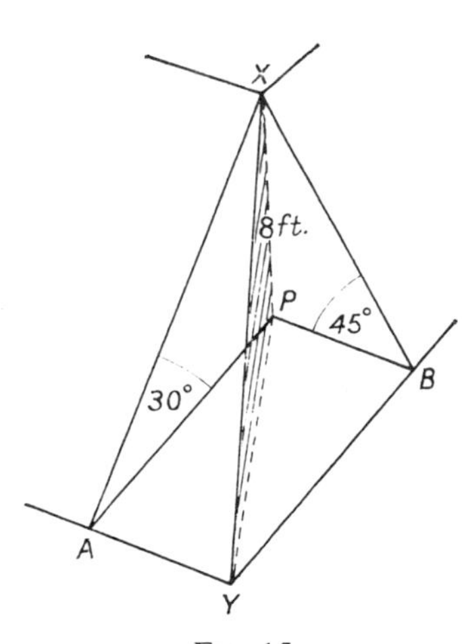

FIG. 15

Let XY be the line of intersection.

Let XA, XB be lines of greatest slope through X.

Let P be the projection of X on the horizontal plane through Y.

Then PY is the projection of XY and XYP is the required angle (see diagram at right).

$$PB = 8 . \tan 45^\circ = 8$$
$$PA = 8 . \tan 60^\circ = 13{\cdot}86$$
$$PY^2 = 8^2 + 13{\cdot}86^2$$
$$= 64 + 192$$
$$= 256$$
$$PY = 16$$
$$\tan X\hat{Y}P = \frac{XP}{PY} = \frac{8}{16} = 0{\cdot}5$$
$$\therefore X\hat{Y}P = 26^\circ\ 34'$$

Note: $APBY$ is a rectangle, for the same kind of reasons as in Example 2.

These three examples illustrate some of the techniques used in three-dimensional problems. Notice that the idea of projection is frequently employed. Each of the problems could have been solved by the method of scale drawing, but each would have required three or four separate drawings for its solution.

Example 3, for instance, needs drawings of $\triangle$ *APX*, $\triangle$ *BPX*, rectangle *APBY* and finally $\triangle$ *YPX*. Even with very careful draughtsmanship it is doubtful if angles could be given with more than half-degree accuracy.

EXERCISE 8A

1. A path up a hillside makes an angle of 17° with the line of greatest slope, and is itself inclined at 17° to the horizontal. At what angle is the hillside inclined to the horizontal?

2. *ABCD* is a square trapdoor of side 2 ft., mounted on a horizontal hinge *AB*. It is opened until the opposite edge, *CD*, is 10 in. above the level of the hinge. What is then the inclination to the horizontal of (i) the plane *ABCD*; (ii) the diagonal *AC*?

3. *VABC* is a pyramid whose base, *ABC*, is an equilateral triangle of side 2 in. $VA = VB = 4$ in. and $VC = 3$ in. Calculate the inclination to the face *ABC* of (i) edge *VC*; (ii) face *VAB*.

4. Fig. 16 shows a tetrahedron *ABCD* in which $\triangle$ *ABC* is equilateral of side 5 cm., and the edge *CD*, which is also of length 5 cm., is perpendicular to the plane of *ABC*. By considering $\triangle$ *MCD*, where *M* is the mid-point of *AB*, find the distance from *C* on to the plane *ABD*.

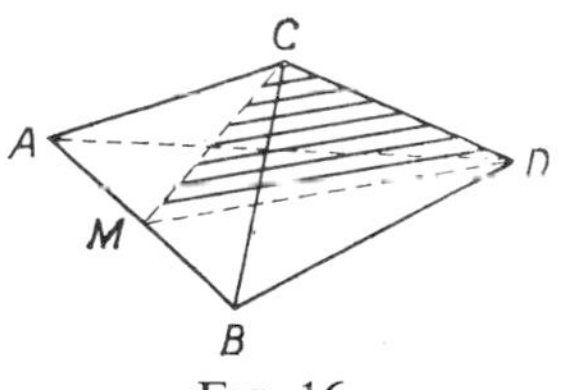

FIG. 16

5. Calculate the volume of a pyramid whose base is a rectangle measuring 6×8 in. and each of whose slant edges is of length 1 ft. 1 in.

6. An aircraft is flying on a steady course at a height of 5,000 ft. An observer spots it due north of him at an elevation of 40°, and watches it until it is due west of him at an elevation of 30°. Calculate:

(i) the bearing on which the aircraft is flying;

(ii) its greatest elevation during this period to the observer (who is stationary on the ground).

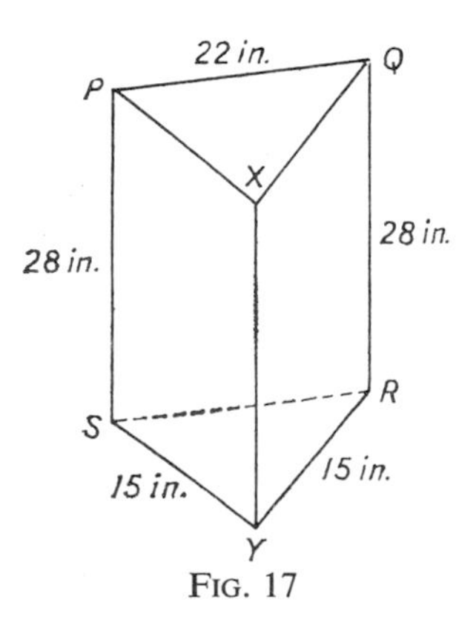

FIG. 17

7. Fig. 17 shows some of the dimensions of a fire-guard to fit a rectangular aperture *PQRS*. The triangle *PQX* is inclined at 45°, and *RSY* at 90°, to the plane *PQRS*. The rod *XY* is parallel to *PS* and *QR*. Calculate the lengths of rods *XP*, *XQ* and *XY*.

8. $\triangle$ *ABC* is equilateral of side 3 ft. Vertex *A* rests on horizontal ground, while *B* and *C* are respectively 6 in. and 18 in. above the ground. Find the angle at which each side of $\triangle$ *ABC* is inclined to the horizontal.

9. A rectangular shelf measuring 1 ft. by 1 ft. 6 in. is mounted horizontally in a corner between two walls and supported by a strut of length 3 ft. 6 in. as shown in Fig. 18. Show that the lower end of the strut is 3 ft. below the shelf and find the angle at which the strut is inclined to the shelf.

10. *VABCD* is a pyramid on a square base, each of whose slant faces is an equilateral triangle. Calculate the angle between adjacent slant faces.

FIG. 18

Plans and Elevations

We now look in rather more detail at the construction of plans and elevations, which are a basic feature of engineering drawings and in frequent use in draughtsmanship generally.

It was remarked on page 86 that the two projections of any point lie on a line at right-angles to the "fold" between the vertical and horizontal planes. It follows that, if the height of any point above the horizontal plane is known, its elevation can be constructed directly from its plan. This process is illustrated in Fig. 19, which represents the following problem:

Given the plan of a square pyramid, whose base lies in the horizontal plane and whose vertical height is $2\frac{1}{2}$ in., construct its elevation.

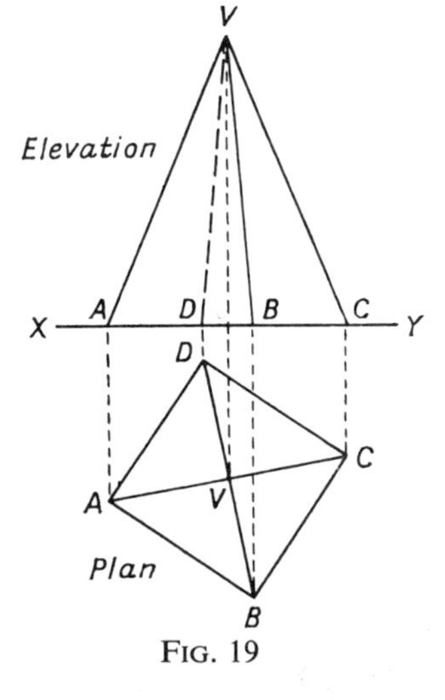

FIG. 19

Notice these points:

1. The lines *AA*, *BB*, *CC*, *DD*, *VV*, are drawn perpendicular to the base-line *XY*, *VV* being produced to a point $2\frac{1}{2}$ in. above *XY*.

In practice it is easy to draw these perpendiculars by using a set-square and T-square on a drawing board. The T-square, sliding down the edge of the drawing board, stays parallel to *XY*, while the set-square, sliding along the T-square, is always perpendicular to *XY*.

2. The edge *VD* of the pyramid is shown on the elevation as a broken line, since this edge is hidden when the figure is viewed from the front.

3. We shall next see how to draw, from a given plan and elevation, correct measurements of various lengths and angles. It should be noticed that neither

of the projections in Fig. 19 give direct measurements of, for example, the length of VB or its inclination to the horizontal.

Auxiliary Views

Fig. 20 shows the plan, AB, and the elevation, A' B', of a line. How can we find its true length and its inclination to the horizontal? We could measure these values directly if the elevation were on a plane parallel to AB, i.e. as viewed from a direction at right-angles to AB. We therefore construct an auxiliary view of the figure as seen from this direction.

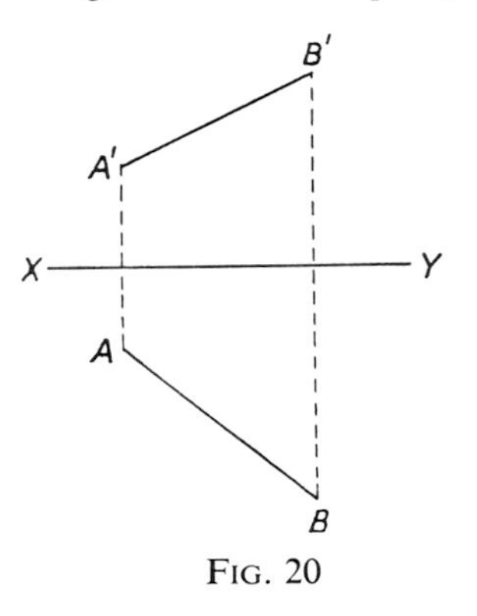

FIG. 20

This is shown in Fig. 21: a new base-line LM has been drawn parallel to AB, and AA'', BB'' have been drawn at right-angles to LM, making the heights h_1 and h_2 equal to those on the original elevation. A'' B'' is the required true length and θ the inclination.

When the new base-line is taken at right-angles to XY, the resulting projection is usually known as a Side View or Side Elevation.

When a side elevation is required, a slightly different method is used on the drawing board, to make easier the construction of perpendiculars. The new base-line is rotated through a right-angle to bring it into line with XY, so that the side and front elevations appear side by side: this has the advantage that heights can be transferred directly from one to the other by means of a T-square. Rotation of the base-line is effected with a pair of compasses.

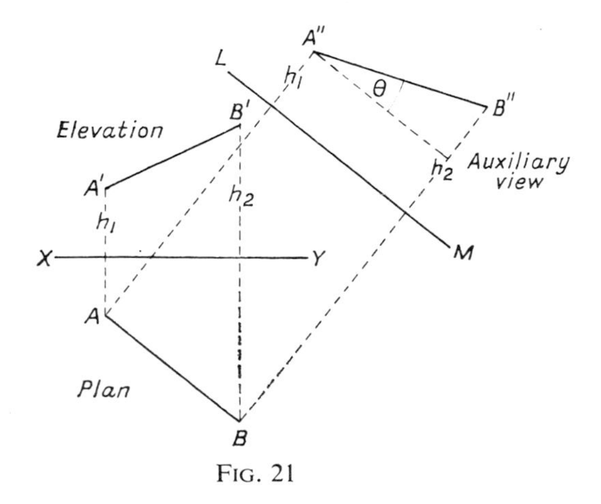

FIG. 21

The procedure is shown in Fig. 22 for a prism standing on a triangular base.

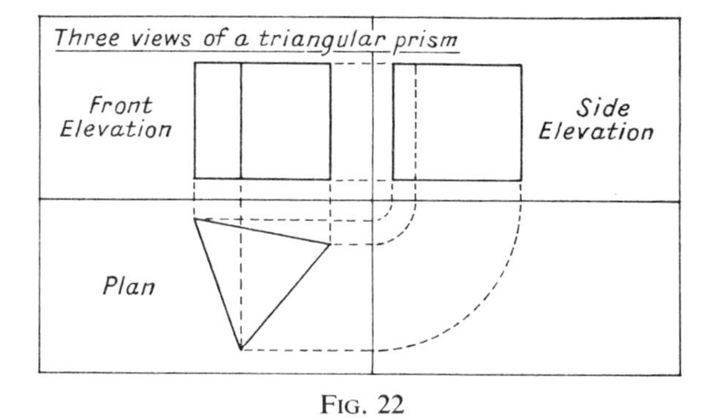

FIG. 22

Here is a worked example showing the use of an auxiliary view.

Example: Fig. 23 shows the plan of a roof whose shape is that of a pyramid on a rectangular base. The triangular faces VAB and VCD are inclined at $40°$ to the horizontal base.

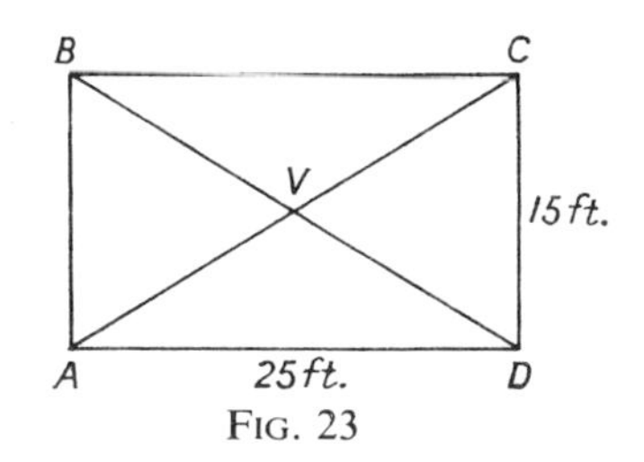

FIG. 23

(i) Draw an elevation on a plane parallel to BC and hence determine the height of V above the plane $ABCD$.

(ii) Draw an auxiliary elevation on a plane parallel to BD and hence find the lengths of edges VB and VD and the angle between them.

The construction of the various views is shown in Fig. 24. The position of V on the elevation is fixed by the intersection of lines drawn at $40°$ to the horizontal. The height h is then found by measurement to be 10·5 ft.

Next a new base-line is drawn parallel to BD and the points B, V, D, are projected on to it at right-angles, the line from V being extended 1·05 in. beyond the base. The auxiliary view here is actually a cross-section of the plane BVD, since the edges VA and VC have not been drawn in.

Measurement of this triangle now gives the results:

$$BV = VD = 18{\cdot}1 \text{ ft.};$$
$$B\hat{V}D = 108°.$$

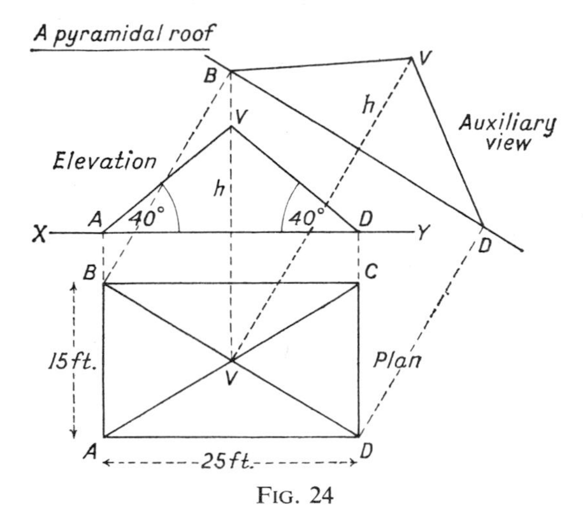

FIG. 24

It is interesting to compare these results with those given by the appropriate trigonometrical calculations:

$$h = 12{\cdot}5 \tan 40^\circ = 10{\cdot}59$$

$$BV = \sqrt{7{\cdot}5^2 + 12{\cdot}5^2 + 10{\cdot}59^2} = 18{\cdot}02$$

$B\hat{V}D$ is twice the angle whose cosine is $\dfrac{10{\cdot}59}{18{\cdot}02}$: $BVD = 108^\circ\ 2'$

EXERCISE 8B

1. Fig. 25 shows a perspective drawing and a plan of a triangular prism. The edge PQ is horizontal and is $1\frac{1}{2}$ in. above the rectangular base.

Draw the plan and from it construct the elevation of the prism on a plane parallel to PA. Find by measurement the true length of the diagonal PA and the angle between it and the plane $ABCD$.

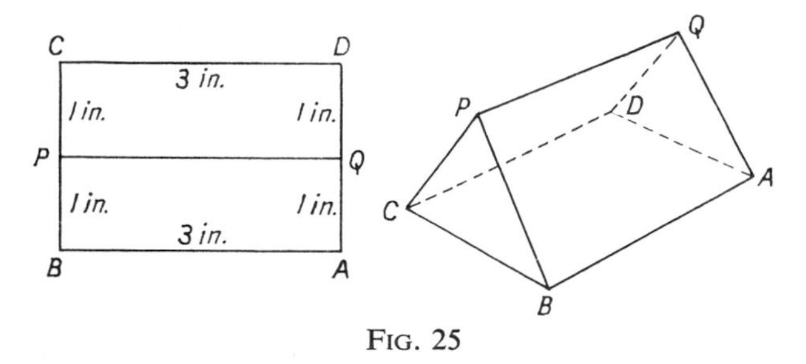

FIG. 25

2. $VABC$ is a pyramid whose base ABC is an equilateral triangle of side 2 in.: VA lies in a vertical plane at right-angles to BC, and is of length 3 in. and inclined at 70° to the base. Draw the plan of the pyramid and the elevation on a vertical plane at right-angles to *BC*. Find from your drawing the height of the pyramid and the angle which face *VBC* makes with the base.

3. Fig. 26 shows the plan of a cube of side $2\frac{1}{2}$ in. whose lower face, *ABCD*, has been tilted about edge *AD* so that it is inclined to the horizontal.

Draw this plan and from it construct the elevation on a plane parallel to *AB*. Hence find the height of edge *QR* above the horizontal plane through *AD*, and the angle at which plane *ABCD* is inclined to the horizontal. Construct also a side view, i.e. the elevation on a plane parallel to *BC*.

4. *VABCD* is a pyramid whose base *ABCD* is a square of side $1\frac{1}{2}$ in. The vertex *V* is 2 in. vertically above the mid-point of *AB*. Draw a plan of the pyramid, and from suitable elevations determine the lengths of edges *VA* and *VC*.

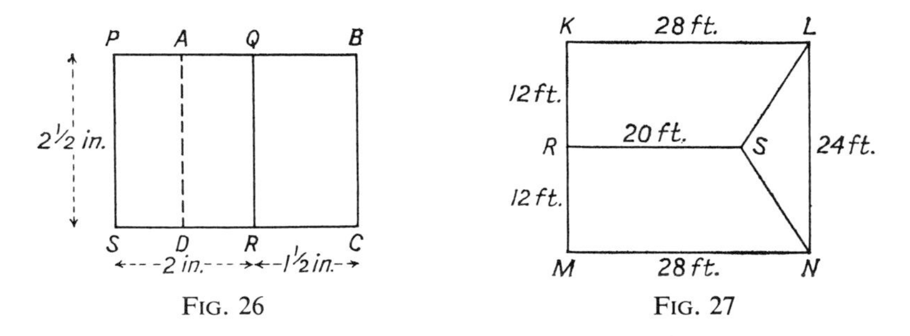

FIG. 26

FIG. 27

5. Fig. 27 shows the plan of a roof truss. *RS* is a horizontal ridge, and the face *LSN* is inclined at 55° to horizontal.

By drawing front and side elevations determine the angle between the faces *RSLK* and *RSNM*.

CHAPTER 9

THE SPHERE

THIS CHAPTER deals with some of the simpler geometrical and trigonometrical properties of the sphere, and in particular of the earth, which is generally regarded as a sphere. The earth is, in fact, slightly flattened at the poles; the technical name for a solid of its shape is a spheroid. We shall not deal with the subject usually known as spherical trigonometry, which is, however, referred to briefly on the next page.

Geometrical Properties

We begin by listing some of the sphere's geometrical properties: most of these should be fairly well known already.

1. The sphere is the locus, in three dimensions, of a point whose distance from a fixed point is given: the fixed point is called the centre, and the given distance the radius, of the sphere.

2. A sphere whose radius is r has a surface area $4\pi r^2$, a volume $\frac{4}{3}\pi r^3$.

3. The section of a sphere by a plane is a circle, whose radius is generally less than that of the sphere. If, however, the plane passes through the centre of the sphere, the circle has a radius equal to that of the sphere, and is called a great circle (Fig. 1).

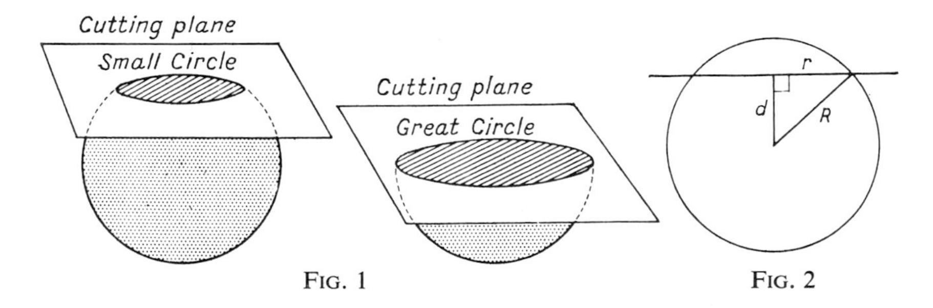

FIG. 1

FIG. 2

4. If the plane is at a distance from the centre of the sphere equal to its radius, then the plane meets the sphere in just one point and is described as a tangent plane (for example—a table top is a tangent plane to a sphere resting on the table). Any line through the point of contact which lies in the tangent plane is also a tangent to the sphere.

5. Figs. 2 and 3 illustrate formulae for circles of section and tangents, both obtained by applying Pythagoras' theorem:
Suppose a sphere has radius R.

(i) A plane whose distance from the centre of the sphere is d cuts the sphere in a circle of radius $r = \sqrt{R^2 - d^2}$.

(ii) From a point at distance d from the centre of the sphere tangents can be drawn whose length is $t = \sqrt{d^2 - R^2}$.

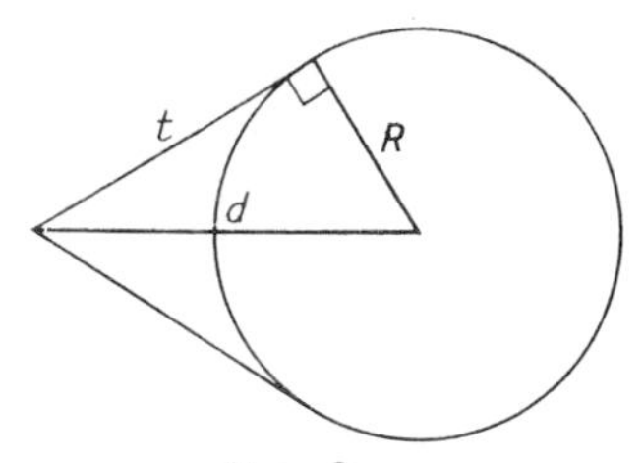

FIG. 3

Fig. 3, of course, is only a cross-section: if all possible tangents were drawn they would form the surface of a cone.

Notice that factorization of the above results leads to formulae

(i) $r^2 = (R - d)(R + d)$;

(ii) $t^2 = (d - R)(d + R)$

which could have been obtained from the theorems of intersecting chords and of secant and tangent respectively, as can be seen from Figs. 3a and 3b.

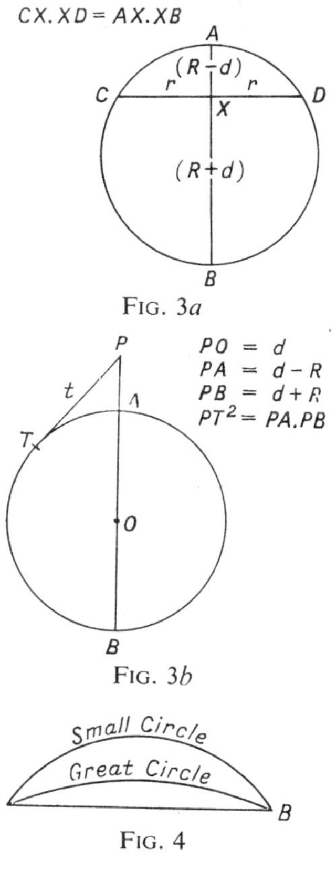

FIG. 3a

FIG. 3b

FIG. 4

Use of these forms of the formulae will often save the step of factorizing the difference of two squares, e.g. in Example 3 on page 97 we could write straight away $SJ^2 = 150 \times 8{,}150$.

6. Given any two points on the surface of a sphere, the shortest path joining them (keeping to the surface) is the shorter arc of a great circle passing through the two points. This is because a curve between two points has the least possible length when it is an arc of the greatest possible radius (Fig. 4): we have seen item 3 (above) that the great circle fulfils this requirement.

Spherical Triangles: Fig. 5 shows three points on the surface of a sphere, each pair being joined by an arc of a great circle. The figure ABC is known as a spherical triangle: it has three sides and three angles (the angle ABC, for instance, is defined as the angle between the planes which contain the arcs

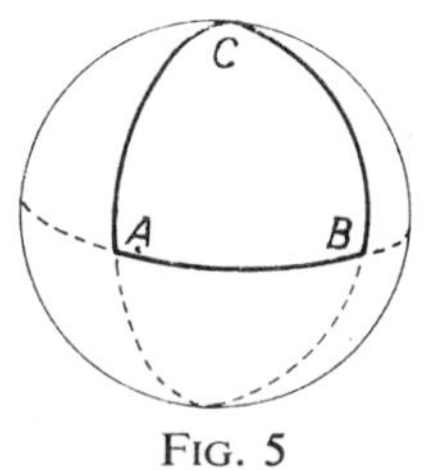

FIG. 5

AB and BC) and in some ways resembles a plane triangle. The relationships between its sides and angles, however, are quite different from those of plane trigonometry (notice, for instance, in Fig. 5 that the sum of the interior angles of ABC is certainly greater than 180°). The study of the properties of spherical triangles forms the starting point for the subject known as "spherical trigonometry."

Some Problems Concerning Spheres

We now work some examples on the various properties listed above.

Example 1. A saucer, whose diameter is 12 cm. and whose greatest depth is 16 mm., forms part of the surface of a sphere. Find the radius of this sphere.

This question is based on Fig. 2. Suppose the sphere has radius R mm. Then the plane of the rim of the saucer is at distance $(R - 16)$ mm. from the centre of the sphere. But the circle of section has radius 60 mm. (Fig. 6).

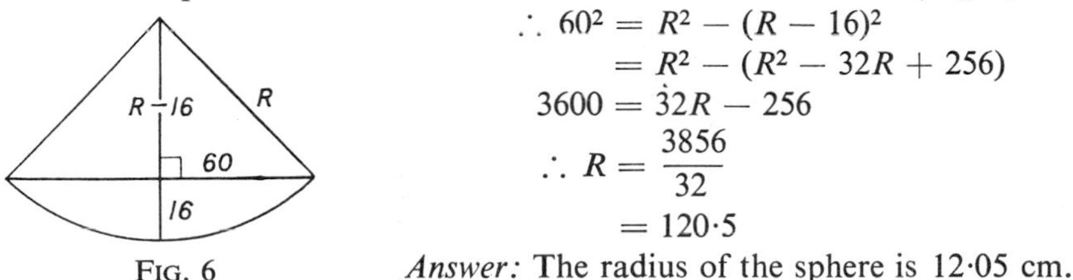

FIG. 6

$$\therefore\ 60^2 = R^2 - (R - 16)^2$$
$$= R^2 - (R^2 - 32R + 256)$$
$$3600 = 32R - 256$$
$$\therefore\ R = \frac{3856}{32}$$
$$= 120{\cdot}5$$

Answer: The radius of the sphere is 12·05 cm.

Example 2. Find the radius of the largest sphere which can be contained inside a hollow cone of height 10 in. and semi-vertical angle 30°.

Let the radius be r in.

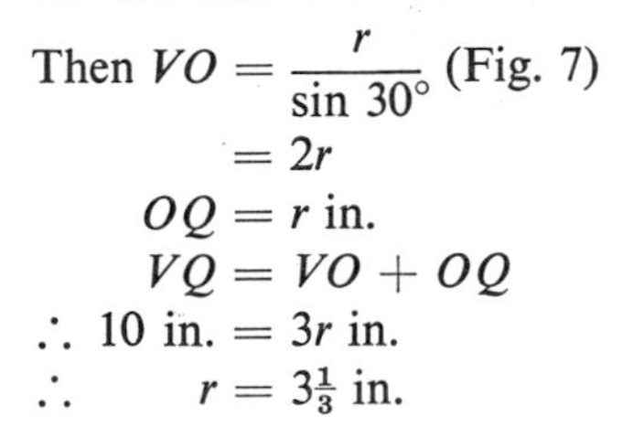

$$\text{Then } VO = \frac{r}{\sin 30^\circ} \text{ (Fig. 7)}$$
$$= 2r$$
$$OQ = r \text{ in.}$$
$$VQ = VO + OQ$$
$$\therefore\ 10 \text{ in.} = 3r \text{ in.}$$
$$\therefore\ r = 3\tfrac{1}{3} \text{ in.}$$

Answer: The radius of the sphere is $3\frac{1}{3}$ in.

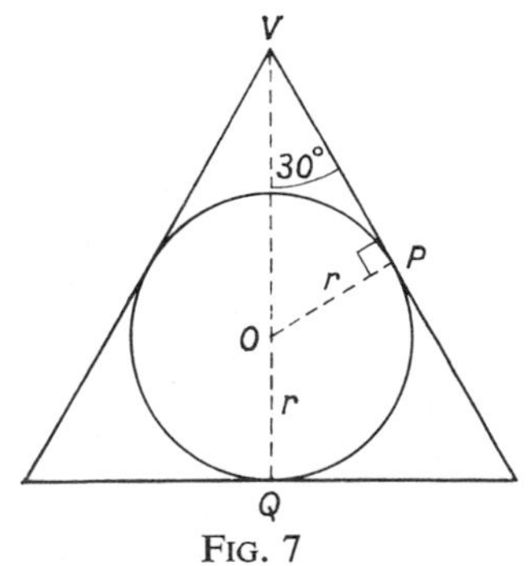

FIG. 7

Example 3. From a satellite 150 miles above the surface of the earth (assumed to be a sphere of radius 4,000 miles), how far away is the horizon?

Let the centre of the earth be O (see diagram) and let H, J be points just visible from the satellite, S.

SH and SJ are tangents to the earth (Fig. 8).

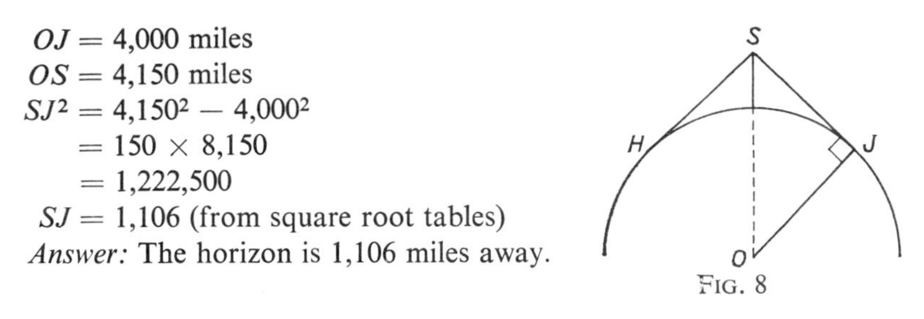

$OJ = 4{,}000$ miles
$OS = 4{,}150$ miles
$SJ^2 = 4{,}150^2 - 4{,}000^2$
$= 150 \times 8{,}150$
$= 1{,}222{,}500$
$SJ = 1{,}106$ (from square root tables)
Answer: The horizon is 1,106 miles away.

FIG. 8

Describing Position in Three-dimensional Terms

These examples have all been solved by considering a plane figure (a cross-section) which reduces the problem to one in two dimensions. In a fully three-dimensional problem, it is necessary to have a standard way of describing the position of any point in space.

Now in two dimensions, we commonly use either:

(i) Distances from two fixed lines (e.g. the co-ordinates x, y on a graph) or, particularly when referring to a map,

(ii) distance from a fixed point and bearing from a fixed direction (e.g. a point is 7 miles away in a direction N. 65° E.).

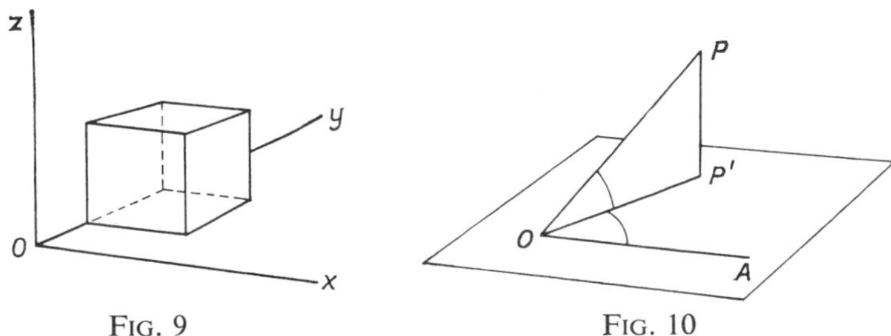

FIG. 9 FIG. 10

In three dimensions, a set of three co-ordinates (x, y, z) would be quite appropriate when dealing, for instance, with a cube (see Fig. 9); but for the sphere a system of *distance*, *bearing* and *elevation* is more useful, as we shall see. This system is illustrated in Fig. 10. P is any point and P' is its projection on a fixed plane. O is a fixed point, and OA a fixed line lying in this plane. Then from O, the point P has a distance OP, a bearing of $A\hat{O}P'$ and an elevation $P'\hat{O}P$.

Points on the Surface of a Sphere

Suppose now that we wish to describe the position of any point on the surface of a sphere. If we take the centre of the sphere as the fixed point O, then the distance OP will always equal the radius of the sphere. So it will only be necessary to state the two angles, AOP' and $P'OP$.

How does this description work out when the sphere in question is the earth?

1. The fixed plane through O meets the sphere in a great circle (see page 95) which is called the *Equator*.

2. The angle which OP makes with the fixed plane is called the *Latitude* of the point P.

3. Just two points have latitudes of 90°, namely the ends of the diameter of the sphere which is perpendicular to the fixed plane. These points are called the *North* and *South Poles*.

4. A plane containing a point P and the poles meets the sphere in a great circle which is called the *Meridian* of P.

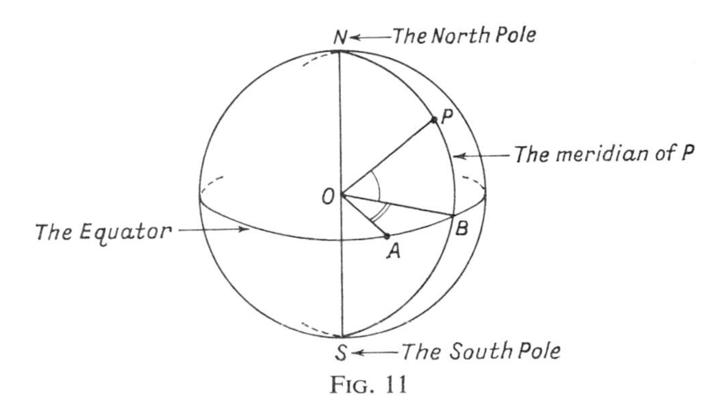

FIG. 11

5. Suppose that the meridian of P meets the Equator at B (Fig. 11). Suppose that the fixed line through O meets the Equator at A. Then $A\hat{O}B$ is called the *Longitude* of the point P.

6. The meridian through A is called the *Greenwich Meridian*. This, of course, like the fixed plane of section 1, is not chosen arbitrarily, but for geographical reasons: the great circle of zero longitude was originally chosen to pass through the site (at that time) of Greenwich Observatory.

7. All points of the same longitude (i.e. the same angle measured in the same direction, E. or W. from A) lie on a common meridian.

8. Suppose P is a point of latitude θ and suppose the radius of the earth is R. Then from Fig. 12 we see that P is at a distance $R.\sin\theta$ from the plane of the Equator. Thus a plane parallel to the Equator and distant $R.\sin\theta$ from it contains all points of latitude θ. But this plane meets the earth in a small circle.

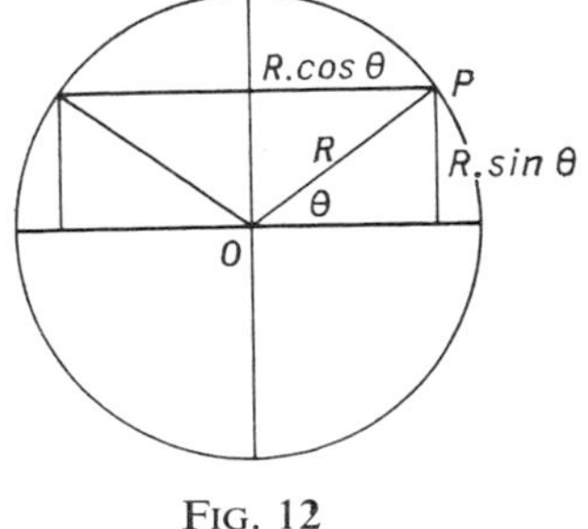

FIG. 12

So all points of the same latitude (i.e. the same angle measured in the same direction, N. or S.) lie on a circle parallel to the Equator, which is called a *Parallel.* The radius of this circle can be found, also from Fig. 12, and is $R.\cos\theta$.

The position of any point on the surface of a sphere can be given, then, by stating its latitude and longitude. Also the surface can be sub-divided, for the purpose of mapping, by a network of intersecting parallels and meridians. Because parallels lie in planes parallel to, and meridians in planes perpendicular to the plane of the Equator, they always cross at right-angles.

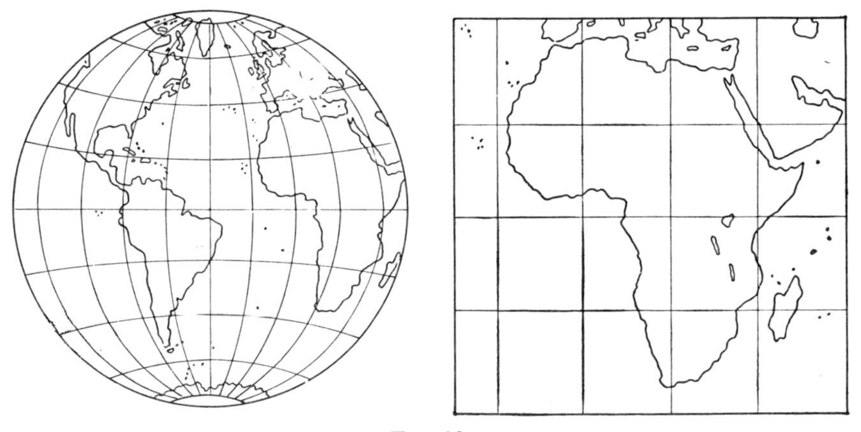

FIG. 13

Over a small region of the earth the curvature of these lines is not very noticeable, and in regional maps they are often drawn as though they were simply two sets of straight lines at right-angles. Compare the two illustrations above, one of a complete globe marked with great and small circles, the other of a map of a small part of it (Fig. 13).

Distances Over the Earth's Surface

The distance from A to B along a great or small circle can be calculated from the radius of the circle and the angle which AB subtends at its centre. If the radius is r and the angle θ (in degrees), the whole of the circumference has length $2\pi r$, and the arc AB, by proportion, has a length $2\pi r \times \dfrac{\theta}{360}$.

So the problem is to determine r and θ.

If the radius of the earth is R, then the radius of the Equator and of the meridians is R, while that of a parallel of latitude θ is $R.\cos\theta$, as shown above.

If two points are on the same meridian, the angle they subtend at its centre is the difference between their latitudes (Fig. 14).

If two points are on the same parallel, the angle they subtend at its centre is the difference between their longitudes (Fig. 15): the required angle PCQ is the angle between the planes NPS and NQS, and this is also the same as angle $P'OQ'$.

If two points have different longitudes *and* different latitudes, the problem of finding even a great circle distance between them involves some three-dimensional trigonometry rather beyond the scope of this book—except in certain special cases; for example, if their longitudes differ by 180°, when a great circle route via one of the poles can be used.

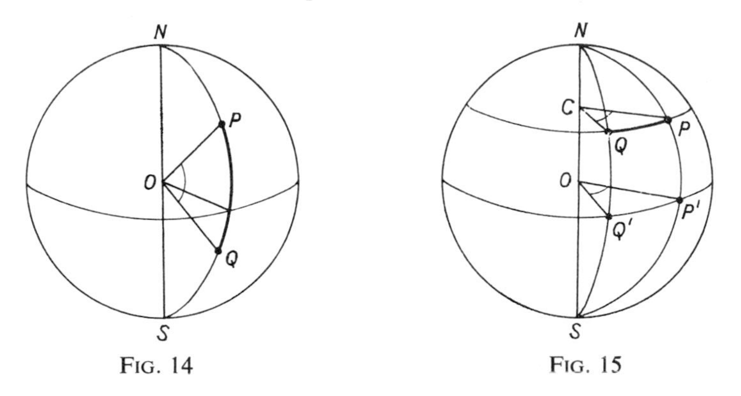

FIG. 14 FIG. 15

The radius of the earth is approximately 3,960 miles, though in some problems one may be told to use a different figure such as 4,000 miles.

The nautical mile is often used in distance problems: it is defined as the length of arc of a great circle which subtends 1 minute at the centre of the earth. Thus, along a great circle the distance in nautical miles is equal to the angle, in minutes, subtended at the centre. Along a parallel of latitude θ, this answer must be reduced by a factor $\cos\theta$. If it is necessary to convert nautical miles into ordinary units, the relation is

$$1 \text{ nautical mile} = 6{,}080 \text{ ft.}$$

Some examples will now be shown of problems concerning the earth.

Example 4. Taking the radius of the earth as 3,960 miles, calculate, correct to three significant figures, the distance between Axminster: 50° 46′ N., 3° 0′ W. and Bishop's Castle: 52° 29′ N., 3° 0′ W.

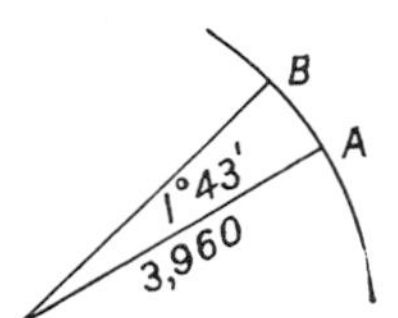

FIG. 16

The two towns lie on the same meridian, and differ in latitude by 1° 43′. The circumference of the meridian is $2\pi \times 3{,}960$ and that of the arc AB (Fig. 16) is:

$$2\pi \times 3{,}960 \times \frac{103}{360\,(60)} \text{ miles}$$

$$= \frac{\pi \times 11 \times 103}{30} \text{ miles} = 118{\cdot}7 \text{ miles}$$

No.	*Log.*
π	0·4971
11	1·0414
103	2·0128
	3·5513
30	1·4771
118·7	2·0742

Answer: The distance is approximately 119 miles.

Example 5. Calculate the distance in nautical miles from Madrid (40° N., 4° W.) to Peking (40° N., 116° E.), along a parallel of latitude.

The parallel of latitude 40° N. is a small circle of radius $R.\cos 40°$ (see Fig. 12, page 99) where R is the radius of the earth.

Its circumference is therefore $2\pi R.\cos 40°$. But $2\pi R$ is the circumference of a great circle, which is 360 × 60 nautical miles (1 n. ml. for each minute of arc).

∴ The circumference of the parallel 40° N. is 360 (60) (cos 40°) n. ml.
∴ Each minute of arc on this circle has a length cos 40° n. ml.
But Madrid and Peking differ in longitude by 120° = 7,200′
∴ The distance is 7,200 × cos 40°
= 5,516 n. ml.

No.	*Log.*
7,200	3·8573
cos 40°	$\bar{1}$·8843
5,516	3·7416

Answer: The distance is approximately 5,520 nautical miles.

Example 6. Two towns, A and B, have the same latitude, 51° 30′ N. and B is 100 miles due east of A. Taking the radius of the earth as 3,960 miles, calculate the difference between their longitudes.

Let the difference be D degrees.

$$\text{Then } 100 = 2\pi \times 3{,}960 \times \cos 51°\,30' \times \frac{D}{360}$$
$$= 2\pi \times 1\dot{1} \times \cos 51°\,30' \times D$$
$$\therefore D = \frac{100}{22\pi \cos 51°\,30'}$$
$$= 2{\cdot}325$$
$$= 2\frac{19{\cdot}5}{60}$$

No.	*Log.*
22	1·3424
π	0·4971
cos 51° 30′	$\bar{1}$·7941
	1·6336
100	2·0000
	1·6336
2·325	0·3664
0·325	$\bar{1}$·5119
60	1·7782
19·5	1·2901

Answer: They differ in longitude by approximately 2° 20′.

Example 7. Fig. 17 shows the orbit of a satellite, a circle passing over the North and South Poles. The orbit does not rotate with the earth. The satellite passes directly over Istanbul (41° 1′ N., 28° 56′ E.) going north: on its next time round it passes over Accra (5° 30′ N., 0° 10′ W.). Calculate its time for one complete orbit, to the nearest minute.

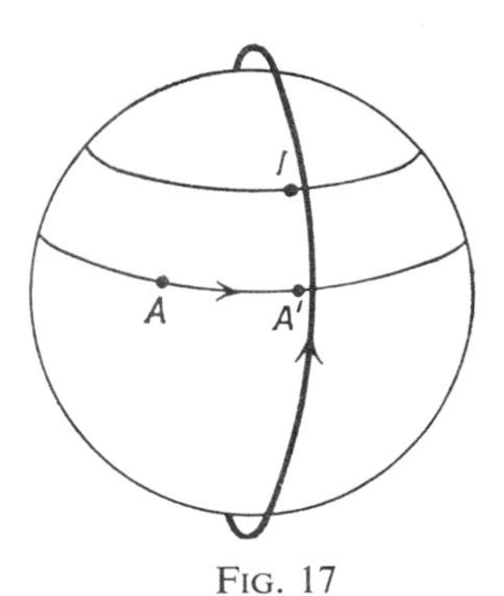

FIG. 17

In travelling from I (Istanbul) to A' (Accra) the satellite has covered 324° 29′ of arc, i.e. a complete orbit minus 35° 31′, the difference in latitude between the two towns.

In this time the earth has turned through 29° 6′, the difference in longitude between the two towns (i.e. Accra has moved from A to A').

∴ The satellite completes an orbit while the earth turns through

$$29°\ 6' \times \frac{360}{324{\cdot}5}$$

But the earth turns through 360° per day, or 1° in 4 minutes.

$$\therefore \text{ Time for 1 orbit} = \frac{4 \times 29{\cdot}1 \times 360}{324{\cdot}5} \text{ minutes.}$$
$$= 129{\cdot}1 \text{ minutes}$$

No.	*Log.*
4	0·6021
29·1	1·4639
360	2·5563
	4·6223
324·5	2·5112
129·1	2·1111

Answer: One orbit takes approximately 2 hours 10 minutes.

Note: Most satellites at relatively low heights circle the earth in a time somewhere near to two hours. Thus, whatever angle their orbits make with the Equator, their paths appear to move about 30° to the west each time they come round.

EXERCISE 9A

This exercise contains examples of most of the types of problem discussed in this chapter, particularly those based on the properties of the sphere and on calculation of great and small circle distances. Unless the question specifies nautical miles, take the radius of the earth as 3,960 miles.

1. Calculate
  (i) the volume;
  (ii) the total surface area;
  of a solid hemisphere whose diameter is 9 in.

2. A satellite travels round a circular orbit, whose radius is 5,000 miles and whose centre is at the centre of the earth, once every 110 minutes. Calculate its speed to the nearest 100 m.p.h.

3. Find the distance to the horizon from a point 1,760 ft. above sea-level, assuming the earth to be a perfect sphere and giving your answer to the nearest mile.

4. Fig. 18 shows a napkin-ring which is part of the surface of a sphere of radius 3 cm. The distance between the circular ends, which are equal and parallel, is 2·5 cm. Find the greatest possible diameter of a cylindrical object which can be passed through this ring.

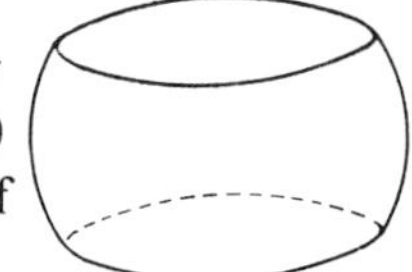

FIG. 18

5. Prove that, due to the rotation of the earth, any point on the Equator is travelling with a speed of 900 knots, and find the latitude of a point whose speed of rotation is 750 knots.

6. Calculate the great circle distance from Hamburg (53° 35′ N., 9° 58′ E.) to Ulm (48° 27′ N., 9° 58′ E.).

7. The latitude of Cairo is 30° N. Calculate to the nearest 10 miles:

(i) its distance from the Equator, measured along its meridian;

(ii) its perpendicular distance from the plane of the Equator.

8. Buenos Aires has a latitude 34° 50′ South, and a longitude 58° 37′ West. Find the latitude and longitude of points:

(i) 50 nautical miles due north of Buenos Aires;

(ii) 50 nautical miles due east of Buenos Aires.

9. The approximate positions of New Orleans and Lhasa are 30° N., 90° W. and 30° N., 90° E., respectively. Find, correct to the nearest 100 miles, the distance between them:

(i) along their parallel of latitude;

(ii) along a meridian through the North Pole;

(iii) in a straight line through the earth's interior.

10. An aircraft flies from London (51° 30′ N., 0° 5′ W.) due west to Cardiff (51° 30′ N., 3° 10′ W.) in 37 minutes. Calculate its average speed in m.p.h.

REVISION SUMMARY

ARITHMETIC AND TRIGONOMETRY

(**A** = *Syllabus A;* **B** = *Syllabus B*)

(A & B) **AVERAGES**

Page

The common meaning of the word "average" applied to a set of numbers is the value each would have *if they were all equal,* in order to achieve the same total. The average of 6, 3 and 15 is 8, since $6 + 3 + 15 = 24$ and $8 + 8 + 8 = 24$.

***Arithmetic Mean.* This is the technical name for the common "average."**

It is defined as: $\dfrac{\text{The total of all the numbers}}{\text{The number of numbers involved}}$

***Average Price.* This is found as** $\dfrac{\text{Total cost}}{\text{Number of articles}}$

A girl bought 3 records at 6s. 9d. each and one at 21s. 9d. What was the average price she paid for a record? 9

***Average Speed.* This is found as** $\dfrac{\text{Total distance}}{\text{Total time}}$

A motorist travels for 2 hr. at 30 m.p.h. and then for a further 3 hr. at 40 m.p.h. What is his average speed for the whole journey? 11

***Density.* The density of a substance is the weight of a specified volume of that substance. Thus the density of water is about $62\frac{1}{2}$ lb. per cu. ft.**

***Average Density.* This is found as** $\dfrac{\text{Total weight}}{\text{Total volume}}$

Two metals whose densities are 420 lb. per cu. ft. and 560 lb. per cu. ft. are alloyed in the ratio 60% to 40% by weight. What is the density of the alloy? 13

***Mixtures.* Tea costing 3s. 8d. per lb. is to be blended with tea costing 4s. per lb. so that the mixture costs 3s. 9d. per lb. Every pound of the cheaper tea will make a profit of 1d., but each pound of the dearer tea will lose 4d., so the qualities must be mixed in the ratio:**

4 (cheaper) : 1 (dearer)

***Harmonic Mean.* To find the harmonic mean of 5 and 10, we say that the average of $\frac{1}{5}$ and $\frac{1}{10}$ is $\frac{3}{20}$, and hence the H.M. required is $\frac{20}{3}$ ($= 6\frac{2}{3}$). If a journey is covered in equal *distances* at different speeds, the average speed is the H.M. of the given speeds: also, if substances of different densities are mixed in equal *weights,* the average density is the H.M. of the given densities.**

Page

Find the average speed for a two-mile journey if the first mile is covered at 20 m.p.h., and the second at 30 m.p.h. 14

Geometric Mean. **$4 \times 9 = 36$, and $\sqrt{36} = 6$. 6 is called the G.M. of 4 and 9.**

(A & B) MENSURATION III

The number π which appears in many formulae cannot be expressed as an exact fraction. Its value is *approximately* 3·14 or $\frac{22}{7}$.

Circles. **Circumference $= 2\pi \times$ radius $= \pi \times$ diameter.**

Area $= \pi r^2$, where r is the radius.

Find (*a*) the circumference, (*b*) the area, of a circle of radius 7 in. 18

Compound Problems. **Do not substitute a value for π until as late as possible in the solution: this often eases the calculations, e.g. to evaluate $23\pi + 5\pi$, first say that this sum is 28π and then put $\pi = \frac{22}{7}$, getting $28 \times \frac{22}{7} = 88$.**

Two concentric circles have radii 27 in. and 20 in. Find the area of the ring enclosed between them. 19

Cylinders. **The area of the *curved* surface of a circular cylinder is given by**

$$\text{area} = 2\pi rh \text{ (} r \text{ is the radius, } h \text{ the height).}$$

Find the *total* area of a closed cylindrical can of radius 2 in. and height 5 in. 21

The volume of a cylinder as above is given by the formula

$$\text{volume} = \pi r^2 h$$

A rain gauge is a cylindrical jar of diameter 3 in. Rain is collected in it by means of a conical funnel of diameter 8 in. If $\frac{5}{8}$ in. of water is collected in the gauge, what is the rainfall at that place? 23

Displacement of Liquid. **If an object is placed in a vessel of uniform cross-section containing liquid, then the rise in level is given by**

$$\text{rise} = \frac{\text{volume of object immersed}}{\text{area of base of vessel}}$$

This formula applies equally when the object is removed and the level falls.

A tank with a square base of side 3 ft. contains water to a depth of 2 ft. A cube of side 18 in. is placed in the tank. How much does the water level rise? 24

Pipes. **When water is flowing out of a pipe, we may use the formula**

rate of discharge = area of cross-section $\times$ speed of flow.

It is vital to reduce all quantities to the same sets of units.

A pipe in which the water flows at 7 ft. per sec. delivers water at a rate 13,750 gal. per hr. Find the diameter of the pipe. 25

Page

(A & B) SQUARES, SQUARE ROOTS AND THE USE OF TABLES

Four figure tables **give values to 4 significant figures and are correct only to 3 significant figures.**

To find the *square* of a number from the squares table:

1. Make an approximation first.

2. Read off the first two digits in the left-hand column.

3. Read across that line until you come to the third digit, and note the number.

4. Continue across that line until you reach the difference column headed with the fourth digit and *add* that to the number noted.

5. Insert the decimal point after consulting the rough check.

6. The square of a number less than one is *less* than that number.

7. Numbers with more than 4 significant figures must be corrected first.

Using tables, work out: $1{\cdot}728^2$

$1{\cdot}3257^2$ — 28

Square Roots. **There are two sets of numbers for each row in the square root table. To find the appropriate set:**

1. Mark off the number, whose square root you wish to find, in pairs from the decimal point.

2. Write above the left-hand figure or figures the biggest number whose square is less than the number there.

3. Put a zero above each of the following pairs, and use this as a rough check to decide which set of numbers to use.

Use tables to evaluate $\sqrt{63,450}$ — 30

$\sqrt{5,942}$ — 31

$\sqrt{0{\cdot}006425}$ — 31

(Notice that the square root of numbers less than one is *bigger* than the number.)

(A) STOCKS AND SHARES

Shares are issued by business firms in order to raise capital.

Nominal Value. **This is the price at which the shares were originally sold, and is printed in the share certificates.**

Dividend. **This is the profit to be divided among the shareholders: it is expressed as a percentage of the nominal value, and each shareholder receives that percentage of the nominal value of his shares.**

Cash Value. **This is the current market price of the shares, which will usually not be the same as the nominal value.**

Page

Yield. **This is the dividend expressed as a percentage of the *cash* value of the shares.**

10% (£1) shares at 30s. means:—

1. **The nominal value is £1.**
2. **The dividend is 10% of £1 (= 2s.).**
3. **The cash value is 30s. This is the price you would have to pay for each share.**
4. **The yield is the dividend (2s.) as a percentage of the cash value (30s.), i.e. $6\frac{2}{3}$%.**

A man invests £200 in Barton's (£1) shares when they stand at 16s. If they pay a dividend of 8%:

(*a*) How many shares does he buy?

(*b*) What is his income?

(*c*) What is his yield? 34

Stocks. **The same terms discussed above apply to stocks; they differ from shares in that:**

1. **They are issued by governments, public corporations, etc.**
2. **The money will be repaid (the stock will be redeemed) eventually.**
3. **The cash value is quoted as the price of £100 stock, but any fractional amount of stock may be bought.**

It is important to write the words "stock" and "cash" to distinguish between nominal and cash values.

6% stock at 60 means that:

1. **£120 cash will buy £200 stock.**
2. **The dividend will be 6% of £200, i.e. £12.**
3. **The yield will be £12 as a percentage of £120, i.e. 10% (often written as £5 per cent, i.e. £5 per £100).**

A man invests £700 in Barchester $4\frac{1}{2}$% stock at 120. What is his income? 36

(A & B) LOGARITHMS

The logarithm of a number is the power to which 10 must be raised to give the number: i.e. if

$$N = 10^L \text{ we say that } L = \log N.$$

A number between 1 and 10 has a logarithm of the form 0.— (found from a log table).

For any logarithm in this form, the numbers whose log it is can be found in an antilog table.

Each multiplication by 10 adds 1 to the log.

Each division by 10 subtracts 1 from the log, but the subtraction is done from the whole number part of the logarithm, leaving a "bar" number if the result is negative.

		Page

Log (M × N) = log M ÷ log N: to multiply, add logarithms.
Log (M ÷ N) = log M − log N: to divide, subtract logarithms.

Multiply 2·345 by 3·178.	Divide 6·563 by 1·732.	42
What is the log of 1,765?	What is the antilog of 4·8432?	44
What is the log of 0·005476?	What is the antilog of $\bar{2}$·2982?	45
Multiply 38·26 by 0·0007251.	Divide 0·4359 by 0·006705.	46

To find the Nth power of a number, multiply its log by N and look up the antilog of the result.
For the Nth root, divide by N.

Calculate $(0{\cdot}7195)^5$. 49
Calculate the cube root of 17·63. 49

To divide a "bar" number by N, it may be necessary to rewrite it as a larger "bar" number (divisible exactly by N) plus a positive number.

(A & B) TRIGONOMETRY

Trigonometrical ratios.

$$\textbf{Tangent} = \frac{\textbf{Opposite}}{\textbf{Adjacent}} \qquad \textbf{Sine} = \frac{\textbf{Opposite}}{\textbf{Hypotenuse}} \qquad \textbf{Cosine} = \frac{\textbf{Adjacent}}{\textbf{Hypotenuse}}$$

Also: Opposite = Hypotenuse × Sine
Adjacent = Hypotenuse × Cosine

Logarithms of these ratios can be looked up directly in log tan., log sin., log cos. tables.
In cosine (and log cos.) tables, figures in the difference columns are *subtracted.*
Angles of elevation and depression are measured from the horizontal.
The sun's altitude = its angle of elevation.

How long will be the shadow cast by a post 9 ft. high when the sun's altitude is 35°? 55
Find the tangent of 71° 43′ 56
A ladder, which reaches 31 ft. 6 in. up a vertical wall, makes an angle of $68\frac{1}{2}°$ with the ground. Calculate the length of the ladder. 59
A straight road rises 485 ft. in a distance of $\frac{3}{4}$ mile (measured along the road). At what angle is it inclined to the horizontal? 59

***Non-right-angled Triangles* can usually be tackled by drawing a perpendicular from one vertex to the opposite side. This method is particularly useful with an isosceles triangle when the perpendicular can bisect the base, also the angle between the equal sides.**

Triangle TAB has $AT = TB$ = 5 ft. 6 in.; AB = 2 ft. 10 in.
By considering the perpendicular from T on to AB, calculate $A\hat{T}B$.
Find also the length of this perpendicular. 61

Page

If the triangle is not isosceles, the methods of the next chapter (i.e. triangle formulae) are probably more convenient.

Other relations.

Cotangent $= \dfrac{1}{\text{Tangent}}$. **Secant** $= \dfrac{1}{\text{Cosine}}$. **Cosecant** $= \dfrac{1}{\text{Sine}}$.

Tangent $= \dfrac{\text{Sine}}{\text{Cosine}}$.

$\sin^2 A + \cos^2 A = 1$.

TRIANGLES

(A & B) ***Triangle Formulae.*** **We use a standard way of lettering the sides and angles: side** a **is the side opposite** A**, etc.**

Where obtuse angles are involved use the following relations:

$\sin A = \sin(180° - A)$; $\cos A = -\cos(180° - A)$,

$\tan A = -\tan(180° - A)$.

Use tables to find (i) the value of sin 137° 49′, 66

(ii) the angle whose tan is minus 0·5486. 67

Important formulae for the triangle are:

(B) The ***cosine rule:*** $a^2 = b^2 + c^2 - 2bc.\cos A$

which can also be written making $\cos A$ **the subject:**

$$\cos A = \frac{b^2 + c^2 - a^2}{2bc}.$$

In triangle ABC, $AB = 4{\cdot}25$ cm., $BC = 6{\cdot}7$ cm. and $\hat{B} = 53°$. Calculate the length AC. 68

(B) The ***sine rule:*** $\dfrac{a}{\sin A} = \dfrac{b}{\sin B} = \dfrac{c}{\sin C}$.

Triangle ABC has $\hat{A} = 39°$, $\hat{B} = 73°$ and $AB = 6{\cdot}1$ in. Calculate the length BC. 71

The ***area*** **of a triangle** ABC **is** $\frac{1}{2}bc.\sin A$**, or in general a half the product of two sides and the sine of the angle between them.**

(B) ***Solution of Triangles.*** **Use the sine rule in preference to the cosine rule if there is a choice, and remember that when two angles are known the third can be found by subtraction of their sum from 180 degrees.**

S.S.S. **Find an angle by cos rule** } **2nd angle by sin rule,**
S.A.S. **Find 3rd side by cos rule** } **3rd by subtraction.**

A.A.S. **Find 3rd angle by subtraction, then the remaining sides by the sin rule.**

When finding an angle by the sine rule, choose an angle ***not*** **opposite the longest side: it is then known to be an acute angle.**

Page

In the "ambiguous" case ($A.S.S.$) we can use the sine rule to find the sine of a second angle: if we are sure that this angle cannot be obtuse we find the third angle by subtraction and the third side by using the sine rule again.

Solve the triangle ABC, given $a = 6{\cdot}7$ cm., $\hat{B} = 53°$ and $c = 4{\cdot}25$ cm. 74

(B) *Algebraic Treatment.* If P is the point (x, y) referred to rectangular axes Ox, Oy, and if the line OP is of length r and makes an angle θ with Ox (anti-clockwise)

$$\cos \theta = \frac{x}{r}, \quad \sin \theta = \frac{y}{r}, \quad \tan \theta = \frac{y}{x}$$

where x and y have their usual signs. These definitions again lead to the results for obtuse angles, and can be used to define the ratios for any angle.

The graphs of $\sin \theta$ and $\cos \theta$ are "sin waves," one being 90° ahead of the other. This fact can be expressed in the form

$$\cos \theta = \sin (\theta + 90°).$$

(B) THREE DIMENSIONS

***Solid Geometry.* The projection of a point on a plane is the foot of the perpendicular from the point on to the plane.**

The projection of a line consists of the projections of all points lying in it.

The angle between a line and a plane is the angle between the line and its projection on the plane.

If two planes are not parallel, they meet in a straight line. The angle between them is the angle between two intersecting lines, one in each plane, which are both perpendicular to this line of intersection.

A hillside slopes uniformly at 12° to the horizontal, and a straight path along it makes an angle of 25° with the line of greatest slope. Find the angle at which the path is inclined to the horizontal. 86

$VABCD$ is a pyramid on a square base $ABCD$ of side 6 in. $VA = VB = 5$ in. and the face VAB is inclined at 60° to the base. Calculate: (i) the volume of the pyramid,
(ii) the angle between planes VBC and $ABCD$. 87

***Plan and elevation.* The projection of a figure on a horizontal plane is called its plan. Any projection on a vertical plane is called an elevation.**

Given the plan of a figure, how would you construct its elevation? 90

For what purpose is an auxiliary view used, and how would you construct one? 91

Page

VABCD is a pyramid on a rectangular base *ABCD*. $AB = 15$ ft. and $BC = 25$ ft. *VAB* and *VCD* are isosceles triangles inclined at 40° to the base. By drawing suitable elevations, determine:
(i) the height of *V* above the base;
(ii) the lengths of edges *VB* and *VD* and the angle between them. 92

THE SPHERE

(A & B) Radius *r*. Surface Area $4\pi r^2$. Volume $\frac{4}{3}\pi r^3$.

A plane whose distance from the centre of a sphere is *d* cuts the sphere in a circle of radius $\sqrt{(R^2 - d^2)}$

$d = 0$ (a diametral plane): radius $= R$ (a great circle),
$d = R$ (a tangent plane): radius $= 0$ (a single point),
Intermediate values of $d =$ a small circle.

From a point at distance *d* from the centre of a sphere, tangents can be drawn whose length is $\sqrt{(d^2 - R^2)}$.

What is meant by a "spherical triangle"? 96

A saucer, whose diameter is 12 cm. and whose greatest depth is 16 mm., forms part of the surface of a sphere. Find its radius. 97

From a satellite 150 miles above the surface of the earth (assumed to be a sphere of 4,000 miles radius), how far away is the horizon? 97

(B) *The Earth* is approximately a sphere of radius 3,960 miles.
The equator is a great circle.
Let *O* be the centre, *P* a point on the surface.
Then the latitude of *P* is the angle which *OP* makes with the plane of the equator.
The poles have latitudes of 90°.
A parallel is a small circle parallel to the plane of the equator; it joins points of equal latitude.
A meridian is a great circle through the poles.
The longitude of a point is the angle between the meridian it lies on and the Greenwich Meridian.

What is the radius of a parallel of latitude θ? 99

What is meant by a "nautical mile"? 101

Taking the radius of the earth as 3,960 miles, calculate, correct to 3 sig. fig., the distance between Axminster (50° 46′ N., 3° 0′ W.) and Bishop's Castle (52° 29′ N., 3° 0′ W.). 101

Calculate the distance in nautical miles from Madrid (40° N., 4° W.) to Peking (40° N., 116° E.) along a parallel of latitude. 102

ALGEBRA AND THE CALCULUS

CHAPTER 1

TRINOMIALS AND QUADRATIC EQUATIONS

THE METHOD of multiplying brackets together was discussed in the last chapter, but for the work which follows it is extremely useful to be able to multiply binomials (*i.e.* brackets containing two terms) in your head, and simply to write down the answer.

So let us go back a little way and look at this process again.

$$\begin{aligned}(2a - 3)(a + 4) &= 2a(a + 4) - 3(a + 4)\\ &= 2a^2 + 8a - 3a - 12\\ &= 2a^2 + 5a - 12\end{aligned}$$

The final answer contains *three terms*, and is called a *trinomial*. The middle term, $+ 5a$, is a combination of the two terms $+ 8a$ and $- 3a$ of the line before, which contained four terms. Now these four terms arose from the following multiplications:

$$\begin{aligned}2a \times a &= 2a^2\\ 2a \times 4 &= 8a\\ - 3 \times a &= - 3a\\ - 3 \times 4 &= - 12\end{aligned}$$

The pairings can be shown diagrammatically as under:

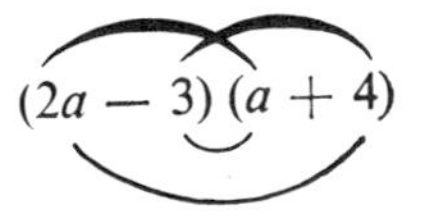

(This diagram has been likened to a face with an inane grin on it, and has been irreverently dubbed "the algebraic expression"). The "eyebrows" give the first and last terms of the answer, and the "mouth" and "chin" give two more terms which combine to give the middle term, $+ 5a$. Thus we can do the multiplication mentally:

(Eyebrows)	$2a^2 \qquad - 12$	(leaving a gap for the middle
(Mouth and chin)	$- 3a + 8a = 5a$	(term
(Fill in the missing term)	$2a^2 + 5a - 12$	

EXERCISE 1A

Multiply the following *mentally:*

1. $(a + 2)(a + 3)$
2. $(b + 6)(b - 4)$
3. $(c + 2)(c - 8)$
4. $(d - 3)(d - 5)$
5. $(e + 2)(2e - 3)$
6. $(f + 6)(3f - 4)$
7. $(2g + 3)(g - 7)$
8. $(3h - 1)(h - 2)$
9. $(3k + 2)(2k - 3)$
10. $(4m - 3)(2m + 3)$
11. $(5n + 2)(3n - 5)$
12. $(2p - 9)(3p - 4)$

Guesswork and Common Sense

The above exercise should convince you that trinomials containing only one letter will factorize into two binomials. The method we use to do the factorization is, surprisingly, guesswork. Guesswork combined, of course, with common sense.

Consider $a^2 + 4a + 3$

We know this came from two brackets ( ) ( )

The "eyebrows" of this multiplication provide the first and last terms,

a^2 and $+ 3$

Now a^2 can only arise here from $a \times a$, so the brackets start

$(a \quad)(a \quad)$

The signs in $a^2 + 4a + 3$ are all positive, so both these brackets must contain a + sign.

$(a + \quad)(a + \quad)$

The number 3 can only arise from 3×1, so the brackets are either

$(a + 3)(a + 1)$

or $(a + 1)(a + 3)$

These come to exactly the same thing (*e.g.* $2 \times 5 = 5 \times 2$), so either will do: the only possible answer is

$(a + 3)(a + 1)$

Now we *must check* by multiplication that this is the correct answer: do this for yourself. This check is vital. If we had been working with

$a^2 + 5a + 3$

the reasoning would have been just the same, and we would have arrived at

$(a + 3)(a + 1)$

as the only possible answer: but it is not the answer in *this* case, hence

$a^2 + 5a + 3$ *has no factors.*

In a more complicated case there may be several possibilities, and then there is no alternative but to try them all until we hit on the right one.

Consider $4b^2 + 16b - 9$

Now $4b^2$ could arise from $4b \times b$

or $2b \times 2b$

and 9 could arise from 9×1

or 3×3 also, the fact that

the last term is negative tells us that one bracket must contain a + sign and the other a − sign, but does not tell us which is which. Altogether there are nine possibilities: we list them below and work out each product.

$$\begin{aligned}
(4b + 3)(b - 3) &= 4b^2 - 9b - 9 \\
(4b - 3)(b + 3) &= 4b^2 + 9b - 9 \\
(4b + 9)(b - 1) &= 4b^2 + 5b - 9 \\
(4b - 9)(b + 1) &= 4b^2 - 5b - 9 \\
(4b + 1)(b - 9) &= 4b^2 - 35b - 9 \\
(4b - 1)(b + 9) &= 4b^2 + 35b - 9 \\
(2b + 3)(2b - 3) &= 4b^2 \qquad\quad - 9 \\
(2b + 9)(2b - 1) &= 4b^2 + 16b - 9 \\
(2b - 9)(2b + 1) &= 4b^2 - 16b - 9
\end{aligned}$$

From this long list we can see that the last but one attempt is the right one, so we can put

$$4b^2 + 16b - 9 = (2b + 9)(2b - 1)$$

It is tedious to have to try all these possibilities, but it is the only way to be sure of finding the correct factors. There is a way in which a little time can be saved, though. Inspection of the above list shows that the attempts go together in pairs [except for $(2b + 3)(2b - 3)$, which is a special case]; each pair differing only in that the signs have been tried in different brackets. The resulting products differ only in the sign of the middle term, not in its numerical value. (Look at the first two attempts to verify this.)

Having listed all the possibilities, then, we work out the first product, find that it gives $-9b$ in the middle, and then need not bother to try the signs the other way round, as we know this will give $+9b$ in the middle, and we want a $16b$ in the middle. Instead, we go on to a different combination of numbers.

If by good fortune we had listed the possibilities the other way up, so that we started with

$$(2b - 9)(2b + 1) = 4b^2 - 16b - 9$$

we should see that the required $16b$ had appeared in the middle, but with the wrong sign: exchange the signs, and we have the answer.

Notice the five steps required in finding the above factors:

1. What possibilities give the first term $(4b^2)$?
2. What possibilities give the last term (9)?
3. What do we know about the signs?
4. List all possible combinations systematically.
5. Multiply out the various cases until the correct one is reached.

The following points help us at step (3):

(a) If both signs of the trinomial are positive $(a^2 + 4a + 3)$, both factors have a + sign: $(a + 3)(a + 1)$.

(b) If the *middle* term is *negative*, and the last term positive ($a^2 - 4a + 3$), *both* factors have a — *sign*: $(a - 3)(a - 1)$.

(c) If the *last* term is negative, the factors have *opposite* signs, order unknown. (The sign of the middle term is of no help in this case.)

With practice you will acquire a knack of factorizing trinomials quite quickly, but however skilful you become, you *must* check your answer by multiplication: a good guess *might* turn out to be wrong.

EXERCISE 1B

Factorize:

1. $2a^2 + 7a + 3$
2. $2a^2 + 5a + 3$
3. $2a^2 - 5a + 3$
4. $2a^2 - 5a - 3$
5. $2a^2 + 5a - 3$
6. $b^2 + 5b + 6$
7. $c^2 - 5c + 4$
8. $d^2 - 3d - 4$
9. $3e^2 - e - 2$
10. $2f^2 - 7f - 4$
11. $3g^2 - 14g + 8$
12. $5h^2 + 13h + 6$
13. $6k^2 - k - 2$
14. $4m^2 + 5m - 6$
15. $6n^2 + 7n - 20$
16. $12p^2 - 7p - 12$

Factorizing Trinomials

Compare these two products:

$$(2x + 3)(x - 6) = 2x^2 - 9x - 18$$
$$(2x + 3y)(x - 6y) = 2x^2 - 9xy - 18y^2$$

The general shape of each expansion is the same: the presence of the letter y in the second case does not affect the numbers involved; hence if we are asked to factorize

$$3a^2 + 5ab - 2b^2$$

we can temporarily ignore the letter b, find in the usual way that

$$3a^2 + 5a - 2 = (3a - 1)(a + 2)$$

and then, replacing the letter b,

$$3a^2 + 5ab - 2b^2 = (3a - b)(a + 2b)$$

Sometimes the trinomial to be factorized is the wrong way round, e.g.

$$6 - a - a^2$$

In such a case do not attempt to reverse the order; work out the factors with the numbers coming before the letters, thus:

$$6 - a - a^2 = (3 + a)(2 - a)$$

EXERCISE 1C

Factorize:

1. $2x^2 - 5xy + 2y^2$
2. $10 + 3b - b^2$
3. $x^2 - 2xy + y^2$
4. $8 - 2c - c^2$

Four Categories of Factorization Problems

This is a convenient moment to review the whole subject of factorization. There are four main types of problem you are likely to meet at this stage of the algebra course.

1. *Simple factors.* These consist of single numbers and letters, e.g.

$$2a^2b - 6ab^2 = 2ab\,(a - 3b)$$

2. *The difference of two squares*, e.g. $4x^2 - 9y^2 = (2x + 3y)\,(2x - 3y)$
3. *Trinomials.* These are done by intelligent guesswork, e.g.

$$2p^2 - p - 3 = (2p - 3)\,(p + 1)$$

4. *Four-term expressions.* Divide these into pairs, e.g.

$$\begin{aligned} a^2 - ab + 3a - 3b &= a\,(a - b) + 3\,(a - b) \\ &= (a + 3)\,(a - b) \end{aligned}$$

It is important to remember that sometimes more than one of these types may occur in the same problem. For example,

$$\begin{aligned} 2a^4 - 2a^2 - 24 &= 2\,(a^4 - a^2 - 12) && \text{Type (1)} \\ &= 2\,(a^2 + 3)\,(a^2 - 4) && \text{Type (3)} \\ &= 2\,(a^2 + 3)\,(a + 2)\,(a - 2) && \text{Type (2)} \end{aligned}$$

When faced with a factorization problem, you should

(a) Look for simple factors and take them out when present. (This is important and often forgotten).
(b) Factorize according to type.
(c) Examine your answer to see if it can be factorized still further.

EXERCISE 1D

Factorize:

1. $2c^2 - 8c - 10$ **2.** $2ax - 2ay - 6x + 6y$ **3.** $b^4 - 26b^2 + 25$

Quadratic Equations

One of the most valuable applications of factorization is in the solution of *quadratic equations*. These are equations in which the unknown appears raised to the power two, i.e. squared. For example

$$x^2 = 4$$

$$\text{and } x^2 - 2x = 12$$

are quadratic equations. But before we can appreciate the connection between these equations and the process of factorization, we must examine some of the peculiar properties of the number 0.

The 0 times table was not one of the tables you learned as a child. It is very easy and very dull:

$$0 \times 1 = 0$$
$$0 \times 2 = 0$$
$$0 \times 3 = 0 \text{ and so on.}$$

In fact, the number 0 does not appear in any of the tables learned at primary school, since the three-times table, for example, starts

$$3 \times 1 = 3$$

rather than $3 \times 0 = 0$

This is less trivial than it might first appear. The number 0 cannot appear in any multiplication unless it appears on both sides. If 0 appears in the multiplication, the answer is 0, and, conversely,

if the answer is 0, *then* 0 *appears in the multiplication.*

If $2 \times a = 0$

then, since the answer to the multiplication is 0, 0 must appear in the multiplication; that is $a = 0$

Similarly, if $xy = 0$

then 0 must appear in the multiplication: we cannot tell which factor is zero, but either $x = 0$ or $y = 0$

If $x(y - 3) = 0$
then either $x = 0$
or $y - 3 = 0$
that is, either $x = 0$ or $y = 3$

If $(a - 2)(a + 6) = 0$
then either $a - 2 = 0$
or $a + 6 = 0$
that is, either $a = 2$ or $a = -6$

Clearly a cannot equal both 2 and -6, but it must be equal to one of them.

EXERCISE 1E

Deduce as much as possible from the following statements:

1. $3x = 0$
2. $2ab = 0$
3. $p(q + 4) = 0$
4. $2y(y - 3) = 0$
5. $(x - 3)(x + 4) = 0$
6. $(2x - 3)(x + 2) = 0$
7. $(a - 2)(a - 3)(a + 5) = 0$

Conversion to Zero Form

We can see from the above examples that if an equation is written in the form

$$\text{(some factors)} = 0$$

then we know that one or other of those factors is itself zero, and from a collection of such facts we can find various possible answers to the equation. Now the equation will probably not be written in this form, but by now we are well equipped to reduce it to factors if it is possible to do so, and hence solve the equation.

$$\text{Thus, if } ab + 2a = 3b + 6$$
$$\text{then } ab + 2a - 3b - 6 = 0$$
$$a(b + 2) - 3(b + 2) = 0$$
$$(a - 3)(b + 2) = 0$$
$$\text{Hence either } a - 3 = 0$$
$$\text{or } b + 2 = 0$$

therefore either $a = 3$ or $b = -2$. Notice the little word "or". If a is *not* 3, then b *must be* -2, but if a *is* 3, then b need not be -2: in fact, b might be any number at all. Suppose a *is* 3, and we choose b to be, say, 14. Then, in the original equation,

$$\text{L.H.S.} = ab + 2a \qquad\qquad \text{R.H.S.} = 3b + 6$$
$$= 42 + 6 \qquad\qquad = 42 + 6$$
$$= 48 \qquad\qquad = 48$$

We see that our solution is perfectly justified. Try checking again with $b = -2$ and $a =$ any number you like.

Now take the equation $\qquad x^2 = 3x + 4$

This can be written $\qquad x^2 - 3x - 4 = 0$ (This is known as writing the equation in zero form)

$$(x - 4)(x + 1) = 0$$
$$\text{Either } x - 4 = 0$$
$$\text{or } x + 1 = 0$$
$$\text{Therefore } x = 4 \text{ or } x = -1$$

Check: $x = 4$ $\qquad$ L.H.S. $= x^2 = 16$

R.H.S. $= 3x + 4 = 12 + 4 = 16$

Check: $x = -1$ $\qquad$ L.H.S. $= x^2 = 1$

R.H.S. $= 3x + 4 = -3 + 4 = 1$

Here we have checked both possible solutions: it is usually sufficient to check only one. We give two more examples to show the correct method of presentation.

(a) Solve the equation $\qquad x = 6x^2 - 2$

Solution: $\qquad x = 6x^2 - 2$

Therefore $6x^2 - x - 2 = 0$ $\qquad$ (We arrange in the natural order with the x^2 term positive.)

$$(3x - 2)(2x + 1) = 0$$
$$\text{Either } 3x - 2 = 0$$
$$3x = 2$$
$$x = \tfrac{2}{3}$$
$$\text{or } 2x + 1 = 0$$
$$2x = -1$$
$$x = -\tfrac{1}{2}$$

Check: $x = \frac{2}{3}$ L.H.S. $= x = \frac{2}{3}$

$$\begin{aligned} \text{R.H.S.} &= 6x^2 - 2 \\ &= 6\left(\tfrac{4}{9}\right) - 2 \\ &= \tfrac{8}{3} - 2 \\ &= \tfrac{2}{3} \end{aligned}$$

Answer: $x = \frac{2}{3}$ or $-\frac{1}{2}$

(b) Solve $x^3 - 5x^2 - 6x = 0$ (This is a *cubic* equation, as it contains a term in x^3; but this should not deter us.)

Solution:

$$\begin{aligned} x^3 - 5x^2 - 6x &= 0 \\ x(x^2 - 5x - 6) &= 0 \\ x(x - 6)(x + 1) &= 0 \\ \text{Either } x &= 0 \\ \text{or } x - 6 &= 0 \\ x &= 6 \\ \text{or } x + 1 &= 0 \\ x &= -1 \end{aligned}$$

Check: $x = -1$ L.H.S. $= x^3 - 5x^2 - 6x$

$$\begin{aligned} &= (-1)^3 - 5(-1)^2 - 6(-1) \\ &= -1 - 5 + 6 \\ &= 0 = \text{R.H.S.} \end{aligned}$$

Answer: $x = 0$ or $x = 6$ or $x = -1$

EXERCISE 1F

Solve the following equations:

1. $x^2 = 5x - 6$
2. $x^2 + 2x = 3$
3. $x^2 + 3x = 0$
4. $x^2 = 4x$
5. $x^2 - 4 = 0$
6. $x^2 = 25$
7. $2x^2 + 3x = 0$
8. $2x^2 - 5x + 2 = 0$
9. $2x^2 = 5x + 3$
10. $2x^2 = 2 - 3x$
11. $12x^2 + 13x = 4$
12. $x^3 - 3x^2 + 2x = 0$
13. $x^2 - 4x + 4 = 0$

Two Solutions or Only One?

You will have realized by now that a quadratic equation has generally two solutions, but the last question in Exercise 1F shows that sometimes there is only one solution. This happens when the factors of the equation after it has been written in zero form are identical. Now the solutions of an equation are often called its *roots*.

Thus the roots of the equation $x^2 = 9$
are 3 and -3, while for the equation

$$x^2 - 6x + 9 = 0$$
$$\text{i.e. } (x - 3)(x - 3) = 0$$

the only root is 3. But the equation $x^2 = -4$ has *no roots*. (No number squared can possibly give a negative answer.) Hence we can say that a quadratic equation can have two roots, but may have only one, or none at all.

This can be well illustrated on a graph. Take a simple quadratic function of x, such as $y = x^2$, drawn below.

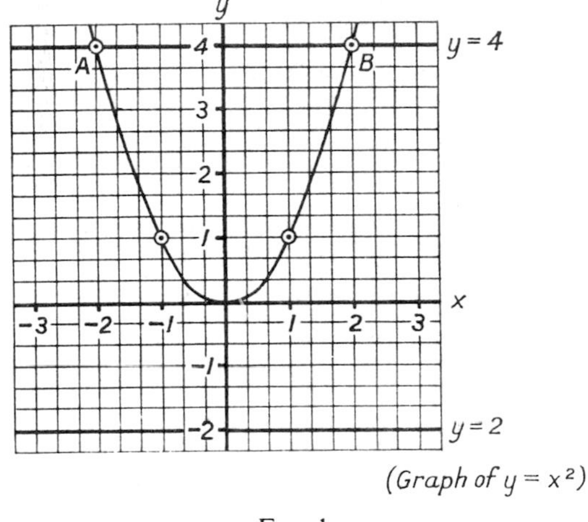

(Graph of $y = x^2$)

FIG. 1

The horizontal line $y = 4$ meets the graph at the two points A and B, and at these two points the co-ordinates satisfy the simultaneous equations

$$y = x^2$$
$$y = 4$$

Now A is $(-2, 4)$ and B is $(2, 4)$, so the solutions of the above equations are $x = -2$, $y = 4$ or $x = 2$, $y = 4$. If we combine the two equations to make one equation $x^2 = 4$, we see that the values of x satisfying this equation are

$$x = 2 \text{ or } x = -2$$

Now the horizontal line $y = 0$ (in other words, the x axis) only just touches the curve at the point (0,0). Hence the only solution of the simultaneous equations

$$y = x^2, \ y = 0$$
$$\text{is } x = 0, \ y = 0$$

Combining the equations, the only solution of

$$x^2 = 0 \text{ is } x = 0$$

Lastly, the horizontal line $y = -2$ does not meet the curve at all, so the simultaneous equations

$$y = x^2, \quad y = -2$$

have no solution, and combining the equations we see that

$$x^2 = -2 \text{ has no solution.}$$

In this example we were able to examine the solutions of three equations. Starting with the graph of $y = x^2$, the three lines $y = 4$, $y = 0$ and $y = -2$ gave us roots (where they exist) of $x^2 = 4$, $x^2 = 0$ and $x^2 = -2$. Similarly, to find the roots of

$$x^2 = 5$$

we must find the points where the graph of $y = x^2$ meets the horizontal line $y = 5$. The x co-ordinates of these points will give us the roots of the equation. Clearly we shall not get an exact answer, but by eye we can estimate the roots as

$$2{\cdot}24 \text{ and } -2{\cdot}24$$

What are the roots of $x^2 = 3$? Check with a table of square roots.

The same process can be applied to other quadratic graphs. Here is a table of values for the function $y = 2x^2 - 3x$,
and here is the graph:

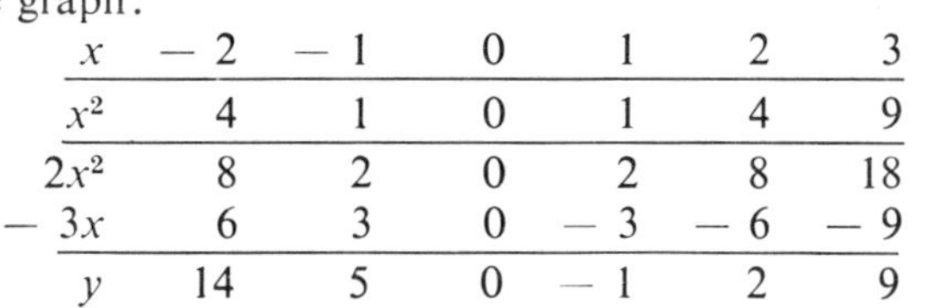

x	-2	-1	0	1	2	3
x^2	4	1	0	1	4	9
$2x^2$	8	2	0	2	8	18
$-3x$	6	3	0	-3	-6	-9
y	14	5	0	-1	2	9

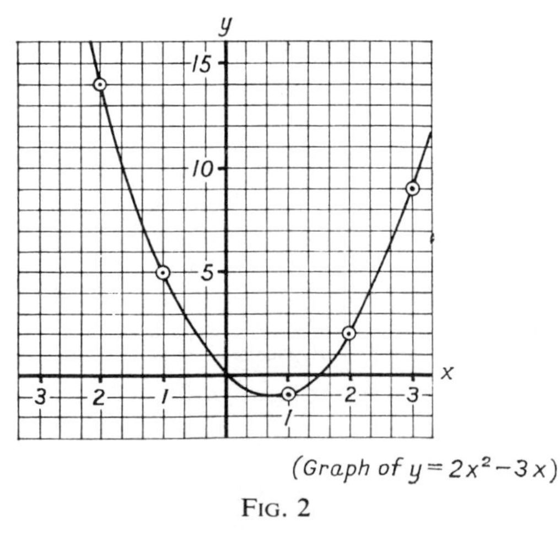

(Graph of $y = 2x^2 - 3x$)

FIG. 2

If we look along the horizontal line $y = 2$ and find the points where it cuts the curve, the x values of those two points will be the roots of the equation

$$2x^2 - 3x = 2$$

Verify that the roots are $-0{\cdot}5$ and 2.

To solve the equation $\quad 2x^2 - 3x = 5$

we find where the curve meets the horizontal line $y = 5$. What are the roots?

When we try to solve the equation

$$2x^2 - 3x = -2$$

we find that the line $y = -2$ *does not meet the curve*, and so the equation has *no solution*.

Use the graph to solve the equation $2x^2 - 3x = 4$ giving answers to one decimal place.

You will see from this that, once a graph has been drawn

$$y = \text{a function of } x$$

we can solve any equation

$$(\text{that function of } x) = (\text{a given number})$$

by simply finding the x co-ordinates of the points where the curve meets the horizontal line

$$y = (\text{the given number})$$

If, however, the equation is not written in that shape, we may have to do some preliminary rearrangement of the equation. Suppose we have already drawn the graph (Fig. 3) of $y = 4 + 2x - x^2$

and we wish to solve $\quad x^2 - 2x = 2$

We first rearrange the equation as $0 = 2 + 2x - x^2$

then add 2 to each side, $2 = 4 + 2x - x^2$

and we have the equation in the correct shape

$$(\text{that function of } x) = 2$$

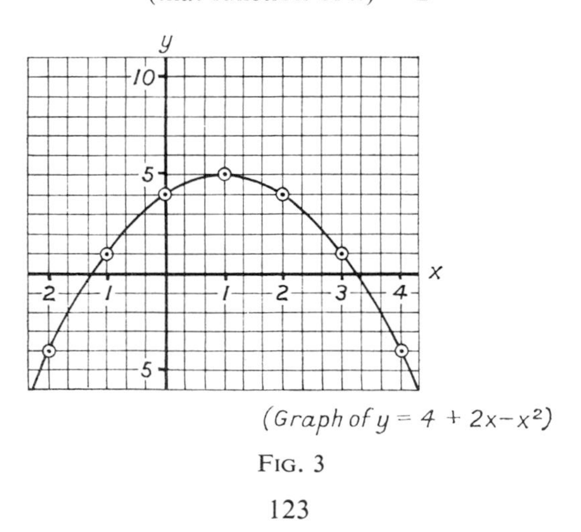

(Graph of $y = 4 + 2x - x^2$)

FIG. 3

So we find where the curve meets the horizontal line

$$y = 2$$

and read off the roots. What are they? Check one of them in the equation. (Since the graph only gives approximate roots, the check will not come out exactly.)

Use the same graph to solve $x^2 - 2x + 1 = 0$, and also $2x^2 - 4x - 3 = 0$. (For the second one, start the re-arrangement by dividing the whole equation by 2.)

EXERCISE 1G

Draw the graph of $y = x^2 - 3x - 4$ for values of x between -3 and 6. Use it to solve the following equations:

1. $x^2 - 3x - 4 = 0$
2. $x^2 - 3x - 5 = 0$
3. $x^2 - 3x - 1 = 0$
4. $3x - x^2 = 1$
5. $6x - 2x^2 = 5$

Translating Facts into Mathematical Form

As with other types, quadratic equations arise from all sorts of problems, and there is no standard method of solution. You must take the facts given and translate them into mathematical form, solve the resulting equation and *check your answer*. Here are some examples.

(a) I think of a number, square it, and subtract 6 from the result. I should have obtained the same answer if I had multiplied the original number by 6 and then added 1. What number did I choose?

Solution: Let x be the number.

$$\text{Then } x^2 - 6 = 6x + 1$$
$$\text{Therefore } x^2 - 6x - 7 = 0$$
$$(x - 7)(x + 1) = 0$$
$$\text{Either } x - 7 = 0$$
$$x = 7$$
$$\text{or } x + 1 = 0$$
$$x = -1$$

Check: $x = 7$

$$7^2 - 6 = 43$$
$$(6 \times 7) + 1 = 43$$

Answer: The number was either 7 or -1.

(There is no reason why I should not have thought of a minus number.)

(b) The length of a garden path exceeds four times the breadth by 3 ft., and the total area is $32\frac{1}{2}$ sq. ft. Find the length and breadth.

Solution: Let the breadth be x ft.
Then the length is $4x + 3$ ft.

Since the area is given as $32\frac{1}{2}$ sq. ft.,

$$x(4x + 3) = 32\tfrac{1}{2}$$
$$4x^2 + 3x = 32\tfrac{1}{2}$$
$$8x^2 + 6x = 65$$
$$8x^2 + 6x - 65 = 0$$
$$(4x + 13)(2x - 5) = 0$$

Either $4x + 13 = 0$

$$4x = -13$$
$$\underline{x = -3\tfrac{1}{4}}$$

or $2x - 5 = 0$

$$2x = 5$$
$$\underline{x = 2\tfrac{1}{2}}$$

Check: $x = 2\frac{1}{2}$

Breadth $2\frac{1}{2}$ ft.
Length $4 \times (2\frac{1}{2}) + 3$ ft.
$= 13$ ft.
Area $= 13 \times 2\frac{1}{2} = 32\frac{1}{2}$ sq. ft.

Answer: Length 13 ft.: breadth $2\frac{1}{2}$ ft.

(Notice that we *reject* the answer $x = -3\frac{1}{4}$, as the breadth cannot be negative.)

(c) A photograph is mounted on a piece of card 8 in. long and 5 in. wide, leaving a border of constant width all round. The area of this border is 22 sq. in. Find its width.

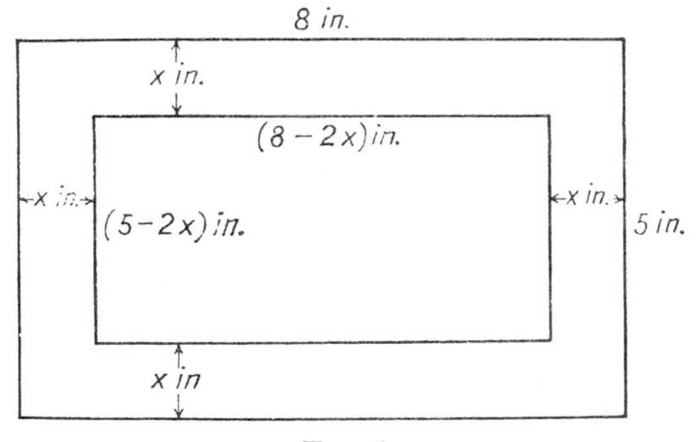

FIG. 4

Solution: Let the width of the border be x in.
Then the length of the photograph is $8 - 2x$ in.,
and its breadth is $5 - 2x$ in.
Hence its area is $(8 - 2x)(5 - 2x)$ sq. in.
and the area of the whole card is $8 \times 5 = 40$ sq. in.

So the area of the border is $40 - (8 - 2x)(5 - 2x)$ sq. in.

$$\therefore 40 - (8 - 2x)(5 - 2x) = 22$$
$$\therefore 40 - (40 - 16x - 10x + 4x^2) = 22$$
$$\therefore 40 - 40 + 16x + 10x - 4x^2 = 22$$
$$\therefore 26x - 4x^2 = 22$$
$$\therefore 4x^2 - 26x + 22 = 0$$
$$\therefore 2x^2 - 13x + 11 = 0$$
$$\therefore (2x - 11)(x - 1) = 0$$
$$\therefore \text{Either } 2x - 11 = 0$$
$$2x = 11$$
$$x = 5\tfrac{1}{2}$$
$$\text{or } x - 1 = 0$$
$$x = 1$$

Check: $x = 5\frac{1}{2}$

The width of the card is only 5 in., so the border cannot be $5\frac{1}{2}$ in. wide. We reject this solution.

Check: $x = 1$

Card 8 in. × 5 in. =	40 sq. in.
Photograph 6 in. × 3 in. =	18 sq. in.
Area of border	22 sq. in.

Answer: The border is 1 in. wide.

(d) The height of a stone above the ground t seconds after it was thrown is given by the formula $h = 30t - 16t^2$, where h is the height in feet. For how long is the stone more than 9 feet above the ground?

Solution: The stone is exactly 9 feet above the ground when $h = 9$, that is, when

$$30t - 16t^2 = 9$$
$$\text{or } 16t^2 - 30t + 9 = 0$$
$$(8t - 3)(2t - 3) = 0$$
$$\text{Either } 8t - 3 = 0$$
$$8t = 3$$
$$t = \tfrac{3}{8}$$
$$\text{or } 2t - 3 = 0$$
$$2t = 3$$
$$t = 1\tfrac{1}{2}$$

Check: $t = 1\frac{1}{2}$

$$\begin{aligned} h &= 30\left(\tfrac{3}{2}\right) - 16\left(\tfrac{3}{2}\right)^2 \\ &= 45 - 36 \\ &= 9 \end{aligned}$$

Therefore the stone is 9 feet above the ground after $\frac{3}{8}$ sec. (on the way up) and again after $\frac{3}{2}$ sec. (on the way down); it is above that height for

$$\frac{3}{2} - \frac{3}{8} \text{ sec.}$$
$$= 1\tfrac{1}{8} \text{ sec.}$$

Answer: The stone is more than 9 feet above the ground for $1\frac{1}{8}$ seconds.

Notice that we did not start this solution with "Let x be . . .", because we were *given* a formula to work with. To set up the equation we took the formula for the height and put it equal to the height required.

EXERCISE 1H

1. I think of a number, square it and then add 4. I would have got the same result if I had added 4 to the number first and then multiplied the sum by 4. Find the number.

2. Find two consecutive odd numbers such that the sum of their squares is 394.

3. Find the sides of a rectangle whose perimeter is 46 ft. and whose area is 120 sq. ft.

4. An *open* cardboard box is 7 in. high, and its length is 5 in. more than its breadth. Its total surface area is 500 sq. in. Find its dimensions.

5. To add up all the whole numbers from 1 to n we can use the formula

$$S = \frac{n}{2}(n + 1)$$

where S is the sum and n is the last number. For example,

$$1 + 2 + 3 + 4 + 5 + 6$$

can be added up by putting $n = 6$ in the formula, thus getting

$$S = \frac{6}{2} \times 7 = 21 \text{ (check this)}$$

What is the last number if the sum comes to 231?

6. In a right-angled triangle, the two shorter sides are respectively 9 in. shorter and 2 in. shorter than the hypotenuse. Find the three sides. (Use the theorem of Pythagoras.)

CHAPTER 2

SIMPLE FRACTIONS; LONG DIVISION

ALGEBRAIC FRACTIONS can involve a lot of laborious manipulation, but if you can handle fractions in arithmetic, then you can handle them in algebra. The processes are the same, and we can group them under three headings, showing the correspondence between arithmetic and algebra. They are Cancelling; Multiplication and Division; Addition and Subtraction.

Cancelling

Basically, cancelling means dividing the top and the bottom of the fraction by the same factor. Thus when we cancel the fraction $\frac{8}{12}$, what we do is to say

$$\frac{8}{12} = \frac{4 \times 2}{4 \times 3}$$

divide by the common factor 4, and obtain the answer $\frac{2}{3}$. The first (probably unconscious) step is to put the top and the bottom of our original fraction into factors. This step is also necessary in algebra, but will have to be done deliberately.

Thus $\dfrac{8}{4a + 8} = \dfrac{4 \times 2}{4\,(a + 2)} = \dfrac{2}{a + 2}$ (dividing top and bottom by 4).

Notice that, although $\frac{8}{12}$ *can* be written as $\dfrac{8}{4 + 8}$ it would be nonsense to "cancel the eights" and say that the answer was

$$\frac{1}{4 + 1} = \frac{1}{5}$$

This is obviously wrong. In the same way, it would be nonsense to "cancel the eights" in

$$\frac{8}{4a + 8}$$

and give the answer $\dfrac{1}{4a + 1}$

Cancelling involves division by common factors, which means that we *must factorize before attempting to cancel.*

Here are some more examples:

$$\frac{3a + 6}{9b - 3} = \frac{3\,(a + 2)}{3\,(3b - 1)} = \frac{a + 2}{3b - 1} \quad \text{(dividing top and bottom by 3)}$$

$$\frac{2x - 6}{x - 3} = \frac{2\,(x - 3)}{(x - 3)} = \frac{2}{1} = 2 \quad \text{(here we divide top and bottom by the common factor } x - 3\text{)}$$

EXERCISE 2A

Reduce the following fractions by cancellation:

1. $\dfrac{2}{2a + 2}$

2. $\dfrac{3b - 6}{3}$

3. $\dfrac{5}{5c - 10}$

4. $\dfrac{4d + 4}{2d - 2}$

5. $\dfrac{2e - 8}{4f - 6}$

6. $\dfrac{2g + 4}{3g + 6}$

7. $\dfrac{3h - 3}{4h - 4}$

8. $\dfrac{2k + 2}{k + 1}$

9. $\dfrac{m - 4}{3m - 12}$

Multiplication and Division

To multiply fractions in arithmetic we simply multiply together the tops and bottoms of each fraction: we do the same in algebra.

$$\frac{2}{3} \times \frac{4}{7} = \frac{8}{21}$$

$$\frac{2}{a - 3} \times \frac{4}{a + 1} = \frac{8}{(a - 3)(a + 1)} = \frac{8}{a^2 - 2a - 3}$$

but it is more usual in algebra *not* to multiply out expressions with brackets when they appear in a fraction, so we would leave the answer as

$$\frac{8}{(a - 3)(a + 1)}$$

Naturally we also use the well-known rule for division by a fraction, "turn it upside down and multiply."

$$\frac{3}{b + 2} \div \frac{4}{b - 3} = \frac{3}{b + 2} \times \frac{b - 3}{4}$$
$$= \frac{3(b - 3)}{4(b + 2)}$$

It is of course possible to cancel before multiplying in some cases:

$$\frac{4}{c - 2} \times \frac{3c - 6}{8} = \frac{4}{c - 2} \times \frac{3(c - 2)}{4 \times 2}$$
$$= \frac{1}{c - 2} \times \frac{3(c - 2)}{2} \quad \text{(cancelling a 4)}$$
$$= \frac{1}{1} \times \frac{3}{2} \quad \text{(cancelling } c - 2\text{)}$$
$$= 1\tfrac{1}{2}$$

EXERCISE 2B

Simplify the following:

1. $\dfrac{3}{a - 4} \times \dfrac{2}{a - 5}$

2. $\dfrac{4}{b + 2} \times \dfrac{b - 6}{3}$

3. $\frac{c+1}{5} \times \frac{10}{c+2}$

4. $\frac{2}{d-2} \div \frac{5}{2d-4}$

5. $\frac{4e+6}{3} \times \frac{9}{6e+9}$

6. $\frac{2f+5}{6} \times \frac{9}{3f-1} \div \frac{8f+20}{6f-2}$

Addition and Subtraction

Again, as in arithmetic, this requires us to express all the fractions in the problem with the same denominator. Just as

$$\frac{2}{3} + \frac{4}{7} = \frac{14}{21} + \frac{12}{21} = \frac{14+12}{21} = \frac{26}{21}$$

so
$$\frac{2}{a+1} + \frac{4}{a+5} = \frac{2(a+5)}{(a+1)(a+5)} + \frac{4(a+1)}{(a+1)(a+5)}$$
$$= \frac{2(a+5)+4(a+1)}{(a+1)(a+5)}$$
$$= \frac{2a+10+4a+4}{(a+1)(a+5)}$$
$$= \frac{6a+14}{(a+1)(a+5)}$$

Example:

$$\frac{2}{3} - \frac{5}{6(b+1)}$$

As a common denominator we choose $6(b+1)$, as 3 will divide into it, leaving a quotient $2(b+1)$. Multiply the top and bottom of the first fraction by $2(b+1)$, and we have

$$\frac{4(b+1)}{6(b+1)} - \frac{5}{6(b+1)}$$
$$= \frac{4(b+1)-5}{6(b+1)}$$

Now we simplify the top of the fraction:

$$= \frac{4b+4-5}{6(b+1)}$$
$$= \frac{4b-1}{6(b+1)}$$

Note the three stages of the working:

1. Choose a common denominator.
2. Express each fraction with that denominator, and hence build up a fraction

$$\frac{(\textit{some long expression})}{(\textit{common denominator})}$$

3. Simplify as far as possible the long expression at the top.

Example:

$$\frac{x+2}{x-3} - \frac{x-4}{x+2}$$

The common denominator will be $(x - 3)(x + 2)$. (Stage 1)
The fraction is equivalent to

$$\frac{(x+2)(x+2)}{(x-3)(x+2)} - \frac{(x-4)(x-3)}{(x-3)(x+2)}$$

$$= \frac{(x+2)(x+2) - (x-4)(x-3)}{(x-3)(x+2)} \qquad \text{(Stage 2)}$$

$$= \frac{(x^2+4x+4) - (x^2-7x+12)}{(x-3)(x+2)}$$

$$= \frac{x^2+4x+4-x^2+7x-12}{(x-3)(x+2)}$$

$$= \frac{11x-8}{(x-3)(x+2)} \qquad \text{(Stage 3)}$$

EXERCISE 2C

Reduce the following to single fractions:

1. $\dfrac{2}{a+2} + \dfrac{3}{a+3}$

2. $\dfrac{4}{b-1} - \dfrac{5}{b+3}$

3. $\dfrac{.3}{2c+5} - \dfrac{2}{5}$

4. $\dfrac{2}{x-y} + \dfrac{4}{x+y}$

5. $\dfrac{x}{x-3} - \dfrac{6}{x-2}$

6. $\dfrac{10}{x} + \dfrac{8}{x+6}$

7. $\dfrac{y}{y-2} - \dfrac{y+3}{y+4}$

8. $\dfrac{d+1}{d+3} - \dfrac{d-2}{d+2}$

The Elimination of Fractions

When we come across an equation involving fractions like those above, we choose a common denominator, as before, and then *multiply each term of the equation by that denominator*. This clears the equation of fractions, and enables us to deal with it in the normal way. Consider

$$\frac{x+4}{x-2} = 6$$

If we multiply both sides by $(x - 2)$ we get

$$x + 4 = 6(x - 2)$$
$$x + 4 = 6x - 12$$
$$12 + 4 = 6x - x$$
$$16 = 5x$$
$$x = 3\tfrac{1}{5}$$

Check:

$$\text{L.H.S.} = \frac{x+4}{x-2} = \frac{7\frac{1}{5}}{1\frac{1}{5}} = 6$$

If we are given $\dfrac{2x-3}{x+2} = \dfrac{x+6}{x+8}$

we multiply both sides by $(x + 2)(x + 8)$
and we get

$$\begin{aligned}(2x-3)(x+8) &= (x+6)(x+2)\\ 2x^2+13x-24 &= x^2+8x+12\\ x^2+5x-36 &= 0\\ (x+9)(x-4) &= 0\\ \text{Either } x+9 &= 0\\ x &= -9\\ \text{or } x-4 &= 0\\ x &= 4\end{aligned}$$

The same process can be extended to equations with three or more fractions in them: for instance,

$$\frac{2}{(x-1)} - \frac{3}{(x+4)} = \frac{4}{7}$$

Here we multiply throughout by $7(x-1)(x+4)$, thus:

$$\frac{2.7(x-1)(x+4)}{(x-1)} - \frac{3.7(x-1)(x+4)}{(x+4)} = \frac{4.7(x-1)(x+4)}{7}$$

which cancels down to

$$14(x+4) - 21(x-1) = 4(x-1)(x+4)$$

(With a little practice the middle line can be left out and you will be able to go straight from the given equation to the present stage of the solution.) Continuing,

$$\begin{aligned}14x+56-21x+21 &= 4(x^2+3x-4)\\ 77-7x &= 4x^2+12x-16\\ 0 &= 4x^2+19x-93\\ 0 &= (4x+31)(x-3)\\ \text{Either } 4x+31 &= 0\\ x &= -7\tfrac{3}{4}\\ \text{or } x-3 &= 0\\ x &= 3\end{aligned}$$

Check: $x = 3$

$$\text{L.H.S.} = \frac{2}{2} - \frac{3}{7} = \frac{4}{7} = \text{R.H.S.}$$

EXERCISE 2D

Solve the following equations:

1. $\dfrac{8}{x+2} = 2$
2. $\dfrac{5}{2x-3} = \dfrac{3}{8}$
3. $\dfrac{2x-4}{3x-5} = 6$
4. $\dfrac{3}{x+7} = \dfrac{x}{3x+5}$
5. $\dfrac{2x-7}{3} = \dfrac{x+6}{3x-4}$
6. $\dfrac{2x-1}{x-3} = \dfrac{5-x}{2x-5}$
7. $\dfrac{3}{x} - \dfrac{4}{x-2} = 7$
8. $\dfrac{20}{x} + \dfrac{18}{x-3} = 6\frac{1}{10}$
9. $\dfrac{x}{x-4} - \dfrac{7}{x+2} = 2\frac{1}{8}$

Steps in Setting-out an Equation

The type of equation that we have just been discussing arises very frequently from certain types of problem; consider this instance:

Example:

A boy can cycle 6 m.p.h. faster than his father can walk. Hence he can get to the nearest village, which is 2 miles away, 18 minutes earlier than his father if they set out at the same time. Find the speed at which the boy cycles.

The essence of this problem is that there are two journeys involved, over known distances, but at different speeds. If we suppose that the boy travels at x m.p.h., then his father travels at $(x - 6)$ m.p.h.

To write down an expression for the time each journey takes, we must use the general formula: $\quad time = \dfrac{distance}{speed}$

so that the boy takes $\dfrac{2}{x}$ hours for his journey, and his father takes $\dfrac{2}{x-6}$ hours.

The times for the two journeys are connected by the given fact that they differ by 18 minutes, that is, $\frac{3}{10}$ of an hour.

Since the father clearly takes the longer time, we can express this fact by saying:

$$(\text{Father's time}) - (\text{Son's time}) = \tfrac{3}{10} \text{ hours}$$

or, using algebra,

$$\frac{2}{x-6} - \frac{2}{x} = \frac{3}{10}$$

The steps used in setting up the equation can be much more clearly seen if the work is tabulated, and you are advised always to do this. Thus, in the present problem, we would set the work out as follows:

	Father	*Son*	
Speed	$x - 6$	x	m.p.h.
Distance	2	2	miles
Time	$\frac{2}{x-6}$	$\frac{2}{x}$	hours

Time difference $\frac{3}{10}$ hours.

There are two points where it is easy to go wrong: first, the time of each journey must be written down by using the formula

$$time = \frac{distance}{speed}$$

as the time fact (here, a difference of 18 minutes) is needed to form an equation: and, secondly, the units must be clear throughout, and consistent. If the speeds are given in miles per hour, then the times must all be written down in hours. Returning to our equation

$$\frac{2}{x-6} - \frac{2}{x} = \frac{3}{10}$$

Multiply throughout by $10x(x - 6)$

$$20x - 20(x - 6) = 3x(x - 6)$$
$$20x - 20x + 120 = 3x^2 - 18x$$
$$0 = 3x^2 - 18x - 120$$
$$0 = x^2 - 6x - 40$$
$$0 = (x - 10)(x + 4)$$
$$x = 10$$

Clearly the solution $x = -4$ can be rejected.

If the boy's speed is 10 m.p.h. he takes 12 minutes to cover the two miles, and his father, at 4 m.p.h., will take 30 minutes for the same distance, the time difference being 18 minutes, as given; thus the answer is checked: the boy cycles at 10 m.p.h.

EXERCISE 2E

1. By increasing his average speed on a 72 mile journey by 4 m.p.h., a motorist can save 12 minutes. What then will be his average speed?

2. To visit relations I have to travel 16 miles on a train and then a further 6 miles on a bus. Including a 6-minute wait for the bus, the whole trip takes me 70 minutes. The train travels at 9 m.p.h. faster than the bus. How fast does it go?

3. On a 120 mile journey the express travels 10 m.p.h. faster than the stopping train and takes 36 minutes less time. What is the speed of the slower train? (Having set up your equation, divide each fraction by 3 to reduce the size of the numbers involved.)

4. The airspeed of a jet plane is 400 m.p.h. One day it flies a 840-mile journey against the wind, and then returns with the wind behind it. The return journey takes 32 minutes less than the outward journey. Find the speed of the wind.

(If the speed of the wind is x m.p.h., then the jet will travel against the wind at a speed of $(400 - x)$ m.p.h.)

Problems Concerning Change of Price and Quantity

The same pattern emerges when we consider problems in which the price of some commodity changes, as in this case:

Example:

The price of a fountain pen was increased by 3s. As a result, a shopkeeper found that he could buy two fewer pens for £9 than had previously been possible. Find the previous price of the pen.

The basic fact here which corresponds to the formula $time = \dfrac{distance}{speed}$ is

$$price = \frac{total\ cost}{number\ of\ articles} \quad \text{or} \quad number\ of\ articles = \frac{total\ cost}{price}$$

Thus we can set out our table like this:

	Before Increase	*After Increase*	
Price	x	$x + 3$	shillings
Total cost	180	180	shillings
Number of articles	$\dfrac{180}{x}$	$\dfrac{180}{x + 3}$	

Difference in number of articles: 2.

Hence we can form the equation

$$\frac{180}{x} - \frac{180}{x + 2} = 2$$

Multiply throughout by $x(x + 3)$,

$$180(x + 3) - 180x = 2x(x + 3)$$
$$540 = 2x^2 + 6x$$
$$0 = x^2 + 3x - 270$$
$$0 = (x + 18)(x - 15)$$
$$\text{so } x = 15$$

Answer: The pens originally cost 15 shillings each.

EXERCISE 2F

1. When the price of an egg goes up by a penny, a housewife finds that she can now buy 3 fewer eggs for 3 shillings than before. Find the price of an egg before the increase.

2. A man bought a quantity of apples for £9. If he had paid 3d. per pound less, he would have obtained 60 lb. more apples. Find the cost of 1 lb. of apples.

3. When a tax of an extra shilling per gallon was imposed on petrol, a motorist found that by reducing his petrol consumption by four gallons per month, he was still spending £4 a month on petrol. How many gallons did he use in a month before the increase?

4. A man was planting 160 fruit trees in an orchard. He found that if he had an extra ten trees he could make two more rows with three trees less in each row. How many rows did he plant if he had the extra ten?

This question is basically the same as the others: complete this table:

	First Case	*Second Case*
Number of rows		
Number of trees		
Number of trees per row		

Long Division in Algebra

We conclude this chapter with an examination of the long division process in algebra. It is very similar to the same process in arithmetic, so we will start by tracing the steps of an arithmetical division, and then follow the same steps in an algebraic one: take

```
17)2642
```

17 into 26 goes 1, and $1 \times 17 = 17$

```
      1
17)2642
   17
```

Take 17 from 26, and bring down the 4

```
      1
17)2642
   17
    94
```

Repeat the steps; 17 into 94 goes 5, and $5 \times 17 = 85$, etc.

```
    155
17)2642
   17
    94
    85
     92
     85
      7
```

Answer: 155 Remainder 7.

Now take $a + 2\overline{)a^3 + 3a^2 - 2a - 20}$

We say a into a^3 goes a^2, and $(a + 2) \times a^2 = a^3 + 2a^2$

$$
\begin{array}{rl}
 & a^2 \\
a + 2 & \overline{)a^3 + 3a^2 - 2a - 20} \\
 & \;\; a^3 + 2a^2
\end{array}
$$

Subtract, and bring down the $- 2a$

$$
\begin{array}{rl}
 & a^2 \\
a + 2 & \overline{)a^3 + 3a^2 - 2a - 20} \\
 & \;\; \underline{a^3 + 2a^2} \\
 & \qquad\quad a^2 - 2a
\end{array}
$$

Repeat the steps:

$$
\begin{array}{rl}
 & a^2 + a \\
a + 2 & \overline{)a^3 + 3a^2 - 2a - 20} \\
 & \;\; \underline{a^3 + 2a^2} \\
 & \qquad\quad a^2 - 2a \\
 & \qquad\quad \underline{a^2 + 2a} \\
 & \qquad\qquad - 4a - 20
\end{array}
$$

Note the signs at the last subtraction. Repeat once more: a into $- 4a$ goes $- 4$, and $(a + 2) \times - 4 = - 4a - 8$

$$
\begin{array}{rl}
 & a^2 + a - 4 \\
a + 2 & \overline{)a^3 + 3a^2 - 2a - 20} \\
 & \;\; \underline{a^3 + 2a^2} \\
 & \qquad\quad a^2 - 2a \\
 & \qquad\quad \underline{a^2 + 2a} \\
 & \qquad\qquad - 4a - 20 \\
 & \qquad\qquad \underline{- 4a - \;\; 8} \\
 & \qquad\qquad\qquad - 12
\end{array}
$$

Answer: Quotient $a^2 + a - 4$ Remainder $- 12$

You will notice that, as in the arithmetic process, there is a cycle of steps which we keep repeating until we reach the end of the sum. But note particularly that at the beginning of each cycle, although we are dividing by $a + 2$, we only use the a to say, e.g. a into a^3 goes a^2, then use the whole $a + 2$ to say $(a + 2) \times a^2 = a^3 + 2a^2$. You will also notice that it is possible to have a negative remainder.

EXERCISE 2G

1. $x^3 - 4x^2 + 3x - 7$ by $x + 3$
2. $2y^3 - 5y^2 - 9y + 18$ by $2y - 3$
3. $x^3 + 2x^2y - 3xy^2 + y^3$ by $x + 2y$

CHAPTER 3

INDICES AND THE THEORY OF LOGARITHMS

IN AN EXPRESSION like x^3, the "3" is the *power* or *index* of x.

You will already know what are usually called the "*Laws of Indices*":

To MULTIPLY powers of a number, ADD the indices.

To DIVIDE powers of a number, SUBTRACT the indices.

To find a POWER OF A POWER of a number, MULTIPLY the indices.

General statements of these rules are:

$$\text{(i) } a^m \times a^n = a^{m+n}; \qquad \text{(ii) } a^m \div a^n = a^{m-n}; \qquad \text{(iii) } (a^m)^n = a^{mn}.$$

The Meaning of a "Root"

$2^2 = 4$, and we call 2 the SQUARE ROOT of 4 (written $\sqrt{4}$);

$5^3 = 125$, and we call 5 the CUBE ROOT of 125 (written $\sqrt[3]{125}$);

$3^4 = 81$, and we call 3 the FOURTH ROOT of 81 (written $\sqrt[4]{81}$); and so on.

In general, if $a^n = b$, a is the *nth root* of b (written $\sqrt[n]{b}$).

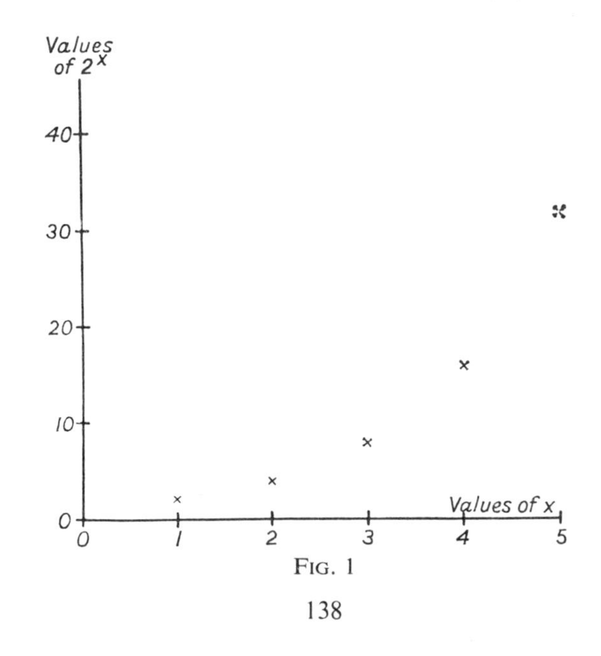

FIG. 1

Introduction

Consider some powers of 2: $2^1 = 2$, $2^2 = 4$, $2^3 = 8$, $2^4 = 16$, $2^5 = 32$. If we make a table showing the powers (x) and the numbers (2^x),

x	1	2	3	4	5
2^x	2	4	8	16	32

and plot these values on a graph, it looks as though we could draw a smooth curve through the points (Fig. 1). Are we justified in doing this? So far, a power of 2 has simply meant the result of multiplying together a number of 2's (2^3 is short for $2 \times 2 \times 2$), so that points on the curve between the ones we have plotted would mean nothing.

Through the years, mathematicians have often come across this sort of thing, and they have never been satisfied just to leave it at that. Can we give sensible meanings to expressions like $2^{1\frac{1}{2}}$, $2^{2\frac{1}{4}}$ and, to extend our graph "backwards," $2^{\frac{1}{2}}$, 2^0, 2^{-1}, etc.? "Sensible" meanings will be ones that fit in with the *Laws of Indices* that are stated above. The "backward" extension is simpler, so we will start with that.

Zero Power and Negative Powers

See if the *pattern* of what we already know suggests what to do.

x	5	4	3	2	1	0	-1	-2	-3
2^x	32	16	8	4	2	?	?	?	?

Try to discover the pattern and fill in values for 2^0, 2^{-1}, etc., before reading any further. (What happens every time x is made 1 smaller?)

If x is decreased by 1, 2^x is divided by 2; and we know $2^1 = 2$. This suggests: $2^0 = 2 \div 2 = 1$;

$$2^{-1} = 1 \div 2 = \tfrac{1}{2};$$

$$2^{-2} = \tfrac{1}{2} \div 2 = \tfrac{1}{4} \left(\text{or } \frac{1}{2^2}\right), \text{ and so on.}$$

Do these values fit in with the *Laws of Indices*?

$2^0 = 1$ fits, since $1 = 2 \div 2 = 2^1 \div 2^1$, which should be 2^{1-1}, or 2^0;

$2^{-1} = \dfrac{1}{2}$ fits, since $\dfrac{1}{2} = 1 \div 2 = 2^0 \div 2^1$, which should be 2^{0-1}, or 2^{-1};

$2^{-2} = \dfrac{1}{2^2}$ fits, since $\dfrac{1}{2^2} = 1 \div 2^2 = 2^0 \div 2^2$, which should be 2^{-2}.

In the same way, we must have $2^{-3} = \dfrac{1}{2^3} = \dfrac{1}{8}$; $2^{-4} = \dfrac{1}{2^4} = \dfrac{1}{16}$;

$$3^0 = 1; \qquad 3^{-1} = \frac{1}{3};$$

$$4^0 = 1; \qquad 4^{-3} = \frac{1}{4^3} = \frac{1}{64}; \text{ and so on.}$$

And so we say: If a is any number, $a^0 = 1$, $a^{-n} = \dfrac{1}{a^n}$.

Fractional Powers

What meaning must we give to these so that they will fit in with the *Laws of Indices*? (We will think of powers of *any* number, *a*.)

We must have $a^{\frac{1}{2}} \times a^{\frac{1}{2}} = a^{\frac{1}{2}+\frac{1}{2}} = a^1$; that is, if we square $a^{\frac{1}{2}}$, it must come to a.

So we say: $a^{\frac{1}{2}}$ means the square root of a ($\sqrt{a}$).

We must have $a^{\frac{1}{3}} \times a^{\frac{1}{3}} \times a^{\frac{1}{3}} = a^{\frac{1}{3}+\frac{1}{3}+\frac{1}{3}} = a^1$; that is, the cube of $a^{\frac{1}{3}}$ must be a.

So we say: $a^{\frac{1}{3}}$ means the cube root of a ($\sqrt[3]{a}$).

In the same way, $(a^{\frac{1}{4}})^4$ must be a.

So we say $a^{\frac{1}{4}}$ means the fourth root of a ($\sqrt[4]{a}$); and so on.

Now, what about $a^{\frac{2}{3}}$, $a^{\frac{3}{4}}$, $a^{1\frac{1}{2}}$, etc.? We can approach these in two ways:

(i) If we square $\sqrt[3]{a}$, that is $a^{\frac{1}{3}}$, we must have $(a^{\frac{1}{3}})^2 = a^{\frac{1}{3}\times 2} = a^{\frac{2}{3}}$

So we say: $a^{\frac{2}{3}}$ means $(\sqrt[3]{a})^2$

(ii) If we cube $a^{\frac{2}{3}}$, we must have $(a^{\frac{2}{3}})^3 = a^{\frac{2}{3}\times 3} = a^2$.

So we say: $a^{\frac{2}{3}}$ means $\sqrt[3]{a^2}$.

These two meanings for $a^{\frac{2}{3}}$ are the same; we have to SQUARE, and we have to find a CUBE ROOT, and it does not matter which we do first.

For similar reasons, we say $a^{\frac{3}{4}}$ means $(\sqrt[4]{a})^3$ or $\sqrt[4]{a^3}$;

$a^{1\frac{1}{2}}$, or $a^{\frac{3}{2}}$ means $(\sqrt{a})^3$ or $\sqrt{a^3}$; and so on.

(Try to write out the arguments fully, as in (i) and (ii).)

In fact, in a fractional power, the *denominator* (bottom) of the fraction is a *root*, while the *numerator* (top) is a *power*. Either may be taken first.

Suppose that we want to work out $8^{\frac{2}{3}}$; we can say either, the *cube root* of 8 is 2, and $2^2 = 4$, or $8^2 = 64$, and the cube root of 64 is 4.

A formal statement of this definition is:

$$a^{\frac{p}{q}} = \sqrt[q]{a^p} \text{ or } (\sqrt[q]{a})^p$$

Here are some more examples. Try to work them out before you look at the results.

(i) $4^{\frac{1}{2}} = \sqrt{4} = 2$.

(ii) $4^{1\frac{1}{2}} = 4^{\frac{3}{2}}$; either $(\sqrt{4})^3 = 2^3 = 8$ or $\sqrt{4^3} = \sqrt{64} = 8$.

(iii) $16^{\frac{1}{4}} = \sqrt[4]{16} = 2$. ($2^4 = 16$, so 2 is the 4th root of 16.)

(iv) $27^{\frac{2}{3}} = (\sqrt[3]{27})^2 = (3)^2 = 9$.

(v) $32^{\frac{3}{5}} = (\sqrt[5]{32})^3 = (2)^3 = 8$. ($2^5 = 32$, so 2 is the 5th root of 32.)

(vi) $10^0 = 1$.

(vii) $7^{-1} = \frac{1}{7}$

(viii) $6^{-2} = \frac{1}{6^2} = \frac{1}{36}$

(ix) $25^{-\frac{1}{2}} = \dfrac{1}{25^{\frac{1}{2}}} = \dfrac{1}{\sqrt{25}} = \dfrac{1}{5}$ (xi) $\left(\dfrac{4}{9}\right)^{\frac{1}{2}} = \sqrt{\dfrac{4}{9}} = \dfrac{2}{3}$

(x) $\left(\dfrac{2}{5}\right)^{-2} = \dfrac{1}{(\frac{2}{5})^2} = \dfrac{1}{\frac{4}{25}} = \dfrac{25}{4}$ or $6\frac{1}{4}$. (xii) $\left(\dfrac{4}{9}\right)^{-\frac{1}{2}} = \dfrac{1}{(\frac{4}{9})^{\frac{1}{2}}} = \dfrac{1}{\frac{2}{3}} = \dfrac{3}{2}$ or $1\frac{1}{2}$

Note: $\left(\dfrac{b}{a}\right)^{-n} = \dfrac{1}{\left(\dfrac{b}{a}\right)^n} = \dfrac{1}{\dfrac{b^n}{a^n}} = 1 \times \dfrac{a^n}{b^n} = \left(\dfrac{a}{b}\right)^n$

So $\left(\dfrac{b}{a}\right)^{-n} = \left(\dfrac{a}{b}\right)^n$ and, in particular, $\left(\dfrac{b}{a}\right)^{-1} = \dfrac{a}{b}$

Thus, in (x), $\left(\dfrac{2}{5}\right)^{-2} = \left(\dfrac{5}{2}\right)^2 = \dfrac{25}{4}$;

in (xii), $\left(\dfrac{4}{9}\right)^{-\frac{1}{2}} = \left(\dfrac{9}{4}\right)^{\frac{1}{2}} = \sqrt{\dfrac{9}{4}} = \dfrac{3}{2}$

See also Example 4 on page 143.

EXERCISE 3A

Write down the values of

1. 7^0

2. 5^{-1}

3. 10^{-3}

4. 3^{-4}

5. $49^{\frac{1}{2}}$

6. $64^{\frac{1}{3}}$

7. $81^{\frac{1}{4}}$

8. $1000^{\frac{1}{3}}$

9. $9^{\frac{3}{2}}$

10. $49^{1\frac{1}{2}}$

11. $100^{1\frac{1}{2}}$

12. $4^{2\frac{1}{2}}$

13. $125^{\frac{2}{3}}$

14. $8^{\frac{4}{3}}$

15. $27^{1\frac{1}{3}}$

16. $16^{\frac{3}{4}}$

17. $16^{1\frac{1}{4}}$

18. $729^{\frac{2}{3}}$

19. $243^{\frac{2}{5}}$

20. $256^{\frac{5}{8}}$

21. $100^{-\frac{1}{2}}$

22. $8^{-\frac{1}{3}}$

23. $(\frac{1}{4})^{-1}$

24. $(\frac{2}{3})^{-3}$

25. $(\frac{9}{16})^{\frac{1}{2}}$

26. $(\frac{8}{125})^{\frac{1}{3}}$

27. $(\frac{1}{9})^{-\frac{1}{2}}$

28. $(\frac{9}{16})^{-\frac{1}{2}}$

29. $(\frac{8}{125})^{-\frac{1}{3}}$

30. $(2\frac{7}{9})^{-\frac{3}{2}}$

Extending the Graph

It is important to understand that we have not *proved* that $a^0 = 1$, $a^{-1} = 1/a$, $a^{\frac{1}{2}} = \sqrt{a}$, etc. Previously, such expressions have had *no meaning*. We have now *defined* meanings for them. What we did was to show how we must define these meanings if we want to be able to use the expressions in the same way as we use a^2, a^3, etc.

We are now able to add as many points as we wish to our graph of 2^x (page 138). The extended graph (Fig. 2) has been drawn using these values:

x	-2	-1	$-\frac{1}{2}$	0	$\frac{1}{4}$	$\frac{1}{2}$	1	$1\frac{1}{2}$	2	$2\frac{1}{2}$	3	$3\frac{1}{2}$	4	$4\frac{1}{2}$	5
2^x	·25	·5	·71	1	1·19	1·41	2	2·83	4	5·66	8	11·31	16	22·63	32

Try to work out the values for yourself, to see if you agree with those given. (Notice that $2^{\frac{1}{2}} = \sqrt{2} = 1{\cdot}4142$ approx.;

$$2^{\frac{1}{4}} = 2^{\frac{1}{2}\times\frac{1}{2}} = (2^{\frac{1}{2}})^{\frac{1}{2}} = \sqrt{1{\cdot}4142};$$
$$2^{1\frac{1}{2}} = 2^{\frac{1}{2}+1} = 2^{\frac{1}{2}} \times 2;$$
$$2^{2\frac{1}{2}} = 2^{1\frac{1}{2}+1} = 2^{1\frac{1}{2}} \times 2; \text{ and so on.)}$$

Clearly, the points we have added fit into the pattern we noticed before, and we can draw a smooth curve*!

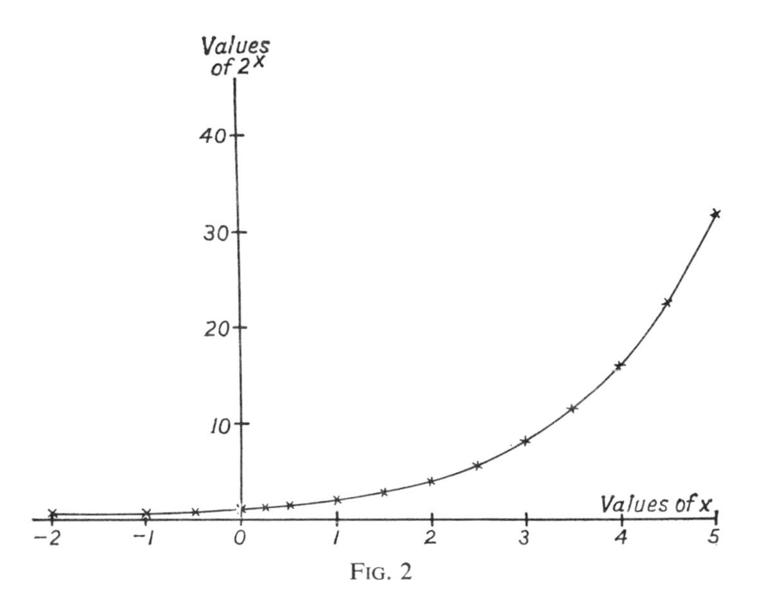

FIG. 2

We can now deal with a^n according to the "laws of indices," whether n is positive or negative, integral (i.e., a whole number) or fractional. The following examples are intended to illustrate this.

Example 1: Express as a power of x: $\dfrac{x^{m+n} \times x^{m-n}}{x^m}$

The expression is $x^{(m+n)+(m-n)-m} = x^m$

Example 2: Express $\sqrt[3]{{\cdot}01}$ as a power of 10.

$$\sqrt[3]{{\cdot}01} = ({\cdot}01)^{\frac{1}{3}} = \left(\frac{1}{10^2}\right)^{\frac{1}{3}} = (10^{-2})^{\frac{1}{3}} = 10^{-2\times\frac{1}{3}} = 10^{-\frac{2}{3}}$$

*Drawing a continuous curve seems to imply that 2^x has a meaning for *all* values of x. In fact, we have only defined the meaning when x is what is called a "rational" number, that is, a whole number or a fraction. If you go on with your studies in mathematics, you will learn that there are other numbers—called "irrational"—which cannot be expressed in this way. $\sqrt{2}$ is an example. To define a meaning for $2^{\sqrt{2}}$ involves much more advanced work.

Example 3: Remove the brackets from $ab\,(a^3b^{-2} + a^{-3}b^2)$, using only positive indices in your answer.

$$ab\,(a^3b^{-2} + a^{-3}b^2) = a^4b^{-1} + a^{-2}b^3$$
$$= \frac{a^4}{b} + \frac{b^3}{a^2}$$

Example 4: Simplify $\left(\frac{64x^6}{y^3}\right)^{\frac{1}{3}} \times \left(\frac{y}{2x}\right)^{-1}$

The expression is $\frac{4x^2}{y} \times \frac{2x}{y} = \frac{8x^3}{y^2}$

EXERCISE 3B

1. Write the following without fractional or negative indices. (Use "root" signs if required.)

(i) $a^{\frac{1}{2}}b^{-\frac{3}{2}}$, (ii) $\frac{a^{-2}}{b^{-2}}$, (iii) $a^{-\frac{2}{5}}b^{\frac{2}{3}}$.

2. Write as a power of x:

(i) $\sqrt[5]{x}$, (ii) $\sqrt[4]{x^3}$, (iii) $\frac{1}{(\sqrt[3]{x})^2}$, (iv) 1.

3. Express as powers of 10:

(i) ·001, (ii) 10,000, (iii) $\sqrt{\cdot 1}$, (iv) 1 millionth.

4. Express in decimal form, using root signs where appropriate:

(i) 10^{-2}, (ii) $3{\cdot}53 \times 10^{-5}$, (iii) $10^{\frac{3}{2}}$, (iv) $10^{-\frac{2}{3}}$.

5. Simplify, using only positive indices in your answers:

(i) $x^3 \times \frac{1}{\sqrt{x}}$, (iii) $(a^2b^{-1})^3 \div (a^{-1}b^3)^{-1}$,

(ii) $(a^{\frac{1}{2}}b^{-1})^{-2}$, (iv) $\frac{x}{y}\,(x^2y^{-1} + x^{-1}y)$.

6. By expressing each number as a power of 12, prove that

$$\sqrt{12^5} \times 144^{-1} \div \sqrt[6]{1728} = 1$$

Logarithms

The use of logarithms to shorten work was explained in Arithmetic, Chapter 5. We can now deal more fully with the *theory* of logarithms.

A logarithm is simply a power, and the rules for working with logs are merely the laws of indices put in a slightly different way.

Consider the statement $2^4 = 16$.

2 is called the *Base*, and 4 is called the *Logarithm of* 16 *to base* 2 (written $\log_2 16$).

Here are some further statements written first in index form, then in logarithmic form:

Index	*Logarithm*
$9 = 3^2$	$\log_3 9 = 2$ ("The log of 9 to base 3 is 2")
$1000 = 10^3$	$\log_{10} 1000 = 3$
$5 = 25^{\frac{1}{2}}$	$\log_{25} 5 = \frac{1}{2}$
$\frac{1}{8} = 2^{-3}$	$\log_2(\frac{1}{8}) = -3$
$\cdot 01 = 10^{-2}$	$\log_{10}(\cdot 01) = -2$

All these are examples of the general statement:

"If $N = a^x$, x is called the 'Logarithm of N to base a (written $\log_a N$)."

We can now justify our statement that the rules for working with logs are merely the laws of indices.

Consider two numbers p and q, and suppose that $\log_a p = x$, $\log_a q = y$. This means $p = a^x$, $q = a^y$.

(i)
$$pq = a^x \times a^y = a^{x+y}$$
$$\text{So } \log_a pq = x + y$$
$$\text{that is, } \log_a pq = \log_a p + \log_a q.$$

("To find the log of the product of two numbers, add the logs of the numbers.")

(ii)
$$\frac{p}{q} = a^x \div a^y = a^{x-y}$$
$$\text{So } \log_a \frac{p}{q} = x - y$$
$$\text{that is, } \log_a \frac{p}{q} = \log_a p - \log_a q.$$

("The log of the quotient of two numbers is the difference of their logs.")

(iii)
$$p^n = (a^x)^n = a^{nx}$$
$$\text{So } \log_a(p^n) = nx,$$
$$\text{that is, } \log_a(p^n) = n \log_a p.$$

("To find the log of a power of a number, multiply the log of the number by the power.")

Note: (i) Since roots may be expressed as powers, finding the logarithms of square roots, cube roots, etc., is covered by this rule.

e.g. $\log_a(\sqrt{p}) = \log_a(p^{\frac{1}{2}}) = \frac{1}{2} \log_a p$.

(ii) Since $a^0 = 1$, $\log 1 = 0$ *whatever the base.*

Often, there is no need to specify the base, and we write simply "log p." The logarithms used in numerical work are logs *to base* 10; this is understood, and not normally stated.

The examples that follow deal with logs to base 10. They are intended partly to help you to understand the theory which has just been explained, partly as revision of the use of logs in arithmetical work.

Example 1: Express as powers of 10: (i) 3, (ii) $5{\cdot}61 \times 10^7$, (iii) $0{\cdot}836$.

(i) From thc table, $\log 3 = {\cdot}4771$, that is, $3 = 10^{\cdot 4771}$.

(ii) From the table, $\log 5{\cdot}61 = {\cdot}7490$, so that $5{\cdot}61 = 10^{\cdot 7490}$.
Hence $5{\cdot}61 \times 10^7 = 10^{\cdot 7490} \times 10^7$
$= 10^{7\cdot 7490}$

(iii) From the table, $\log {\cdot}836 = \bar{1}{\cdot}9222$
$= -1 + {\cdot}9222$
$= -{\cdot}0778$
$\therefore \quad {\cdot}836 = 10^{-\cdot 0778}$

Note: In using log tables to express numbers as powers of 10, we have given the powers as *decimals*, but our definition of fractional powers includes decimal fractions, of course.

Thus $49^{\frac{1}{2}}$ (= 7) could be written as $49^{\cdot 5}$;
$16^{\frac{1}{4}}$ (= 2) could be written as $16^{\cdot 25}$;
$27^{\frac{1}{3}}$ (= 3) could be written as $27^{\cdot 3333}$;
$27^{\frac{2}{3}}$ (= 9) could be written as $27^{\cdot 6667}$;
$10^{\cdot 4771} = 10^{\frac{4771}{10000}}$ means $\sqrt[10000]{10^{4771}}$;
$10^{\cdot 7490} = 10^{\frac{749}{1000}}$ means $\sqrt[1000]{10^{749}}$; and so on.

In the last four of these the decimal power is approximate, correct to 4 significant figures.

Example 2: Given that $\log_{10}2 = {\cdot}30103$, $\log_{10}3 = {\cdot}47712$, find, *without using tables*: (i) $\log_{10}12$, (ii) $\log_{10}\sqrt{6}$, (iii) $\log_{10}5$, (iv) $\log_{10}{\cdot}54$.

(We can do this because 12, $\sqrt{6}$, 5, ·54 can all be expressed as products, quotients or powers of 2, 3 and 10.)

(i) $\text{Log}_{10}12 = \log_{10}(2^2.3)$
$= \log_{10}(2^2) + \log_{10}3$
$= 2\log_{10}2 + \log_{10}3$
$= 2.{\cdot}30103 + {\cdot}47712$
$= {\cdot}60206 + {\cdot}47712$
$= 1{\cdot}07918$

(ii) $\text{Log}_{10}\sqrt{6} = \log_{10}(6^{\frac{1}{2}})$
$= \frac{1}{2}\log_{10}6$
$= \frac{1}{2}(\log_{10}2 + \log_{10}3)$
$= \frac{1}{2}({\cdot}30103 + {\cdot}47712)$
$= \frac{1}{2}({\cdot}77815)$
$= {\cdot}38908$ to 5 sig. fig.

(iii) $\text{Log}_{10}5 = \log_{10}(10 \div 2)$
$= \log_{10}10 - \log_{10}2$
$= 1 - {\cdot}30103$ ($\log_{10}10$ is 1, since $10^1 = 10$)
$= {\cdot}69897$

(iv) $\text{Log}_{10}\cdot 54 = \log_{10}\dfrac{54}{100}$

$= \log_{10}(2 \times 3^3 \div 10^2)$
$= \log_{10}2 + 3\log_{10}3 - 2$
$= \cdot 30103 + 1\cdot 43136 - 2$
$= -2 + 1\cdot 73239$
$= -1 + \cdot 73239$
$= \bar{1}\cdot 73239$ or $- \cdot 26761$

Example 3: Use 4-figure tables to find the values of (i) $2^{\frac{3}{4}}$, (ii) x, where $x^3 = 8\cdot 16 \times 10^{-7}$.

(The solutions are given first as statements showing the logarithmic theory, then in the column form normally used for arithmetical work.)

(i) $\text{Log } 2^{\frac{3}{4}} = \frac{3}{4}\log 2$
$= \frac{3}{4} \times \cdot 3010$
$= \dfrac{\cdot 9030}{4}$
$= \cdot 2258$ to 4 sig. fig.
$\therefore 2^{\frac{3}{4}} = 1\cdot 682$

No.	*Log.*
2	$\cdot 3010$
	$\times 3$
	$4)\cdot 9030$
$2^{\frac{3}{4}} = 1\cdot 682$	$\cdot 2258$

(ii) $x^3 = 8\cdot 16 \times 10^{-7}$
$\therefore x = \sqrt[3]{8\cdot 16 \times 10^{-7}}$
$= (8\cdot 16 \times 10^{-7})^{\frac{1}{3}}$
$\therefore \log x = \frac{1}{3}\log(8\cdot 16 \times 10^{-7})$
$= \frac{1}{3}\{\log(10^{-7}) + \log 8\cdot 16\}$
$= \frac{1}{3}\{(-7) + \cdot 9117\}$
$= \frac{1}{3}\{(-9) + 2\cdot 9117\}$ (See Arithmetic, page 49.)
$= -3 + \cdot 9706$
$= \bar{3}\cdot 9706$
$\therefore x = \cdot 009346$

No.	*Log.*
$8\cdot 16$	$\cdot 9117$
10^{-7}	$\bar{7}\cdot 0000$
	$3)\bar{7}\cdot 9117$
$\cdot 009346$	$\bar{3}\cdot 9706$

EXERCISE 3C

N.B.: Throughout this exercise, the logarithms are to base 10. Tables should *not* be used in Nos. 1-4.

1. Write down the values of:
(i) $\log 100$, (ii) $\log(\sqrt[3]{10})$, (iii) $\log \cdot 001$, (iv) $\log(10^5)$, (v) $\log 1$.

2. Find x if:
(i) $\log x = 4$, (ii) $\log x = \frac{1}{2}$,
(iii) $\log x = -2$, (iv) $\log x = 0$.

3. Given that $\log 3 = \cdot 47712$, $\log 5 = \cdot 69897$, calculate:
(i) $\log 27$, (ii) $\log 15$, (iii) $\log 75$,
(iv) $\log\sqrt{15}$, (v) $\log 2$, (vi) $\log \cdot 18$.

4. Simplify:

(i) $\frac{\log 16}{\log 2}$ (iii) $\log 30 - \log 3$,

(ii) $\log 20 + \log 5$, (iv) $\log 2 + \log \frac{1}{2}$,

5. Express:

(i) 53·4, (ii) ·0581 as powers of 10.

In No. 6, 7 and 8, answers should be given correct to 3 sig. fig.

6. Use logs to calculate:

(i) $4^{\frac{2}{3}}$, (ii) $\sqrt[5]{\cdot 6538}$, (iii) $\frac{75{\cdot}8 \times (\cdot 8519)^2}{\sqrt[3]{\cdot 044} \times 269{\cdot}3}$

7. If $x^4 = \frac{(\cdot 3219)^2}{\sqrt[3]{1{\cdot}76}} + \frac{\sqrt{\cdot 0093}}{\cdot 048}$ find x.

(Remember that logs can *not* be used to perform addition or subtraction.)

8. Calculate: $\left(\log \frac{15{\cdot}86}{\cdot 68}\right) \div (\log (2{\cdot}53)^3)$

Large and Small Numbers

In scientific work, very large and very small numbers are usually written expressed in the form

$$a \times 10^n$$

where "a" is in standard form (see page 44) and "n" is a whole number.

236,000,000 would be expressed as $2{\cdot}36 \times 10^8$,

·00000517 would be expressed as $5{\cdot}17 \times 10^{-6}$,

and so on.

Try to see why these are correct before you read the explanation which follows.

$$236{,}000{,}000 = 2{\cdot}36 \times 100{,}000{,}000 \text{ (the decimal point is moved 8 places)}$$
$$= 2{\cdot}36 \times 10^8$$
$$\cdot 00000517 = 5{\cdot}17 \div 1{,}000{,}000 \text{ (the decimal point is moved 6 places)}$$
$$= 5{\cdot}17 \div 10^6$$
$$= 5{\cdot}17 \times \frac{1}{10^6}$$
$$= 5{\cdot}17 \times 10^{-6}$$

Notice that $\log (2{\cdot}36 \times 10^8) = \log 2{\cdot}36 + \log 10^8$
$$= \cdot 3729 + 8$$
$$= 8{\cdot}3729$$
$$\log (5{\cdot}17 \times 10^{-6}) = \log 5{\cdot}17 + \log 10^{-6}$$
$$= \cdot 7135 + (-6)$$
$$= \bar{6}{\cdot}7135$$

In fact, when a number is expressed in this way, *the whole number part of its log is the power of* 10.

Example: A unit used for distances to stars is the "light-year," that is, the distance travelled by light in a year. How many miles is this? (The speed of light is 186,000 miles per second.)

In 1 sec., light travels 186,000 miles.

$\therefore$ in 1 year it travels $(186{,}000 \times 60 \times 60 \times 24 \times 365)$ miles

$= 5{\cdot}87 \times 10^{12}$ miles approx.

(This is nearly 6 million million)

No.	*Logs.*
186,000	5·2695
60	1·7782
60	1·7782
24	1·3802
365	2·5623
$5{\cdot}866 \times 10^{12}$	12·7684

EXERCISE 3D

You may not understand some of the things mentioned in this exercise. Never mind; the calculations are quite straightforward.

Unless otherwise stated, answers should be given in the above form if appropriate, with "a" correct to 3 sig. fig.

1. The speed of light in a vacuum is 3×10^8 metres-per-second. So the wave-length (λ metres) and frequency (f cycles-per-second) are connected by the formula

$$f\lambda = 3 \times 10^8$$

If the wave-length of blue light is 4×10^{-7} metres, calculate the frequency. (That is, if $\lambda = 4 \times 10^{-7}$, find f.)

2. The same formula applies to radio waves. According to the *Radio Times*, B.B.C. Light Programme wave-lengths and frequencies are

(i) $\lambda = 1500, f = 2 \times 10^5$;

(ii) $\lambda = 247, f = 1{\cdot}214 \times 10^6$.

In each case, multiply the two figures together to see if they give the correct product, 3×10^8.

3. In electrical theory, the formula $f = \dfrac{1}{2\pi\sqrt{LC}}$ occurs. Calculate f when $L = 1{\cdot}7 \times 10^{-4}$, $C = 10^{-10}$.

(L henrys is the inductance of a tuned circuit, C farads is the capacitance, f cycles-per-second is the frequency.)

4. The distance of the star Sirius from the earth is about 5×10^{13} miles. How long, to the nearest half-year, does light from Sirius take to reach us. (Use the result of the Example at the top of this page.)

5. Astronomers use a unit of distance called a "parsec." It is about $1 \cdot 92 \times 10^{13}$ miles. There is a galaxy of stars (about 10^{11} of them!) which is about 450,000 parsecs away. How many miles is this? Answer to 1 sig. fig. only. (It looks very impressive written out in full, with all the '0's.)

6. If the length of a piece of metal is L_0 cm. when its temperature is 0°C., then when it is heated to t°C., the expansion is

$$L_0 \alpha t \text{ cm.},$$

where α is a constant for any particular metal. For brass, $\alpha = 19 \times 10^{-6}$.

If a brass wire is 150 cm. long at 0°C., how much will it expand when it is heated to 20° C.?

(α is called the "coefficient of linear expansion.")

7. If m grams is the mass of a moving body, v cm.-per-sec. is its speed, E ergs its "kinetic energy," then

$$E = \tfrac{1}{2} mv^2.$$

The mass of an electron is $9 \cdot 108 \times 10^{-28}$ grams. How fast must it move for its energy to be 1 erg? (That is, find v when $E = 1$, $m = 9 \cdot 108 \times 10^{-28}$)

8. The scale of a map of Europe was 1 to 2×10^7—that is, 1 inch on the map represented 2×10^7 inches on the ground. How many miles is this to the inch?

CHAPTER 4

LINEAR AND QUADRATIC FUNCTIONS

THE IDEAS of *Functions* and *Variables* were introduced in Book 1. They are two of the most important ideas in mathematics. All the way through scientific and technical work runs a need for understanding mathematical functions and how they behave. The rest of our work in algebra will be largely a study of certain simple functions.

First, we must make sure that we are quite clear about what the word "function" means. You met "linear functions"—ones whose graphs are straight lines—in Book 1. Take $2x - 3$ as an example. We use "y" to stand for the value of the function, and write $y = 2x - 3$.

If we choose a value for x, we can work out the corresponding value of y; for example, if $x = 5$, $y = 7$. x is called the "*independent variable*," y is called the "*dependent variable.*"

This is the essential thing about functions. If, when we *choose* a particular value of x, we can always find *one*, definite corresponding value of y, we say that "*y is a function of x.*"

Here are two rather different examples; each of them shows you something important about functions.*

1. Look at this table:

Race ..	100 yd.	220 yd.	$\frac{1}{4}$ mile	$\frac{1}{2}$ mile	1 mile	3 miles
Time ..	9·2 sec.	20·0 sec.	45·7 sec.	1 min. 46·8 sec.	3 min. 54·5 sec.	13 min. 10·0 sec.

This table shows world record times, up to January, 1962, for various races commonly run in Britain. If we use x to stand for the number of yards, y for the number of seconds, we can write the table as:

x	100	220	440	880	1760	5280
y	9·2	20·0	45·7	106·8	234·5	790·0

There is *one* value of y for *each* value of x; so *y is a function of x.*

*These examples are put in to help you to have a proper understanding of the idea of a function. For the G.C.E. "O" level exam., it would not matter if you missed them out.

Note: (i) There are only six different values of x. These six values make up what is called the "DOMAIN" of the independent variable, x.

(ii) There are also six values of y. They make up what is called the "RANGE" of the function, y.

(iii) There is no *formula* giving y in terms of x.

(iv) In this example, if we *choose* a particular value of y, there is always *one* corresponding value of x. So we could think of x as a function of y. This doesn't generally happen (see Example 2).

2. Here is a schedule of parcel charges:

Weight of parcel, not exceeding	2 *lb.*	3 *lb.*	4 *lb.*	5 *lb.*	6 *lb.*	7 *lb.*	8 *lb.*	11 *lb.*	15 *lb.*	18 *lb.*	22 *lb.* (*max.*)
Charge	2s. 0d.	2s. 3d.	2s. 6d.	2s. 9d.	3s. 0d.	3s. 3d.	3s. 6d.	3s. 9d.	4s. 0d.	5s. 9d.	6s. 6d.

If we use "w" to stand for the number of ounces in the weight, "p" for the number of pence in the postage, we can write the table as

	Not over										
w	32	48	64	80	96	112	128	176	240	288	352
p	24	27	30	33	36	39	42	45	48	69	78

Given a particular value of w, we can find *one*, definite, corresponding value of p. For example, if $w = 64$, $p = 30$; if $w = 70$, $p = 33$. So, *p is a function of w.*

Theoretically, the *domain* of the independent variable w is any number (including fractions) not greater than 352. But packets weighing not more than 26 oz. can be sent more cheaply by letter-post. In practice, too, weights of parcels can only be measured to a certain degree of accuracy, depending on the scales used. If the scales could measure weights to the nearest ounce, the *domain* of w would really be 27, 28, 29, 30 . . . and so on up to . . . 350, 351, 352.

The *range* of p is the integers (that is, whole numbers) 24, 27, 30, 33, 36, 39, 42, 45, 48.

Note: (i) As in Example 1, there is no single formula giving p in terms of w.

(ii) If we are given a particular value of p, we cannot say what the corresponding value of w is. If, for example, $p = 39$, all we can say is that w is more than 96 but not more than 112. So w is not a function of p. (This is different from Example 1.)

These examples have been put in simply to make clear exactly what we mean in mathematics when we say "*y is a function of x*":

(a) If we choose a particular value of x, we must be able to find ONE (but only one) definite, corresponding value of y.

(b) There MAY be a formula giving y in terms of x, but this is not necessary.

Now, we have to study some simple types of functions, all *with* formulae, to tell us how to work out the value of the function when we have chosen a particular value of x. We must understand how each type of function behaves, that is, how the value of the function changes as x changes. This means that we should know, as soon as we see the formula, what sort of pattern the graph of the function forms. We must be able to give a *rough sketch* of the graph, without having to do a lot of accurate plotting. Even when you have to plot a graph accurately, if you know what its shape should be before you start, it will help you to avoid silly mistakes.

We shall assume in this work that x can be any real number (this includes numbers like $\sqrt{2}$ and π, as well as ones like $0, 5, -2, \frac{3}{4}, -\frac{23}{31}$, and so on). Of course, in some problems the domain of x will be restricted to a particular set of values. In the example in Book 1 (page 234) about the stone being thrown up, the formula was only valid for values of t between 0 and 5 ("t" was used for the independent variable instead of x). In the one about the electric fire, later in this chapter, "h" and "u" must both be positive.

There are some words which we shall use quite often:
Parts of a formula separated by + or − are called TERMS.

$3x + 1$ has two terms, $3x$ and 1;

$x^2 + 5x - 2$ has three terms, x^2, $5x$ and -2.

The number multiplying a power of x is called its COEFFICIENT, and a number on its own is called a CONSTANT TERM.

In $3x + 1$, the coefficient of x is 3, the constant term is 1.

In $x^2 + 5x - 2$, the coefficient of x^2 is 1, the coefficient of x is 5, the constant term is -2.

Linear Functions

In Book 1 you learnt that the graph of any function of the form $mx + c$, where m and c are constants, is a straight line. So this is called a "linear function." There are two particular things to notice: (a) the gradient of the line is m; (b) it cuts the y-axis where $y = c$. First, we will revise that work.

$2x - 1$ and $5 - \frac{1}{2}x$ are examples of functions of this type.
In the first, $m = 2, c = -1$;
in the second, $m = -\frac{1}{2}, c = 5$.

We use "y" to stand for the value of the function, and write

$$y = 2x - 1$$
$$\text{or } y = 5 - \tfrac{1}{2}x$$

We choose values for x, and work out the corresponding values of y. For example:

(i) $y = 2x - 1$

x	-2	-1	0	1	2
y	-5	-3	-1	1	3

(ii) $y = 5 - \frac{1}{2}x$

x	-2	-1	0	1	2
y	6	$5\frac{1}{2}$	5	$4\frac{1}{2}$	4

We need not have chosen only whole numbers for x, of course. In (i), when $x = 1\frac{3}{4}$, $y = 2\frac{1}{2}$; in (ii), when $x = -\frac{1}{2}$, $y = 5\frac{1}{4}$; and so on.

We plot points corresponding to the various pairs of values of x and y: in (i), the points $(-2, -5)$, $(-1, -3)$, $(0, -1)$, etc.; in (ii), the points $(-2, 6)$, $(-1, 5\frac{1}{2})$, $(0, 5)$, etc.

(Remember that when we talk of the point $(-2, -5)$, we mean the point for which "x" is -2 and "y" is -5.)

Since equal changes in x produce equal changes in y, we find in each case that the points lie on a straight line.

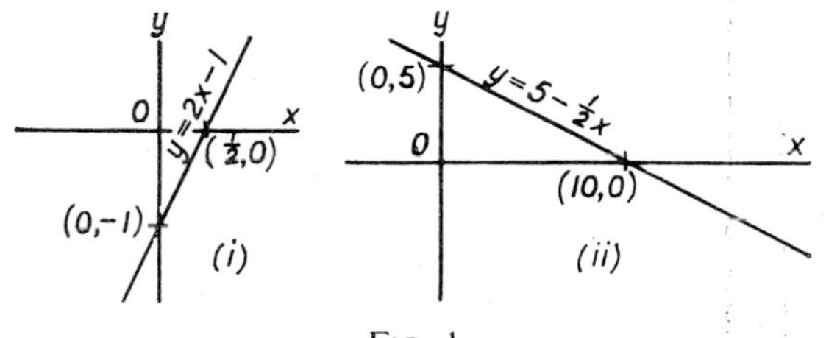

FIG. 1

In (i), where $y = 2x - 1$, as x increases in 1's, y increases in 2's; we say that the gradient of the line is 2.

In (ii), where $y = 5 - \frac{1}{2}x$, as x increases in 1's, y decreases in $\frac{1}{2}$'s; we say that the gradient of the line is $-\frac{1}{2}$.

In fact, the coefficient of x tells us the gradient.

Let us prove that this is so, instead of relying on the pattern suggested by particular cases. A mathematician is never satisfied until he has proved that what he suspects is in fact true; he knows that special cases can be very misleading.

Suppose $y = mx + c$

If x has any particular value, say k, then $y = mk + c$

If x increases by 1, becoming $k + 1$, then $y = m(k + 1) + c$

$= mk + m + c$

i.e. $y = mk + c + m$

So y increases by m's as x increases by 1's, and the gradient of the line is m.

When $x = 0$, $y = c$, so the line passes through the point $(0, c)$; that is, it cuts the y-axis where $y = c$.

The line (i) cuts the y axis at $(0, -1)$; the line (ii) cuts it at $(0, 5)$.

Notice also that on line (i), $y = 0$ when $x = \frac{1}{2}$;
on line (ii), $y = 0$ when $x = 10$.

The Gradient of a Line

We must think a little more about this. We have said that if, when x increases in 1's, y increases in m's, the gradient of the line is m.

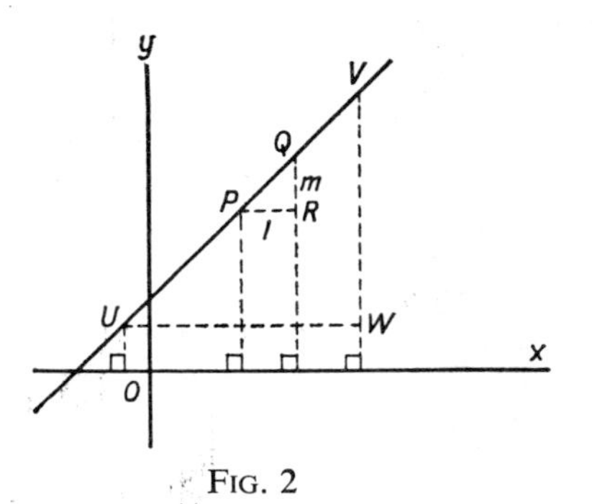

FIG. 2

Suppose P and Q (Fig. 2) are points on a line $y = mx + c$, with an x-difference of 1 (PR), and therefore a y-difference of m (RQ).

If we take *any* two other points U and V on the line, $\triangle UWV$ is similar to $\triangle PRQ$.

So $\dfrac{WV}{UW} = \dfrac{RQ}{PR} = m$; that is, the difference in y between U and V, divided by the difference in x, is equal to the gradient. In fact, this *is* what we *mean* by the gradient:

Take *any* 2 points on a line; then

$$\frac{\text{the difference in } y}{\text{the difference in } x}$$

is called the "*Gradient*" of the line.

On $y = 2x - 1$ take, say, the points $(-2, -5)$ and $(2, 3)$: Difference in x (between -2 and 2) is 4; difference in y (between -5 and 3) is 8; gradient $= \frac{8}{4} = 2$ (Fig. 3(i)).

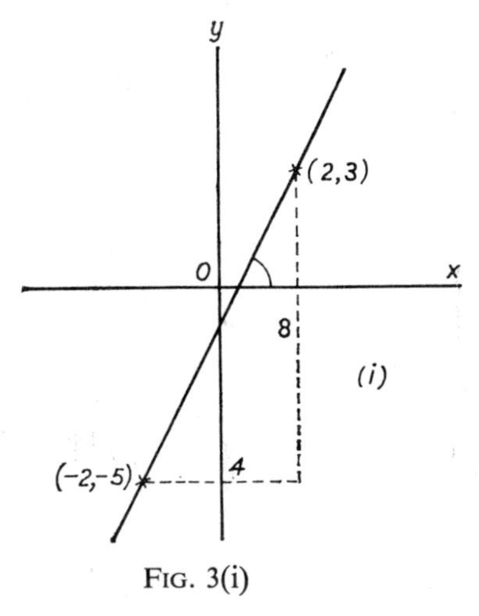

FIG. 3(i)

On $y = 5 - \frac{1}{2}x$, take, say, the points $(-1, 5\frac{1}{2})$ and $(2, 4)$ (Fig. 3(ii)). Difference in x (between -1 and 2) is 3; difference in y (between $5\frac{1}{2}$ and 4) is $-1\frac{1}{2}$; gradient $= \frac{-1\frac{1}{2}}{3} = -\frac{1}{2}$. (In this case the difference in y is negative, since y decreases as x increases.)

These values for the gradient agree with what we had before.

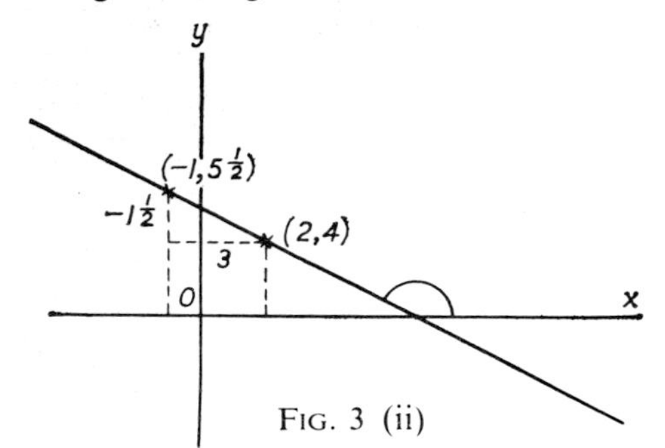

FIG. 3 (ii)

Can you see that the gradient of a line is the tangent of the angle between the line and the positive direction of the x-axis? (In (ii), this angle is obtuse, so its tangent is negative.) Perhaps we should point out that a line when actually drawn on graph paper does not usually make this theoretical angle with the x-axis, because different scales are taken on the two axes.

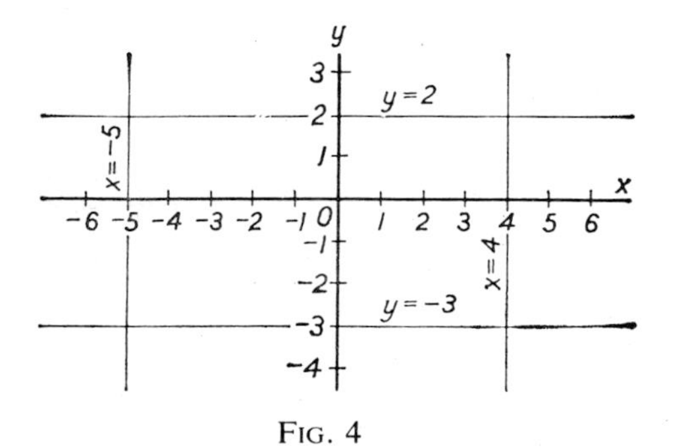

FIG. 4

When a line is *parallel to the x-axis*, its *gradient is zero*, since y does not change.

Its equation is "y = a constant" ($m = 0$).

When a line is parallel to the y-axis, we cannot really say that it has a gradient, but we do sometimes call the gradient "infinite," since we can think of y as changing by any amount we like, without x changing at all. The equation of the line is "x = a constant" (Fig. 4).

We shall be using this work on gradients frequently in the next few chapters, so please make sure that you are clear about it.

Direct Proportion

We are going to think now about linear functions such as $2x$, $5x$, $\frac{1}{3}x$; in fact, mx, where "m" is any constant. (Here the "c" is 0, so that the graph is a straight line through the origin.)

Imagine a 2-kilowatt electric fire—that is, one that uses 2 units of electricity per hour—kept switched on continuously to warm a room. We will make a table showing the amounts of electricity used.

No. of hours for which fire is on	0	1	2	3	4	5	6	7	8	9	10
No. of units used	0	2	4	6	8	10	12	14	16	18	20

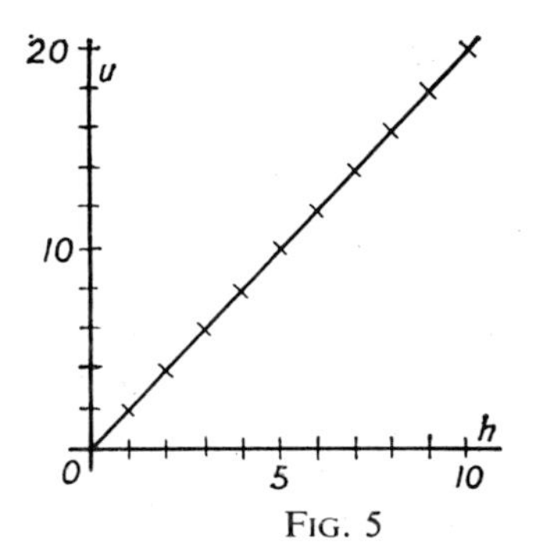

FIG. 5

The number of units is always twice the number of hours. Doubling the number of hours (say, from 4 to 8) doubles the number of units. In fact, whatever the number of hours is multiplied or divided by, the number of units is multiplied or divided by the same amount. (Try this for yourself, and see that it is, in fact, so.)

If we call the number of hours "h" and the number of units "u," then in each case $u = 2h$ (Fig. 5).

(Does this include the special case $h = 0$, $u = 0$?) If we plot the values of h and u on a graph, the points lie on a straight line through the origin.

When two variables are connected in this way, so that $y = mx$, or $\frac{y}{x} = m$, where m is a constant, we say that "y is directly proportional to x," or "y varies directly as x." (Sometimes the word "directly" is left out.)

In the example above, u is proportional to h. We shall meet this idea of "direct proportion" again in Chapter 13.

EXERCISE 4A

Note.—In graphs, "Draw" means calculate values and plot accurately, "Sketch" means show the shape of the graph without accurate plotting.

1. Draw graphs of the following functions, using the same axes and scales for all of them:

$$3x, \quad 3x + 2, \quad 3x + 5, \quad 3x - 1, \quad 3x - 4$$

(Since you know that all the graphs will be straight lines, it is only necessary in each case to plot two points and rule the line joining them. Take two points as far apart as possible—why?—and plot a third point as a check on your calculations and plotting.) What do you notice about all these graphs?

2. Repeat No. 1 for $x + 3$, $\frac{1}{2}x + 3$, $2x + 3$, $3 - x$, $3 - 2x$. Draw also the line $y = 3$. (Use the same scale on the x- and y-axes. You will then get a true picture of the gradient of each line.)

3. What are the values of the function $4x - 3$, (i) when $x = -2$, (ii) when $x = 5$? State the co-ordinates of the corresponding points on the graph $y = 4x - 3$.

Find also the co-ordinates of the points where the line crosses the axes, i.e. where $x = 0$ and where $y = 0$.

Mark these two pairs of points on a sketch of the graph, and verify, for each pair, that $\frac{\textit{change in } y}{\textit{change in } x}$ gives the correct value of the gradient.

4. Repeat No. 3 for the function $5 - 3x$.

5. Many practical problems involve linear *inequalities.* The equation of the graph in No. 4, $y = 5 - 3x$, can be written $3x + y = 5$. Can you shade in, on your diagram for No. 4, the region in which x and y are both positive, and $3x + y > 5$? (">" means "is greater than.")

6. If a temperature measured on the Centigrade scale is $C°$, and the same temperature measured on the Fahrenheit scale is $F°$, then

$$F = \tfrac{9}{5}C + 32$$

What is F when $C = 0$? What is C when $F = 212$? (These two temperatures are the freezing point and boiling point of water.)

Draw the graph $F = \frac{9}{5}C + 32$, and use it to find (i) the value of F when $C = 60$ (check by calculation), (ii) the "normal" body temperature, 98·4° F., on the Centigrade scale (i.e. what is C when $F = 98{\cdot}4$?)

Quadratic Functions

A "quadratic function" is one whose formula contains an "x^2" term, but no higher power of x (and no negative power). So it *may* have an "x" term and a constant term. If we call the coefficient of x^2, "a"; the coefficient of x, "b"; and the constant term, "c"; the function is

$$y = ax^2 + bx + c$$

Some examples are $y = x^2$ ($a = 1, b = 0, c = 0$),
$y = \frac{1}{2}x^2 + 3$ ($a = \frac{1}{2}, b = 0, c = 3$),
$y = 3x^3 - 5x - 4$ ($a = 3, b = -5, c = -4$),
$y = 80x - 16x^2$ ($a = -16, b = 80, c = 0$).

Can you see why these graphs have the same general shape?

First, we will choose some values of x, say whole numbers from -4 to $+4$. Next, we will work out the corresponding values of several functions. (Please check by working the values out for yourself, and see if you can find one that is wrong.)

x	-4	-3	-2	-1	0	1	2	3	4
(i) x^2	16	9	4	1	0	1	4	9	16
(ii) x^2+1	17	10	5	2	1	2	5	10	17
(iii) x^2-1	15	8	2	0	-1	0	3	8	15
(iv) $(x-1)^2$	25	16	9	4	1	0	1	4	9
(v) $(x+1)^2$	9	4	1	0	1	4	9	16	25
(vi) $2x^2$	32	18	8	2	0	2	8	18	32
(vii) $\frac{1}{2}x^2$	8	$4\frac{1}{2}$	2	$\frac{1}{2}$	0	$\frac{1}{2}$	2	$4\frac{1}{2}$	8
(viii) $-x^2$	-16	-9	-4	-1	0	-1	-4	-9	-16

FIG. 6

Now, what do the graphs of these functions look like?

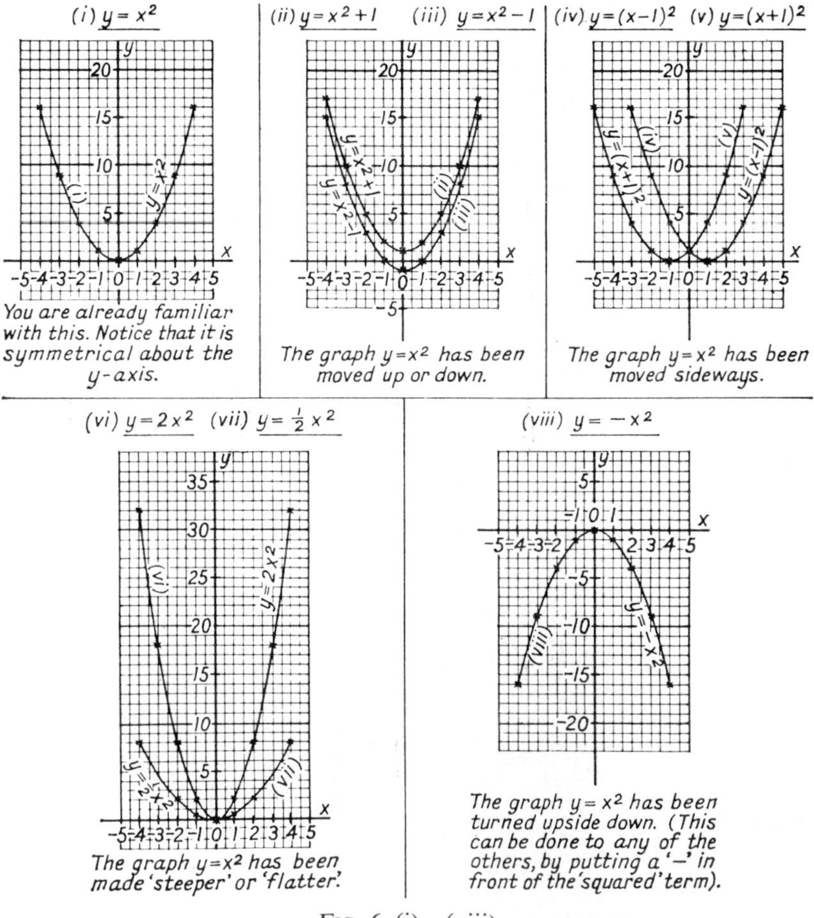

FIG. 6 (i)—(viii)

The wrong value is that for $x^2 - 1$ at $x = -2$; it should be 3, not 2.

The graphs are all basically the same curve, which is called a "PARABOLA." The lowest or highest point is called the "VERTEX."

Do you see how all these graphs can be obtained from $y = x^2$ by moving it up or down, to right or left, steepening or flattening it, or turning it upside down?

We will try the effect of doing several of these things in turn (Fig. 7).

(a) $y = x^2$.

(b) $y = (x - 2)^2$: the curve is moved sideways, the vertex is at (2, 0).

(c) $y = \frac{1}{2}(x - 2)^2$: the curve is made "shallower."

(d) $y = \frac{1}{2}(x - 2)^2 + 3$: the curve is moved up, the vertex is at (2, 3).

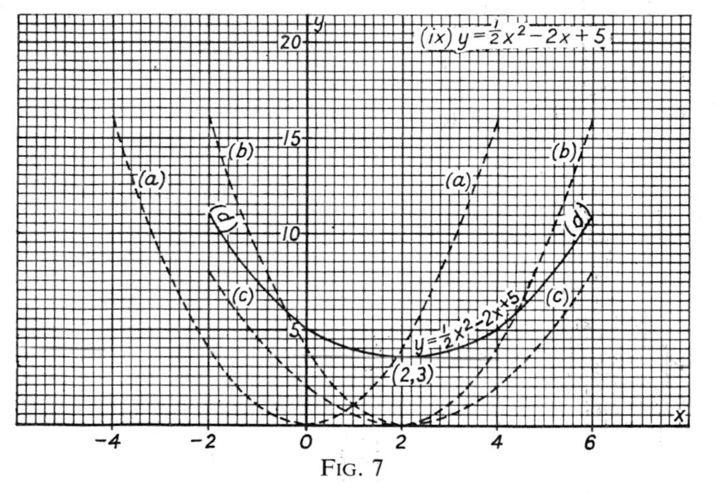

FIG. 7

If we multiply out the formula of this function, we get

$$y = \tfrac{1}{2}(x^2 - 4x + 4) + 3$$
$$= \tfrac{1}{2}x^2 - 2x + 2 + 3,$$
$$\text{i.e. } y = \tfrac{1}{2}x^2 - 2x + 5 \quad \ldots\ldots\ldots\ldots\ldots\ldots\ldots \text{(ix)}$$

Here we have the function in the "standard" form, $y = ax^2 + bx + c$, with $a = \frac{1}{2}$, $b = -2$, $c = 5$—and we have seen that its graph is still basically the same curve as $y = x^2$.

Now, if you start with any formula of this sort, you can always reverse the argument and put it in a form like (d). For example, suppose

$$y = 1 - 6x - 3x^2 \quad \ldots\ldots\ldots\ldots\ldots\ldots\ldots \text{(x)}$$
$$\text{Then } y = 1 - 3(x^2 + 2x)$$
$$= 1 - 3(x^2 + 2x + 1) + 3^*$$
$$\text{i.e. } y = -3(x + 1)^2 + 4$$

**Note.*—The "1" is put inside the bracket to make a perfect square; it is multiplied by -3, so the $+3$ is put in to make up for it. If you don't quite follow this, multiplying out and collecting up will show you that it is correct.

So the graph is built up from $y = -x^2$ as shown in Fig. 8. Its vertex is at $(-1, 4)$.

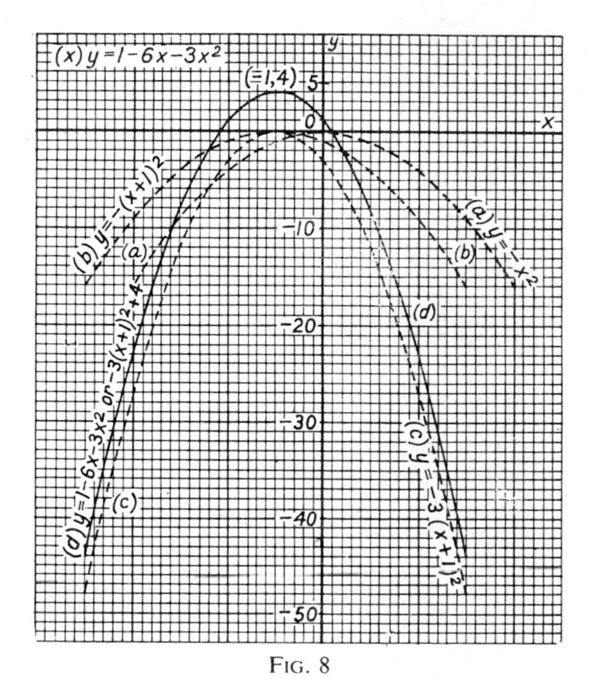

FIG. 8

Similarly the graph of *any* quadratic function is a parabola.

If the coefficient of x^2 is positive, as in (i) to (vii) and in (ix), the vertex is the lowest point (we call it a "minimum" point).

If the coefficient of x^2 is negative, as in (viii) and (x), the curve is "upside down" and the vertex is the highest point (we call it a "maximum" point).

Notice that all these curves are symmetrical about the line through the vertex parallel to the y-axis. (We call this line the "axis" of the parabola.)

This should help you to know at once, when you see a quadratic function, what its graph is like. You ought to be able to *sketch* it without accurate plotting.

Notice that it may cross the x-axis at two points, as in (iii) and (x); "touch" the x-axis at one point, as in (i) and in (iv) to (viii); or not meet the x-axis at all, as in (ii) and (ix). We shall return to this point in Chapter 12.

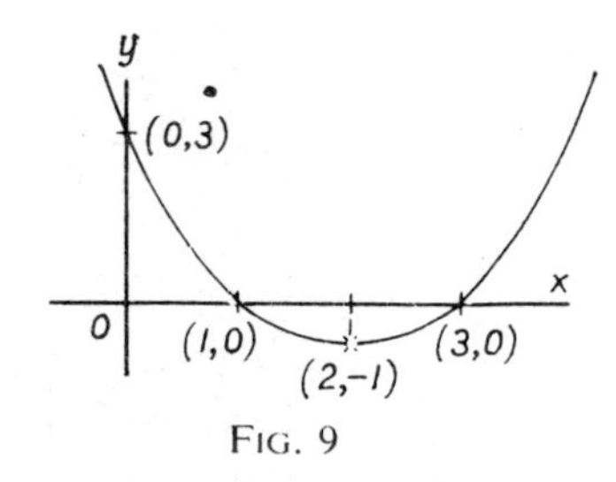

FIG. 9

Often, it is enough just to find out where the curve crosses the axes as in this case (Fig. 9): $y = x^2 - 4x + 3$ ....(xi)

i.e. $y = (x - 1)(x - 3)$

$y = 0$ when $(x - 1)(x - 3) = 0$

i.e. when $x - 1 = 0$ or $x - 3 = 0$, i.e. when $x = 1$ or 3.

So the curve crosses the x-axis at (1, 0) and (3, 0).

When $x = 0$, $y = 3$; so the curve crosses the y-axis at (0, 3).

Notice that, from the symmetry of the curve, the minimum point must be where $x = 2$ (and $y = -1$).

Example: $y = 4x - x^2$, or $x(4 - x)$................(xii)

$y = 0$ when $x(4 - x) = 0$ i.e. when $x = 0$ or 4 (Fig. 10).

Since the coefficient of x^2 is -1, the curve must have a maximum point. By symmetry, this must be where $x = 2$ (and $y = 4$).

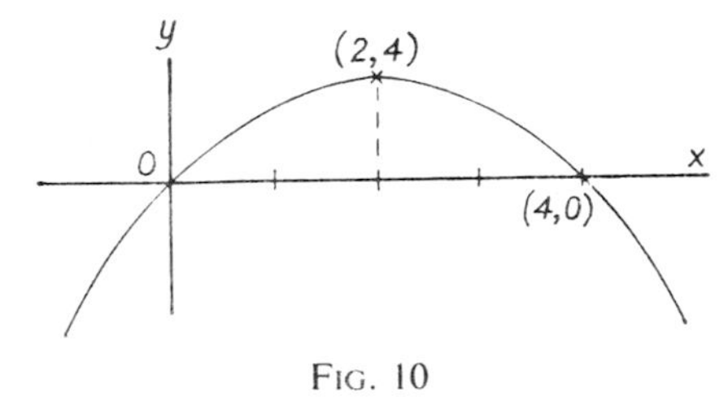

FIG. 10

We hope you now feel familiar with linear and quadratic functions. We shall deal with some other types of function in Chapter 8, after we have learnt some new ideas which are helpful in sketching their graphs.

EXERCISE 4B

1. Draw graphs of the functions (i) x^2, (ii) $(x + 2)^2$, (iii) $3(x + 2)^2$, (iv) $3(x + 2)^2 - 4$.

Show that (iv) is $3x^2 + 12x + 8$.

What are the co-ordinates of the vertex of the curve $y = 3x^2 + 12x + 8$?

2. Draw graphs of (i) $-x^2$, (ii) $-(x - 3)^2$, (iii) $2 - (x - 3)^2$.

What does (iii) become when it is multiplied out? Where is the vertex and what is the equation of the axis of the graph of (iii)?

3. Sketch the graph $y = 2x^2 - x - 3$, showing where it crosses the axes.

By considering the symmetry of the curve, say where the maximum or minimum point must be (i.e. where $x = ?$, $y = ?$); which is it?

4. Repeat No. 3 for (i) $y = 8 + 2x - x^2$, (ii) $y = 5x - x^2$.

5. Structural engineers have to know all about the stresses and strains set up in beams which carry heavy loads. If a 30-foot beam, supported at each end, carries an evenly-spread load of 4 tons per foot, the "bending moment" (M) at a distance x feet from either end is given by

$$M = 2x^2 - 60x$$

Sketch the graph of this function for values of x from 0 to 30. Verify that

M is zero at both ends of the beam (i.e. when $x = 0$ or 30).

What is the greatest (negative) value of M, and where does it occur? (Algebraically, this means finding the *minimum* value, but it is the greatest numerically.)

6. If a stone is thrown straight up at 80 ft.-per-sec., its *upward* speed (v ft./sec.) and its height above the ground (s ft.), t sec. later are given approximately by

$$v = 80 - 32t$$
$$s = 80t - 16t^2$$

Draw graphs of these functions for values of t from 0 to 5.

Noticing the various values of v and s, can you describe how the stone moves in these 5 sec.?

CHAPTER 5

GRADIENTS AND RATES OF CHANGE

YOU MAY find this chapter rather "wordy" and difficult; if so, go right through it, trying to grasp the general trend of the argument, without worrying if you do not understand every detail. Then study it a second time, writing out the worked examples as you go. This should make it clearer.

We will start by looking again at the example of "direct proportion" on page 156. We plotted a graph showing the number of units of electricity used by a 2-kilowatt fire (i.e. one which uses 2 units an hour) and the time it is on. This diagram (Fig. 1) shows the same graph (OA) and corresponding ones for 1-kilowatt and 3-kilowatt fires (OB and OC). Do you agree that the last two are correct? Their equations are $u = h$ and $u = 3h$.

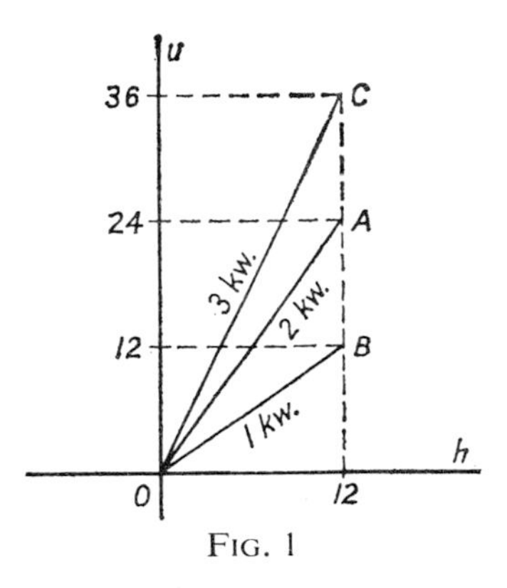

FIG. 1

Clearly, the steepness of the slope of a line indicates the rate of consumption of electricity—the faster electricity is being used, the steeper the slope.

Now, "steepness" and "slope" are vague words. We already know that we measure them in a definite way by the "gradient" of a line. So, the gradient of a line shows the rate of consumption:

The gradient of OA is 2; consumption, 2 units per hour;
The gradient of OB is 1; consumption, 1 unit per hour;
The gradient of OC is 3; consumption, 3 units per hour.

Now, consider another example. Imagine that it were possible for a man to walk at a steady speed of 4 miles per hour, to cycle at a steady speed of 12 m.p.h., or to drive a car at a steady speed of 30 m.p.h. If we call the time for which he moves, t hours; and the distance he goes, d miles, the graphs of d against t will be as shown. Please think about this, and see whether you agree. What are the equations of these lines?

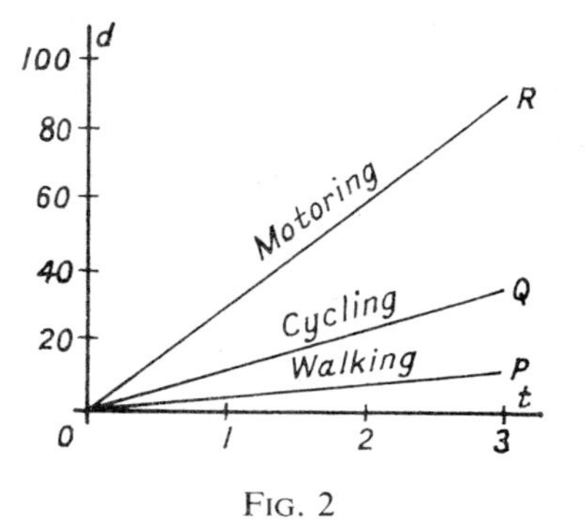

FIG. 2

Do the gradients of the lines show anything this time? Clearly, they show the speed; the greater the speed, the greater the gradient.

The line OP represents distances travelled in different times at a speed of 4 m.p.h.; its equation is $d = 4t$; its gradient is 4.

OQ represents movement at 12 m.p.h.; its equation is $d = 12t$; its gradient is 12.

OR represents movement at 30 m.p.h.; its equation is $d = 30t$; its gradient is 30.

In both these examples the gradient of a line represents the rate at which something is changing: the rate at which the number of units of electricity used is increasing (so many units per hour), or the rate at which the distance travelled is increasing (so many miles per hour)—which we usually call the "speed."

Look, now, at this table, which shows the lengths of the sides of various squares, and their perimeters, that is, the distance round the outside.

Length of side (*inches*)	1	2	3	4	5	6	7	8	9	10
Perimeter (*inches*) . .	4	8		16		24	28			40

(Can you fill in the missing figures?)

Call the length of the side x in., the perimeter y in.; plot the various points (x, y) (Fig. 3). The graph is again a straight line through the origin (when $x = 0$, $y = 0$); its equation is $y = 4x$, and its gradient 4. Every increase of 1 in x produces an increase of 4 in y.

We use the word "rate" here in a rather different sense, without any reference to time. In fact, we say:

"The rate of change of y relative to x is 4," meaning simply what we have just said, that any change in x produces a change 4 times as great in y.

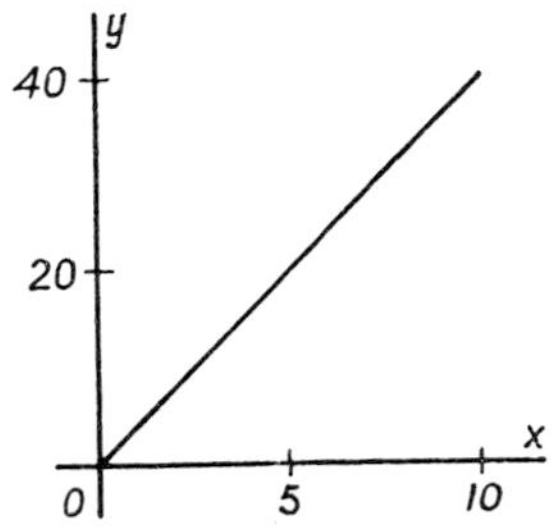

(You *can* think of time as coming in to it if you like, because if you imagine a square to be growing in size, y increases 4 *times as fast* as x.)

FIG. 3

These examples show that the gradient of a line tells us how fast things change; it represents the rate at which one variable changes relative to the other. What happens if the graph is a curve instead of a straight line? We will take another example involving distance and time. Such a graph is usually called a "space-time" graph, with "s" units standing for the distance—or "space"—covered and "t" units for the time.

Here are some figures showing how a bicycle started off, free-wheeling down a hill.

Time, t sec. ..	0	1	2	3	4	5
Distance, s ft.	0	0·6	2·1	4·7	9·6	19·3

How far did the bicycle go in each second? (Remember that all the distances in the table are measured *from the starting point.*)

First second ($t = 0$ to $t = 1$), 0·6 feet;
Second second ($t = 1$ to $t = 2$), 1·5 feet (i.e. 2·1 — 0·6);
Third second ($t = 2$ to $t = 3$), 2·6 feet (i.e. 4·7 — 2·1);
Fourth second ($t = 3$ to $t = 4$), 4·9 feet (i.e. 9·6 — 4·7);
Fifth second ($t = 4$ to $t = 5$), 9·7 feet (i.e. 19·3 — 9·6).

Clearly, the bicycle moved faster and faster. How does this affect the space-time graph (Fig. 4)?

As the speed increases, the curve slopes up more steeply, which agrees with what we found when the space-time graphs were straight lines. Can we still say that the gradient represents the speed? If we hope to do so, we must decide exactly what we mean by the speed of the bicycle at any particular time, say when $t = 3$.

We will lead up to this by studying the *average* speed over short intervals of time after $t = 3$, and seeing how each quantity we mention is represented on the diagram.

First, here is a short explanation of the diagram. P, Q, R and S are the points *on the curve* for which $t = 3$, 4, $3\frac{1}{2}$ and $3\frac{1}{4}$ respectively. The tangent to

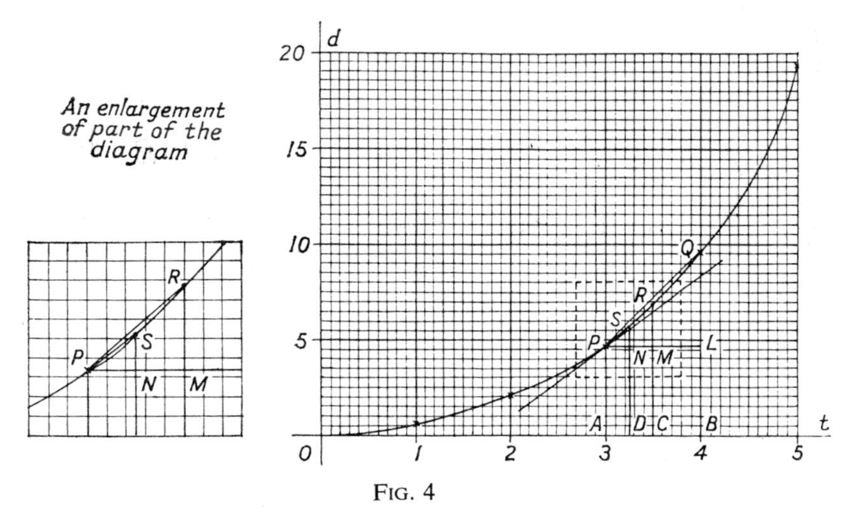

FIG. 4

the curve at P, and the straight line PQ, are shown in the main diagram. The enlargement shows the straight lines PR and PS; the curve has had to be distorted slightly so that PR and PS could be distinguished in print from the curve itself. Because of this, the tangent at P has been left out of the enlargement.

Distances, Times and Speeds	*Represented on the Graph By*
$t = 3$ to $t = 4$	
Distance travelled $= 9{\cdot}6 - 4{\cdot}7 = 4{\cdot}9$ ft.	$BQ - AP = BQ - BL = LQ$.
Time taken $= 1$ sec.	AB or PL.
Average speed $= \frac{4{\cdot}9}{1} = 4{\cdot}9$ ft.-per-sec.	$\frac{LQ}{PL}$ *which is the gradient of the line PQ.*
$t = 3$ to $t = 3\frac{1}{2}$ (reading from the graph, when $t = 3\frac{1}{2}$ the total distance is $6{\cdot}7$ ft.)	
Distance travelled $= 6{\cdot}7 - 4{\cdot}7 = 2{\cdot}0$ ft.	$CR - AP = CR - CM = MR$.
Time taken $= \frac{1}{2}$ sec.	AC or PM.
Average speed $= \frac{2{\cdot}0}{\frac{1}{2}} = 4{\cdot}0$ ft.-per-sec.	$\frac{MR}{PM}$ *which is the gradient of the line PR.*
$t = 3$ to $t = 3\frac{1}{4}$ (reading from the graph, when $t = 3\frac{1}{4}$ the total distance is $5{\cdot}5$ ft.)	
Distance travelled $= 5{\cdot}5 - 4{\cdot}7 = 0{\cdot}8$ ft.	$DS - AP = DS - DN = NS$.
Time taken $= \frac{1}{4}$ sec.	AD or PN.
Average speed $= \frac{0{\cdot}8}{\frac{1}{4}} = 3{\cdot}2$ ft.-per-sec.	$\frac{NS}{PN}$ *which is the gradient of the line PS.*

If we go on in the same way, taking shorter and shorter intervals of time after $t = 3$, the average speed must be getting nearer and nearer to the actual speed when $t = 3$.*

As we do this, the lines ("chords" of the curve) whose gradients represent the average speed get closer and closer to the tangent to the curve at P. So, the gradient of the tangent at P represents the actual speed at time $t = 3$.

This rather difficult idea will probably be clearer if, instead of figures found by *observing* how far the bicycle moves, we take a *formula* giving the distance (s feet) moved by a body in t sec. You may know, for instance, that if a body falls in a vacuum, the formula is approximately $s = 16t^2$. To illustrate the new ideas we are trying to introduce, we will take as simple a formula as possible, $s = t^2$. (If a marble is rolled down a smooth groove in a plank, the distance it rolls can be made to fit this formula quite closely, by adjusting the slope of the plank.)

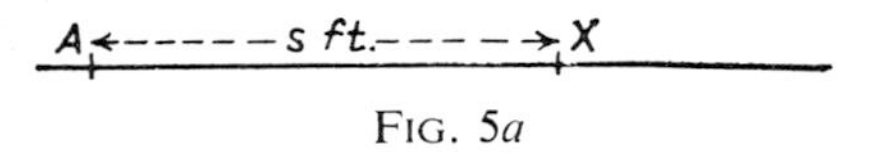

FIG. 5*a*

Given: A body (X) is moving in a straight line, starting from a point A, so that, t seconds later, its distance from A is s feet, where

$$s = t^2.$$

To Find: (i) The speed of the body after 3 seconds.

(ii) A formula giving the speed after t seconds.

(i) As before, we will find the *average* speed over a small interval of time after $t = 3$. Call this small interval h sec., so that at the end of it, $t = 3 + h$.

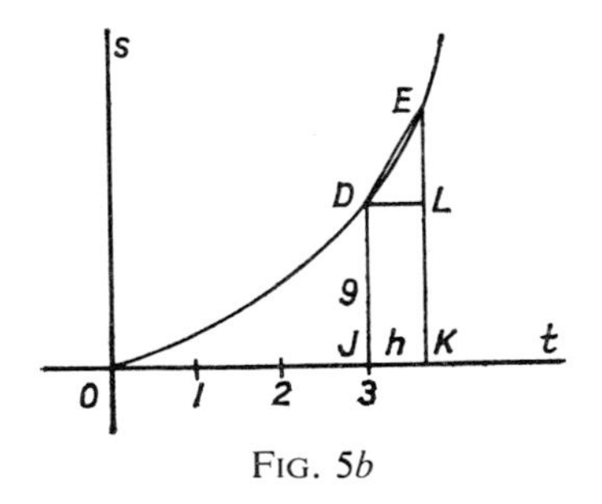

FIG. 5*b*

*In fact, this "limiting value" that the average speed approaches *is* what we mean by the "speed when $t = 3$"; this is the only way we can define it.

Distances, Times and Speeds	*Represented on the Graph By*
After 3 sec., distance from $A = 9$ ft., i.e. when $t = 3$, $s = 9$	D is the point (3, 9), i.e., $OJ = 3$, $JD = 9$
When $t = 3 + h$, $s = (3 + h)^2$ $= 9 + 6h + h^2$ So in h sec. (from $t = 3$ to $t = 3 + h$), the distance moved is $6h + h^2$ ft. (from where $s = 9$ to where $s = 9 + 6h + h^2$)	E is the point $(3 + h, 9 + 6h + h^2)$, i.e. $OK = 3 + h$, $KE = 9 + 6h + h^2$ $JK = OK - OJ = h$, $\therefore DL = h$ $LE = KE - KL$ $= KE - JD$ $= (9 + 6h + h^2) - 9$ $LE = 6h + h^2$
Average speed $= \dfrac{6h + h^2}{h}$ ft./sec. $= 6 + h$ ft./sec.	Gradient of chord $DE = \dfrac{6h + h^2}{h}$ $= 6 + h$
By taking h small enough, the average speed can be made as near to 6 ft./sec. as we wish.*	By taking h small enough, the gradient of the chord can be made as near to 6 as we wish. But the smaller we take h, the closer the chord DE will lie to the *tangent* to the curve at D.
So the actual speed when $t = 3$ must be 6 ft./sec.	*So the gradient of the tangent at D must be* 6.

WE SEE THAT THE GRADIENT OF THE TANGENT AT D REPRESENTS THE SPEED WHEN $t = 3$.

(ii) We shall go through the same argument that we used in (i), but now we have to think about where the body is and how fast it is moving after *any* time—which we call "t" sec.—instead of one *particular* time.

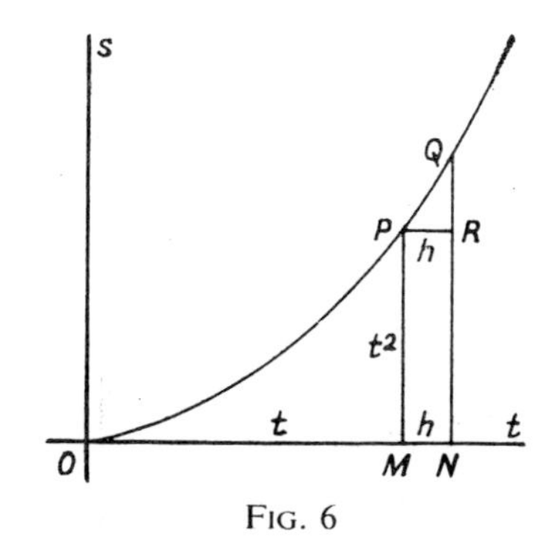

FIG. 6

*For example, if $h = \cdot 1$; that is, if we think of the time-interval from $t = 3$ to $t = 3{\cdot}1$, the average speed is 6·1 ft./sec. If $h = \cdot 01$, the average speed is 6·01 ft./sec., and so on.

Distances, Times and Speeds	*Represented on the Graph By*
After t sec., distance $= t^2$ ft.	P is the point (t, t^2), i.e. $CM = t$, $MP = t^2$
After $t + h$ sec., distance $= (t + h)^2$ ft., i.e. $t^2 + 2th + h^2$ ft.	Q is the point $(t + h, t^2 + 2th + h^2)$, i.e. $ON = t + h$, $NQ = t^2 + 2th + h^2$.
So in h sec. (from t to $t + h$) the distance moved is $2th+h^2$ ft. (from where $s = t^2$ to where $s = t^2 + 2th + h^2$).	$MN = ON - OM = h, \therefore PR = h$ $RQ = NQ - NR$ $= NQ - MP$ $= (t^2 + 2th + h^2) - t^2$ $\therefore RQ = 2th + h^2$
Average speed $= \dfrac{2th + h^2}{h}$ ft./sec. $= 2t + h$ ft./sec.	Gradient of chord $PQ = \dfrac{2th + h^2}{h}$ $= 2t + h$
By taking h small enough, the average speed can be made as near as we please to $2t$ ft./sec.	By taking h small enough, the gradient of the chord PQ can be made as near to $2t$ as we please. But, the smaller we take h, the closer PQ will lie to the *tangent* to the curve at P.
So the actual speed at time "t" must be 2t ft./sec.	*So the gradient of the tangent at P must be 2t.*
AGAIN, WE SEE THAT THE GRADIENT OF THE TANGENT AT P REPRESENTS THE SPEED AFTER TIME "t."	

Note how each step on the right represents exactly the corresponding step on the left. Notice what we have done:

We called the time "t" secs.

We have shown that if the distance formula is t^2 *feet*, the speed formula is $2t$ *ft./sec.*

After 1 sec., that is, when $t = 1$, the speed is 2 ft./sec.;

After 5 sec., the speed is 10 ft./sec.;

After $3\frac{1}{2}$ sec., the speed is 7 ft./sec.; and so on.

This, of course, is a trivial example; we had to take a very simple one to illustrate the new ideas. But these ideas are extremely important; we shall return to this point later.

We have now been through the same argument three times. It is a difficult one to understand. Read the three examples through several times and think about them carefully. If you can really grasp the argument, you will have dealt with the main difficulty in what follows in the next few chapters.

As we found in our examples where the graphs were straight lines, the same argument, with some alterations in the wording, shows that the gradient of the tangent at a point of any graph gives the rate at which the "y" is changing relative to the "x."

If the "y" represents speed and the "x" time, the gradient gives the rate at which the speed is changing at any particular time, i.e. the "acceleration" (so many m.p.h. per second, say).

If the "y" represents quantity of electricity used in time "x," the gradient gives the *rate of consumption of electricity* (so many units per hour).

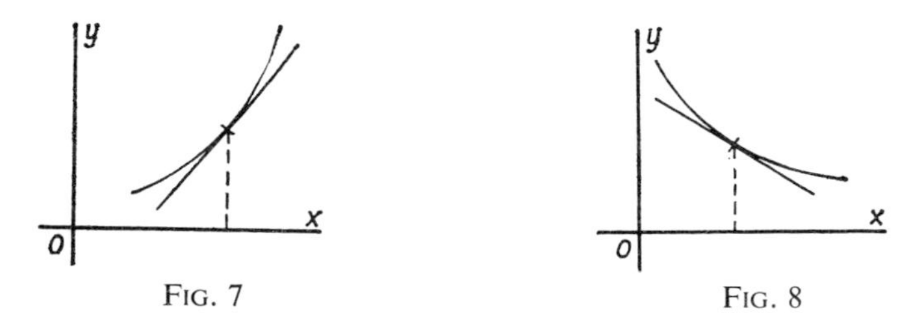

FIG. 7 FIG. 8

Don't forget that a line may have a negative gradient—and "y" may get less as "x" gets bigger. If "y" represents the temperature of a liquid, "x" the time, the gradient at any point gives the rate at which the substance is cooling at the particular time (so many degrees per minute, say).

It is hoped that these examples will give some idea of why the study of tangents to curves is important.

"The gradient of a curve at any point" means the gradient of the tangent at that point.

The next few chapters deal with the *calculation* of gradients when the equations of curves are known (and vice versa). We shall only use graphs of simple functions, but the ideas have applications in every branch of science and technology. This chapter is intended just as an introduction; there will be exercises in the other ones.

CHAPTER 6

DIFFERENTIATION

WE MUST now study the calculation of gradients in some detail. We shall use the same method as on page 169, to which please refer. Since h represented a *small* interval of time, Q was a point on the curve *near to P*. We calculated the gradient of the chord PQ—we will call this the "average gradient" between P and Q. Then we found the actual gradient at P (i.e. the gradient of the tangent there) by considering what happened to the average gradient when the time-interval was very short, that is, when Q was very close to P.

We will start by explaining the notation that is normally used. It seems complicated at first, but it has been in use since these ideas were first introduced, and you will find that the notation has many advantages, so it is worth making the effort to master it.

We start with a point P on a curve; its co-ordinates are (x, y), that is, $OL = x$, $LP = y$ (Fig. 1).

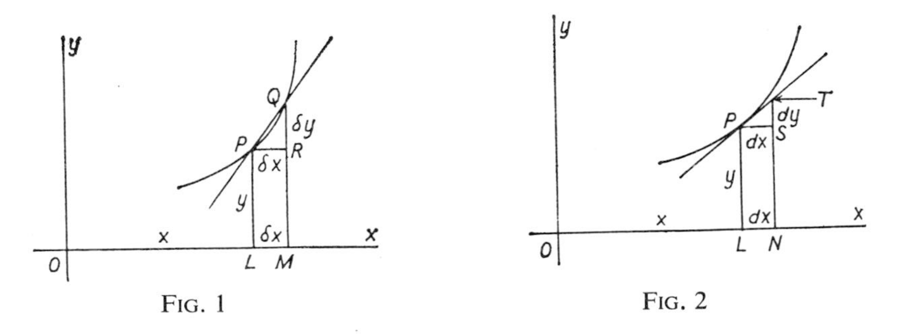

FIG. 1 FIG. 2

Take a point Q on the curve near to P. We call the difference in x (LM or PR) between P and Q, "δx" (pronounced "delta x").

δ (delta) is the Greek letter corresponding to our "d"; it is used to stand for "the difference in." δx does NOT mean $\delta \times x$; you must think of it as one single symbol δx, meaning "the difference in x."

Similarly, the difference in y (RQ) is called "δy" ("delta y").

Using this notation, the gradient of the line PQ is $\frac{\delta y}{\delta x}$ and the co-ordinates of Q are $(x + \delta x, y + \delta y)$, that is, $OM = x + \delta x$, $MQ = y + \delta y$.

Notice that, since Q is *any* point on the curve near to P, we can *choose* any small value of δx. When, however, we have chosen a particular δx (or, we have chosen a particular point Q), the corresponding δy will be fixed. What we shall do is to work out a formula giving δy in terms of δx.

Now, we shall be trying to find the gradient of the *tangent* at P, so we have a similar notation, but using *English* letters, for differences in x and y between points on the tangent (Fig. 2).

The difference in x between P and T (LN or PS) is called "dx" (dee x).

The difference in y between P and T (ST) is called "dy" (dee y).

So the gradient of the tangent PT is $\frac{dy}{dx}$.

As before, remember that dx, dy are *single symbols* meaning "the difference in x" and "the difference in y." As with δx, dx can be *chosen* to have any value we like, but when dx has been chosen, the corresponding dy will be fixed. In fact, though, we shall not think about dx and dy separately at all.

We shall simply use $\frac{dy}{dx}$ to stand for "the gradient of the tangent."

It is usually referred to as "dy by dx."

Now, we will use this notation to work out a formula for the gradient at any point of the curve $y = x^2$. (We have already done this on page 169. using t and s instead of x and y; s stood for a number of seconds, t for a number of feet, and the gradient gave the speed in feet-per-second.)

We will use the same diagram (Fig. 1), without bothering for the moment about the actual shape of the graph.

For any point on this curve (the y-co-ord.) = (the x-co-ord.)^2. Now, the co-ordinates of P are (x, y), those of Q are $(x + \delta x, y + \delta y)$;

$$\text{so } y = x^2 \quad \ldots\ldots\ldots\ldots (1)$$

$$\text{and } y + \delta y = (x + \delta x)^2 \quad \ldots\ldots (2)$$

$$\text{Line (2) is} \quad y + \delta y = x^2 + 2x(\delta x) + (\delta x)^2$$

$$\text{Line (1) is} \quad y = x^2$$

$$\text{Subtracting, } \delta y = 2x(\delta x) + (\delta x)^2$$

$$\therefore \text{ gradient of } PQ = \frac{\delta y}{\delta x} = 2x + \delta x$$

By choosing δx small enough, we can make the gradient of PQ as close as we please to $2x$.

But, the smaller we make δx (that is, the closer Q is to P), the closer PQ will be to the tangent at P. So the gradient of the tangent at P must be $2x$;

$$\text{that is, } \frac{dy}{dx} = 2x.$$

Consider this argument very carefully, until you are quite sure that you have understood it; it is fundamental in all the work of this chapter.

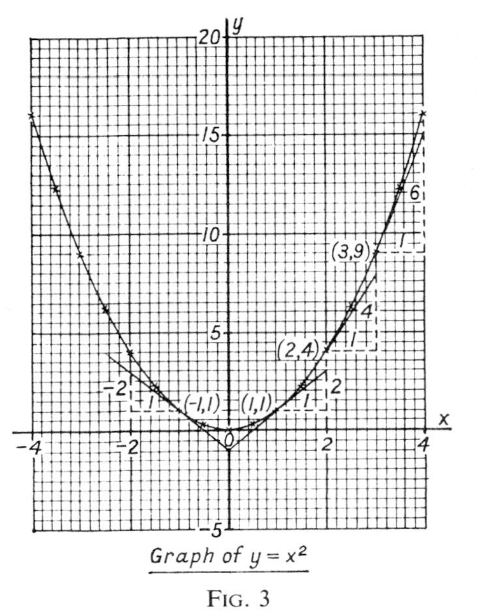

FIG. 3

Let us see how what we have just done fits in with the graph of $y = x^2$, which we are already familiar with. We will substitute various values of x in our "gradient formula," to find the gradients of the tangents at various points.

Do you see the significance of $\frac{dy}{dx}$ the gradient formula, in relation to the graph? Beginners often confuse $\frac{dy}{dx}$, the *gradient* of the tangent at a point on a curve, with y, the *co-ordinate* of the point. Try to get the distinction clear.

We have been referring all the time to the "graph of $y = x^2$" or the "curve $y = x^2$." Normally, we are only interested in a graph because it gives a picture of how a function of x behaves as x changes. It is the *function* that really concerns us.

Values of x	*Values of $\frac{dy}{dx}$*	*Representation on the Graph*
1	$2 \times 1 = 2$	At the point on the curve where $x = 1$, i.e. the point (1, 1), gradient of tangent = 2.
2	$2 \times 2 = 4$	At the point where $x = 2$, i.e. the point (2, 4), gradient of tangent = 4.
3	$2 \times 3 = 6$	At the point (3, 9), gradient = 6.
0	$2 \times 0 = 0$	At the point (0, 0), gradient = 0, i.e. the tangent is parallel to the x-axis. In fact, the curve touches the *x-axis* at this point, the x-axis *is* the tangent.
-1	$2 \times (-1) = -2$	At the point $(-1, 1)$, gradient of tangent $= -2$, i.e. the tangent slopes downwards, with y decreasing by 2 for every increase of 1 in x, and so on.

Starting with the function x^2, we have found a new function, $2x$, which is the "gradient formula" for the graph $y = x^2$.

This gradient formula is called the "DERIVED FUNCTION," or "DERIVATIVE" (because it is derived from the original function). Remember that it indicates how the value of the function (y) changes as x changes—and often the rate of change is more important than the actual value of the function. (Chap. 5.) The process of finding the derived function is called "DIFFERENTIATION."

Our next step will be to differentiate several simple types of function, using the same diagram and notation that we used for x^2,

y standing for the *given* function,

$\frac{dy}{dx}$ standing for the *derived* function.

Please do not just read. Always draw a diagram and write down the argument, trying to do each step yourself first. If you find any step difficult to understand, see what you are finding *on the graph* (Fig. 4).

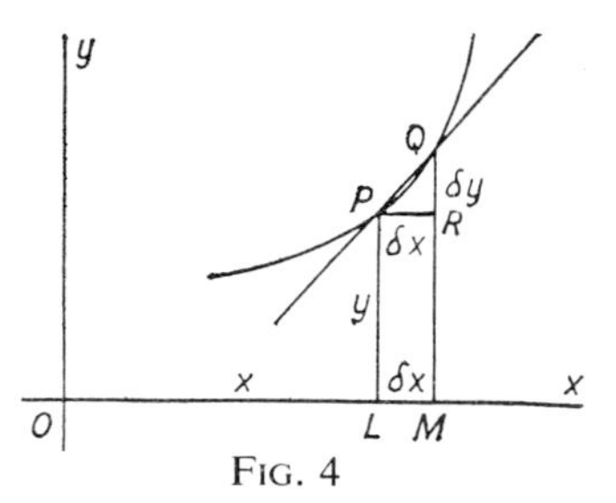

FIG. 4

We start with a particular value of x, and the corresponding value of the function (y); these are represented on the graph by a point P, with co-ordinates (x, y).

We increase x by a small amount δx; this changes the value of the function by a small amount δy. This is represented on the graph by a point Q, near to P, with co-ordinates $(x + \delta x, y + \delta y)$.

I. Functions like $2x^2$, $3x^2$, $\frac{1}{2}x^2$, etc.

Look back to page 172, where we found that if $y = x^2$, $\frac{dy}{dx} = 2x$.

Can you see that if we start with "a number of times x^2," the right-hand side of each equation will be multiplied by that number, so that $\frac{dy}{dx}$ will be "that number $\times$ $2x$"?

Try it yourself several times, with different numbers, before reading any farther.

We will take $y = 5x^2$ ....(1)

Then $y + \delta y = 5\,(x + \delta x)^2$*

$= 5\,\{x^2 + 2x\,(\delta x) + (\delta x)^2\}$,

that is, $y + \delta y = 5x^2 + 10x\,(\delta x) + 5\,(\delta x)^2$ ....(2)

*The value of the function is always $5 \times$ (the value of x)^2; or, on the graph (the y-co-ord.) $= 5 \times$ (the x-co-ord.)^2.

Subtracting line (1) from line (2),

$$\delta y = 10x(\delta x) + 5(\delta x)^2,$$

$$\therefore \frac{\delta y}{\delta x} = 10x + 5(\delta x).$$

By choosing δx small enough, we can make $\frac{\delta y}{\delta x}$ as close as we please to $10x$.

So, $\frac{dy}{dx} = 10x$

(We shall not write the argument quite as fully each time as we did on page 172. Refer back to that page if you are at all doubtful.)

Similarly, if $y = 2x^2$, $\frac{dy}{dx} = 4x$;

if $y = 3x^2$, $\frac{dy}{dx} = 6x$;

if $y = \frac{1}{2}x^2$, $\frac{dy}{dx} = x$ (i.e. $1x$); and so on.

We can say: if $y = ax^2$, where "a" is any constant, $\frac{dy}{dx} = 2ax$.

Try to go through the differentiation process for the function ax^2!

II. Functions of the type $mx + c$, where m and c are constants

$$y = mx + c \quad \ldots\ldots\ldots\ldots\ldots\ldots (1)$$

$$y + \delta y = m(x + \delta x) + c$$

$$\text{i.e. } y + \delta y = mx + m(\delta x) + c \quad \ldots\ldots\ldots\ldots (2)$$

Subtracting line (1) from line (2),

$$\delta y = m(\delta x),$$

$$\therefore \frac{\delta y}{\delta x} = m.$$

This is constant, so $\frac{dy}{dx} = m$.

You knew this already.

$$mx + c$$

is a linear function; its graph is a straight line of gradient m. See page 153. (When the graph is a straight line, $\frac{dy}{dx}$ stands for the gradient of the line itself.)

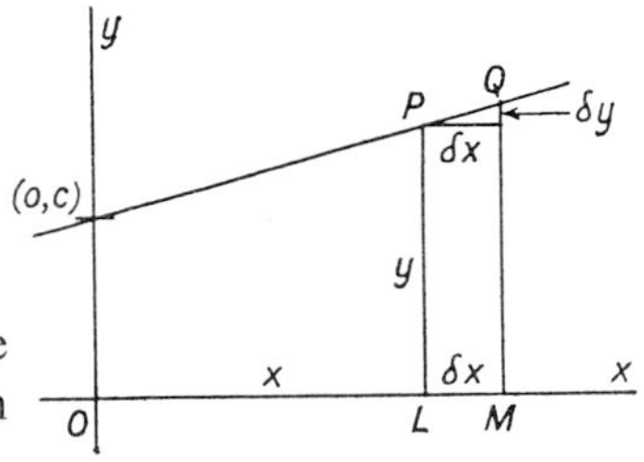

FIG. 5

Notice that the "c" disappears—it does not affect the gradient. We should expect this, because the only effect of changing c is to move the line parallel to itself so that it cuts the y-axis at a different point.

If $y = x$, $y = x + 1$, $y = x - 3$, etc., $\frac{dy}{dx} = 1$;

If $y = -2x$, $y = 5 - 2x$, etc., $\frac{dy}{dx} = -2$; and so on.

There are two special cases to note:

(a) (taking $c = 0$) if $y = mx$, $\frac{dy}{dx} = m$

the graph is a straight line through the origin (Fig. 6).

(b) (taking $m = 0$) if $y = c$, $\frac{dy}{dx} = 0$

the graph is a line parallel to the x — axis (Fig. 7).

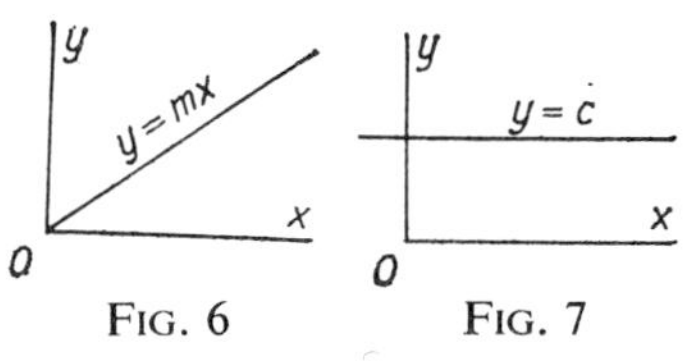

FIG. 6 FIG. 7

III. Any quadratic function

Take, for example, $x^2 - 4x + 3$ (Fig. 8).

We know that, if $y = x^2$, $\frac{dy}{dx} = 2x$;

if $y = -4x$, $\frac{dy}{dx} = -4$;

if $y = 3$, $\frac{dy}{dx} = 0$.

What do you think the derivative will be in this case?

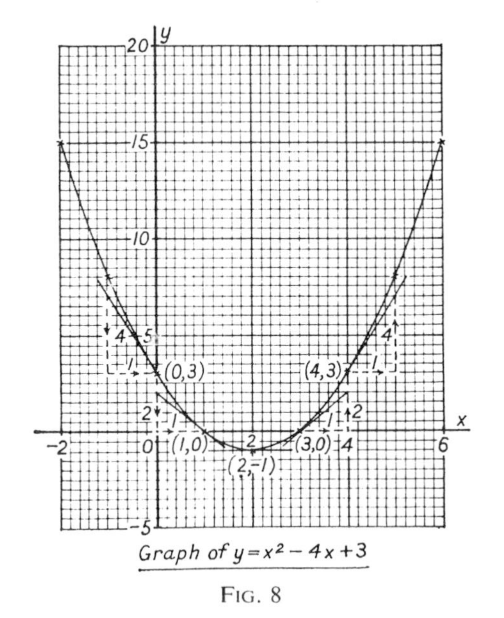

FIG. 8

We will differentiate by our usual process and then check our answers.

$$y = x^2 - 4x + 3 \quad \ldots\ldots\ldots\ldots\ldots\ldots (1)$$

$$y + \delta y = (x + \delta x)^2 - 4(x + \delta x) + 3 \quad \ldots\ldots\ldots\ldots (2)^*$$

Line (2) is $y + \delta y = x^2 + 2x(\delta x) + (\delta x)^2 - 4x - 4(\delta x) + 3$,

Line (1) is $y \quad = x^2 \quad - 4x \quad + 3$.

Subtracting, $\delta y = 2x(\delta x) + (\delta x)^2 - 4(\delta x)$,

$$\therefore \frac{\delta y}{\delta x} = 2x + \delta x - 4.$$

By choosing x small enough, we can make $\frac{\delta y}{\delta x}$ as close to $2x - 4$ as we please. So, $\frac{dy}{dx} = 2x - 4$. (Did you guess correctly?)

Let us pause at this point to see, as we did on page 173, how values of the gradient found from this derived function tie up with the graph of $y = x^2 - 4x + 3$, which we discussed and sketched on pages 160-161.

(i) When $x = 1$, $\frac{dy}{dx} = -2$; that is, the gradient (of the tangent) at the point (1,0) is -2.

(ii) When $x = 3$, $\frac{dy}{dx} = +2$; the gradient at (3, 0) is $+2$.

These results mean that the tangents at the two points make equal angles with the x-axis, but slope in opposite directions—which agrees with the symmetry of the graph (Fig. 8).

(iii) $\frac{dy}{dx} = 0$ when $x = 2$. When $x = 2$, $y = -1$.

This mean that the tangent at the point $(2, -1)$ is parallel to the x-axis; $(2, -1)$ is a minimum point on the curve.

(iv) When $x = 0$, $\frac{dy}{dx} = -4$; when $x = 4$, $\frac{dy}{dx} = +4$. Again, this agrees with considerations of symmetry.

EXERCISE 6A

1. (i) Differentiate "from first principles"—that is, as above—the function $x^2 - 2x - 15$. (Before you start, write down what you think the derived function will turn out to be.)

*This is the step that many people find difficult. Remember that for any particular value of x, the value of the function is worked out as:

(value of x)^2 $-$ 4 (value of x) + 3.

This is what we have done in Line (2), taking "$x + \delta x$" as the value of x and calling the new value of the function, "$y + \delta y$."

Or, referring to the graph, we could say, ("y" of Q) = ("x" of Q)^2 $-$ 4 ("x" of Q) + 3.

(ii) *Sketch* the graph of $y = x^2 - 2x - 15$, giving the co-ordinates of the points where it crosses the axes.

(iii) Calculate the gradients at these points. Add the tangents there to your sketch, and see that your calculated results agree with the sketch.

(iv) Find the co-ordinates of the point on the curve at which $\dfrac{dy}{dx} = 0$.

Sketch the tangent there. What sort of point is this?

2. Answer the same question for the function $3x - x^2$.

3. Differentiate from first principles the function $ax^2 + bx + c$, where a, b and c are constants.

All the examples we have done so far are particular cases of this function, with a, b and c having special values. You should find that the derived function is $2ax + b$.

Check that the results in all the special cases agree with this formula.

It should be clear by now that if the original function has more than one term, we can write down the derived function by simply differentiating the separate terms.

Thus, if $y = 3x^2 - 7x + 2$, $\dfrac{dy}{dx} = 6x - 7$;

if $y = x - 2x^2$, $\dfrac{dy}{dx} = 1 - 4x$;

if $y = \frac{1}{2}x^2 + 8$, $\dfrac{dy}{dx} = x$; and so on.

A constant term does not affect the gradient.

IV. The function x^3

Using the same notation as before,

$$y = x^3 \quad \ldots\ldots(1)$$

$$\text{and } y + \delta y = (x + \delta x)^3,$$

$$\text{that is, } y + \delta y = x^3 + 3x^2(\delta x) + 3x(\delta x)^2 + (\delta x)^3 \quad \ldots\ldots(2)$$

[Please check this by multiplying out $(x + \delta x)(x + \delta x)^2$, that is,

$$(x + \delta x)\{x^2 + 2x(\delta x) + (\delta x)^2\}]$$

Subtracting line (1) from line (2),

$$\delta y = 3x^2(\delta x) + 3x(\delta x)^2 + (\delta x)^3,$$

$$\therefore \frac{\delta y}{\delta x} = 3x^2 + 3x(\delta x) + (\delta x)^2.$$

By choosing δx small enough, we can make $\dfrac{\delta y}{\delta x}$ as close as we please to $3x^2$.

$$\text{So, } \frac{dy}{dx} = 3x^2.$$

EXERCISE 6B

Show that if $y = 2x^3$, $\dfrac{dy}{dx} = 6x^2$;

if $y = 3x^3$, $\dfrac{dy}{dx} = 9x^2$; and so on.

In fact:

If $y = ax^3$, where "a" is any constant, $\dfrac{dy}{dx} = 3ax^2$.

V. The function $\frac{1}{x}$

$$y = \frac{1}{x} \quad \ldots\ldots\ldots\ldots\ldots\ldots\ldots\ldots(1)$$

$$y + \delta y = \frac{1}{x + \delta x} \quad \ldots\ldots\ldots\ldots\ldots\ldots(2)$$

Subtracting line (1) from line (2),

$$\delta y = \frac{1}{x + \delta x} - \frac{1}{x}$$

$$= \frac{x - (x + \delta x)}{x(x + \delta x)}$$

$$= \frac{x - x - \delta x}{x(x + \delta x)}$$

that is, $\delta y = \dfrac{-\delta x}{x(x + \delta x)}$

$$\therefore \frac{\delta y}{\delta x} = \frac{-1}{x(x + \delta x)}$$

By choosing δx small enough, we can make $\dfrac{\delta y}{\delta x}$ as close as we please to $\dfrac{-1}{x.x}$ i.e. $-\dfrac{1}{x^2}$

$$\text{So, } \frac{dy}{dx} = -\frac{1}{x^2}$$

We shall see the significance of the minus sign when we consider this function and its graph in Chapter 8.

Similarly, if $y = \dfrac{3}{x}$ (i.e. $3.\dfrac{1}{x}$), $\dfrac{dy}{dx} = -\dfrac{3}{x^2}$;

if $y = \dfrac{1}{2x}$ (i.e. $\dfrac{1}{2}.\dfrac{1}{x}$), $\dfrac{dy}{dx} = -\dfrac{1}{2x^2}$ and so on.

In fact:

If $y = \dfrac{a}{x}$ where "a" is any constant, $\dfrac{dy}{dx} = -\dfrac{a}{x^2}$.

VI. The function $\frac{1}{x^2}$

$$y = \frac{1}{x^2} \quad \ldots\ldots\ldots\ldots\ldots\ldots\ldots\ldots\ldots\ldots \quad (1)$$

$$y + \delta y = \frac{1}{(x + \delta x)^2} \quad \ldots\ldots\ldots\ldots\ldots\ldots\ldots\ldots \quad (2)$$

Subtracting line (1) from line (2),

$$\begin{aligned} \delta y &= \frac{1}{(x+\delta x)^2} - \frac{1}{x^2} \\ &= \frac{x^2 - (x+\delta x)^2}{x^2(x+\delta x)^2} \\ &= \frac{x^2 - \{x^2 + 2x(\delta x) + (\delta x)^2\}}{x^2(x+\delta x)^2} \\ &= \frac{x^2 - x^2 - 2x(\delta x) - (\delta x)^2}{x^2(x+\delta x)^2} \end{aligned}$$

that is, $\delta y = \frac{-2x(\delta x) - (\delta x)^2}{x^2(x+\delta x)^2}$ $\therefore \frac{\delta y}{\delta x} = \frac{-2x - \delta x}{x^2(x+\delta x)^2}$

By choosing δx small enough, we can make $\frac{\delta y}{\delta x}$ as close as we please to $\frac{-2x}{x^2 . x^2}$, that is, $-\frac{2}{x^3}$. So $\frac{dy}{dx} = -\frac{2}{x^3}$.

Similarly, if $y = \frac{4}{x^2}$ (i.e. $4 . \frac{1}{x^2}$), $\frac{dy}{dx} = -\frac{8}{x^3}$

if $y = \frac{1}{3x^2}$ (i.e. $\frac{1}{3} . \frac{1}{x^2}$), $\frac{dy}{dx} = \frac{-2}{3x^2}$ and so on.

In fact: If $y = \frac{a}{x^2}$ where "a" is any constant, $\frac{dy}{dx} = \frac{-2a}{x^3}$.

Let us summarize what we have found.

y	$\frac{dy}{dx}$
x^3	$3x^2$
x^2	$2x^1$ ("x" is x^1)
x	1
1	0
$\frac{1}{x}$	$-\frac{1}{x^2}$
$\frac{1}{x^2}$	$-\frac{2}{x^3}$

Can we see a pattern in the results, so that we don't have to learn all the derived functions as separate items?

Can you guess what $\frac{dy}{dx}$ is if $y = x^4$? It is $4x^3$.

In fact, we can show that for *any* power of x (n, say),

$$\text{if } y = x^n,\ \frac{dy}{dx} = nx^{n-1}.$$

Remembering that $1 = x^0$, $\frac{1}{x} = x^{-1}$, $\frac{1}{x^2} = x^{-2}$, etc., we can see that all our results fit into this pattern.

y	$\frac{dy}{dx}$
x^3	$3x^2$
x^2	$2x$ (i.e. $2x^1$)
x (i.e. x^1)	1 (i.e. $1x^0$)
1 (i.e. x^0)	0
$\frac{1}{x}$ (i.e. x^{-1})	$-\frac{1}{x^2}$ (i.e. $-1.x^{-2}$)
$\frac{1}{x^2}$ (i.e. x^{-2})	$-\frac{2}{x^3}$ (i.e. $-2.x^{-3}$)

Remember also:

(i) That multiplying y by a number multiplies $\frac{dy}{dx}$ by that number;

(ii) if y has more than one term, $\frac{dy}{dx}$ is made up of the derivatives of the separate terms.

We can now *write down* the derivatives of simple functions without going through the process of differentiation from first principles.

Examples:

y	$\frac{dy}{dx}$
$4x^3 - 3x + 2$	$12x^2 - 3$
$x^2 + \frac{1}{x}$	$2x - \frac{1}{x^2}$
$\frac{1}{3}x^3 - x^2 - \frac{6}{x}$	$x^2 - 2x + \frac{6}{x^2}$

(Differentiating $-\frac{6}{x}$ that is, $-6.\frac{1}{x}$ or $-6.x^{-1}$, gives $+6.x^{-2}$.)

y	$\frac{dy}{dx}$
$\frac{1}{2}x^2 - 8 - \frac{1}{2x^2}$	$x + \frac{1}{x^3}$

(Differentiating $\frac{-1}{2x^2}$ that is, $-\frac{1}{2}.\frac{1}{x^2}$ or $-\frac{1}{2}x^{-2}$, gives $+1.x^{-3}$.)

Beginners sometimes use as a rule for differentiating, "*Multiply by the power and reduce the power by* 1."

The important thing is not to let this become purely a mechanical process, without understanding what it is all about. Chapters 7, 8 and 10 should help to strengthen your understanding of the significance of the derived function.

EXERCISE 6C

Write down (that is, without differentiating from first principles) the derived functions of the following:

1. $2x^2 + 4x - 5$

2. $7 - 10x - 8x^2$

3. $6x - x^3$

4. $\frac{1}{3}x^3 + \frac{1}{2}x^2 + x + 1$

5. $6x^3 - x + \frac{1}{x}$

6. $\frac{1}{4}x^2 + 2 + \frac{1}{x^2}$

7. $2x^3 - 5x^2 + 7x - 1$

8. $2 - 3x - \frac{2}{x^2}$

9. $4x + 17 - \frac{x^3}{6}$

10. $3 - \frac{1}{3x} + \frac{3}{x^2}$

CHAPTER 7

MAXIMUM AND MINIMUM VALUES

WE HAVE already referred to the highest or lowest point of the graph of a quadratic function as a maximum or minimum point.

In Chapter 4, on page 160, we sketched the graph

$$y = x^2 - 4x + 3;$$

it had a minimum point at $(2, -1)$. This means that when $x = 2$, the value of the function $x^2 - 4x + 3$ (namely, -1) is less than it is for other values of x near to 2. We say that "the function $x^2 - 4x + 3$ has a minimum value of -1 when $x = 2$."

Similarly (see page 161), the function $4x - x^2$ has a maximum value of 4 when $x = 2$.

You may have wondered why we said above that the value of $x^2 - 4x + 3$ "is less than it is for other values of x near to 2." Why not simply, "-1 is the least value"? After all, -1 *is* the least value that $x^2 - 4x + 3$ can ever have, and in the same way 4 is the greatest value that $4x - x^2$ can ever have.

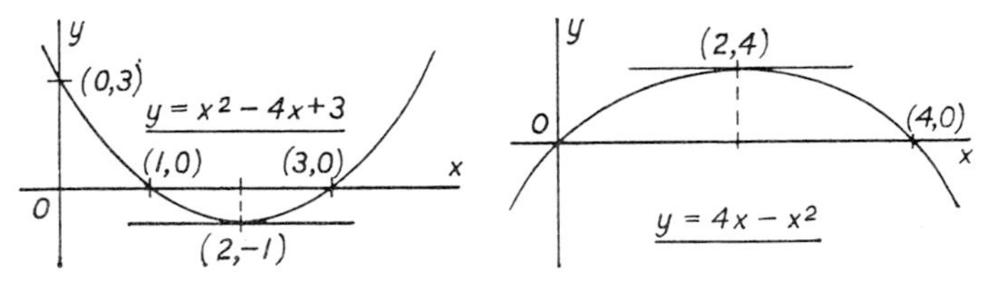

FIG. 1

However, a maximum value of a function is not necessarily its greatest value, nor a minimum value its least. In Fig. 2, P is not the highest point on the graph; it does not represent the greatest value of the function (which gets bigger and bigger as x increases), but we still call P a maximum point, and say that the function has a maximum value.

Similarly, Q, though not the lowest, is a minimum point; the function has a minimum value.

Tops of "hills" represent maximum values, bottoms of "valleys" represent minimum values.

If, when x has a particular value—call it "c"—the value of y is greater than it is for all other values of x close to c, we say that "y has a maximum value when $x = c$."

If, when $x = c$, the value of y is less than it is for all other values of x close to c, we say that "y has a minimum value when $x = c$."

Maximum and minimum points on a curve are called "*turning points.*"

To find maximum or minimum values of a function is often an important practical problem. There is a simple example of this in Question 5 of the exercise at the end of Chapter 4; the beam is most likely to break at the point where the "bending moment" is greatest. Of course, at this stage, we can deal only with very simple functions, but the same method is used with more complicated functions which arise in practical applications.

How can we find out when a function has a maximum or a minimum value? We cannot generally appeal to considerations of symmetry as we did in the examples above.

In Fig. 2 the tangents to the curve at the maximum and minimum points are drawn. They are both parallel to the x-axis (their gradients are *zero*).

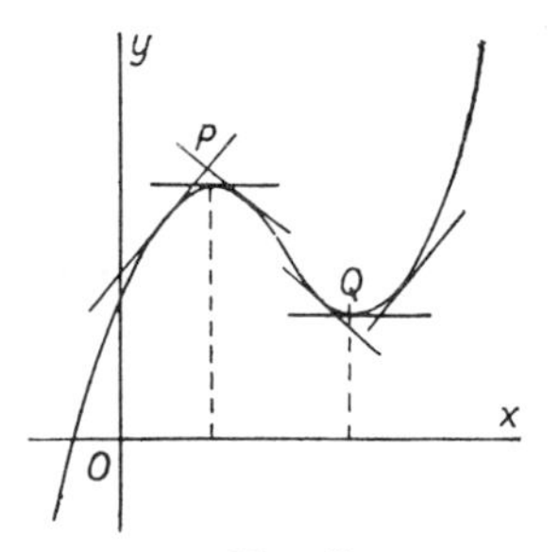

FIG. 2

Look again, too, at the examples from Chapter 4. $x^2 - 4x + 3$ has a minimum value of -1 when $x = 2$.

Now, if $y = x^2 - 4x + 3$,

$$\frac{dy}{dx} = 2x - 4.$$

When $x = 2$, $\frac{dy}{dx} = 0$—that is, the gradient is 0, and the tangent is parallel to the x-axis.

$4x - x^2$ has a maximum value of 4 when $x = 2$.

Now, if $y = 4x - x^2$,

$$\frac{dy}{dx} = 4 - 2x.$$

When $x = 2$, $\frac{dy}{dx} = 0$—that is, the gradient is 0, and the tangent is parallel to the x-axis.

Here, then, is a test we can use to find maximum and minimum values:

At a turning point on a curve, the gradient is zero.

Having found where the gradient is zero, how can we decide whether the point concerned is a maximum or a minimum one? We shall study the gradient of the tangent on either side of the turning point. (See Fig. 2.)

Remember that if a line slopes upwards from left to right (that is, if y increases as x increases), its gradient is positive. (See Chapter 4, page 153.)

So, if a line slopes down from left to right, its gradient is negative.

Fig. 2 shows that for a maximum point, the gradient is positive to the left, negative to the right; for a minimum point, it is negative to the left, positive to the right. "To the left" means "when x has a slightly smaller value"; "to the right" means "when x has a slightly larger value."

Let us summarize all this:

"y" stands for any function of x; we will use "c" to stand for any particular value of x.

y has a *maximum* value when $x = c$ if

(i) $\dfrac{dy}{dx} = 0$ when $x = c$, and

(ii) $\dfrac{dy}{dx}$ changes from positive to negative as x increases through the value c.

y has a *minimum* value when $x = c$ if

(i) $\dfrac{dy}{dx} = 0$ when $x = c$, and

(ii) $\dfrac{dy}{dx}$ changes from negative to positive as x increases through the value c.

Example 1:

(i) Show that the function $x^2 - 5x + 6$ has a minimum value when $x = 2\frac{1}{2}$.

(ii) Calculate this minimum value.

(iii) Sketch the graph of $x^2 - 5x + 6$.

(i) Let $y = x^2 - 5x + 6$;

then $\dfrac{dy}{dx} = 2x - 5$.

$\dfrac{dy}{dx} = 0$ when $2x - 5 = 0$,

i.e. when $2x = 5$,

$x = 2\frac{1}{2}$.

When $x < 2\frac{1}{2}$, $\dfrac{dy}{dx}$ is negative (for example, when $x = 2$, $\dfrac{dy}{dx} = -1$).

When $x > 2\frac{1}{2}$, $\dfrac{dy}{dx}$ is positive (for example, when $x = 3$, $\dfrac{dy}{dx} = 1$).

(This means that the graph $y = x^2 - 5x + 6$ runs "downhill" to the left of the point where $x = 2\frac{1}{2}$, "uphill" to the right.)

So y has a minimum value when $x = 2\frac{1}{2}$.

(ii) When $x = 2\frac{1}{2}$, $y = (2\frac{1}{2})^2 - 5(2\frac{1}{2}) + 6$

$= 6\frac{1}{4} - 12\frac{1}{2} + 6 = -\frac{1}{4}$

So the minimum value of y is $-\frac{1}{4}$.

OCL/M2—M

(iii) When $x = 0$, $y = 6$.

Also, $y = (x - 2)(x - 3)$,

$\therefore y = 0$ when $(x - 2)(x - 3) = 0$,

i.e. when $x - 2 = 0$ and when $x - 3 = 0$

i.e. when $x = 2$ and when $x = 3$.

We can now sketch the graph (Fig. 3).

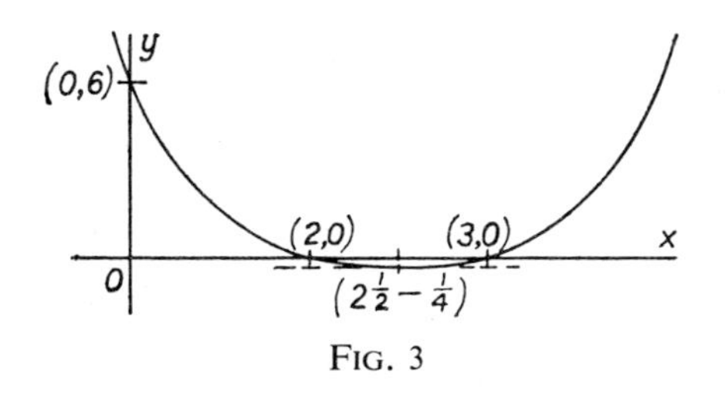

FIG. 3

Notice that in this case, since $y = 0$ when $x = 2$ and when $x = 3$, our knowledge of the symmetry of the graph of a quadratic function tells us that there must be a minimum point where $x = 2\frac{1}{2}$.

Example 2:

Find the maximum and minimum values of the function $x^3 - 3x^2 + 5$, distinguishing between them.

$$\text{Let } y = x^3 - 3x^2 + 5.$$

$$\text{Then } \frac{dy}{dx} = 3x^2 - 6x$$

$$= 3x(x - 2)$$

$\frac{dy}{dx} = 0$ when $x = 0$ and when $x = 2$. {See Note (*a*) (page 187).}

When $x = -\frac{1}{10}$, $\frac{dy}{dx} = 3(-\frac{1}{10})(-2\frac{1}{10})$, which is positive.

When $x = +\frac{1}{10}$, $\frac{dy}{dx} = 3(+\frac{1}{10})(-1\frac{1}{10})$, which is negative.

{See Note (b) (page 187).}

This means that the gradient changes from positive to negative as x increases through the value 0.

Also, when $x = 0$, $y = 5$.

So y has a maximum value of 5 when $x = 0$.

When $x = 1\frac{9}{10}$, $\frac{dy}{dx} = 3(1\frac{9}{10})(-\frac{1}{10})$, which is negative.

When $x = 2\frac{1}{10}$, $\frac{dy}{dx} = 3(2\frac{1}{10})(\frac{1}{10})$, which is positive.

This means that the gradient changes from negative to positive as x increases through the value 2.

Also, when $x = 2$, $y = 2^3 - 3(2^2) + 5 = 1$.
So y has a minimum value of 1 when $x = 2$.
Here is a sketch of the graph $y = x^3 - 3x^2 + 5$ (Fig. 4):

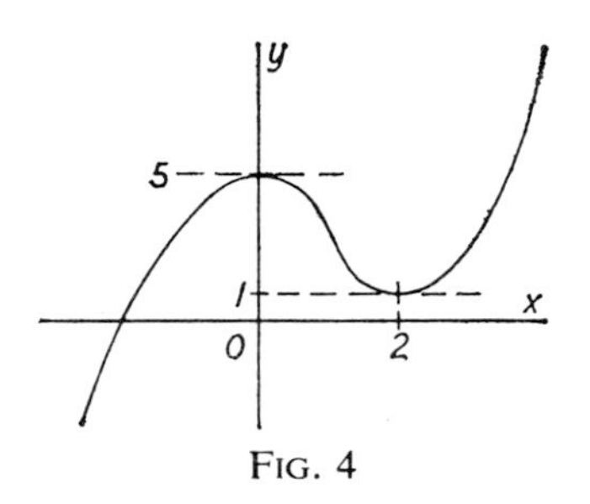

FIG. 4

We shall deal more fully with the graphs of cubic functions in Chapter 8.

Note:

(a) In finding out when $\frac{dy}{dx} = 0$, we have solved the quadratic equation $3x(x - 2) = 0$, by the method used in Chapter 1.

$$3x = 0 \text{ or } x - 2 = 0$$
$$\therefore x = 0 \text{ or } \quad x = 2$$

It is useful to be able to do this just by looking at the factors, without writing the equation down. If the product is to be 0, one of the factors must be 0.

(b) We took particular values of x in deciding how the gradient changed at the turning point. It is better, if you can, to argue generally, in this way:

$\frac{dy}{dx} = 3x(x - 2)$; consider the signs of the factors separately.

If $x < 0$, $\frac{dy}{dx}$ is $(-)(-)$, which is positive;

if $0 < x < 2$*, $\frac{dy}{dx}$ is $(+)(-)$, which is negative;

if $x > 2$, $\frac{dy}{dx}$ is $(+)(+)$, which is positive.

So the gradient changes from positive to negative as x increases through 0, and from negative to positive as x increases through 2.

This general information about the gradient agrees with our sketch of the graph $y = x^3 - 3x^2 + 5$.

It is important to realize that the gradient of a curve may be zero without there being a turning point.

*This means that x lies between 0 and 2.

For example, if $y = x^3$; $\frac{dy}{dx} = 3x^2$. So $\frac{dy}{dx} = 0$ when $x = 0$, but $\frac{dy}{dx}$ is *positive* on both sides of $x = 0$. The graph $y = x^3$ is as shown in Fig. 5 (see also Chapter 8, Fig. 1, page 193). A point like O is called a "point of inflexion."

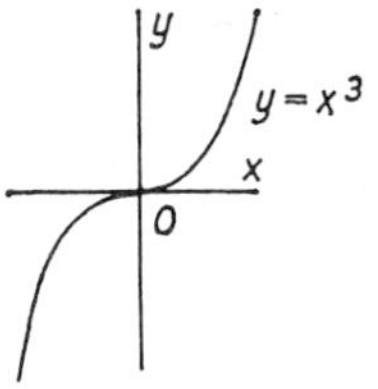

FIG. 5

EXERCISE 7A

Use the method of Example 1 to find the maximum or minimum values of the functions in Nos. 1-6. In each case, sketch the graph of the function.

1. $x^2 - 3x - 4$ **3.** $2x - x^2 - 1$ **5.** $8x - 2x^2 - 11$

2. $x^2 + 6x + 10$ **4.** $5x - x^2$ **6.** $3x^2 + 8x$

Find the maximum and minimum values of the following, distinguishing between them:

7. $\frac{3}{2}x^2 - \frac{1}{3}x^3 + 2$ **8.** $2x^3 - 3x^2 - 12x$ **9.** $x^3 - 12x$

(We shall consider the graphs of functions of this type in the next chapter.)

Maximum and Minimum Problems

Example 3: Divide 12 into two parts so that the sum of their squares is as small as possible.

Discussion: If we take 1 and 11, the sum of the squares is $1 + 121 = 122$;
If we take 2 and 10, the sum of the squares is $4 + 100 = 104$;
and so on.

We will call one of the parts x, express the sum of the squares as a function of x, and then find the minimum value of the function.

Solution: Let one part be x; then the other is $12 - x$.
The sum of their squares is $x^2 + (12 - x)^2$

$$= x^2 + 144 - 24x + x^2$$
$$= 2x^2 - 24x + 144.$$

Let $y = 2x^2 - 24x + 144$

$$\text{Then } \frac{dy}{dx} = 4x - 24, \quad \frac{dy}{dx} = 0 \text{ when } x = 6$$

When $x < 6$, $\frac{dy}{dx}$ is negative.
When $x > 6$, $\frac{dy}{dx}$ is positive.
} The gradient changes from negative to positive as x increases through the value 6.

So y has a minimum value (of 72) when $x = 6$.

The sum of the squares is least when the 12 is divided into two equal parts of 6 each.

Example 4:

A length of thin metal sheeting 20 in. wide is to be bent up at each side to form an open rectangular gutter. What is the greatest possible area of the cross-section of the gutter?

Discussion:

If $\frac{1}{2}$ in. is bent up at each side, 19 in. will be left for the width of the base;

$$\text{area} = (19 \times \tfrac{1}{2}) \text{ sq. in.}$$
$$= 9\tfrac{1}{2} \text{ sq. in. (Fig. 6a).}$$

If 1 in. is bent up at each side,

$$\text{area} = (18 \times 1) \text{ sq. in.}$$
$$= 18 \text{ sq. in. (Fig. 6b) and}$$

so on.

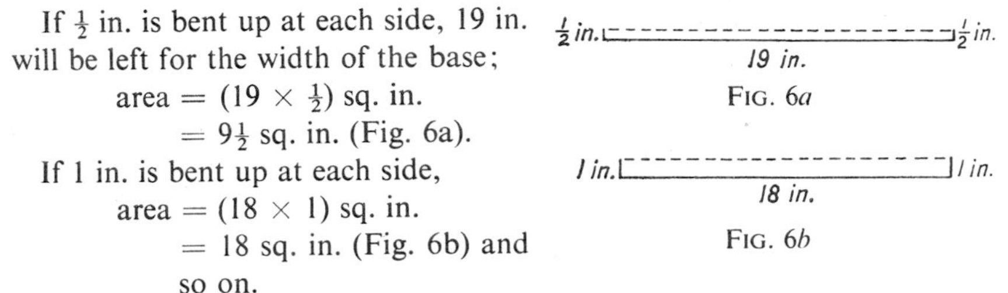

FIG. 6*a*

FIG. 6*b*

Clearly, the area of the cross-section depends on the depth of the gutter. We will call the depth x in.; then we can express the area as a function of x, and so find its maximum value.

Solution:

Call the depth of the gutter x in.; then its width is $(20 - 2x)$ in.

The area of cross-section is $x(20 - 2x)$ sq. in. (Fig. 6c).

i.e. $20x - 2x^2$ sq. in.

Let $y = 20x - 2x^2$.

Then $\frac{dy}{dx} = 20 - 4x$.

$\frac{dy}{dx} = 0$ when $x = 5$.

x in. | x in. (20−2x) in. x in. | x in.
← 20 in. →

FIG. 6*c*

When $x < 5$, $\frac{dy}{dx}$ is positive.
When $x > 5$, $\frac{dy}{dx}$ is negative.
} The gradient changes from positive to negative as x increases through the value 5.

So y has a maximum value when $x = 5$.

When $x = 5$, $y = 50$, and this is the maximum value.

The greatest possible area of the cross-section is 50 sq. in. (when the gutter is 5 in. deep, 10 in. wide).

Example 5:

A closed tin, with a square base, is to be made from thin sheet metal and is to have a capacity of 125 cu. in. Find the dimensions of the tin requiring the least metal sheet. (Ignore any overlap.)

Solution:

Call the side of the square base x in., the height h in.; then the volume is x^2h cu. in.

$$\text{So } x^2h = 125 \quad \ldots\ldots\ldots\ldots\ldots\ldots\ldots\ldots (1)$$

The base and top are each x^2 sq. in. in area, the four sides each xh sq. in. So the total area of metal sheet used is $(2x^2 + 4xh)$ sq. in.

$$\text{Let } y = 2x^2 + 4xh.$$

Here we have y as a function of *two* variables, x and h.
However, they are connected by equation (1), so that

$$h = \frac{125}{x^2}$$

$$\text{So } y = 2x^2 + 4x.\frac{125}{x^2}$$

$$\text{i.e. } y = 2x^2 + \frac{500}{x}$$

$$\frac{dy}{dx} = 4x - \frac{500}{x^2}$$

$$\frac{dy}{dx} = 0 \text{ when } 4x = \frac{500}{x^2}$$

$$\text{i.e. when } 4x^3 = 500$$

$$x^3 = 125$$

$$x = 5$$

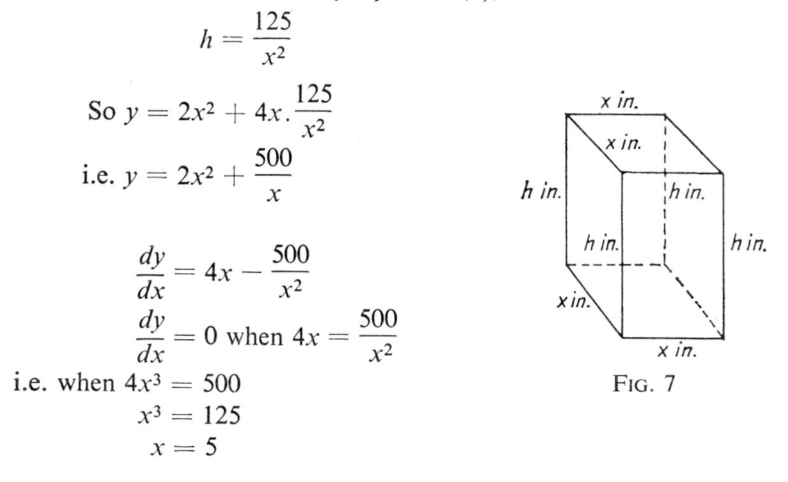

Fig. 7

If $x < 5$, the $4x$ is smaller, while the $\frac{500}{x^2}$ is bigger, so $\frac{dy}{dx}$ is negative.

If $x > 5$, the $4x$ is bigger, while the $\frac{500}{x^2}$ is smaller, so $\frac{dy}{dx}$ is positive.

The gradient changes from negative to positive as x increases through the value 5.

So y has a minimum value when $x = 5$.

Also, when $x = 5$, $h = 5$ {from equation (1)}.

So the tin requiring the least metal sheet is a cube, 5 in. by 5 in. by 5 in.

EXERCISE 7B

N.B.: Do not omit the proof that, when x has the value you find by putting $\frac{dy}{dx} = 0$, y has a maximum or minimum value, as required.

1. If the sum of two numbers is 20, what is the greatest possible value of their product?

2. If the product of two positive numbers is 36, what is the least possible value of their sum?

(Call one x, then the other is $\frac{36}{x}$, and their sum is $x + \frac{36}{x}$.)

3. A double sheep-pen, in two equal parts as shown, is to be made with 200 ft. of fencing, a hedge being used as one side.

Show that $z = 100 - 2x$, and hence that the total area of the pen is $200x - 4x^2$ (Fig. 8).

Find the maximum area.

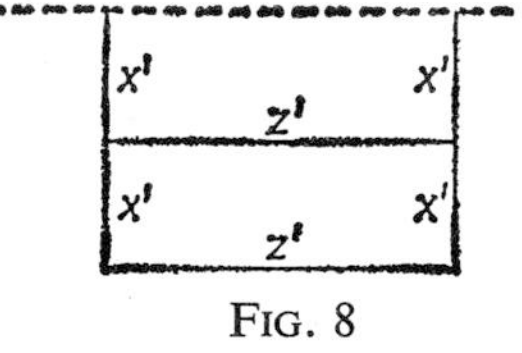

FIG. 8

4. If the area of a rectangle is 25 sq. in., what is the smallest perimeter it can have?

5. A sheet of thin cardboard, 8×5 in., has squares of side x in. cut out from each corner (Fig. 9). An open rectangular box of depth x in. is then formed from the remainder.

Show that the volume of the box is $4x^3 - 26x^2 + 40x$ sq. in.

Hence find the maximum volume.

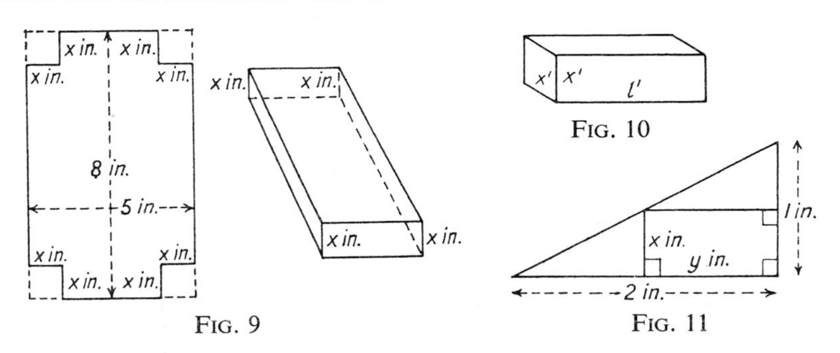

FIG. 9

FIG. 10

FIG. 11

6. The sum of the length and girth of a parcel sent by post must not exceed 6 ft. Find the maximum volume of a parcel with square cross-section.

(Call the side of the square x ft.; and show that the greatest length is $6 - 4x$ ft.; hence express the volume as a function of x.) (Fig. 10).

7. An open rectangular box with a square base (without a lid), made from thin cardboard, is to have a volume of 4 cu. ft.

Find the dimensions of the box requiring the smallest area of cardboard.

8. Use the properties of similar triangles to show that, in Fig. 11, $y = 2 - 2x$.

Hence find the maximum area of the rectangle.

CHAPTER 8

FURTHER FUNCTIONS AND THEIR GRAPHS*

Cubic Functions

BY A "cubic function" of x we mean one whose formula contains x^3, but no higher powers of x (and no negative powers).

Example 1: The simplest cubic function is x^3 itself. Here is a table giving some values of this function:

x	-3	$-2\frac{1}{2}$	-2	$-1\frac{1}{2}$	-1	$-\frac{1}{2}$	0	$\frac{1}{2}$	1	$1\frac{1}{2}$	2	$2\frac{1}{2}$	3
x^3	-27	$-15{\cdot}6$	-8	$-3{\cdot}4$	-1	$-{\cdot}1$	0	${\cdot}1$	1	$3{\cdot}4$	8	$15{\cdot}6$	27

(*N.B.:* You must always work out enough values to make sure that the points you plot (Fig. 1) are close enough together for you to be able to draw the graph accurately. If you use a large scale, such as 1 in. to 1 for x, it will certainly not be sufficient to take only "whole number" values of x.)

Where they are not whole numbers, the values of x^3 have been given correct to one place of decimals.

We had already noted in Chapter 7 that the gradient of the graph $y = x^3$ is 0 when $x = 0$.

Now $\frac{dy}{dx} = 3x^2$, so that at all other points the gradient is positive.

* *Note:* If you are working on "Syllabus A," you need only concern yourself with accurate plotting of the graphs of the functions discussed in this chapter. The following sections are important:

Examples 1, 2 and 3 (but ignore references to "$\frac{dy}{dx}$" and maximum or minimum values).

Exercise 8A, Nos. 1-3.

The discussion of "Division by Zero" and "The function $\frac{1}{x}$" (pages 197 and 198).

Exercise 8B, No. 1.

You will find more examples on the drawing of graphs in Chapter 12 under "Graphical Solution of Equations." See Examples 4-6, and Exercise 12C (pages 231-235).

Our drawing of the graph agrees with this, since y everywhere increases as x increases, and it confirms the sketch we gave on page 188.

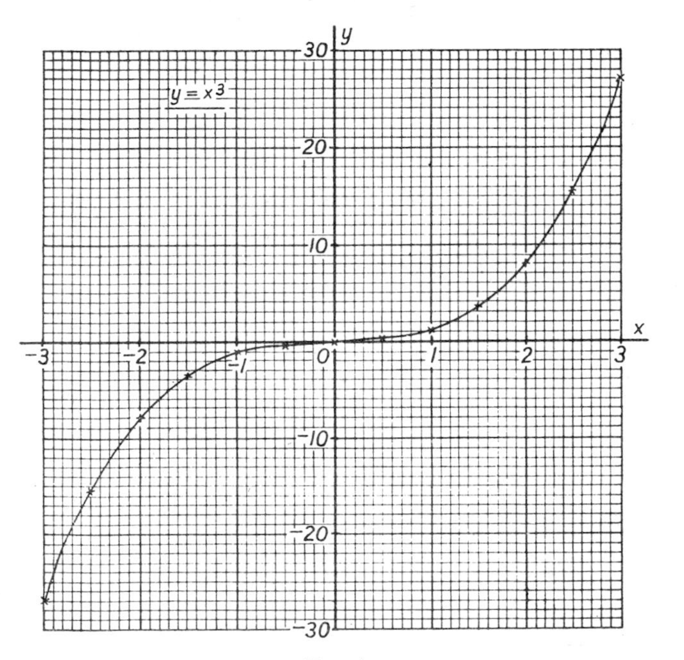

FIG. 1

Example 2: The function $x^3 - 3x^2 + 5$.

x	-2	-1	0	1	2	3	4
x^3	-8	-1	0	1	8	27	64
$-3x^2$	-12	-3	0	-3	-12	-27	-48
5	5	5	5	5	5	5	5
$y = x^3 - 3x^2 + 5$	-15	1	5	3	1	5	21

Clearly, there is a value of x between -2 and -1 for which $y = 0$. (Fig. 2, overleaf.)

We had already discovered (page 187) that this function has a maximum value of 5 when $x = 0$ and a minimum value of 1 when $x = 2$. The graph $y = x^3 - 3x^2 + 5$ has *two* turning points (Fig. 2).

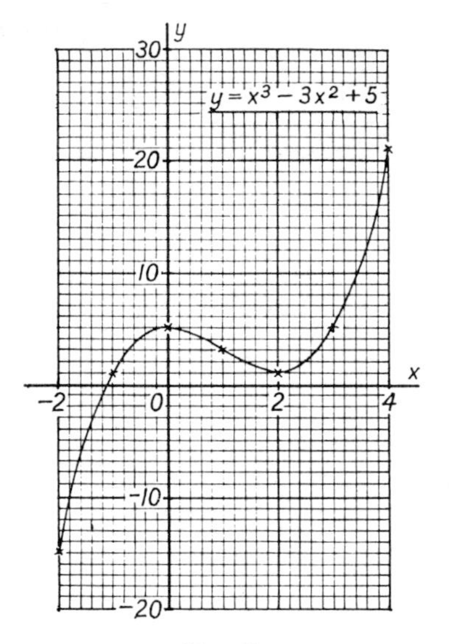

FIG. 2

Now, whenever y is a cubic function of x, $\frac{dy}{dx}$ is a quadratic function. When you put $\frac{dy}{dx} = 0$, you have a quadratic equation, which cannot have more than two solutions. (In this case, $\frac{dy}{dx} = 3x^2 - 6x$; $\frac{dy}{dx} = 0$ when $3x^2 - 6x = 0$.)

So the graph of a cubic function cannot have more than two turning points.

It may have *one* point only where the gradient is zero (see Example 1); or it may not have any (see Exercise 8A, No. 7, on page 197).

Example 3: The function $(x + 1)(2 - x)(x - 3)$.

As usual, we will use "y" to stand for the value of the function.

(i) The idea that you have used in solving quadratic equations, namely, that if a product of factors is zero, one of the factors must be zero, is a very important general principle.

In this case, we can see at once that $y = 0$ when $x + 1 = 0$, $2 - x = 0$ or $x - 3 = 0$, i.e. when $x = -1$, when $x = 2$ and when $x = 3$.

(ii) $y = -x^3 + 4x^2 - x - 6$ (please check this by multiplying out). So when $x = 0$, $y = -6$.

(iii) When x is very large (positive or negative), the "$-x^3$" term will be much larger than any of the others, so that it alone will tell us whether y is positive or negative.

(For example, when $x = 100$, the four terms are $-1{,}000{,}000$; $40{,}000$; -100 and -6; we need only to look at the first to see that y is negative.)

When x is positive, $-x^3$ is negative, so that when x is large and positive, y is numerically large but negative.

When x is negative, $-x^3$ is positive, so when x is numerically large but negative, y is large and positive.

We can now sketch the graph $y = (x + 1)(2 - x)(x - 3)$ with confidence.

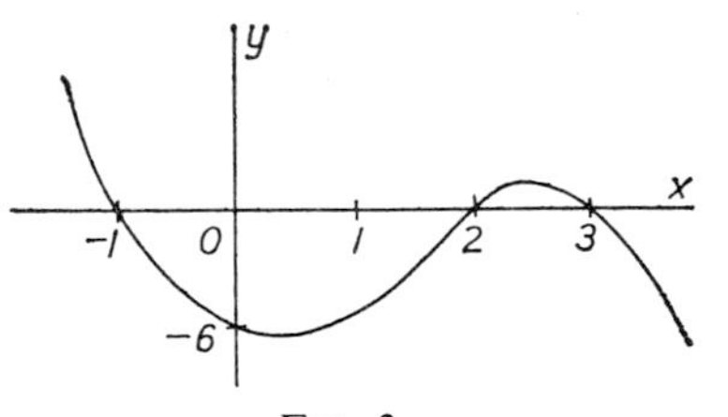

FIG. 3

The argument used in (iii) tells us that the graph of a cubic function will always be above the x-axis at one end, below it at the other. Which end is which depends on whether the "x^3" term is positive (as in Example 2) or negative (as in Example 3).

You will not be asked at this level to give rough sketches of the graphs of cubic functions unless it is easy to see at least where y is 0 or where the turning points are. Some hints are given for the examples in Exercise 8A.

Example 4:

(i) Find the gradient of the graph $y = x^3 - 2x^2 + x$ at the origin.

(ii) Show that the curve *touches* the x-axis where $x = 1$.

(iii) Find the other point on the curve at which the tangent is parallel to the tangent at the origin.

(iv) Sketch the graph.

(We shall discuss various methods of factorizing cubic expressions in Chapter 14. In this case the factorization is simple, since x is a common factor, and the remaining quadratic factor can be factorized further.)

$$\begin{aligned} y &= x(x^2 - 2x + 1) \\ &= x(x - 1)^2 \end{aligned}$$

(i) When $x = 0$, $y = 0$, so the curve passes through the origin.

$$\frac{dy}{dx} = 3x^2 - 4x + 1$$

When $x = 0$, $\frac{dy}{dx} = 1$, i.e. *the gradient of the tangent at the origin is* 1.

(ii) When $x = 1$, $y = 0$, so the curve meets the x-axis where $x = 1$.

Also, when $x = 1$, $\dfrac{dy}{dx} = 0$, so the x-axis is the tangent to the curve at the point $(1, 0)$; i.e., *the curve touches the x-axis where* $x = 1$.

(iii) To find where the tangent is parallel to the tangent at the origin, is to find where the gradient is 1. See (i).

Now $\dfrac{dy}{dx} = 1$ when $3x^2 - 4x + 1 = 1$

i.e. when $3x^2 - 4x = 0$,

$x(3x - 4) = 0$,

$x = 0$ or $\frac{4}{3}$.

When $x = \frac{4}{3}$, $y = \frac{4}{3}(\frac{1}{3})^2 = \frac{4}{27}$

(using $y = x(x - 1)^2$.)

So *the tangent at the point* $(\frac{4}{3}, \frac{4}{27})$ *is parallel to the tangent at the origin.*

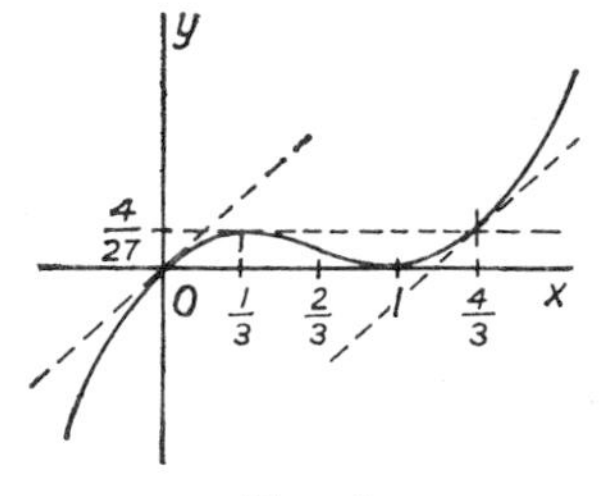

FIG. 4

(iv) $\dfrac{dy}{dx} = 0$ when $3x^2 - 4x + 1 = 0$,

i.e. when $(3x - 1)(x - 1) = 0$,

$3x - 1 = 0$

or $x - 1 = 0$,

$x = \frac{1}{3}$ or 1.

When $x = \frac{1}{3}$, $y = \frac{1}{3}(-\frac{2}{3})^2 = \frac{4}{27}$.

Clearly, $(\frac{1}{3}, \frac{4}{27})$ is a maximum point, $(1, 0)$ a minimum point.

(As we found the turning points solely to help in sketching the graph, we did not *prove* what sort of point each is; the information we had already gave a clear enough indication for our purpose.)

EXERCISE 8A

1. Draw the graph $y = -x^3$ from $x = -3$ to $x = +3$, using scales of 1 in. to 1 on the x-axis and 1 in. to 10 on the y-axis. From your graph, read off the value of y when $x = 2{\cdot}2$, and the value of x when $y = 20$.

(Remember the warning in Example 1 about plotting enough points. The values you read from the graph will test the accuracy of your plotting.)

2. Draw the graph $y = (x + 2)(x - 1)(x - 3)$ from $x = -3$ to $x = +4$, using the same scales as in the preceding question.

Use the graph to find three values of x for which $y = 2$.

(In working out values of y, do *not* multiply out the algebraical expression. It is much easier to use the factors as given. Your table of values should show the different values of $x + 2$, $x - 1$, $x - 3$ and then of their product, thus:

x	-3	$-2\frac{1}{2}$ ....
$x+2$	-1	....
$x-1$	-4	....
$x-3$	-6	....
y	-24	....

You will definitely *not* have plotted the turning points. It is important to join the points you have plotted according to the "feel" of a smooth curve.)

3. Sketch the graph of the function $x^3 - 6x^2 + 8x$, showing the points where it crosses the axes.

(Factorize as in Example 4.)

4. (i) Show that the graph $y = 3x^2 + x^3$ *touches* the x-axis at the origin.

(ii) Find the point at which this curve crosses the x-axis (i.e. the other point at which $y = 0$), and the gradient at that point.

(iii) Find another point where the tangent is parallel to the one at the point you found in (ii).

(iv) Find the point, other than the origin, at which the gradient is zero.

(v) Sketch the graph, making use of what you have found in parts (i) to (iv).

5. Repeat Question 3 for the function $-x^3 + 6x^2 - 5x$.

6. Repeat Question 3 for the function $x^3 - 4x^2 + 4x$.

7. Show that the gradient of the graph $y = x^3 + x$ at the origin, is 1.

Explain why the gradient is greater than 1 at every other point of the curve, and why the gradient increases continuously as you move away from the origin in either direction.

Hence sketch the curve.

(The origin is a point of inflexion—see page 188—at which the direction of curvature changes. The tangent there crosses the curve.)

8. Sketch the graph $y = x^3 + 1$.

Hyperbolic Functions

We will now give a few examples of functions whose graphs are curves called "hyperbolas."

First, we must think about *Division by Zero.*

What is, say, $1 \div 0$, or $\frac{1}{0}$?

If we ask, "What is $10 \div 2$?", we are asking, "How many 2's make 10?;" in other words, "$2 \times ? = 10$."

Consider $1 \div 0$ from this point of view: $0 \times ? = 1$.

Clearly, there is no answer to this, since any number of times 0, is 0.

So, *division by zero is impossible.**

Example 5: The function $\frac{1}{x}$.

We cannot take $x = 0$; the function has no value when $x = 0$. This means that the graph of the function has a break in it when $x = 0$.

Notice, however, that when x is very small, the value of the function is very large. When $x = \frac{1}{10}$, $\frac{1}{x} = 10$; when $x = \frac{1}{100}$, $\frac{1}{x} = 100$; and so on.

When $x = 1$, $y = 1$. As x gets bigger, y gets smaller (never quite reaching 0). As x gets smaller, y gets bigger. If x is $-$, y is $-$.

A table of values and accurate plotting confirm these general conclusions.

x	-4	-3	-2	-1	$-\frac{1}{2}$	$-\frac{1}{3}$	$-\frac{1}{4}$	0	$\frac{1}{4}$	$\frac{1}{3}$	$\frac{1}{2}$	1	2	3	4
$\frac{1}{x}$	$-\frac{1}{4}$	$-\frac{1}{3}$	$-\frac{1}{2}$	-1	-2	-3	-4	-	4	3	2	1	$\frac{1}{2}$	$\frac{1}{3}$	$\frac{1}{4}$

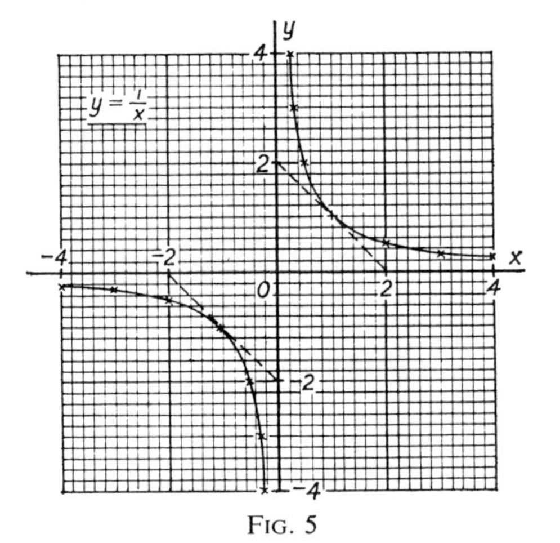

FIG. 5

Notice that, if $y = \frac{1}{x}$ (i.e. x^{-1}), $\frac{dy}{dx} = -\frac{1}{x^2}$ (i.e. $-1 . x^{-2}$).

Since x^2 must be positive, this means that the gradient of the curve is

* This argument applies to $\frac{a}{0}$, where "a" is *any* number except 0. What happens, though, with $\frac{0}{0}$?

$$0 \times ? = 0$$

The answer is, any number you like! We say that $\frac{0}{0}$ is "indeterminate."

always negative. Our drawing (Fig. 5) agrees with this, too, since y always decreases as x increases.

When $x = 1$ or -1, the gradient is -1.

You will find functions of this type in Chapter 13, where we shall consider "inverse variation."

Example 6: The function $x + \frac{1}{x}$

Various points can help us to sketch the graph $y = x + \frac{1}{x}$.

(i) The curve has a "break" when $x = 0$.

Near $x = 0$, the "x" term is small, but the $\frac{\text{"1"}}{x}$ term is large (positive when x is positive, negative when x is negative).

(ii) If we try to find where $y = 0$, we have $x + \frac{1}{x} = 0$,

$\therefore\ x^2 + 1 = 0$, which is impossible, since x^2 is always positive.

So the curve does not cross the x-axis.

(iii) When x is numerically large ($+$ or $-$), the $\frac{1}{x}$ term is small, so the curve is close to the line $y = x$.

When x is large and $+$, $y = x +$ (something small), so the curve is above the line $y = x$.

When x is numerically large but $-$, $y = x -$ (something small), so the curve is below the line $y = x$.

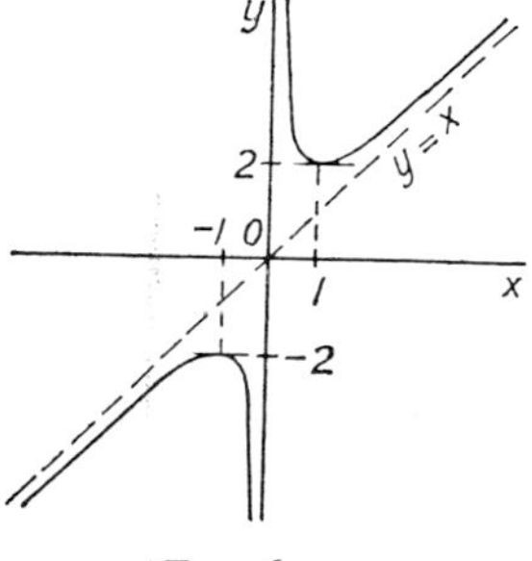

FIG. 6

(iv) $\frac{dy}{dx} = 1 - \frac{1}{x^2}$; so $\frac{dy}{dx} = 0$ when $x^2 = 1$, i.e. when $x = 1$ or -1.

Can you prove that y has a *maximum* value of -2 when $x = -1$, and a *minimum* value of 2 when $x = 1$? (Fig. 6).

(Does this seem strange? Remember that there is a break in the curve.)

Curve Sketching

Here is a summary of the methods we have used to help us to sketch the graphs of various functions. It is put in the form of questions for you to ask yourself when dealing with a particular function. You will not normally need to use all of them.

(a) Is this a "standard" curve whose shape I know?
(b) What is y when x is 0?
(c) For what values of x is $y = 0$?
(d) Are there any "breaks" in the curve?

(e) What happens when x is numerically large (+ or —)?

(f) Are there any maximum or minimum points?

You can always work out a few particular values of y if necessary; and it sometimes helps to know the gradient at particular points.

Other Types of Function

We have only considered a few simple types of function, all with formulae involving powers of x up to x^3 or down to x^{-1}. The hints in Exercise 8B should help you to extend this work slightly.

There are, of course, quite different types of function. Here are three examples with sketches of their graphs.

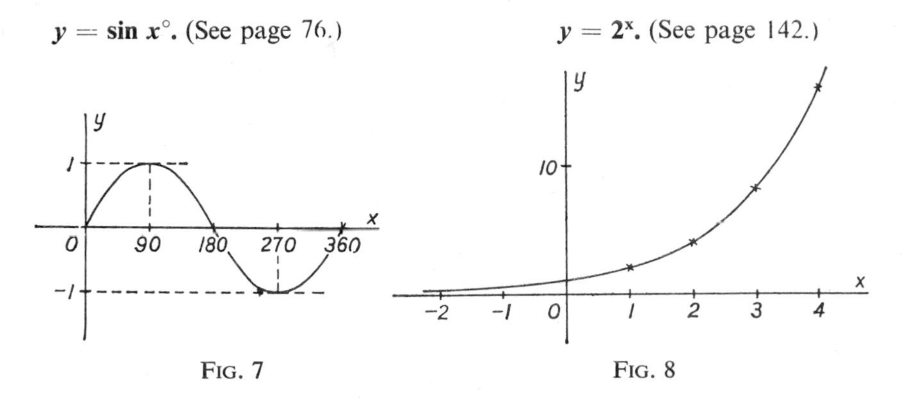

FIG. 7

FIG. 8

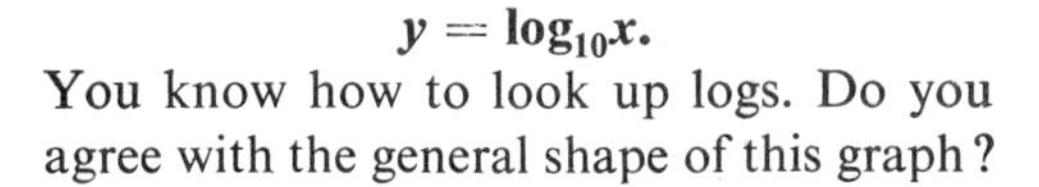

$y = \log_{10}x$.

You know how to look up logs. Do you agree with the general shape of this graph?

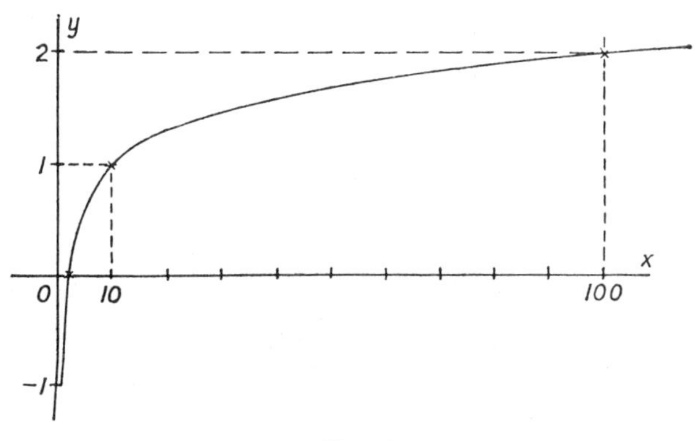

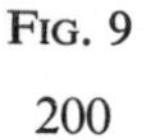

FIG. 9

EXERCISE 8B

1. Draw the graph $y = -\frac{1}{x}$, plotting at least the points for which $x = \pm\frac{1}{5}, \pm\frac{1}{4}, \pm\frac{1}{3}, \pm\frac{1}{2}, \pm 1, \pm 2, \pm 3, \pm 4, \pm 5.$

Use scales of 1 in. to 1 on each axis if your paper is large enough; otherwise, 1 in. to 2.

Calculate the gradient at the points $(1, -1)$ and $(-1, 1)$. Draw lines through these points with the appropriate gradient. The fact that these lines should be tangents to the curve will serve as a check on the accuracy of your drawing.

2. Sketch the graphs $y = \frac{1}{x^2}$ and $y = -\frac{1}{x^2}$.

(Compare Example 5 and Question 1, but remember that x^2 is always positive.)

3. Sketch the graph $y = x - \frac{1}{x}$.

(See Example 6. We found that $y = x + \frac{1}{x}$ did not cross the x-axis, but did have turning points. You should find that this graph does cross the x-axis but does not have turning points. Can you see how the two curves are related to each other?)

4. Sketch the graph $y = \frac{3}{x} - 2$.

(Notice that y is nearly -2 when x is numerically large.)

CHAPTER 9

INTEGRATION

WE HAVE learnt how to "differentiate" a given function; that is, how to find the "derived function," or gradient formula. We must now tackle the opposite problem; given a derived function $\left(\frac{dy}{dx}\right)$, to find the original function (y). This problem often arises practically, when the rate of change of some quantity is known, and a formula giving the value of the quantity itself is required.

Arbitrary Constants

Suppose we know that the derived function is $2x$; what can we say about the original function?

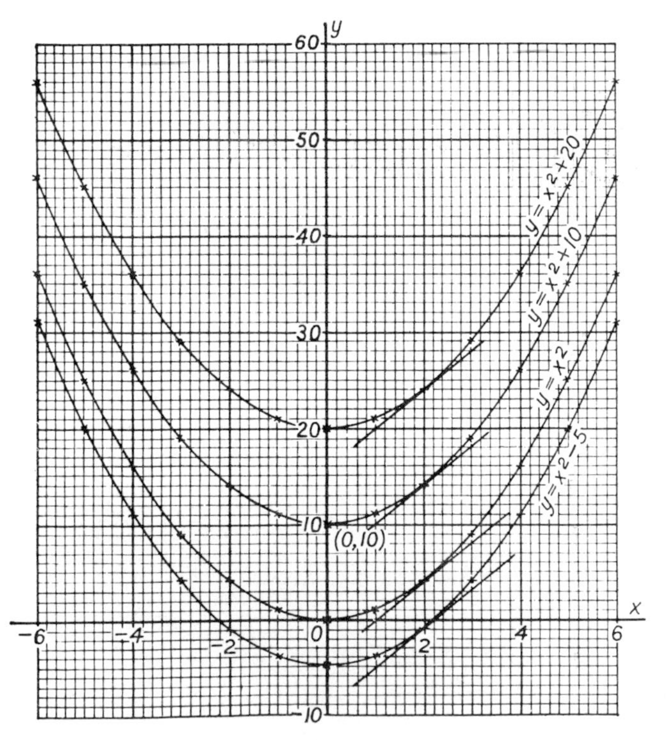

FIG. 1

We know that if $y = x^2$, $\dfrac{dy}{dx} = 2x$; so the original function *could* be x^2.

But suppose $y = x^2 + 10$, $x^2 + 20$, $x^2 - 5$, $x^2 - \frac{1}{3}$, or $x^2 +$ any constant (positive or negative).

In all these cases, too, $\dfrac{dy}{dx} = 2x$. In fact, if $\dfrac{dy}{dx} = 2x$, then $y = x^2 + c$, where "c" is called an "*arbitrary constant,*" since it can have *any* value.

This process of "reverse differentiation" is called "*integration.*"

Clearly, whenever we integrate, the function we find always includes an arbitrary constant, since the derivative of a constant is zero.

Graphical illustration helps to make this clear. We know that the effect of adding a constant to a function is merely to move its graph bodily up or down, without altering its shape. Fig. 1 shows the graphs of some of the functions mentioned above. The tangents to all these curves at points with a particular value of x, are parallel—the graphs have the same gradient at these points.

Finding Particular Constants

We may have further information that tells us what the constant must be in a particular case.

Suppose, for example, we know not only that $\dfrac{dy}{dy} = 2x$, but also that $y = 10$ when $x = 0$.

Then the constant must be 10, and $y = x^2 + 10$.

Referring to the graphs, we have found the particular one of the above "family" of graphs which passes through the point (0, 10).

If, on the other hand, we know that $y = 0$ when $x = 0$, so that the graph passes through the origin, then $c = 0$, and $y = x^2$.

Similarly, if we know the value of y corresponding to *any* one value of x, we can find c, and hence y in terms of x. See Examples 2 and 3 on pages 205 and 206.

It is most important always to include this constant of integration, or, if it is zero, to explain *why* you have left it out.

Rule for Integration

In Chapter 6 we proved these results:

If $y = x^3$, $\dfrac{dy}{dx} = 3x^2$; so if $y = \frac{1}{3}x^3$, $\dfrac{dy}{dx} = x^2$.

If $y = x^2$, $\dfrac{dy}{dx} = 2x$; so if $y = \frac{1}{2}x^2$, $\dfrac{dy}{dx} = x$.

If $y = x$, $\dfrac{dy}{dx} = 1$

If $y = \frac{1}{x}$, $\frac{dy}{dx} = -\frac{1}{x^2}$; so if $y = -\frac{1}{x}$, $\frac{dy}{dx} = \frac{1}{x^2}$.

If $y = \frac{1}{x^2}$, $\frac{dy}{dx} = -\frac{2}{x^3}$; so if $y = -\frac{1}{2x^2}$, $\frac{dy}{dx} = \frac{1}{x^3}$.

Hence (i) if $\frac{dy}{dx} = x^2$, $y = \frac{1}{3}x^3 + c$;

(ii) if $\frac{dy}{dx} = x$, $y = \frac{1}{2}x^2 + c$;

(iii) if $\frac{dy}{dx} = 1$, $y = x + c$;

(iv) if $\frac{dy}{dx} = \frac{1}{x^2}$, $y = -\frac{1}{x} + c$;

(v) if $\frac{dy}{dx} = \frac{1}{x^3}$, $y = -\frac{1}{2x^2} + c$.

The general result is

if $\frac{dy}{dx} = x^n$, $y = \frac{x^{n+1}}{n+1} + c$, where c is an arbitrary constant.

(You can check by the general rule for differentiation given on page 181.) (i) and (ii) obviously fit into this pattern. The others do so, too, since

(iii) is "if $\frac{dy}{dx} = x^0$, $y = x^1 + c$";

(iv) is "if $\frac{dy}{dx} = x^{-2}$, $y = \frac{x^{-1}}{-1} + c$";

(v) is "if $\frac{dy}{dx} = x^{-3}$, $y = \frac{x^{-2}}{-2} + c$".

Notice that "$\frac{dy}{dx} = \frac{1}{x}$" (i.e. x^{-1}) is missing. If we try to apply the general formula in this case, we have "$y = \frac{x^0}{0} + c$," which is meaningless, since we cannot divide by zero. When you go on with this work, you will learn later that $\frac{1}{x}$ as a *derived function* comes from a quite different type of original function (nothing to do with x^n).

We know that multiplying a power of x by a constant merely multiplies its derivative by that constant; so, of course, a similar rule applies in reverse.

If $\frac{dy}{dx} = 2x^2$, $y = \frac{2}{3}x^3 + c$;

if $\frac{dy}{dx} = 5x$, $y = \frac{5x^2}{2} + c$;

if $\dfrac{dy}{dx} = -3$, $y = -3x + c$;

if $\dfrac{dy}{dx} = \dfrac{4}{x^2}$ (i.e. $4x^{-2}$), $y = -\dfrac{4}{x} + c$ (i.e. $\dfrac{4x^{-1}}{-1} + c$);

if $\dfrac{dy}{dx} = \dfrac{1}{3x^3}$ (i.e. $\frac{1}{3}x^{-3}$), $y = -\dfrac{1}{6x^2} + c$ (i.e. $\frac{1}{3}.\dfrac{x^{-2}}{-2} + c$); and so on.

In general, if $\dfrac{dy}{dx} = ax^n$, $y = \dfrac{ax^{n+1}}{n+1} + c$.

"To integrate, increase the power by 1, and divide by the new power."

As with differentiation, it is most important not to apply this rule blindly, but to think about the meaning of what you are doing.

Example 1: Find functions of x of which the derived functions are

(i) $6x^2 - 4x + 3$. (ii) $5 - \dfrac{2}{x^2}$.

In each case, call the required function y.

(i) $\dfrac{dy}{dx} = 6x^2 - 4x + 3$, $\therefore y = \dfrac{6x^3}{3} - \dfrac{4x^2}{2} + 3x + c$,

i.e. $y = 2x^3 - 2x^2 + 3x + c$.

(ii) $\dfrac{dy}{dx} = 5 - \dfrac{2}{x^2}$, i.e. $\dfrac{dy}{dx} = 5 - 2.x^{-2}$.

$$\therefore y = 5x - \frac{2x^{-1}}{-1} + c,$$
$$= 5x + 2x^{-1} + c,$$

i.e. $y = 5x + \dfrac{2}{x} + c$.

Example 2: y is a function of x such that $\dfrac{dy}{dx} = 1 - 3x^2$. When $x = 2$, $y = 0$.

Express y in terms of x, and find the value of y when $x = 3$.

$$\frac{dy}{dx} = 1 - 3x^2$$
$$\therefore y = x - x^3 + c.$$

When $x = 2$, $y = 0$; $\quad \therefore 0 = 2 - 8 + c$,

$\therefore c = 6$.

Hence $\quad y = x - x^3 + 6$.

When $x = 3$, $\quad y = 3 - 27 + 6$ i.e. $y = -18$.

Example 3: The gradient of a curve is given by the function $4 - 2x$. The curve passes through the origin. Find:

(i) the equation of the curve;
(ii) the point other than the origin at which it crosses the x-axis;
(iii) the point where the gradient is 0.

Sketch the curve.

(i) $\frac{dy}{dx} = 4 - 2x$.

$\therefore\ y = 4x - x^2$. (There is no constant, since the curve passes the origin, i.e. $y = 0$ when $x = 0$.)

(ii) (We have to find where $y = 0$, so we factorize.)

$y = x(4 - x)$.

$y = 0$ when $x = 0$ or $4 - x = 0$,

i.e. when $x = 0$ and when $x = 4$.

So *the curve crosses the x-axis at the point* (4, 0).

(iii) $\frac{dy}{dx} = 4 - 2x$.

$\frac{dy}{dx} = 0$ when $x = 2$.

When $x = 2$, $y = 4.2 - 2^2 = 8 - 4 = 4$.

So *the gradient is zero at the point* (2, 4).

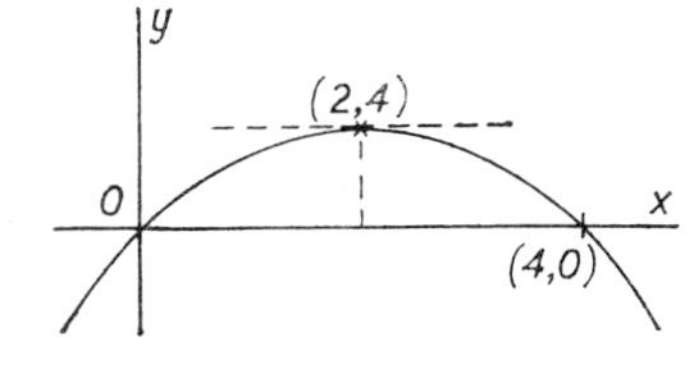

FIG. 2

You will find further work on integration in the next two chapters.

EXERCISE 9A

Write down functions of x of which the derived functions are given in Nos. 1-8.

1. $3x + 1$

2. $12x^2 + 12x - 8$

3. $(x - 2)^2$

4. $5 - 4x^2$

5. $(x - \frac{1}{x})^2$

6. $5 + \frac{2}{x^3}$

7. $\frac{1}{2}x - \frac{2}{5}x^2$

8. $\frac{1}{2x^2} - \frac{2}{3x^3}$

9. If $\frac{dy}{dx} = 2x - 2$, and if $y = 5$ when $x = -2$, find y in terms of x.

10. y is a function of x such that $\frac{dy}{dx} = 6x^2 + 3$, and $y = 3$ when $x = 1$. Find (i) the formula for y; (ii) the value of y when $x = 2$.

11. The gradient of a curve is given by the function $4 + 6x - 3x^2$, and the curve passes through the point $(2, -6)$. Find the equation of the curve.

(*Note:* Since the curve passes through $(2, -6)$, $y = -6$ when $x = 2$.)

12. The gradient of a curve, which passes through the origin, is given by $\frac{dy}{dx} = 9 - 3x^2$. Find (i) the gradient at the origin; (ii) the equation of the curve; (iii) the points, other than the origin, at which the curve crosses the x-axis. Sketch the curve.

CHAPTER 10

DISTANCES, VELOCITIES AND ACCELERATIONS

WE INTRODUCED our ideas of gradients of curves in Chapter 5 by asking how we could find the speed of a body at any instant, when we knew how far it had gone at various times.

We found that the gradient of a tangent to a space-time graph represents the speed of the body. In other words, if we know the distance travelled as a function of the time, then the *derived function* gives the speed.

We will state the argument again, using the notation for small changes and derived functions which we introduced in Chapter 6.

First, there are two things we must be clear about:

(a) In Chapters 6 to 9 we have always used x to stand for the independent variable, y for the dependent variable, δx and δy for small changes in x and y, $\frac{dy}{dx}$ for the derived function. Now, of course, there is nothing sacred about x and y; any letters may be used. As in Chapter 5, we shall call the time, t sec., and the distance (or "space") travelled, s feet. So we shall use "δs" and "δt" to stand for small changes in s and t, $\frac{ds}{dt}$ to stand for the derived function.

(b) We shall talk about the "*velocity*" of a body; this includes a statement of the *direction* in which the body is moving, as well as its speed. If a body moves in a straight line, motion in one direction is taken as positive, motion in the opposite direction as negative. Suppose, for example, that a stone is thrown straight up, and that we take the upward direction as positive.

At some instant the stone has a velocity of + 50 ft./sec., say; that is, it is moving upwards with a speed of 50 ft./sec. A short time later, it will have a velocity of — 50 ft./sec.; that is, it will be moving downwards at 50 ft./sec.

Now, let us return to the example of Chapter 5.

Example 1: A body moves in a straight line, starting from a point A, so that, t sec. later, its distance from A is s ft.,

where $s = t^2$

Find the velocity after t sec.

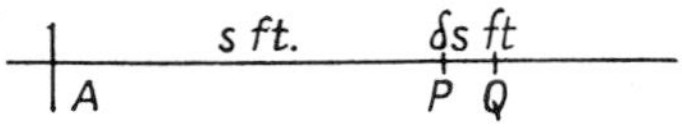

Suppose that, after t sec., the body has reached a point P, where

$AP = s$ ft. (Fig. 1).

Then $s = t^2$ . . . .(1)

s ft. δs ft
A P Q

FIG. 1

Now suppose that after a further short time δt sec., the body has reached Q, where $PQ = \delta s$ ft., so that $AQ = (s + \delta s)$ ft.

Then $s + \delta s = (t + \delta t)^2$ . . . .(2)

Equation (2) is $s + \delta s = t^2 + 2t(\delta t) + (\delta t)^2$

Equation (1) is $s = t^2$

Subtracting, $\delta s = 2t(\delta t) + (\delta t)^2$

The average velocity during this short time δt sec. is

$$\frac{\delta s}{\delta t} = 2t + \delta t \text{ ft./sec.}$$

This average velocity can be made as close as we like to $2t$ ft./sec. by choosing δt small enough.

So the actual velocity at time t (when the body is at P) is $2t$ ft./sec. Now $2t$ is the derived function of t^2, and it is denoted by $\frac{ds}{dt}$.

In the same way we can obtain the general result:

Suppose that a body is moving in a straight line, so that after t sec. its distance from a fixed point in the line is s ft., and its velocity v ft./sec. Then if s is known as a function of t, v is given by the derived function; that is

$$v = \frac{ds}{dt}$$

We have already stated this in graphical terms: If P is any point on the space-time graph, representing where the body is at a particular time, the gradient of the tangent at P represents the velocity at that time.

Example 2: A stone is thrown vertically upwards at 80 ft./sec.; t sec. later its height above the ground is s ft. (Fig. 2), where

$$s = 80t - 16t^2$$

Find:

(i) the velocity after 1, 2, 3, 4 and 5 sec., interpreting the results;
(ii) when the stone stops rising, and the greatest height it reaches;
(iii) how long it is in the air.

(i) (First, we must find a formula giving the velocity after t sec.)

Let the velocity at time t be v ft./sec., then $v = \frac{ds}{dt}$.

$$\text{Now } s = 80t - 16t^2$$

$$\therefore v = \frac{ds}{dt} = 80 - 32t$$

When $t = 1$, $v = 80 - 32 = 48$; the stone is moving upwards at 48 ft./sec.
When $t = 2$, $v = 80 - 64 = 16$; the stone is moving upwards at 16 ft./sec.
When $t = 3$, $v = 80 - 96 = -16$; the stone is moving down at 16 ft./sec.
When $t = 4$, $v = 80 - 128 = -48$; the stone is moving down at 48 ft./sec.
When $t = 5$, $v = 80 - 160 = -80$; the stone is moving down at 80 ft./sec.

(ii) $v = 0$ when $80 - 32t = 0$

i.e. when $32t = 80$

$$t = \tfrac{80}{32} = 2\tfrac{1}{2}$$

The stone stops rising after $2\frac{1}{2}$ sec.

(After this, v becomes negative and the stone starts falling.)

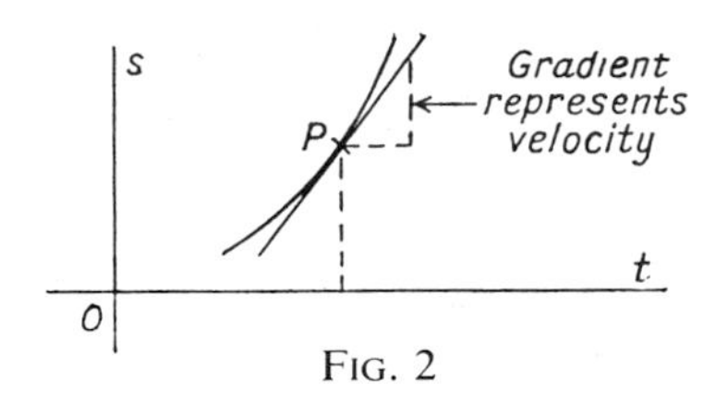

FIG. 2

When $t = 2\frac{1}{2}$, $s = 80\,(2\tfrac{1}{2}) - 16\,(2\tfrac{1}{2})^2$
$= 80\,(2\tfrac{1}{2}) - 16\,(6\tfrac{1}{4})$
$= 200 - 100$
$= 100$

The stone reaches a height of 100 *ft.*

(iii) (Notice that s ft. is not the total distance travelled, but the height above the ground at any particular time. This means that when the stone reaches the ground again, $s = 0$.)

$s = 0$ when $80t - 16t^2 = 0$
i.e. when $16t\,(5 - t) = 0$
i.e. when $t = 0$ or $t = 5$

($t = 0$ when the stone is first thrown up; $t = 5$ is the solution we want.)

The stone is in the air for 5 sec.

EXERCISE 10A

Questions 1, 2 and 4 refer to a body moving in a straight line, s ft. being its distance from a fixed point (O) of the line, v ft./sec. its velocity at time t sec.

1. $s = 3t^2$. Find:

(i) the distance from O at the start and after 5 sec.;

(ii) the average velocity during the first 5 sec.;

(iii) the actual velocity when $t = 0, 1, 2, 3, 4$ and 5.

2. $s = t^2 - 6t + 12$.

(i) Find where the body is at the start, and show that it is moving towards O.

(ii) Find when it stops, before moving away from O again.

(iii) What is its minimum distance from O?

(iv) What is its velocity, and where is it, after 6 sec.?

3. A stone is thrown vertically upwards at 64 ft./sec., t sec. later its height above the ground is s ft., where

$$s = 64t - 16t^2.$$

(i) What is the velocity after t sec.?

(ii) For how long is the stone rising, and what is the greatest height it reaches?

(iii) When does it return to ground level, and with what speed does it reach the ground?

4. $s = t^3 - 6t^2 + 9t$.

(i) Find the values of t for which $s = 0$.

(ii) Write down and factorize a formula giving v in terms of t, and find when and where the body is at rest.

(iii) Using the results of (i) and (ii), describe how the body moves between the times $t = 0$ and $t = 3$.

Acceleration

Acceleration is rate of change of velocity. If a car reaches a speed of 30 m.p.h. from rest in 5 sec., its "average acceleration" is 6 m.p.h. per sec.; if the velocity of a body changes from 10 ft./sec. to 50 ft./sec. (a change of 40 ft./sec.) in 10 sec., its average acceleration is 4 ft./sec. per sec.; and so on.

The expression "feet per sec. per sec." tends to be confusing. It simply means that the velocity changes at the rate of so many ft.-per-sec. every second. It is usually abbreviated to "ft./sec./sec." or ft./sec.^{2}.

Now, what exactly do we mean if we say that the acceleration of a body *at a particular instant* is so many ft./sec./sec.? We will take a simple example and deal with it in exactly the same way as we did with velocity.

Example 3: A body moves in a straight line so that, after t sec., its velocity is v ft./sec., where

$$v = 3t^2 - 4.$$

Find the acceleration after t sec.

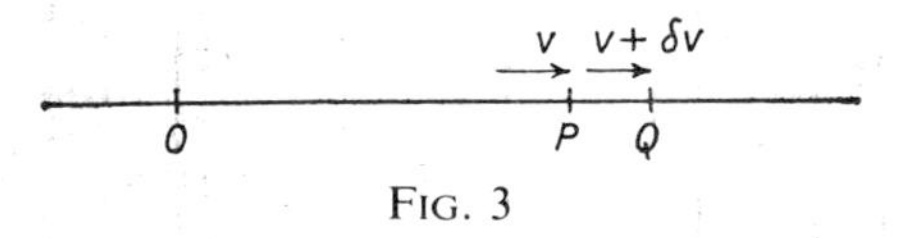

FIG. 3

After t sec., the velocity is v ft./sec.; suppose that after a further short time, δt sec., the velocity has increased by a small amount δv ft./sec., so that it is $(v + \delta v)$ ft./sec. (Fig. 3).

$$\text{Then } v + \delta v = 3(t + \delta t)^2 - 4$$
$$= 3\{t^2 + 2t(\delta t) + (\delta t)^2\} - 4$$

$$\text{i.e.}\quad v + \delta v = 3t^2 + 6t\,(\delta t) + 3\,(\delta t)^2 - 4$$
$$\text{Also, } v = 3t^2 \qquad\qquad\qquad\qquad - 4$$
$$\therefore \delta v = \qquad 6t\,(\delta t) + 3\,(\delta t)^2$$

The average acceleration during this short time δt sec. is

$$\frac{\delta v}{\delta t} = 6t + 3\,(\delta t) \text{ ft./sec./sec.}$$

This average acceleration can be made as close as we please to $6t$ ft./sec./sec. by choosing δt small enough.

So the actual acceleration at time t is $6t$ ft./sec./sec. Now $6t$ is the derived function of $3t^2 - 4$, and it is denoted by $\dfrac{dv}{dt}$.

In the same way, we can obtain the general result:

Suppose that a body is moving in a straight line so that, t sec. after starting, its velocity is v ft./sec. and its acceleration "a" ft./sec./sec., then

$$a = \frac{dv}{dt}.$$

Graphically, this means that if P is any point on the velocity-time graph, representing the velocity of the body at a particular time, the gradient of the tangent at P represents the acceleration of the body at that time.

Example 4: A body moves in a straight line so that, t sec. after it passes a fixed point (A), its distance from A is s ft., where

$$s = 12t - t^2.$$

Find formulae giving the velocity and acceleration after t sec.; sketch and interpret the space-time, velocity-time and acceleration-time graphs. (Fig. 4).

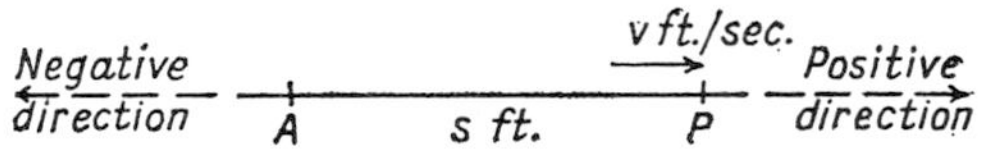

Negative direction — A — s ft. — P (v ft./sec. →) — Positive direction

FIG. 4

Let the velocity after t sec. be v ft./sec.; then $v = \dfrac{ds}{dt}$.

$$\text{Now } s = 12t - t^2$$
$$\therefore v = \frac{ds}{dt} = 12 - 2t$$

The velocity after t sec. is $(12 - 2t)$ ft./sec.

Let the acceleration after t sec. be "a" ft./sec./sec.; then $a = \dfrac{dv}{dt}$.

$$\text{Now } v = 12 - 2t$$
$$\therefore a = \frac{dv}{dt} = -2$$

The acceleration is constant. -2 ft./sec.^{2}

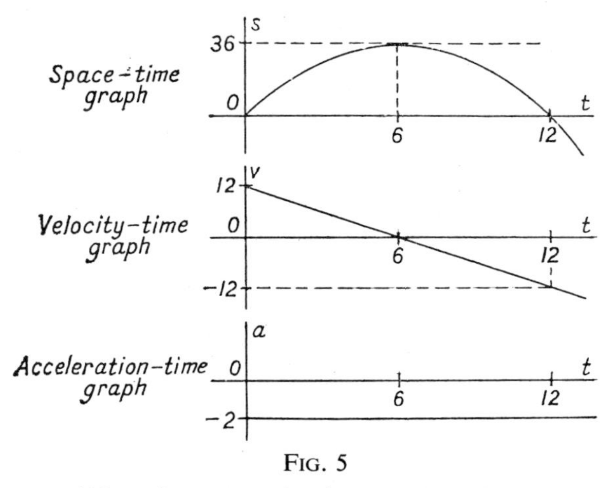

FIG. 5

Notice: (i) $s = t(12 - t)$, so $s = 0$ when $t = 0$ and when $t = 12$.

The maximum value of s occurs when $\frac{ds}{dt} = 0$, i.e. when $v = 0$; this is when $t = 6$. When $t = 6$, $s = 36$. When $t > 12$, s is negative.

(ii) When $t = 0$, $v = 12$.

v decreases steadily, becoming 0 when $t = 6$, afterwards negative; when $t = 12$, $v = -12$.

Interpretation: The body moves outwards from A in the positive direction, starting at 12 ft./sec. Its speed decreases steadily until it stops after 6 sec., 36 ft. from A. It then starts to move back with steadily increasing speed, passing through A again at 12 ft./sec. after a further 6 sec. (i.e. when $t = 12$). Afterwards, it moves away from A in the negative direction.

N.B.: When the body is moving forwards (in the positive direction), the negative acceleration means that it is *slowing down*, but when it is moving backwards the negative acceleration means that its speed is getting faster (in the negative direction).

EXERCISE 10B

These questions refer to a body moving as in Exercise 10A.

1. $v = t^2 - 5t + 8$.

(i) What is the initial velocity (i.e. the velocity when $t = 0$)?

(ii) What is the acceleration at time t sec.?

(iii) What is the initial acceleration? So what happens to the velocity at first?

(iv) When is the acceleration zero? So what is the minimum velocity?

(v) What are the velocity and acceleration when $t = 5$?

2. $s = 15t - 3t^2$.

Find formulae giving the velocity and acceleration after t sec.; sketch and interpret the space-time, velocity-time and acceleration-time graphs.

3. $s = 2t^2 - 6t + 5$.

Find v as a function of t, and find the (constant) acceleration. Find the value of v when $t = 0, 1, 2$ and 3, and verify that the changes in the velocity between these times agree with your figure for the acceleration. Find also when and where the body is momentarily at rest.

4. $s = 12t - t^3$.

Show that the body moves outwards from 0 for 2 sec. and then returns. What is its greatest positive distance from 0, and what is its velocity when it passes through 0 on the return journey? What is the acceleration at the instant when it is at rest?

Finding the Distance Formula

With the notation we have been using,

$$v = \frac{ds}{dt}, \; a = \frac{dv}{dt}.$$

Suppose it is the velocity formula that we know, and the distance formula that we wish to find.

Our problem is: given $\frac{ds}{dt}$, to find s. In other words, it is one of *integration*.

Similarly, if we know "a" (i.e. $\frac{dv}{dt}$) and require v, we have again to integrate.

In the following examples the first step in each solution is a careful statement of what is given and what has to be found. If you always follow this procedure, you should be able to avoid the common mistake of confusing differentiation with integration, and vice versa.

Example 5: A marble rolls down a groove in a sloping board, starting from rest at a point 1 ft. from the top, and moving with a constant acceleration of 2 ft./sec./sec. Find:

(i) how fast the marble is moving after $1\frac{1}{2}$ sec.;

(ii) how far from the top of the board it then is;

(iii) how long it takes to roll down the groove if the board is 10 ft. long.

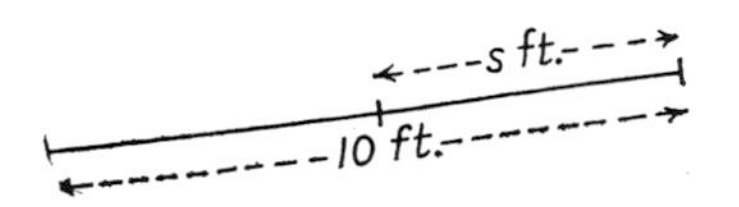

FIG. 6

Suppose that, t sec. after the marble starts to move, its velocity is v ft./sec. and it is s ft. from the top of the board.

(i) (We must first find the formula giving v in terms of t.)

We *know* the acceleration, i.e. $\frac{dv}{dt}$; we have to find v. So we must integrate.

$$\frac{dv}{dt} = 2$$

$$\therefore v = 2t.$$ (There is no constant, since the marble starts from rest, i.e. $v = 0$ when $t = 0$.)

When $t = 1\frac{1}{2}$, $v = 3$.
So the velocity after $1\frac{1}{2}$ sec. is 3 ft./sec.

(ii) (We must first find the formula giving s in terms of t.)

We *know* the velocity (i.e. $\frac{ds}{dt}$); we have to find s. Again, we must integrate.

$$\frac{ds}{dt} = 2t$$

$$\therefore s = t^2 + c$$

When $t = 0$, $s = 1$; $\therefore 1 = 0 + c$, i.e. $c = 1$.

$$\text{So } s = t^2 + 1$$

When $t = 1\frac{1}{2}$, $s = (1\frac{1}{2})^2 + 1 = 3\frac{1}{4}$.

So after $1\frac{1}{2}$ sec., the marble is $3\frac{1}{4}$ ft. from the top of the board.

(iii) At the bottom of the groove, $s = 10$

$$\text{i.e. } t^2 + 1 = 10$$
$$\therefore t^2 = 9$$
$$\therefore t = 3$$

The ball takes 3 sec. to roll down the groove.

Example 6: A body can move in a straight line. A stop-watch is started when it is at A, 4 ft. from a fixed point O of the line. When the watch shows t sec., the velocity of the body is $(3t^2 - 6t)$ ft./sec.

(i) Verify that the body starts from rest, is at rest again at O, 2 sec. later, and afterwards moves out from O again.

(ii) Find where it is, its velocity and its acceleration after 3 sec. and after 4 sec.

(iii) Find the average velocity in the interval $t = 2$ to $t = 4$ and verify that this is *not* the same as the velocity when $t = 3$.

We will take the direction from O to A as positive. At time t sec., let the distance from O be s ft., the velocity v ft./sec., the acceleration "a" ft./sec. (Fig. 7).

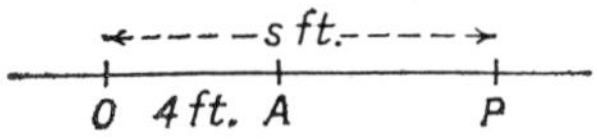

FIG. 7

(i) We are concerned here with the *velocity* (v ft./sec.) and *position* (s ft. from O) of the body. We know v, i.e. $\frac{ds}{dt}$, and we have to find s; we must integrate.

$$v = 3t^2 - 6t = 3t(t - 2) \quad \ldots\ldots\ldots\ldots(1)$$

$$\text{i.e. } \frac{ds}{dt} = 3t^2 - 6t$$

$$\therefore s = t^3 - 3t^2 + c$$

Now $s = 4$ when $t = 0$ $\therefore c = 4$.

$$\text{So } s = t^3 - 3t^2 + 4 \quad \ldots\ldots\ldots\ldots(2)$$

From (1): When $t = 0$, $v = 0$, so the body starts from rest.
When t is between 0 and 2, v is negative, so the body moves back towards O.
When $t = 2$, $v = 0$. }
From (2): When $t = 2$, $s = 0$. } Hence the body is at rest again at O when $t = 2$.
When $t > 2$, v is positive, so the body moves out from O again.

(ii) We are concerned here with "a," as well as with v and s. We know v, we must find "a," i.e. $\frac{dv}{dt}$; we must differentiate.

$$v = 3t^2 - 6t$$

$$\therefore a = \frac{dv}{dt} = 6t - 6 \quad \ldots\ldots\ldots\ldots(3)$$

When $t = 3$, $s = 3^3 - 3.3^2 + 4 = 27 - 27 + 4 = 4$;
$v = 3.3(3 - 2) = 9.1 = 9$;
$a = 18 - 6 = 12$.

The body is 4 ft. from O (at A again), moving with velocity 9 ft./sec. and acceleration 12 ft./sec./sec.

When $t = 4$, $s = 4^3 - 3.4^2 + 4 = 64 - 48 + 4 = 20$;
$v = 3.4(4 - 2) = 12.2 = 24$;
$a = 24 - 6 = 18$.

The body is 20 ft. from O, moving with velocity 24 ft./sec. and acceleration 18 ft./sec./sec.

(iii) When $t = 2$, $s = 0$; when $t = 4$, $s = 20$.
Distance travelled = 20 ft.; time = 2 sec.
So average velocity = 10 ft./sec. (The velocity when $t = 3$ is 9 ft./sec.)

All the examples in this chapter are, of course, completely artificial. However, the basic ideas introduced here, that velocity is rate of change of distance and acceleration is rate of change of velocity, lie behind all investigations into the way in which bodies move.

EXERCISE 10C

The same notation is used as in Exercises 10A and 10B. Unless otherwise stated, the questions refer to a body moving as in these exercises.

1. A stone is thrown up from the ground at 100 ft./sec. (i.e. $v = 100$ when $t = 0$). The gravitational pull of the earth causes a downward acceleration of 32 ft./sec./sec. (i.e. $a = -32$). Find formulae giving the velocity of the stone and its height above the ground after t sec. Find also after how long it stops rising, the greatest height reached and when it returns to ground level.

2. The body starts from O and moves so that after t sec. its velocity is $8 - 2t$ ft./sec. Find the acceleration, and the distance from O after t sec. Describe how the body moves during the first 8 sec.

3. $a = \frac{1}{2}t$.

Initially (i.e. when $t = O$), the body is 5 ft. from O in the positive direction, but is moving back towards O at 1 ft./sec. Find formulae giving v and s in terms of t. Find also after how long the body stops moving back, and what is its least distance from O.

4. $v = 5t - t^2$.

(i) Find the velocity at the end of each of the first 5 sec.

(ii) When is the acceleration zero, and what is the velocity at this time?

(iii) If, at the start, the body is 2 ft. from O, find s in terms of t.

(iv) What can you say about the velocity after $t = 5$? What is the greatest value of s?

CHAPTER 11

AREAS AND VOLUMES

THE PROBLEM of finding areas bounded by curved lines exercised men's minds for many hundreds of years. Integration provides a method of doing this when the boundary is a curve whose equation is known. We can then find the area between the curve and the axes (Fig. 1).

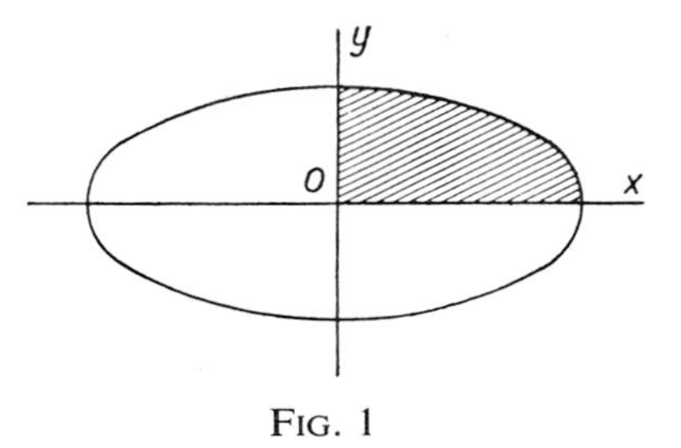

FIG. 1

For example, the oval shape known as an "ellipse" comes from a fairly simple formula giving y in terms of x. To find its area, we can find the shaded part between the curve and the axes, and then multiply by 4. (This example is too hard to include here.)

With our present knowledge, we can only take very simple—and artificial—examples. The method is of wide, genuine practical use, however.

Example 1: Find the area bounded by the curve $y = x^2 + 1$, the x- and y-axes and the line $x = 3$ (i.e., the area *DOKE* in Fig. 2a).

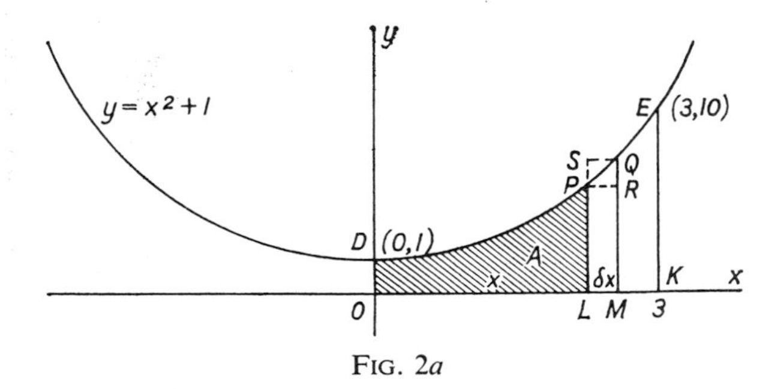

FIG. 2*a*

Let P be any point (x, y) on the curve between D and E, L the foot of the perpendicular from P to the x-axis.

The area $DOLP$ is clearly a function of x—it depends on where P is. We will call this function "A," and will try to find the formula giving A in terms of x. Then, by putting $x = 3$, that is, by taking P to be at E, we shall find the area we want.

Now suppose Q $(x + \delta x, y + \delta y)$ is any other point on the curve near to P. We shall use δA to stand for the small area $PLMQ$, the change in A caused by the small change δx in x. δA is greater than the area of the rectangle $PLMR$, but less than the area of $SLMQ$.

But $LP = y$, $LM = \delta x$, so rectangle $PLMR = y\delta x$.
Also, $MQ = y + \delta y$, so rectangle $SLMQ = (y + \delta y)\delta x$.
So δA is between $y\delta x$ and $(y + \delta y)\delta x$.
$\therefore \dfrac{\delta A}{\delta x}$ is between y and $y + \delta y$.

By choosing δx, and therefore δy, small enough (that is, by choosing Q close enough to P), we can make $\dfrac{\delta A}{\delta x}$ as close as we please to the derived function $\dfrac{dA}{dx}$, and $y + \delta y$ as close as we please to y.*

Hence, since $\dfrac{\delta A}{\delta x}$ is always between y and $y + \delta y$, we must have

$$\frac{dA}{dx} = y$$

$$\text{i.e. } \frac{dA}{dx} = x^2 + 1.$$

We can now find A by integrating.

$$A = \tfrac{1}{3}x^3 + x + c.$$

*In case you do not understand this, we will sketch a graph showing the values of A for different values of x.

In Fig. 2a, when P is at D, i.e. when $x = 0$, $A = 0$. As P moves out to the right, that is, as x increases, A increases. When x has the value represented by OL, the value of "A" is area $DOLP$.

In Fig. 2b, if P' is the point on the "area" graph corresponding to P, the length LP' represents A (area $DOLP$).

If Q' is the point corresponding to Q, MQ' represents $A + \delta A$ (area $DOMQ$), $R'Q'$ represents δA (area $PLMQ$).

Also $P'R' = LM = \delta x$.

So $\dfrac{\delta A}{\delta x}$ is the gradient of the chord $P'Q'$.

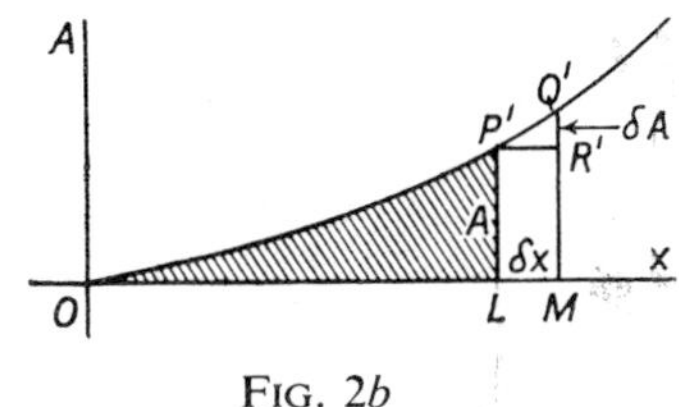

FIG. 2b

By choosing δx small enough, we can make $\dfrac{\delta A}{\delta x}$ as close as we please to the gradient of the tangent at P', i.e. to $\dfrac{dA}{dx}$

When $x = 0$, that is, when P is at D, $A = 0$; so $c = 0$, and

$$A = \tfrac{1}{3}x^3 + x$$

When $x = 3$,

$$\begin{aligned} A &= \tfrac{1}{3}.27 + 3 \\ &= 9 + 3 \\ &= 12 \end{aligned}$$

The required area is 12 units.

The argument which we used to show that $\frac{dA}{dx} = y$ did not depend on the equation of the particular curve; it applies to any curve (Fig. 3).

If DE is an arc of a curve, DH and EK the perpendiculars from D and E to the x-axis, then to find area $DHKE$, we start from

$$\frac{dA}{dx} = y,$$

"A" being the function of x giving area $DHLP$, where P is any point on the curve between D and E.

Note: DH, PL and EK are called the "ordinates" of D, P and E respectively.

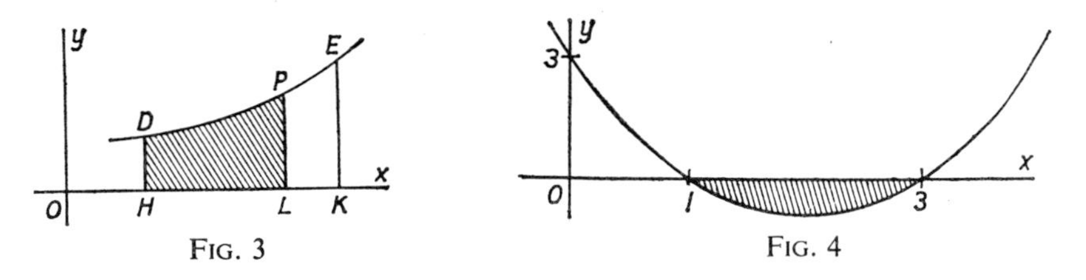

FIG. 3 FIG. 4

Example 2: Find the area enclosed between the curve $y = x^2 - 4x + 3$ and the x-axis.

In order to understand what is required, we must make a sketch (Fig. 4).

$y = (x - 1)(x - 3)$. The curve crosses the x-axis where $x = 1$ and where $x = 3$; when $x = 0$, $y = 3$. (See Chapter 4.)

$$\frac{dA}{dx} = y$$

$$\text{i.e. } \frac{dA}{dx} = x^2 - 4x + 3$$

$$\therefore A = \tfrac{1}{3}x^3 - 2x^2 + 3x + c$$

When $x = 1$, $A = 0$ $\therefore$ $0 = \tfrac{1}{3} - 2 + 3 + c$

$$\therefore c = -1\tfrac{1}{3}$$

$$\text{and } A = \tfrac{1}{3}x^3 - 2x^2 + 3x - 1\tfrac{1}{3}$$

When $x = 3$,

$$\begin{aligned} A &= \tfrac{1}{3}.27 - 2.9 + 3.3 - 1\tfrac{1}{3} \\ &= 9 - 18 + 9 - 1\tfrac{1}{3} \\ &= -1\tfrac{1}{3}. \end{aligned}$$

N.B.: The minus sign merely means that the area is *below the x-axis.*

Example 3: Find the area enclosed between the curve $y = 4x - x^2$ and the line $y = x$.

You should be able to sketch $y = 4x - x^2$ easily (see Chapter 4, page 161, if necessary).

$y = x$ is a straight line through the origin; first, we must find the point E where it meets the curve again.

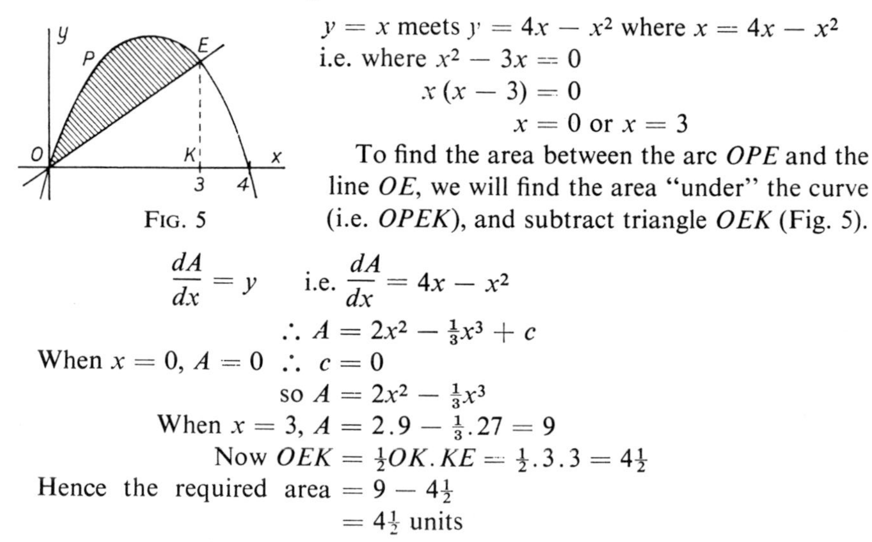

FIG. 5

$y = x$ meets $y = 4x - x^2$ where $x = 4x - x^2$
i.e. where $x^2 - 3x = 0$

$$x(x-3) = 0$$

$$x = 0 \text{ or } x = 3$$

To find the area between the arc OPE and the line OE, we will find the area "under" the curve (i.e. $OPEK$), and subtract triangle OEK (Fig. 5).

$$\frac{dA}{dx} = y \quad \text{i.e. } \frac{dA}{dx} = 4x - x^2$$

$$\therefore A = 2x^2 - \tfrac{1}{3}x^3 + c$$

When $x = 0$, $A = 0$ $\therefore c = 0$

$$\text{so } A = 2x^2 - \tfrac{1}{3}x^3$$

$$\text{When } x = 3,\ A = 2.9 - \tfrac{1}{3}.27 = 9$$

$$\text{Now } OEK = \tfrac{1}{2}OK.KE = \tfrac{1}{2}.3.3 = 4\tfrac{1}{2}$$

Hence the required area $= 9 - 4\frac{1}{2}$

$= 4\frac{1}{2}$ units

EXERCISE 11A

N.B.: It is essential always to make a sketch. Otherwise, you cannot be clear about what you are asked to find.

1. Find the area bounded by the curve $y = x^2$, the x-axis and the line $x = 4$.

2. Sketch the curve $y = x^2 - 4$ for positive values of x. The curve crosses the x-axis at P, the y-axis at Q. O is the origin. Find the area bounded by the curve and the lines OP, OQ. Explain the negative result.

3. Find the area enclosed between the curve $y = 5x - x^2 - 4$ and the x-axis.

4. Find the area enclosed between the curve $y = x^2 - x - 6$ and the x-axis.

5. Sketch the graph $y = \dfrac{1}{x^2}$ for positive values of x. Calculate:

(i) the area bounded by the curve, the x-axis, the line $x = 1$ and the line $x = 3$;

(ii) the area bounded by the curve, the line $y = 1$ and the line $x = 3$.

6. Find the area enclosed by the curve $y = 6x - x^2$ and the line $y = 2x$.

7. Find the area cut off from the curve $y = 3x^2 + 2$ by the line $y = 14$.

8. Sketch on the same diagram, the curves $y = \frac{4}{x^2}$ and $y = \frac{x^2}{4}$. Find their points of intersection and calculate the area enclosed between the two curves and the line $x = 4$.

Volumes

Many vessels and solids have an axis of symmetry and circular cross-sections at right-angles to it. We can think of them as being formed by rotating a plane area about the axis. For instance, we could think of the part of a cone shown in the diagram as formed by rotating the shaded area through 360° about the axis AB (Fig. 6a).

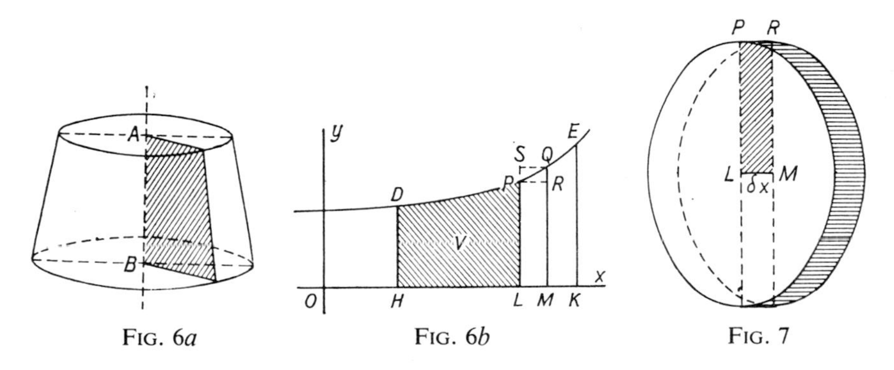

FIG. 6*a* FIG. 6*b* FIG. 7

Solids like this are called "*solids of revolution*"; if we know equations for the boundaries of the area rotated, we can find their volume by integration in a way similar to our method of finding areas.

Using the same notation as in Fig. 3, suppose that we want to find the volume formed by rotating the area $DHKE$ through 360° about the x-axis.

Let $P\,(x, y)$ be any point on the curve between D and E (i.e. $OL = x$, $LP = y$). Let V stand for the volume formed by rotating area $DHLP$; then V is a function of x. If $Q\,(x + \delta x, y + \delta y)$ is another point on the curve near to P, we shall use δV to stand for the extra volume formed by rotating the small area $PLMQ$ (Fig. 6b).

Now, δV is greater than the volume formed by rotating rectangle $PLMR$, but less than that formed by rotating $SLMQ$.

These last two are thin cylindrical discs. The smaller, shown in Fig. 7, has radius y (i.e. LP) and thickness δx (i.e. LM); so its volume is $\pi y^2 \delta x$. (Volume of cylinder $= \pi r^2 h$.)

Similarly, the larger has radius $y + \delta y$ (i.e. MQ) and thickness δx; so its volume is $\pi (y + \delta y)^2 . \delta x$. Hence δV is between $\pi y^2 \delta x$ and $\pi (y + \delta y)^2 . \delta x$.

$\therefore \frac{\delta V}{\delta x}$ is between πy^2 and $\pi (y + \delta y)^2$.

By choosing δx, and therefore δy, small enough (that is, by choosing Q close enough to P), we can make $\frac{\delta V}{\delta x}$ as close as we please to $\frac{dV}{dx}$, and $\pi (y + \delta y)^2$ as close as we please to πy^2.

Hence, since $\frac{\delta V}{\delta x}$ is always between πy^2 and $\pi(y + \delta y)^2$, we must have

$$\frac{dV}{dx} = \pi y^2$$

If you find this difficult to follow, the footnote on page 218 may help. It applies in exactly the same way here, if you replace "area" and "A" by "volume" and "V" throughout.

Example 4: The area enclosed by the curve $y = x^2 + 1$, the x-axis, the line $x = 1$ and the line $x = 3$, is rotated through 360° about the x-axis. Find the volume of the resulting solid of revolution.

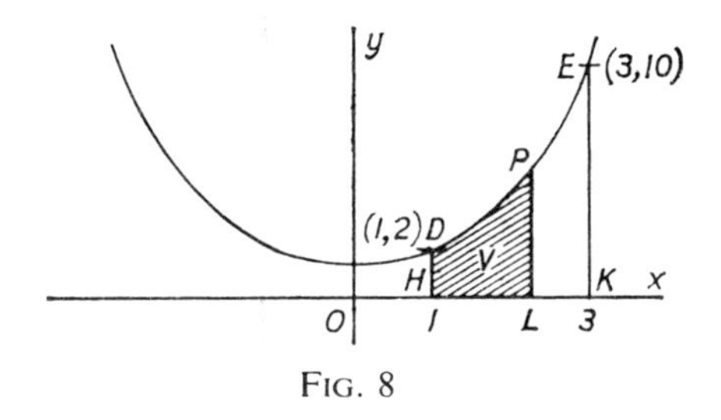

FIG. 8

Using the same notation as before, D is the point (1, 2), E is (3, 10); $P(x, y)$ is any point on the curve between D and E (Fig. 8).

Call the volume formed by rotating the area $DHLP$, V; then

$$\frac{dV}{dx} = \pi y^2$$

$$\text{i.e. } \frac{dV}{dx} = \pi (x^2 + 1)^2$$

$$= \pi (x^4 + 2x^2 + 1)$$

$$\therefore V = \pi \left(\frac{x^5}{5} + \frac{2x^3}{3} + x + c\right)$$

$V = 0$ when $x = 1$ $\quad \therefore 0 = \pi (\frac{1}{5} + \frac{2}{3} + 1 + c)$

$$\therefore c = -1\tfrac{13}{15}$$

$$\text{and } V = \pi \left(\frac{x^5}{5} + \frac{2x^3}{3} + x - 1\tfrac{13}{15}\right)$$

When $x = 3$, $V = \pi\left(\frac{243}{5} + \frac{2.27}{3} + 3 - 1\frac{13}{15}\right)$

$= \pi\,(48\frac{3}{5} + 18 + 3 - 1\frac{13}{15}) = 67\frac{11}{15}\pi$ units.

Note: (a) In Chapter 9 we did not integrate powers of x higher than x^2. However, we did point out that, in general, if $\frac{dy}{dy} = x^n$, $y = \frac{x^{n+1}}{n+1} + c$: "increase the power by 1, and divide by the new power." So integrating x^4 does not cause any difficulty.

(b) Since π is a constant factor multiplying each term, it is simplest to leave it as a common factor, as we have done here. It will usually be sufficient to give the volume as a multiple of π.

Example 5: A barrel is 4 ft. high, 4 ft. in diameter at its widest part, 3 ft. in diameter at the ends (Fig. 9). The barrel can be thought of as formed by rotating a curve with equation $y = a - bx^2$ about the x-axis. Find the equation of the curve and the capacity of the barrel to the nearest $\frac{1}{10}$ cu. ft.

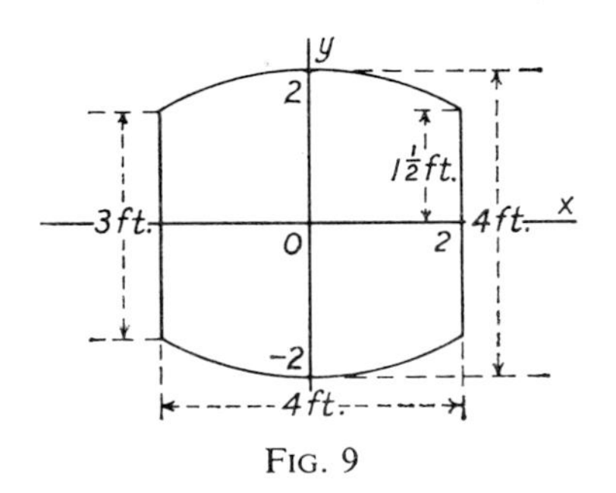

FIG. 9

The dimensions given mean that when $x = 0$, $y = 2$ and when $x = 2$, $y = 1\frac{1}{2}$.

So $\left.\begin{aligned} 2 &= a \\ 1\tfrac{1}{2} &= a - 4b \end{aligned}\right\}$ whence $b = \frac{1}{8}$ (please check).

Hence the equation of the curve is $y = 2 - \frac{1}{8}x^2$

Since the curve is symmetrical about the y-axis, we will find the capacity of half the barrel (from $x = 0$ to $x = 2$), and then double it.

Using V as before, $\frac{dV}{dx} = \pi y^2$

i.e. $\frac{dV}{dx} = \pi\,(2 - \frac{1}{8}x^2)^2$

$= \pi\,(4 - \frac{1}{2}x^2 + \frac{1}{64}x^4)$

$\therefore V = \pi\left(4x - \frac{1}{2}\cdot\frac{x^3}{3} + \frac{1}{64}\cdot\frac{x^5}{5}\right)$ (There is no constant, since $V = 0$ when $x = 0$.)

$$= \pi\left(4x - \frac{x^3}{6} + \frac{x^5}{320}\right)$$

When $x = 2$, $V = \pi\,(8 - \frac{8}{6} + \frac{32}{320})$

$$= \pi\,(8 - 1\tfrac{1}{3} + \tfrac{1}{10})$$

$$= \pi\,.\,6\tfrac{23}{30}$$

Hence the capacity of the barrel $= 13\frac{8}{15}\pi$ cu. ft.

$$= 13{\cdot}53\,.\,3{\cdot}14 \text{ cu. ft.}$$

$$= 42{\cdot}5 \text{ cu. ft.}$$

Example 6: We will use this method to prove the formula for the volume of a sphere.

Think of the sphere as formed by rotating a circle with centre at the origin and radius r, about the x-axis (Fig. 10).

If (x, y) is any point on the circle, then by Pythagoras' theorem,

$$x^2 + y^2 = r^2$$

$$\therefore\ y^2 = r^2 - x^2$$

As in Example 5, we shall take $V = 0$ when $x = 0$, so that we shall first find the volume of half the sphere.

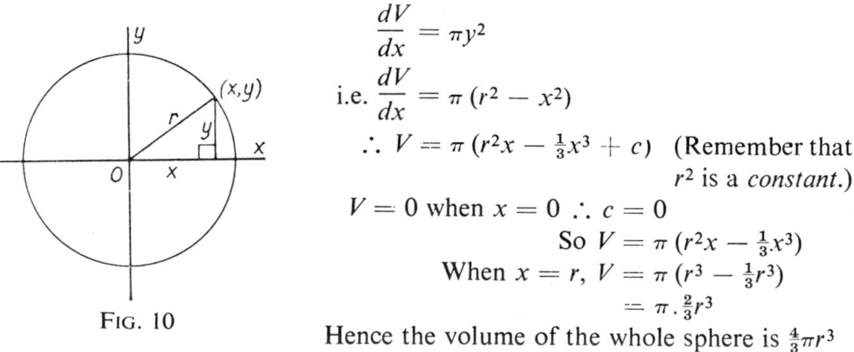

FIG. 10

$$\frac{dV}{dx} = \pi y^2$$

i.e. $$\frac{dV}{dx} = \pi\,(r^2 - x^2)$$

$\therefore\ V = \pi\,(r^2x - \frac{1}{3}x^3 + c)$ (Remember that r^2 is a *constant.*)

$V = 0$ when $x = 0$ $\therefore\ c = 0$

So $V = \pi\,(r^2x - \frac{1}{3}x^3)$

When $x = r$, $V = \pi\,(r^3 - \frac{1}{3}r^3)$

$$= \pi\,.\,\tfrac{2}{3}r^3$$

Hence the volume of the whole sphere is $\frac{4}{3}\pi r^3$

EXERCISE 11B

Except in No. 6, answers may be left as multiples of π.

1. Find the volume formed when the area between the curve $y = x^2$, the x-axis and the line $x = 3$, is rotated through 360° about the x-axis.

2. Find the volume of the solid of revolution formed when the area enclosed by the x-axis and the curve $y = 2x - x^2$ is rotated about the x-axis.

3. Repeat Question 1 for the area between the curve $y = \dfrac{1}{x}$ and the lines $y = 0$, $x = \frac{1}{4}$ and $x = 4$.

4. Find the volume formed by rotating about the x-axis the area enclosed by the curve $y = 3 - x^2$ and the line $y = 2$.

(*Hint:* First find the limiting values of x; then find the volume formed by rotating the whole area "under" the curve; subtract the volume of the cylinder formed by rotating the area under the line.)

5. Prove that the volume of a right circular cone of base-radius r and height h is $\frac{1}{3}\pi r^2 h$.

Take the axis of the cylinder as x-axis, the vertex of the cone as origin. Consider the cone as formed by rotating the area between the line $y = \frac{r}{h}x$ (why this?) about the x-axis (Fig. 11).

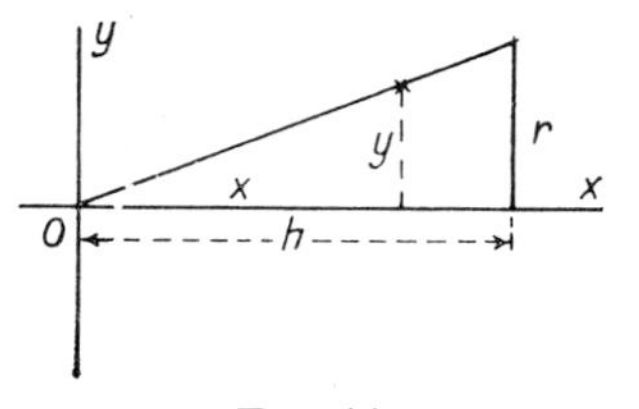

FIG. 11

6. Sketch the curve $y^2 = 9x$ for values of x from 0 to 6.

(*N.B.*: $y = \pm 3\sqrt{x}$, so there are two values of y for each value of x.)

The inside surface of a bowl is formed by rotating about the x-axis the portion of this curve cut off by the line $x = 6$. (The bowl is turned on its side.) The units being inches, find the capacity of the bowl to the nearest cubic inch.

CHAPTER 12

FURTHER WORK ON EQUATIONS; IDENTITIES

IN CHAPTERS 4 to 11 we have developed and used various ideas about functions and their derived functions. We have often wanted to know what value of the independent variable (x or t) gave a function a particular value, generally 0. So, we have often solved equations. Some examples are:

(i) (From Chapter 4):

$y = x^2 - 4x + 3$; $y = 0$ when $(x - 1)(x - 3) = 0$.

(ii) (From Chapter 7):

$y = x^2 - 5x + 6$, so $\dfrac{dy}{dx} = 2x - 5$; $\dfrac{dy}{dx} = 0$ when $2x - 5 = 0$.

(iii) (From Chapter 10): $s = 80t - 16t^2$; $s = 0$ when $80t - 16t^2 = 0$.

In (ii), a linear equation, that is, one involving a function whose graph is a straight line, has to be solved. The equations in (i) and (iii) are quadratic equations—the functions involved contain terms in x^2 or t^2.

In each case, the basic thing is the *function*, whose value is a variable, depending on the value of x. The *equation* is concerned with one particular value of the function only.

In this chapter we return to the study of equations.

I. Quadratic Equations: Completing the Square

Example 1. Consider the function $x^2 + 6x + 4$ and its graph.

If $y = x^2 + 6x + 4$, then $y = 4$ when $x = 0$. If you have studied Chapters 5-7, you will be able to show that the minimum point is $(-3, -5)$ (Fig. 1).

Where does the curve cross the x-axis? In other words, when is y equal to 0? We have to solve the equation

$$x^2 + 6x + 4 = 0$$

We cannot factorize, since there are no factors of 4 which add up to 6. We must look for another method.

One is suggested by the fact that "x squared" is involved. We think of x^2 as representing the area of a square with sides x units, and then try to make the whole left-hand side of the equation represent the area of a square.

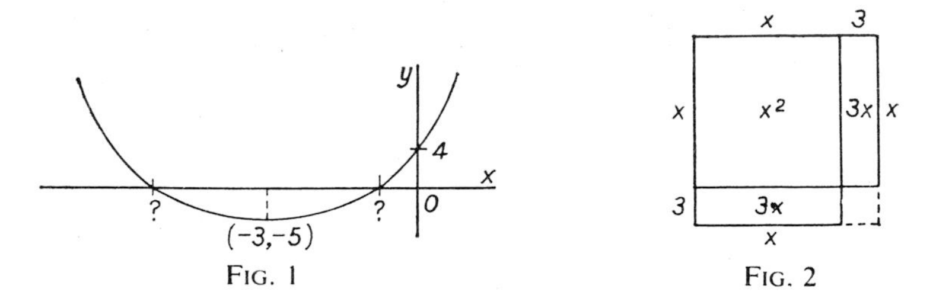

FIG. 1

FIG. 2

First, think of the "$6x$" as two rectangles, each x units by 3 units (area $3x$), placed as shown (Fig. 2).

To make up a complete square, with sides $x + 3$ units, area $(x + 3)^2$, what extra area do we want? Clearly, 9 units (sides 3 by 3).

The equation is $\quad x^2 + 6x + 4 = 0.$

We want the left-hand side to be $x^2 + 6x + 9$, so we add 5 to both sides:

$$x^2 + 6x + 9 = 5, \quad \text{i.e. } (x + 3)^2 = 5.$$

We can now solve the equation approximately by taking the square root of both sides. There is no exact solution, since 5 has no exact square root; we will work to 2 places of decimals. From square root tables, $\sqrt{5} \simeq 2{\cdot}24$.

Remember that, since "$(-) \times (-) = (+)$," any positive number has two square roots. $\sqrt{16} = 4$ or -4, and so on. This is written "± 4," and read as "plus or minus 4." So we find two solutions to our equation, as expected (see Fig. 1).

$$x + 3 = \pm\sqrt{5}$$

$$\therefore x + 3 = 2{\cdot}24 \quad \text{or} \quad x + 3 = -2{\cdot}24$$

$$\therefore x = 2{\cdot}24 - 3 \text{ or} \quad x = -2{\cdot}24 - 3$$

$$= -{\cdot}76 \qquad\qquad = -5{\cdot}24$$

Can we discover a simple rule for "completing the square" without having to draw a diagram each time?

$(x + 3)^2 = x^2 + 6x + 9$; that is, $x^2 + 6x + 3^2 = (x + 3)^2$;
$(x + 4)^2 = x^2 + 8x + 16$; that is, $x^2 + 8x + 4^2 = (x + 4)^2$;
$(x - 1)^2 = x^2 - 2x + 1$; that is, $x^2 - 2x + 1^2 = (x - 1)^2$;
$(x - 2)^2 = x^2 - 4x + 4$; that is, $x^2 - 4x + 2^2 = (x - 2)^2$; and so on.

In fact, if c is any number, and we start with $x^2 + cx$ or $x^2 - cx$, to complete the square we must *add* $\left(\frac{c}{2}\right)^2$.

$$x^2 + cx + \left(\frac{c}{2}\right)^2 = \left(x + \frac{c}{2}\right)^2$$

$$x^2 - cx + \left(\frac{c}{2}\right)^2 = \left(x - \frac{c}{2}\right)^2$$

(Please check by multiplying out the right-hand side in each case.)

***Example* 2.** Solve the equation $x^2 - 3 = 10x$, giving the roots correct to 1 place of decimals.

(The solutions to an equation—the values of x that make it true—are called the "roots" of the equation.)

$$x^2 - 3 = 10x$$
$$\therefore x^2 - 10x = 3$$
$$\therefore x^2 - 10x + (5)^2 = 3 + (5)^2$$
$$\text{i.e. } (x - 5)^2 = 28$$
$$\therefore x - 5 = \pm \sqrt{28}.$$

$$\text{So } x - 5 \simeq 5{\cdot}3 \qquad \text{or } x - 5 \simeq -5{\cdot}3$$
$$x \simeq 5{\cdot}3 + 5 \qquad x \simeq -5{\cdot}3 + 5$$
$$= 10{\cdot}3. \qquad = -{\cdot}3.$$

EXERCISE 12A

Solve the following equations, giving the roots correct to 2 places of decimals.

1. $x^2 + 4x = 3$ **3.** $x^2 + 12x - 2 = 0$ **5.** $x^2 + 7x + 1 = 0$

2. $x^2 - 2x = 5$ **4.** $x^2 + 7 = 6x$ **6.** $3x^2 - 60x = 10$

In No. 6, first make the coefficient of x^2 unity—that is, 1—by dividing both sides of the equation by 3.

Solution by Formula

The method of "completing the square" is quick and easy when the coefficient of x^2 is 1. Otherwise, it can become a little more complicated. We will now use it to solve an equation with letters standing for the coefficients; then, we can use the solution as a *formula* for solving quadratic equations.

Suppose that all the terms of an equation have been collected on one side, leaving 0 on the other. With the notation for quadratic functions used in Chapter 4, the equation will then be

$$ax^2 + bx + c = 0.$$

Divide both sides by "a," to make the coefficient of x^2, 1:

$$x^2 + \frac{b}{a}x + \frac{c}{a} = 0.$$

Subtract $\frac{c}{a}$ from both sides (to leave the "x^2" and "x" terms on their own:

$$x^2 + \frac{b}{a}x = -\frac{c}{a}\cdot$$

Now, $\frac{1}{2}$ of $\frac{b}{a}$ is $\frac{b}{2a}$; so add $\left(\frac{b}{2a}\right)^2$ to both sides:

$$x^2 + \frac{b}{a}x + \left(\frac{b}{2a}\right)^2 = -\frac{c}{a} + \left(\frac{b}{2a}\right)^2$$

$$= -\frac{c}{a} + \frac{b^2}{4a^2}$$

$$= \frac{b^2 - 4ac}{4a^2}$$

So $\left(x + \frac{b}{2a}\right)^2 = \frac{b^2 - 4ac}{4a^2}$

Take the square root of both sides: $x + \frac{b}{2a} = \pm \frac{\sqrt{b^2 - 4ac}}{2a}$

(Remember that to find the square root of a fraction we must take the square root of the numerator and of the denominator; e.g. $\sqrt{\frac{4}{9}} = \pm \frac{2}{3}$).

So $x = -\frac{b}{2a} + \frac{\sqrt{b^2 - 4ac}}{2a}$ or $-\frac{b}{2a} - \frac{\sqrt{b^2 - 4ac}}{2a}$

$= \frac{-b + \sqrt{b^2 - 4ac}}{2a}$ or $\frac{-b - \sqrt{b^2 - 4ac}}{2a}$

We will summarize this as:

If $ax^2 + bx + c = 0$,

$$x = \frac{-b \pm \sqrt{b^2 - 4ac}}{2a}$$

If you wish to use this formula you must learn it by heart. If you write it down each time you use it, this will help you to learn it. In any case, it is wise always to start by stating what you are going to substitute for a, b and c.

Example 3. Solve the equations (i) $x^2 + 5x + 2 = 0$, (ii) $5x = 2 + \frac{6}{x}$, giving the roots correct to 2 places of decimals.

(i) $x^2 + 5x + 2 = 0$

Use formula $x = \frac{-b \pm \sqrt{b^2 - 4ac}}{2a}$, with $a = 1$, $b = 5$, $c = 2$.

$$x = \frac{-5 \pm \sqrt{5^2 - 4.1.2}}{2}$$

$$= \frac{-5 \pm \sqrt{25 - 8}}{2} = \frac{-5 \pm \sqrt{17}}{2}$$

$$\simeq \frac{-5 + 4{\cdot}123}{2} \text{ or } \frac{-5 - 4{\cdot}123}{2}$$

$$= \frac{-{\cdot}877}{2} \text{ or } \frac{-9{\cdot}123}{2}$$

{*Note:* $-5 + 4{\cdot}123$
$= -(5 - 4{\cdot}123)$
$= -{\cdot}877$}

$\simeq -{\cdot}438$ or $-4{\cdot}561$

To 2 places of decimals, $x = -{\cdot}44$ or $-4{\cdot}56$.

(ii) $$5x = 2 + \frac{6}{x}$$

$\therefore 5x^2 = 2x + 6$ (multiplying both sides by x)

$\therefore 5x^2 - 2x - 6 = 0$

Use formula $x = \dfrac{-b \pm \sqrt{b^2 - 4ac}}{2a}$, with $a = 5$, $b = -2$, $c = -6$.

$$x = \frac{-(-2) \pm \sqrt{(-2)^2 - 4.5(-6)}}{10}$$

$$= \frac{2 \pm \sqrt{4 + 120}}{10}$$

Note the "+" sign under the square root. A common mistake is to forget that "$-4ac$" can be positive and to write, for example, $\sqrt{4 - 120} = \sqrt{-116}$. A negative number, of course, has no square root. If you find yourself looking for one, it means either that the equation has no solutions or that you have made a mistake—probably the latter!

$$x = \frac{2 \pm \sqrt{124}}{10}$$

$$\simeq \frac{2 + 11{\cdot}14}{10} \text{ or } \frac{2 - 11{\cdot}14}{10}$$

$$= \frac{13{\cdot}14}{10} \text{ or } \frac{-9{\cdot}14}{10}$$

$$= 1{\cdot}314 \text{ or } -{\cdot}914$$

To 2 places of decimals, $x = 1{\cdot}31$ or $-{\cdot}91$.

EXERCISE 12B

Solve the following equations. If you have to approximate, give the roots correct to 2 places of decimals. (*Some of the equations can be solved by factorization; if you can see the factors easily, it is better to use this method.*)

1. $x^2 + 3x + 1 = 0$
2. $3x^2 + 4x - 3 = 0$
3. $2x^2 - 5x + 2 = 0$
4. $2x^2 = x + 8$
5. $5x^2 - 7x = 12$
6. $9x = 4x^2 + 4$
7. $x^2 + 6x + 2 = 0$
8. $5 - x = 6x^2$
9. $3x + \dfrac{1}{x} = 10$
10. $\dfrac{5}{2x} = x - 3$
11. $8x - 2x^2 = 0$
12. $4x^2 - 9 = 0$

II. Graphical Solution of Equations

Most equations can only be solved approximately; as we have already seen in quadratics. Simple equations, involving only "x" itself, present no difficulty. Apart from these, it is only for quadratic equations that a simple formula exists giving the solution in all cases. For others, a convenient method is to use graphs of functions involved in the equations.

This idea was introduced in Chapter 1; we shall now extend that work, often in fact using quadratics to illustrate methods—you can then check the results by the formula—and solving inequalities as well as equations.

Example 4. Draw the graph $y = 5x^2 - 2x - 6$ for values of x between -2 and $+2$.

Using this graph, (i) solve the equation $5x^2 - 2x - 6 = 0$, and state the range of values of x for which $5x^2 - 2x - 6 < 0$; also solve the equations, (ii) $5x^2 - 2x - 9 = 0$; (iii) $5x^2 - 2x = 2$; (iv) $15x^2 - 6x = 27$; (v) $4x - 10x^2 + 9 = 0$.

Using the same axes, draw the straight line $y = 9 - 3x$.

(vi) For what range of values of x is $5x^2 - 2x - 6 < 9 - 3x$?

(vii) What equation in x can be solved by considering the points of intersection of the two graphs (that is, the points where they meet)?

x	-2	$-1\frac{1}{2}$	-1	$-\frac{1}{2}$	0	$\frac{1}{2}$	1	$1\frac{1}{2}$	2
x^2	4	2·25	1	·25	0	·25	1	2·25	4
$5x^2$	20	11·25	5	1·25	0	1·25	5	11·25	20
$-2x$	4	3	2	1	0	-1	-2	-3	-4
-6	-6	-6	-6	-6	-6	-6	-6	-6	-6
y	18	8·25	1	$-3·75$	-6	$-5·75$	-3	2·25	10

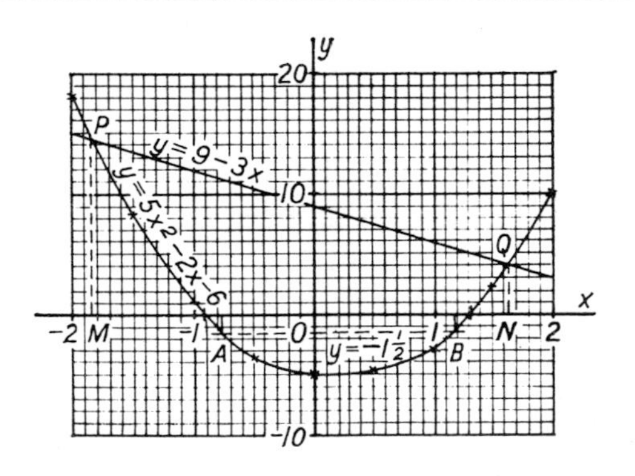

FIG. 3

You know already that we can read off directly from the graph the roots of any equation which can be put in the form "$5x^2 - 2x - 6$ = a constant."

(i) $$5x^2 - 2x - 6 = 0 \text{ (i.e., } y = 0)$$

$$\therefore x = -·9 \text{ or } 1·3$$

(Compare the values found by using the formula on page 230.)

Also $5x^2 - 2x - 6 < 0$ (i.e., y is negative) for all values of x between $-·9$ and $+1·3$ (Fig. 3).

(ii) and (iii) have the same x^2 and x terms as (i), so we have only to add to or subtract from both sides:

(ii) $5x^2 - 2x - 9 = 0$

$5x^2 - 2x - 6 = 3$ (adding 3 to both sides)

$\therefore x = 1{\cdot}56$ or $-1{\cdot}16$

(iii) $5x^2 - 2x = 2$

$5x^2 - 2x - 6 = -4$ (subtracting 6 from both sides)

$\therefore x = {\cdot}86$ or $-{\cdot}46$

(iv) $15x^2 - 6x = 27$

(Here the x^2 term is 3 times $5x^2$, the x term is 3 times $-2x$; so we start by dividing both sides by 3.)

$$\therefore 5x^2 - 2x = 9$$

and the equation turns out to be the same as in (i).

(v) $4x - 10x^2 + 9 = 0$

(Here the x^2 term is -2 times $5x^2$, the x term is -2 times $-2x$; so we start by dividing both sides by -2.)

$\therefore -2x + 5x^2 - 4\frac{1}{2} = 0$

i.e. $5x^2 - 2x - 4\frac{1}{2} = 0$

$\therefore 5x^2 - 2x - 6 = -1\frac{1}{2}$ (subtracting $1\frac{1}{2}$ from both sides)

$x = -{\cdot}77$ or $1{\cdot}17$

(We could use this graph in the same way for any equation in which the x^2 and x terms were the same number of times $5x^2$ and $-2x$.)

(vi) The values used in plotting the line $y = 9 - 3x$ were

x	-2	0	2
y	15	9	3

two to give the line, the third as a check.

P and Q are the points of intersection of the graphs $y = 5x^2 - 2x - 6$ and $y = 9 - 3x$.

At P, $x = -1{\cdot}84$; at Q, $x = 1{\cdot}62$.

(Notice that, in reading from the graph, *estimates* have been made of the x-co-ordinates of P and Q to $\frac{1}{10}$ of a small square; that is, to $\frac{1}{100}$ in., which represents ·01. The calculated values are $-1{\cdot}83$ and $1{\cdot}63$.)

Between P and Q, the curve is below the line. This means that the "y" of the curve is less than the "y" of the line, i.e. $5x^2 - 2x - 6 < 9 - 3x$.

So, $5x^2 - 2x - 6 < 9 - 3x$ when x has any value between $-1{\cdot}84$ and $+1{\cdot}62$.

(vii) At P and Q, the "y's" of the two graphs are the same; that is, $5x^2 - 2x - 6 = 9 - 3x$. (The value of each function is represented by MP or NQ.) So the roots of this equation—that is, the values of x which make the two sides equal—are the "x" of P and the "x" of Q.

$$5x^2 - 2x - 6 = 9 - 3x$$
that is, $5x^2 + x - 15 = 0$
when $x = -1{\cdot}84$ or $1{\cdot}62$

We have here an important general method. If the graphs of two functions of x meet at a point, the x-co-ordinate of this point is a root of the equation formed by putting the two functions equal.

Notice also that if we read the y-co-ordinates of P and Q as well as the x's, we have the solutions of the *simultaneous* equations

$$\left.\begin{array}{l} y = 9 - 3x, \\ y = 5x^2 - 2x - 6 \end{array}\right\} \begin{array}{l} \text{viz., } x = -1{\cdot}84,\ y = 14{\cdot}5 \\ \text{and } x = 1{\cdot}62,\ y = 4{\cdot}1 \end{array}$$

We shall refer to this in the next section.

Using the above method, we can solve *any* quadratic equation by drawing a line across the graph $y = x^2$.

Example 5. Solve in this way the equations:

(i) $x^2 + x - 9 = 0$.

(ii) $8x^2 - x - 20 = 0$, giving the roots correct to 1 place of decimals.

(iii) Explain what happens if you try to solve $2x^2 - 2x + 1 = 0$.

(The values used in plotting the various graphs are not printed. Please check them.)

(i) $x^2 + x - 9 = 0$
$\therefore x^2 = 9 - x$

We draw the line $y = 9 - x$, and find where it meets $y = x^2$.
$x = -3{\cdot}5$ or $2{\cdot}5$.

(ii) $8x^2 - x - 20 = 0$
$\therefore 8x^2 = x + 20$
$\therefore x^2 = \frac{1}{8}x + 2\frac{1}{2}$.

We draw the line $y = \frac{1}{8}x + 2\frac{1}{2}$ and find where it meets $y = x^2$.
$x = -1{\cdot}5$ or $1{\cdot}6$.

(iii) $2x^2 - 2x + 1 = 0$
$\therefore 2x^2 = 2x - 1$
$\therefore x^2 = x - \frac{1}{2}$.

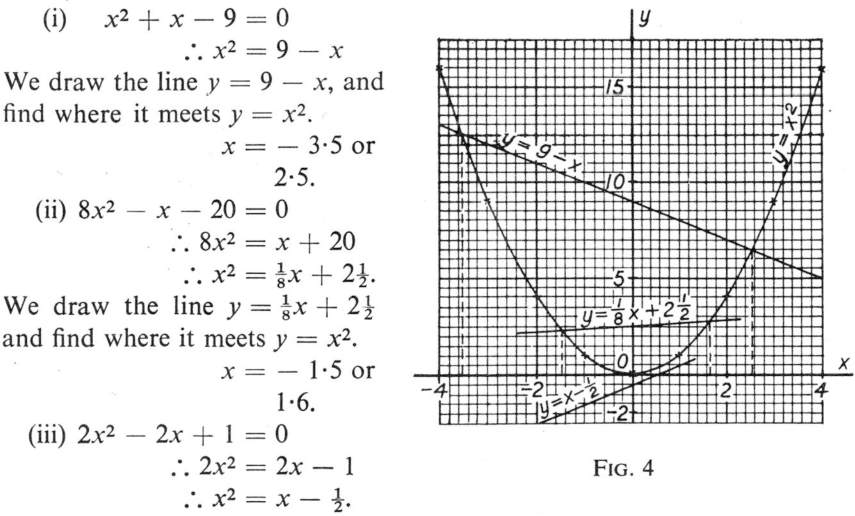

FIG. 4

We draw the line $y = x - \frac{1}{2}$ and find that it does not meet $y = x^2$. The equation has no roots.

(If we try to use the formula, with $a = 2$, $b = -2$, $c = 1$, we find

$$x = \frac{2 \pm \sqrt{-4}}{2}$$

and there is no square root of -4.)

Example 6. Using the same scales and axes, draw the graphs $y = \dfrac{8}{x+2}$ and $y = \frac{1}{2}(11 - 3x)$ from $x = -1$ to $x = 4$.

Explain how:

(i) the roots of the equation $3x^2 - 5x - 6 = 0$;

(ii) the range of values of x for which $3x^2 - 5x - 6 < 0$, may be found from these graphs, and solve the equation.

x	-1	$-\frac{1}{2}$	0	$\frac{1}{2}$	1	$1\frac{1}{2}$	2	$2\frac{1}{2}$	3
$\dfrac{8}{x+2}$	8	5·33	4	3·2	2·67	2·29	2	1·78	1·6
$\frac{1}{2}(11 - 3x)$	7				4				1

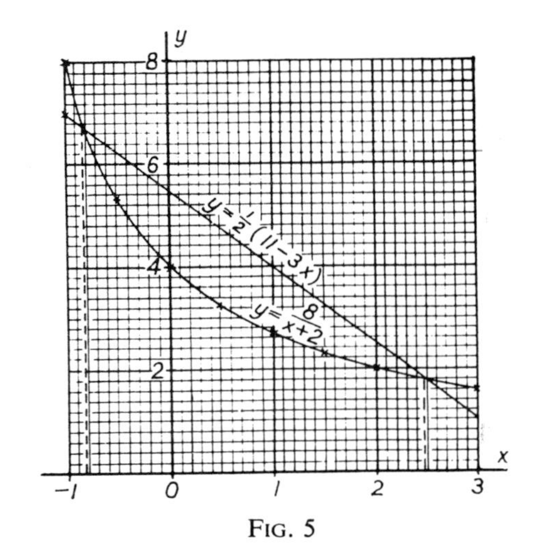

FIG. 5

(i) The graphs meet where $\dfrac{8}{x+2} = \dfrac{11 - 3x}{2}$

i.e. where $16 = (11 - 3x)(x + 2)$

or $16 = 22 - 3x^2 + 5x$

or $3x^2 - 5x - 6 = 0$

The x-co-ordinates of the points of intersection are therefore the roots of this equation.

From the graphs, $x = -·82$ or $2·50$.
(Calculated values are $-·81$, $2·48$.)

(ii) When x has any value between $-\cdot 82$ and $2{\cdot}50$, the curve is below the line; that is,

$$\frac{8}{x+2} < \frac{11-3x}{2}$$

$$\therefore\ 16 < (11-3x)(x+2)$$

$$\text{i.e. } 16 < 22 - 3x^2 + 5x$$

$$\therefore\ 3x^2 - 5x - 6 < 0$$

So this inequality is satisfied by *any value of x between* $-\cdot 82$ *and* $2{\cdot}50$.

EXERCISE 12C

N.B.: Remember that, to draw a reasonably accurate graph, you should plot at least one point for each *half-inch* along the x-axis.

1. Draw the graph $y = x^3$ from $x = -2$ to $x = 2$, using scales of 1 in. to 1 unit for x and 1 in. to 2 units for y.

Using the same axes, draw the line $y = 3x + 1$ and hence solve the equation

(i) $x^3 - 3x - 1 = 0$.

Solve in the same way, by drawing an appropriate straight line in each case, the equations

(ii) $x^3 - 3x + 2 = 0$;

(iii) $2x^3 + x - 10 = 0$.

(*Note:* Any equation which can be put in the form $x^3 = mx + c$ can be solved approximately in this way, by drawing the line $y = mx + c$ across the graph $y = x^3$.)

2. Using scales of 1 in. to 1 for x and 1 in. to 2 for y, draw on the same axes the graphs $y = (x+1)(3-x)$ and $2x - 3y + 1 = 0$, from $x = -2$ to $x = 4$.

(First, write the second equation in the form $y =$ *****.)

(i) For what range of values of x is $(x+1)(3-x)$ positive?

(ii) For what range of values of x is $(x+1)(3-x) > \dfrac{2x+1}{3}$?

(iii) What are the values of x at the points of intersection of the two graphs? Show that these values are the solutions of the equation $3x^2 - 4x - 8 = 0$.

3. Draw the graph $y = \dfrac{10}{x}$, using scales of 1 in. to 1 unit for x and 1 in. to 10 units for y. Plot the points for which $x = \pm\frac{1}{3}, \pm\frac{1}{2}, \pm 1, \pm 1\frac{1}{2}, \pm 2, \pm 2\frac{1}{2}, \pm 3$.

(Remember that there is no value of y when $x = 0$.)

On the same axes draw the line $y = 4x + 2$.

What equation in x can be solved by considering the points where these graphs meet? Read off its roots as accurately as you can.

4. Using the same axes, and scales of 1 in. to 1 unit on each, draw the graphs $y = \dfrac{4}{x+1}$ and $4x + 5y = 16$, from $x = 0$ to $x = 4$.

For what values of x is $\dfrac{16-4x}{5} > \dfrac{4}{x+1}$?

Show how these graphs may be used to solve the equation

$$x^2 - 3x + 1 = 0$$

and give the solutions.

5. Draw the graph $y = x^2(3 - x)$ from $x = -2$ to $x = 4$, using scales of 1 in. to 1 unit for x and 1 in. to 5 units for y.

(i) For what value of x is $y = 7$?

How many roots have the equations:

(ii) $x^2(3 - x) = 5$; (iii) $x^2(3 - x) = 4$; (iv) $x^2(3 - x) = 2$?

By drawing a line across the graph, solve the equation $x^2(3 - x) = 4 - 2x$.

6. Draw on the same axes the graphs $y = \dfrac{12}{x+2}$ and $y = x^2 + 1$ from $x = -1$ to $x = 3$, using scales of 1 in. to 1 unit for x and 1 in. to 2 units for y.

(i) Use the first graph to find $\dfrac{12}{3{\cdot}2}$.

Use the second graph to find:

(ii) $2{\cdot}3^2$; (iii) $\sqrt{7}$.

(iv) Use both graphs to find a root of the equation $x^3 + 2x^2 + x - 10 = 0$.

III. Further Simultaneous Equations

You already know how to solve linear simultaneous equations in two unknowns. We shall now use the method of "Substitution" in cases where *one* of the equations is of the second degree.*

We have already solved the equations $y = 5x^2 - 2x - 6$, $y = 9 - 3x$ by a graphical method (page 235); the equations were represented by a curve and a line which met in two points, so that there were two solutions. We shall find that this is generally so.

Example 7. Solve the equations $4xy = 35$ ....(1)

$x = 6 - y$ ....(2)

The linear equation gives x in terms of y; we substitute directly for x in equation (1).

*A linear equation is one involving only x and y, the graph of which is therefore a straight line, e.g. $3x + 2y = 5$, which may be written $y = 2\frac{1}{2} - 1\frac{1}{2}x$.

A "second degree" or "quadratic" equation is one involving at least one second degree term, x^2, xy or y^2, e.g. $2x^2 - xy + y^2 = 1$.

The problem is generally more difficult if *both* equations are quadratic. There is then no general method which can always be used.

Substituting $6 - y$ for x in equation (1),

$$4(6 - y)y = 35$$

i.e. $4y(6 - y) = 35$ (The order of multiplication does not matter)

$$\therefore 24y - 4y^2 = 35$$

$$\therefore -4y^2 + 24y - 35 = 0$$

$\therefore 4y^2 - 24y + 35 = 0$ (Multiplying both sides by -1)

$$\therefore (2y - 5)(2y - 7) = 0$$

$$\therefore 2y - 5 = 0 \quad \text{or} \quad 2y - 7 = 0$$

$$2y = 5 \qquad 2y = 7$$

$$y = 2\tfrac{1}{2} \qquad y = 3\tfrac{1}{2}$$

Substituting in equation (2),

when $y = 2\frac{1}{2}$, $x = 6 - 2\frac{1}{2} = 3\frac{1}{2}$;
when $y = 3\frac{1}{2}$, $x = 6 - 3\frac{1}{2} = 2\frac{1}{2}$.

Answer: $x = 3\frac{1}{2}$, $y = 2\frac{1}{2}$
or $x = 2\frac{1}{2}$, $y = 3\frac{1}{2}$.

Example 8. Solve the equations

$$x^2 + y^2 + 6y = 4 \ldots\ldots\ldots\ldots\ldots\ldots(1)$$

$$2x - y = 7 \ldots\ldots\ldots\ldots\ldots\ldots(2)$$

(Here we must first use equation (2) to find one unknown in terms of the other. The coefficient of x in equation (2) is 2, the coefficient of y is -1; so we will find y in terms of x, thus avoiding fractions.)

$$2x - y = 7$$

Adding y to both sides, $2x = 7 + y$

Subtracting 7 from both sides, $2x - 7 = y$

i.e. $y = 2x - 7$ ....(3)

Substituting in equation (1),

$$x^2 + (2x - 7)^2 + 6(2x - 7) = 4$$

i.e. $x^2 + 4x^2 - 28x + 49 + 12x - 42 = 4$

$$\therefore 5x^2 - 16x + 3 = 0$$

$$\therefore (x - 3)(5x - 1) = 0$$

$$\therefore x - 3 = 0 \quad \text{or} \quad 5x - 1 = 0$$

$$x = 3 \qquad 5x = 1$$

$$x = \tfrac{1}{5}$$

Substituting in equation (3),

when $x = 3$, $y = 6 - 7 = -1$;
when $x = \frac{1}{5}$, $y = \frac{2}{5} - 7 = -6\frac{3}{5}$.

Answer: $x = 3$, $y = -1$
or $x = \frac{1}{5}$, $y = -6\frac{3}{5}$

Example 9. Solve the equations

$$x^2 + xy - 2y^2 = 4 \quad \ldots\ldots\ldots (1)$$
$$2x + 3y = 7 \quad \ldots\ldots\ldots (2)$$

(Here, we cannot avoid fractions; it would be equally convenient—or inconvenient!—to find x or y from equation (2).)

$$2x + 3y = 7$$
$$\therefore 3y = 7 - 2x$$
$$\therefore y = \frac{7 - 2x}{3} \quad \ldots\ldots\ldots (3)$$

Substituting in equation (1),

$$x^2 + x\left(\frac{7 - 2x}{3}\right) - 2\left(\frac{7 - 2x}{3}\right)^2 = 4$$
$$\text{i.e. } x^2 + \frac{x(7 - 2x)}{3} - \frac{2(7 - 2x)^2}{9} = 4$$

Multiplying both sides by 9,

$$9x^2 + 3x(7 - 2x) - 2(7 - 2x)^2 = 36$$
$$\therefore 9x^2 + 21x - 6x^2 - 2(49 - 28x + 4x^2) = 36$$
$$\therefore 9x^2 + 21x - 6x^2 - 98 + 56x - 8x^2 = 36$$
$$\therefore -5x^2 + 77x - 134 = 0$$
$$\therefore 5x^2 - 77x + 134 = 0$$
$$\therefore (x - 2)(5x - 67) = 0$$
$$\therefore x - 2 = 0 \quad \text{or} \quad 5x - 67 = 0$$
$$x = 2 \qquad\qquad 5x = 67$$
$$x = 13\tfrac{2}{5}$$

Substituting in equation (3),

$$\text{when } x = 2, \quad y = \frac{7 - 4}{3} = 1;$$
$$\text{when } x = 13\tfrac{2}{5}, \quad y = \frac{7 - 26\tfrac{4}{5}}{3} = \frac{-19\tfrac{4}{5}}{3} = -6\tfrac{3}{5}.$$

Answer: $x = 2,\ y = 1$ or $x = 13\tfrac{2}{5},\ y = -6\tfrac{3}{5}$

EXERCISE 12D

Solve the following pairs of simultaneous equations:

1. $y - x = 2,$
$xy = 15.$

2. $x^2 + y^2 = y + 4,$
$y = x + 2.$

3. $y^2 + 4x = 5,$
$x + 2y = 3.$

4. $x^2 - 2xy - 9 = 3y,$
$3x - y = 5.$

5. $x^2 - y^2 = 12,$
$x - 2y = 0.$

6. $13x^2 - 4y^2 = 16,$
$3x + 2y = 0.$

7. $2x^2 - xy - y^2 = 0,$
$5x + 2y = 4.$

8. $6x^2 - 9y^2 - 10y = 5,$
$2x - 3y = 1.$

IV. Equations With Letters

It is a good idea to test your understanding of the processes involved in solving equations by applying them to equations with letters, instead of numbers. We shall use "x" and "y" to stand for unknowns, "a", "b", "c" etc., to stand for the coefficients. We have to find x and/or y in terms of the other letters.

The main thing to remember is always to apply the "principle of fairness" —treat both sides of the equation alike!

Example 10. Solve for x the following equations:

(i) $\frac{a}{x} = \frac{b}{c}$; (ii) $px - a = b - qx$; (iii) $\frac{x-a}{b} = \frac{x-b}{a}$.

(i) $\frac{a}{x} = \frac{b}{c}$

$\therefore\ ac = bx$ (multiplying both sides by xc, to clear fractions).

$\therefore\ \frac{ac}{b} = x$ (dividing both sides by b). i.e. $x = \frac{ac}{b}$

(ii) $px - a = b - qx$

$\therefore\ px = a + b - qx$ (adding a to both sides).

$\therefore\ px + qx = a + b$ (adding qx to both sides, so that all terms containing x are on one side, all terms without x on the other).

$\therefore\ (p + q)x = a + b$ (With numerical coefficients we can say, for example, $2x + 5x = 7x$. Here, we can only say $px + qx = (p + q)x$—taking out the common factor x.)

$\therefore\ x = \frac{a+b}{p+q}$ (dividing both sides by $p + q$).

(iii) $\frac{x-a}{b} = \frac{x-b}{a}$

$\therefore\ a(x - a) = b(x - b)$ (multiplying both sides by ab).

$\therefore\ ax - a^2 = bx - b^2$ (we must multiply out so that we can separate the terms with x from those without).

$\therefore\ ax - bx = a^2 - b^2$ (adding a^2 to, and subtracting bx from, both sides).

$\therefore\ (a - b)x = a^2 - b^2$ (taking out the common factor x).

$\therefore\ x = \frac{a^2 - b^2}{a - b}$ (dividing both sides by $a - b$).

$= \frac{(a-b)(a+b)}{a-b}$ (factorizing the numerator, to see if any simplification is possible).

i.e. $x = a + b$

Example 11.

(i) Solve for x and y the simultaneous equations

$$bx + ay = a^2 + b^2$$
$$ax - by = a^2 + b^2$$

(ii) Solve for x the equation $x^2 + ab = ax + bx$

(i)
$$bx + ay = a^2 + b^2 \quad \dots\dots\dots\dots(1)$$
$$ax - by = a^2 + b^2 \quad \dots\dots\dots\dots(2)$$

Make the coefficients of y equal (but opposite in sign) by multiplying both sides of equation (1) by b, both sides of equation (2) by a:

$$b^2x + aby = a^2b + b^3$$
$$a^2x - aby = a^3 + ab^2$$

Adding,
$$a^2x + b^2x = a^3 + a^2b + ab^2 + b^3$$
$$\therefore (a^2 + b^2)x = a^2(a + b) + b^2(a + b)$$
$$= (a + b)(a^2 + b^2)$$
$$\therefore x = a + b \text{ (dividing both sides by } a^2 + b^2\text{)}$$

Substituting for x in equation (1),

$$b(a + b) + ay = a^2 + b^2$$
$$\text{i.e. } ab + b^2 + ay = a^2 + b^2$$
$$\therefore ay = a^2 - ab \text{ (subtracting } ab + b^2 \text{ from both sides).}$$
$$= a(a - b)$$
$$\therefore y = a - b \quad \text{(dividing both sides by } a\text{).}$$

(ii) This is a quadratic equation; we will write the terms in our usual order:

$$x^2 - ax - bx + ab = 0$$
$$\therefore x(x - a) - b(x - a) = 0$$
$$\therefore (x - a)(x - b) = 0$$
$$\therefore x - a = 0$$
$$\text{or } x - b = 0 \therefore x = a \text{ or } b.$$

EXERCISE 12E

Solve for x the equations in Nos. 1-8

1. $\dfrac{p}{x} = \dfrac{x}{q}$
2. $ax - c = bx + d$
3. $\dfrac{x - a}{a} = \dfrac{x + b}{b}$
4. $\dfrac{x}{2a} + \dfrac{x}{3a} = 10$
5. $\dfrac{a}{bx} + \dfrac{b}{ax} = 1$
6. $\dfrac{x + a}{x - a} = 3$
7. $\dfrac{x - a}{b} + \dfrac{x - b}{a} = 2$
8. $\dfrac{ax + c}{bx - d} = \dfrac{ax - d}{bx + c}$

Solve for x and y the equations in Nos. 9-12.

9. $2x - y = a,$
$5x - 3y = a.$

10. $bx + ay = 2ab,$
$ax - by = a^2 - b^2.$

11. $x - ay = b(a + b),$
$x + by = a(a + b).$

12. $ax + by = \dfrac{a^3 + b^3}{ab},$
$bx + ay = a + b.$

Solve for x the equations in Nos. 13-16.

13. $x^2 + cx + dx + cd = 0$

14. $x^2 + qx = px + pq$

15. $\dfrac{a}{x + b} + \dfrac{b}{x + a} = 1$

16. $\dfrac{a}{x - a} + \dfrac{b}{x - b} = 1 + \dfrac{ab}{(x - a)(x - b)}$

V. Transformation of Formulae

Consider the formula $C = \frac{5}{9}(F - 32)$, where C° and F° are the same temperature measured on the Centigrade and Fahrenheit scales respectively.

The formula is stated in a form suitable for changing Fahrenheit temperatures to Centigrade; that is, given F, to find C.

If, however, we want to convert Centigrade temperatures to Fahrenheit it would be more convenient to have the formula in the form "F = ***." The formula is simply an equation, a statement that two expressions are equal; we have to solve the equation, regarding F as the unknown. This is known as "making F the subject of the formula."

$$C = \tfrac{5}{9}(F - 32)$$

$\therefore \frac{9}{5}C = F - 32$ (multiplying both sides of the equation by $\frac{9}{5}$).

$\therefore \frac{9}{5}C + 32 = F$ (adding 32 to both sides).

That is, $F = \frac{9}{5}C + 32$.

In carrying out this process we are merely solving equations with letters, as in the last section. We will draw attention to the unknown by using bold type.

Example 12. (i) Make r the subject of the formula $V = \frac{1}{3}\pi r^2 h$.

(ii) Make g the subject of the formula $T = 2\pi\sqrt{\dfrac{l}{g}}$.

(In each case, the right-hand side of the formula consists of one term only.)

(i) $V = \frac{1}{3}\pi \mathbf{r}^2 h$

$\therefore 3V = \pi \mathbf{r}^2 h$ (multiplying both sides by 3, to clear fractions).

$\therefore \dfrac{3V}{\pi h} = \mathbf{r}^2$ (dividing both sides by πh).

i.e. $\mathbf{r}^2 = \dfrac{3V}{\pi h}$

$\therefore \mathbf{r} = \sqrt{\dfrac{3V}{\pi h}}$ (taking the square root of each side).

(ii) When the unknown is under a square root sign, both sides must be squared. It is wise first to have the square root on its own.

$$T = 2\pi\sqrt{\frac{l}{g}}$$

$$\therefore \quad \frac{T}{2\pi} = \sqrt{\frac{l}{g}} \quad \text{(dividing both sides by } 2\pi\text{).}$$

$$\therefore \quad \frac{T^2}{4\pi^2} = \frac{l}{g} \quad \text{(squaring both sides).}$$

$$\therefore \quad \frac{T^2 g}{4\pi^2} = l \quad \text{(multiplying both sides by } g\text{).}$$

$$\therefore \quad g = \frac{4\pi^2 l}{T^2} \quad \text{(multiplying both sides by } \frac{4\pi^2}{T^2}\text{).}$$

Example 13. Make:

(i) f the subject of the formula $s = ut + \frac{1}{2}ft^2$;

(ii) P the subject of the formula $A = P + \dfrac{PRT}{100}$;

(iii) w the subject of the formula $E = \dfrac{wa}{(w + W)b}$.

(i)

$$s = ut + \tfrac{1}{2}ft^2$$

$$\therefore \; s - ut = \tfrac{1}{2}ft^2 \quad \text{(subtracting } ut \text{ from both sides, to leave on its own the term containing the unknown).}$$

$$\therefore \; 2(s - ut) = ft^2 \quad \text{(multiplying both sides by 2).}$$

$$\therefore \; \frac{2(s - ut)}{t^2} = f \quad \text{(dividing both sides by } t^2\text{).}$$

i.e.

$$f = \frac{2(s - ut)}{t^2}$$

(ii)

$$A = P + \frac{PRT}{100}$$

$$\therefore \; 100A = 100P + PRT \quad \text{(multiplying by 100, to clear fractions).}$$

(Here the terms containing the unknown are already alone on one side of the equation. With numerical coefficients, e.g. $100P + 50P$, we should say "$150P =$ ***." In doing this, we should in effect be taking P as a common factor: $P(100 + 50)$. This is what we shall do here.)

$$100A = P(100 + RT)$$

$$\therefore \; \frac{100A}{100 + RT} = P \quad \text{(dividing both sides by } 100 + RT\text{).}$$

i.e.

$$P = \frac{100A}{100 + RT}$$

(iii) $$E = \frac{wa}{(w + W)b}$$

$\therefore (w + W)bE = wa$ (multiplying both sides by $(w + W)b$).

$\therefore wbE + WbE = wa$ (multiplying out the bracket so that we can separate the terms containing w from those without it).

$\therefore WbE = wa - wbE$ (subtracting wbE from both sides. This is preferable to "$wbE - wa = - WbE$").

$= w(a - bE)$

$\therefore \frac{WbE}{a - bE} = w$ (dividing both sides by $a - bE$).

i.e. $$w = \frac{WbE}{a - bE}$$

EXERCISE 12F

In each case, make the letter indicated the subject of the given formula.

1. $V = \pi r^2 h$; h.

2. $V = \frac{4}{3}\pi r^3$; r.

3. $T = 2\pi\sqrt{\frac{I}{C}}$; (i) I, (ii) C.

4. $Q = \frac{1}{R}\sqrt{\frac{L}{C}}$; C.

5. $v = u + ft$; f.

6. $v^2 = u^2 + 2fs$; (i) u, (ii) s.

7. $I = \frac{V}{\sqrt{R^2 + X^2}}$; R.

8. $V = \frac{E_1 R_3}{R_1 + R_3}$; R_3.

9. $E = \sqrt{\frac{I_1}{I_1 + I_2}}$; I_1.

10. $L = \frac{R^2 + r^2}{4R}$; r.

11. $E = \frac{9KN}{N + 3K}$; (i) K, (ii) N.

12. $i_2 = I.\frac{R + 2r}{R + 21r}$; (i) R, (ii) r.

VI. Identities

In this chapter we have been concerned with statements of equality—which we call "equations"—and the particular values of "x" which make them true—called the "roots" of the equation.

It may not always be possible to find values of x to make such a statement true.

If, on the other hand, the expressions on either side of the "equals" sign are in fact the same, the statement will be true for *all* values of x. It is then called an "*Identity*."

These points are illustrated as follows:

Example 14. One of the following three statements is an equation, one is an identity, and one is not true for any value of x. Find out which is which, and solve the equation.

(i) $x(x+1)(x+2)-(x-1)x(x+1)=3x^2+3x$;
(ii) $x(x+1)(x+2)-(x-1)x(x+1)=6$;
(iii) $x(x+1)(x+2)-(x-1)x(x+1)=3x^2+3x+1$.

(i) The statement is

$$x(x^2+3x+2)-x(x^2-1)=3x^2+3x$$
$$\text{i.e. } x^3+3x^2+2x-x^3+x=3x^2+3x$$
$$\text{i.e. } 3x^2+3x=3x^2+3x$$

The two sides are in fact the same algebraical expression, so the statement will be true for all values of x. It is an "identity."

(When $x=2$, for example, L.H.S. $=2.3.4-1.2.3=24-6=18$,
R.H.S. $=3.2^2+3.2=12+6=18$.)

(ii) The L.H.S. is the same as before; the statement is

$$3x^2+3x=6$$
$$\text{i.e. } 3x^2+3x-6=0 \quad \text{(subtracting 6 from both sides),}$$
$$\text{or } x^2+x-2=0 \quad \text{(dividing both sides by 3),}$$
$$\text{or } (x+2)(x-1)=0$$

This is true when $x=-2$ and when $x=1$; the statement is an equation, with two solutions (or "roots").

(iii) The statement is

$$3x^2+3x=3x^2+3x+1$$
$$\text{i.e. } 0=1 \text{ (subtracting } 3x^2+3x \text{ from both sides).}$$

This can never be true! Whatever value is given to x, the right-hand side will be one more than the left-hand side.

When you progress further with your mathematics, you will find that you frequently need to express a function in a different form. The next example indicates a way of doing this.

Example 15.

(i) Find constants a and b such that $2x+7=a(x-1)+b(x+2)$ for all values of x.

(ii) If $x^3=ax+bx(x-1)+cx(x-1)(x-2)$ for all values of x, find the constants a, b and c.

(iii) Find constants a and b such that $8x-2x^2-11=a-2(x+b)^2$. Hence find the maximum value of the expression.

(In each case, the statement is to be an identity; the two sides must be the same algebraical expression.)

(i) $$a(x-1)+b(x+2) = ax - a + bx + 2b$$
$$= (a+b)x + (2b-a)$$

This is to be the same expression as $2x+7$.

So we must have $a + b = 2$

$2b - a = 7$

Solving these simultaneous equations, you should find $b = 3$, $a = -1$.

Check: The R.H.S. becomes $-1(x-1) + 3(x+2)$, which is $2x+7$, as required.

(ii) $$ax + bx(x-1) + cx(x-1)(x-2)$$
$$= ax + bx^2 - bx + cx(x^2 - 3x + 2)$$
$$= ax + bx^2 - bx + cx^3 - 3cx^2 + 2cx$$
$$= cx^3 + (b-3c)x^2 + (a-b+2c)x$$

This is to be the same algebraical expression as x^3, i.e. $1x^3$.

So we must have $c = 1$ ....(1)

$b - 3c = 0$ ....(2)

$a - b + 2c = 0$ ....(3)

Substituting for c in equation (2), $b - 3 = 0$, $\therefore b = 3$.

Substituting for b and c in equation (3), $a - 3 + 2 = 0$, $\therefore a = 1$.

So, $a = 1$, $b = 3$, $c = 1$.

Check: The R.H.S. becomes $x + 3x(x-1) + x(x-1)(x-2)$. If you multiply this out and collect up like terms, you will find that this comes to x^3, as required.

(iii) $$a - 2(x+b)^2 = a - 2(x^2 + 2bx + b^2)$$
$$= a - 2x^2 - 4bx - 2b^2$$
$$= (a - 2b^2) - 2x^2 - 4bx$$

This is to be $8x - 2x^2 + 11$; so we must have

$a - 2b^2 = 11$ ....(1)

$-4b = 8$ ....(2)

From equation (2), $b = -2$.

Substituting in equation (1), $a - 8 = 11$, $\therefore a = 19$.

We now have $8x - 2x^2 + 11 = 19 - 2(x-2)^2$.

When $x = 2$, the R.H.S. is $19 - 0 = 19$. For all other values of x, since $(x-2)^2$ is *positive*, we shall be taking something away from the 19.

So, 19 is the maximum value of the expression (when $x = 2$).

EXERCISE 12G

1. Find out which of the following statements is an equation (and solve it), which is an identity and which is never true.

(i) $2x(x+2)(x-1) - (x+1)(2x^2-3) = 5 - x$.

(ii) $\dfrac{4}{x-2} + \dfrac{5}{x-1} = \dfrac{3x^2 - 8}{(x-2)(x-1)} - 3.$

(iii) $\dfrac{1}{x-2} - \dfrac{2}{x+1} = \dfrac{1}{2}.$

2. Find constants a and b such that $x - 4 = ax + b(x + 2)$ for all values of x.

3. If $p(2x - 1) + q(2x + 1) = 6x - 5$ for all values of x, find the constants p and q.

4. Find constants c, d and e such that

$$n^2 + 1 = cn(n - 1) + dn + e$$

for all values of n.

5. Find constants a and b such that

$$3x^2 - 6x + 4 = 3(x + a)^2 + b$$

for all values of x.

Hence find the minimum value of $3x^2 - 6x + 4$.

6. If $a(x - 3)^2 + b(x - 3) = 2x^2 - 9x + c$ for all values of x, find a, b and c.

CHAPTER 13

VARIATION

Direct Variation

If x and y are two variables whose *ratio* is constant,

$$\text{i.e. if } \frac{y}{x} = m, \text{ or } y = mx,$$

where m is a constant, we say that "y varies directly as x," or "y is directly proportional to x." (See Chapter 4, page 156.)

Either of these phrases is denoted by the symbol "$\propto$." So the statement "$y \propto x$" is equivalent to the *equation* $y = mx$.

The graph of y as a function of x is, of course, a straight line through the origin, m being the gradient of the line.

We have now to extend the idea of "direct variation." Think, as an example, of a series of similar rectangles, each with its length twice its breadth. Calling the breadth x in., the area y sq. in., we have

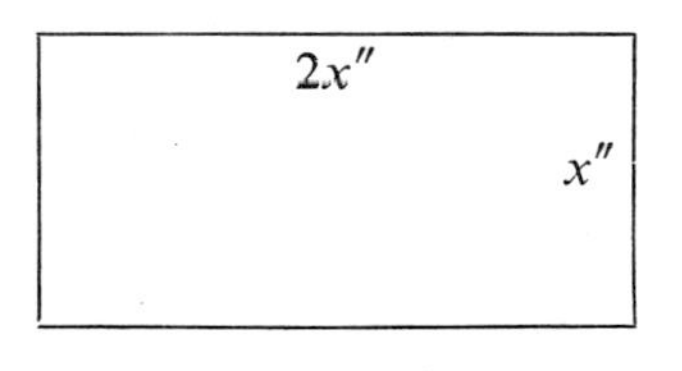

Breadth in in. (x) *Length in in.* ($2x$)	1 2	2 4	3 6	4 8	5 10	6 12
Area in sq. in. (y)	2	8	18	32	50	72

The ratio $\frac{y}{x}$ is *not* constant, so y is not directly proportional to x. Suppose, however, that we tabulate the values of x^2 with those of y:

x^2	1	4	9	16	25	36
y	2	8	18	32	50	72

The ratio $\frac{y}{x^2}$ *is* constant; in fact $\frac{y}{x^2} = 2$, or $y = 2x^2$. In this case, we say that "y is proportional to x^2."

In fact, if n is any given power of x, and if x and y vary so that $\frac{y}{x^n}$ is constant, we say that "y is directly proportional to x^n" or "y varies directly as x^n." (We pointed out in Chapter 4 that the word "directly" is often omitted.)

We shall use "k" for the constant in future, and translate "$y \propto x^n$" as "$y = kx^n$."

Example 1. The table shows approximately (neglecting air resistance) the velocity (v ft./sec.) with which a ball dropped from various heights (h ft.) reaches the ground.

h	1	4	9	16
v	8	16	24	32

Verify that, for these values, $v \propto \sqrt{h}$, and, assuming that this is generally true, write down the formula giving v in terms of h.

We have to show that $\frac{v}{\sqrt{h}}$ is constant.

$$v = 8 \text{ when } \sqrt{h} = 1; \frac{v}{\sqrt{h}} = 8.$$

$$v = 16 \text{ when } \sqrt{h} = 2; \frac{v}{\sqrt{h}} = 8.$$

$$v = 24 \text{ when } \sqrt{h} = 3; \frac{v}{\sqrt{h}} = 8.$$

$$v = 32 \text{ when } \sqrt{h} = 4; \frac{v}{\sqrt{h}} = 8.$$

We see that v *is* proportional to $\sqrt{h}$; the required formula is

$$v = 8\sqrt{h}$$

Example 2. If $y \propto x^2$, and $y = 40$ when $x = 4$, find:

(i) an equation connecting x and y;
(ii) the value of y when $x = 3$;
(iii) the value of x when $y = 250$.

(i) Since $y \propto x^2$, $y = kx^2$, where k is a constant.
When $x = 4$, $y = 40$; $\therefore 40 = k.16$

$$\therefore k = \tfrac{40}{16} = \tfrac{5}{2}$$

Hence the required equation is $y = \frac{5}{2}x^2$ ....(1)

(ii) Substituting in equation (1), when $x = 3$, $y = \frac{5}{2}.9 = 22\frac{1}{2}$.

Note: If we had not had to find the equation first, it would have been quicker to proceed as follows:

$$\text{Since } y \propto x^2, \frac{y}{x^2} \text{ is constant.}$$

When $x = 4$, $y = 40$;
when $x = 3$, $y = ?$ (p, say).

$$\therefore \frac{p}{3^2} = \frac{40}{4^2}$$

$$\therefore p = \tfrac{40}{16} \times 9 = 22\tfrac{1}{2}$$

(iii) When $y = 250$,

$$250 = \tfrac{5}{2}x^2$$

$$\therefore 5x^2 = 500$$

$$\therefore x^2 = 100$$

$$\therefore x = 10$$

Example 3. Show that the weight of a solid sphere of given material varies as the cube of its radius.

If the weight of such a sphere of radius 1 cm. is 297 gm., find to the nearest 10 gm. the weight of one of radius 2 cm.

If the radius of a sphere is r cm., its volume is $\frac{4}{3}\pi r^3$ cu. cm. Suppose that 1 c.c. of the given material weighs w gm. Then, if we call the weight of the sphere W gm., we shall have

$$W = \tfrac{4}{3}\pi r^3 w$$

$$\therefore \frac{W}{r^3} = \frac{4}{3}\pi w, \text{ which is constant.}$$

So the weight varies as the cube of the radius.

When $r = 1$, $W = 297$;
when $r = 2$, $W = ?$ (x, say).

Hence, since $\frac{W}{r^3}$ is constant,

$$\frac{x}{2^3} = \frac{297}{1^3}$$

$$\text{i.e. } \frac{x}{8} = 297$$

$$\therefore x = 2376$$

The weight of the sphere of radius 2 cm. is 2380 gm. approx.

Inverse Variation

Consider the time taken to travel a given distance—20 miles, say—at various speeds:

Speed (v *m.p.h.*)	4	5	8	10	12	16	20	30	40
Time (t *hours*)	5	4	$2\frac{1}{2}$	2	$1\frac{2}{3}$	$1\frac{1}{4}$	1	$\frac{2}{3}$	$\frac{1}{2}$

The equation connecting v and t is

$$t = \frac{20}{v}, \text{ or } vt = 20.$$

If v is *doubled,* t is *halved,* and so on. This time, the *product* of v and t (not their ratio) is constant.

We say that "*t varies inversely as v*" or "*t is inversely proportional to v.*"

Notice that the formula can be written

$$t = 20 \cdot \frac{1}{v}, \text{ or } \frac{t}{\frac{1}{v}} = 20$$

so that t varies directly as $\frac{1}{v}$, and this inverse proportion relationship is sometimes written "$t \propto \frac{1}{v}$."

If n is any given power of x, and if x and y vary so that $y.x^n$ is constant, we say that "y varies inversely as x^n" or "y is inversely proportional to x^n," and write

$$y \propto \frac{1}{x^n}, \text{ or } y = \frac{k}{x^n}, \text{ where } k \text{ is a constant.}$$

Example 4. If y is inversely proportional to the cube root of x, and $y = 5$ when $x = 27$, find (i) the formula connecting x and y, (ii) the value of x when $y = 3$.

(i) Let the formula be $\quad y = \frac{k}{\sqrt[3]{x}}$

When $x = 27$, $y = 5$; $\quad \therefore 5 = \frac{k}{\sqrt[3]{27}} = \frac{k}{3}$

$$\therefore k = 15$$

So the formula is $\quad y = \frac{15}{\sqrt[3]{x}}$

(ii) When $y = 3$, $\quad 3 = \frac{15}{\sqrt[3]{x}}$

$$\therefore 3.\sqrt[3]{x} = 15$$

$$\therefore \sqrt[3]{x} = 5$$

$$\therefore x = 125$$

Example 5. The weight of a body (that is, the force with which it is pulled towards the earth) varies inversely as the square of its distance from the centre of the earth. If a boulder on the seashore weighs 1 ton, what would it weigh if it could be carried to the top of Mount Everest? Take the radius of the earth as 4,000 miles, the height of Mount Everest as $5\frac{1}{2}$ miles.

Call the distance from the centre of the earth d miles; the weight w lb.

When $d = 4000$, $\quad w = 2240$.

When $d = 4005\frac{1}{2}$, $w = $? (x, say).

Since w varies inversely as d^2, we know that wd^2 is constant. Hence, if the required weight is x lb.,

$$x.(4005\tfrac{1}{2})^2 = 2240.4000^2$$

$$\therefore x = \frac{2240.(4000)^2}{(4005{\cdot}5)^2}$$

$$= \frac{2240.16000000}{16044000}$$

$$= 2234 \text{ lb. approx.}$$

EXERCISE 13A

1. If $y \propto x^3$, and $y = 6$ when $x = 2$, find (i) the value of y when $x = 4$, (ii) the value of x when $y = 162$.

2. If $y \propto \frac{1}{x^2}$, and $y = 1\frac{1}{4}$ when $x = 4$, find y in terms of x, and the value of y when $x = \frac{1}{2}$.

3. The cost of cementing the base of a circular fish-pond varies as the square of the diameter of the pond. If the cost is 12 shillings when the diameter is 4 ft., find the cost when the diameter is 6 ft.

4. The number of swings made per minute by a simple pendulum is inversely proportional to the square root of its length. If a pendulum 4 ft. long swings 27 times a minute, find, to the nearest whole number, the number of swings made by one 3 ft. long.

5. If a given voltage is applied to an electrical circuit, the current (I amps) is inversely proportional to the resistance (R ohms). If $I = 4$ when $R = 50$, calculate (i) the value of I when $R = 20$, (ii) the value of R if $I = 6\frac{1}{4}$.

6. When you look out to sea, the distance of the horizon (d miles) is proportional to the square root of your height (h feet) above sea level. At height 6 ft., the distance is 3 miles. Express d in terms of h, and find the distance of the horizon from a height of 96 ft.

Joint Variation

The volume of a cylinder is given by the formula $V = \pi r^2 h$. Suppose that we have a number of cylinders, all with the same radius but with different heights; then $\frac{V}{h} = \pi r^2$, which is constant, so that $V \propto h$.

If, on the other hand, we have cylinders all of the same height but with different radii, then $\frac{V}{r^2} = \pi h$, which is constant, so that $V \propto r^2$.

We say that "V varies directly as the height and as the square of the radius." This is an example of "Joint Variation."

Example 6. The electrical resistance of a wire of given material varies directly as its length and inversely as the square of its diameter. The resistance of a piece of copper wire of diameter $\frac{1}{20}$ in. and length 1 yd. is $\frac{1}{60}$ ohm. Find the resistance of a similar wire 10 ft. long and $\frac{1}{25}$ in. in diameter.

Call the resistance R ohms, the length L ft., the diameter D in. We are told $R \propto L$ and $R \propto \frac{1}{D^2}$; this means that $R = \frac{kL}{D^2}$, where k is a constant.

When $L = 3$ and $D = \frac{1}{20}$, $R = \frac{1}{60}$;

$$\therefore \frac{1}{60} = \frac{k.3}{(\frac{1}{20})^2} = \frac{3k}{\frac{1}{400}}$$

$$\therefore \frac{1}{60} = 1200k$$

$$\therefore k = \frac{1}{72000}$$

$$\text{Hence } R = \frac{1}{72000} \cdot \frac{L}{D^2}$$

When $L = 10$ and $D = \frac{1}{25}$,

$$R = \frac{1}{72000} \times \frac{10}{(\frac{1}{25})^2}$$

$$= \frac{10}{72000} \times 625$$

$$= \frac{25}{288}$$

$$= \cdot 09 \text{ approx.}$$

The resistance is ·09 ohms approx.

Partial Variation

If a formula giving one quantity (y, say) in terms of another (x) contains two or more terms, y will not vary either directly or inversely as any power of x, but the separate terms may do so. This is called "Partial Variation."

Example 7. y varies partly as x and partly inversely as x^2. When $x = 1, y = 7$; when $x = 2, y = 7$. Find the value of y when $x = 4$.

(We must first find y in terms of x.)

The first term varies as x; call it mx, where m is a constant.

The second term varies inversely as x^2; call it $\frac{n}{x^2}$, where n is a constant.

$$\text{Then } y = mx + \frac{n}{x^2}$$

When $x = 1, y = 7$; $\therefore m + n = 7$

When $x = 2, y = 7$; $\therefore 2m + \frac{n}{4} = 7$

Solving these simultaneous equations, you should find $m = 3, n = 4$.

$$\text{Hence } y = 3x + \frac{4}{x^2}$$

When $x = 4$, $y = 12\frac{1}{4}$.

Example 8. The resistance to the motion of a car is partly constant and partly varies as the square of the velocity. At 20 m.p.h. the resistance is 46 lb. wt., at 40 m.p.h. it is 94 lb. wt. Find the resistance at 60 m.p.h.

Call the resistance R lb. wt. when the velocity is v m.p.h.

Then $R = p + qv^2$, where p and q are constants.

When $v = 20$, $R = 46$; $\therefore 46 = p + 400q$ ....(1)

When $v = 40$, $R = 94$; $\therefore 94 = p + 1600q$ ....(2)

$$\text{Subtracting, } 48 = 1200q$$

$$\therefore q = \tfrac{48}{1200} = \tfrac{1}{25}.$$

Substituting in equation (1), $46 = p + 16$, $\therefore p = 30$

$$\text{Hence } R = 30 + \tfrac{1}{25}v^2$$

$$\text{When } v = 60,\ R = 30 + \tfrac{1}{25}.3600$$

$$= 30 + 144 = 174$$

The resistance at 60 m.p.h. is 174 lb. wt.

EXERCISE 13B

1. The volume of a cone varies directly as its height and as the square of its base-radius. What would be the effect on the volume of doubling the height and multiplying the base-radius by 3?

If a cone 1 ft. high and with base-radius $3\frac{1}{2}$ in. has a volume of 154 cu. in., what is the volume of a cone 9 in. high and base-radius 7 in.?

2. If p varies directly as x and as the cube of y, and inversely as the square root of z, and if $p = 72$ when $x = 3$, $y = 2$, $z = 4$, find the value of p when $x = 1\frac{1}{2}$, $y = 6$ and $z = 144$.

3. The work done in stretching an elastic string varies directly as the square of the extension and inversely as the natural length of the string. If $\frac{2}{3}$ ft.-lb. wt. of work is needed to produce an extension of 3 in. in a string of natural length 3 ft., find the work required to double the length of a similar string of natural length 2 ft.

4. In a certain machine, the effort (P lb. wt.) required to raise a load (W lb.) is partly constant and partly varies as the load. If an effort of 30 lb. wt. is needed to raise a load of 50 lb., and an effort of 35 lb. wt. to raise a load of 100 lb., find the formula giving P in terms of W, and the load that can be raised by an effort of 65 lb. wt.

5. If y varies partly as x and partly as x^2, and if the values of y when $x = 4$ and 5 are 56 and 85 respectively, find the value of y when $x = 3$.

6. The length (s ft.) of a wire stretched (but sagging) between two points L ft. apart on the same level, varies partly as L and partly inversely as L. If $s = 100{\cdot}24$ when $L = 100$ and $s = 200{\cdot}12$ when $L = 200$, find s when $L = 300$.

CHAPTER 14

FRACTIONS AND FACTORS

THE VALUE of a fraction is unchanged if the numerator and the denominator are multiplied or divided by the same factor ($\frac{2}{3} = \frac{4}{6} = \frac{6}{9}$; $\frac{9}{12} = \frac{3}{4}$; and so on).

Putting this general idea into symbols, we can write $\frac{a}{b} = \frac{ax}{bx}$.

This principle of "equivalent fractions" is the basis of nearly all work with fractions. It is important to remember that in using the relationship the other way round $\left(\frac{ax}{bx} = \frac{a}{b}\right)$, to simplify a fraction by "cancelling," we are *dividing* numerator and denominator. To find out what will divide into an algebraic expression is to find out its *factors*. Always factorize!

Example 1: Simplify (i) $\frac{x^2 - 3x}{x^2 - 9}$ (ii) $\frac{2x^3 - 5x^2 + 2x}{x^3 - 2x^2 + x - 2}$

(i) $\frac{x^2 - 3x}{x^2 - 9} = \frac{x(x-3)}{(x+3)(x-3)} = \frac{x}{x+3}$

(ii) $\frac{2x^3 - 5x^2 + 2x}{x^3 - 2x^2 + x - 2} = \frac{x(2x^2 - 5x + 2)}{x^2(x-2) + (x-2)}$

$= \frac{x(2x-1)(x-2)}{(x-2)(x^2+1)}$

$= \frac{x(2x-1)}{x^2+1}$ (dividing numerator and denominator by $x - 2$).

(The methods of factorization used here were explained fully in Book I.)

If $x = 5$, $y = 3$, what are the values of $x - y$, $y - x$, $x + y$, $-x - y$? (Please work them out before looking at the footnote.*)

We asked this because the relationships between these expressions often trip people up. These relationships are, of course (!),

(a) $y - x = -x + y = -(x - y)$, so that $\frac{x-y}{y-x} = \frac{x-y}{-(x-y)} = -1$.

(b) $-x - y = -(x + y)$, so that $\frac{x+y}{-x-y} = \frac{x+y}{-(x+y)} = -1$.

*+ 2, − 2, + 8, − 8.

Example 2: Simplify $\dfrac{x^3 - x^2 - 2x}{12x^2 - 3x^4}$

The expression $= \dfrac{x(x^2 - x - 2)}{3x^2(4 - x^2)} = \dfrac{x(x-2)(x+1)}{3x^2(2-x)(2+x)}$

$= \dfrac{(-1)(x+1)}{3x(2+x)}$ {dividing numerator and denominator by $x(2-x)$}

$= \dfrac{-x-1}{3x(2+x)}$

Addition and Subtraction

As in arithmetic, we must first arrange the fractions with a common denominator, which will have to contain all the factors of each separate denominator.

Example 3: Simplify (i) $\dfrac{x+1}{x^2-4} - \dfrac{1}{x+2}$

(ii) $\dfrac{x+y}{x-y} - \dfrac{x-y}{x+y}$

(iii) $\dfrac{1}{2x+1} - \dfrac{2}{x-3} + \dfrac{5x-1}{2x^2-5x-3}$

(iv) $\dfrac{2x-9}{2x^2-6x+4} - \dfrac{2x+3}{6x^2-10x-4} - \dfrac{2x}{3x^2-2x-1}$

(i) The expression $= \dfrac{x+1}{(x-2)(x+2)} - \dfrac{1}{x+2}$

$= \dfrac{x+1}{(x-2)(x+2)} - \dfrac{x-2}{(x-2)(x+2)}$ (multiplying numerator and denominator of the second fraction by $x - 2$)

$= \dfrac{(x+1)-(x-2)}{(x-2)(x+2)}$

$= \dfrac{x+1-x+2}{(x-2)(x+2)}$

$= \dfrac{3}{(x-2)(x+2)}$

(ii) The expression $= \dfrac{(x+y)^2}{(x-y)(x+y)} - \dfrac{(x-y)^2}{(x+y)(x-y)}$

$= \dfrac{(x+y)^2 - (x-y)^2}{(x+y)(x-y)}$

$= \dfrac{(x^2+2xy+y^2) - (x^2-2xy+y^2)}{(x+y)(x-y)}$

$= \dfrac{x^2+2xy+y^2-x^2+2xy-y^2}{(x+y)(x-y)} = \dfrac{4xy}{x^2-y^2}$

Alternatively, after the second line, we could go on,

$$= \frac{\{(x + y) - (x - y)\}\ \{(x + y) + (x - y)\}}{(x + y)\ (x - y)}$$

$$= \frac{(x + y - x + y)\ (x + y + x - y)}{(x + y)\ (x - y)}$$

$$= \frac{(2y)\ (2x)}{(x + y)\ (x - y)}$$

$$= \frac{4xy}{(x + y)\ (x - y)}$$

(See page 259.)

(iii) The expression $= \dfrac{1}{2x + 1} - \dfrac{2}{x - 3} + \dfrac{5x - 1}{(2x + 1)\ (x - 3)}$

(The denominator of the third fraction has both the other denominators as factors, so we can use it as our common denominator. We will multiply numerator and denominator of the first fraction by $x - 3$, those of the second by $2x + 1$.)

The expression $= \dfrac{x - 3}{(2x + 1)\ (x - 3)} - \dfrac{2\ (2x + 1)}{(2x + 1)\ (x - 3)} + \dfrac{5x - 1}{(2x + 1)\ (x - 3)}$

$$= \frac{(x - 3) - 2\ (2x + 1) + (5x - 1)}{(2x + 1)\ (x - 3)}$$

$$= \frac{x - 3 - 4x - 2 + 5x - 1}{(2x + 1)\ (x - 3)}$$

$$= \frac{2x - 6}{(2x + 1)\ (x - 3)}$$

$= \dfrac{2\ (x - 3)}{(2x + 1)\ (x - 3)}$ (We factorize the numerator, to see whether any factor "cancels.")

$$= \frac{2}{2x + 1}$$

(iv) The expression

$$= \frac{2x - 9}{2\ (x^2 - 3x + 2)} - \frac{2x + 3}{2\ (3x^2 - 5x - 2)} - \frac{2x}{3x^2 - 2x - 1}$$

$$= \frac{2x - 9}{2\ (x - 1)\ (x - 2)} - \frac{2x + 3}{2\ (x - 2)\ (3x + 1)} - \frac{2x}{(x - 1)\ (3x + 1)}$$

{Factors appearing in the denominators are 2, $x - 1$, $x - 2$, $3x + 1$; so our lowest common denominator is $2\ (x - 1)\ (x - 2)\ (3x + 1)$. We must multiply the first denominator—and numerator—by $3x + 1$, the second by $x - 1$, the third by $2\ (x - 2)$.}

$$\text{The expression} = \frac{(2x-9)(3x+1)}{2(x-1)(x-2)(3x+1)} - \frac{(2x+3)(x-1)}{2(x-1)(x-2)(3x+1)} - \frac{2x.2(x-2)}{2(x-1)(x-2)(3x+1)}$$

$$= \frac{(2x-9)(3x+1)-(2x+3)(x-1)-4x(x-2)}{2(x-1)(x-2)(3x+1)}$$

$$= \frac{(6x^2-25x-9)-(2x^2+x-3)-(4x^2-8x)}{2(x-1)(x-2)(3x+1)}$$

$$= \frac{6x^2-25x-9-2x^2-x+3-4x^2+8x}{2(x-1)(x-2)(3x+1)}$$

$$= \frac{-18x-6}{2(x-1)(x-2)(3x+1)}$$

$$= \frac{-6(3x+1)}{2(x-1)(x-2)(3x+1)}$$

$$= \frac{-3}{(x-1)(x-2)}$$ {dividing numerator and denominator by $2(3x+1)$.}

Multiplication and Division

Remember that in multiplication and division of fractions, mixed numbers must first be expressed as improper fractions ($2\frac{3}{4} \div 3\frac{1}{3} = \frac{11}{4} \div \frac{10}{3} = \frac{11}{4} \times \frac{3}{10}$, etc.). The algebraical generalization of this is brought out in parts (ii) and (iii) of Example 4.

Example 4: Simplify (i) $\dfrac{x^2-2x}{2x^2+x-1} \times \dfrac{x+1}{x^3-4x}$

(ii) $\left(\dfrac{1}{b^2} - \dfrac{1}{a^2}\right) \div \left(\dfrac{1}{a} + \dfrac{1}{b}\right)$

(iii) $\left(\dfrac{1}{x^2+x-2} + \dfrac{1}{x^2-x-6}\right) \times \left(\dfrac{3-2x}{2-x} - x\right)$

(i) $$\text{The expression} = \frac{x(x-2)}{(2x-1)(x+1)} \times \frac{x+1}{x(x^2-4)}$$

$$= \frac{x(x-2)}{(2x-1)(x+1)} \times \frac{x+1}{x(x-2)(x+2)}$$

$$= \frac{1}{(2x-1)(x+2)}$$

(ii) $$\text{The expression} = \left(\frac{a^2-b^2}{a^2b^2}\right) \div \left(\frac{a+b}{ab}\right)$$

$$= \frac{(a-b)(a+b)}{a^2b^2} \times \frac{ab}{a+b} = \frac{a-b}{ab}$$

(iii) The expression

$$= \left\{ \frac{1}{(x+2)(x-1)} + \frac{1}{(x+2)(x-3)} \right\} \times \left(\frac{3-2x}{2-x} - \frac{x}{1} \right)$$

$$= \left\{ \frac{x-3}{(x+2)(x-1)(x-3)} + \frac{x-1}{(x+2)(x-1)(x-3)} \right\} \times \left\{ \frac{3-2x}{2-x} - \frac{x(2-x)}{2-x} \right\}$$

$$= \frac{(x-3)+(x-1)}{(x+2)(x-1)(x-3)} \times \frac{(3-2x)-x(2-x)}{2-x}$$

$$= \frac{x-3+x-1}{(x+2)(x-1)(x-3)} \times \frac{3-2x-2x+x^2}{2-x}$$

$$= \frac{2x-4}{(x+2)(x-1)(x-3)} \times \frac{x^2-4x+3}{2-x}$$

$$= \frac{2(x-2)}{(x+2)(x-1)(x-3)} \times \frac{(x-1)(x-3)}{-(x-2)}$$

$$= \frac{2}{-(x+2)}$$

$$= -\frac{2}{x+2}$$

EXERCISE 14A

Simplify the following as far as possible:

1. $\dfrac{t^2+2t}{t^2}$

2. $\dfrac{x^2-1}{x-1}$

3. $\dfrac{x^3-25x}{x+5}$

4. $\dfrac{x^3-x^2-2x}{12x^2-3x^4}$

5. $\dfrac{2x^2-5xy+2y^2}{3x^2-5xy-2y^2}$

6. $\dfrac{3x^2+11x-4}{2x^2+11x+12}$

7. $\dfrac{3}{x-1} - \dfrac{2}{x+2}$

8. $\dfrac{1}{x-3} - \dfrac{1}{x-2}$

9. $\dfrac{1}{2x-5} - \dfrac{1}{2x}$

10. $\dfrac{x-1}{4x-3} + \dfrac{x+1}{3x+4}$

11. $\dfrac{x}{x-y} - \dfrac{y}{x+y}$

12. $\dfrac{y}{x-y} + \dfrac{x}{x+y}$

13. $\dfrac{1}{2x-1} + \dfrac{1}{x+4} + \dfrac{9}{2x^2+7x-4}$

14. $\dfrac{x^2-xy}{x^2-y^2} \times \dfrac{(x+y)^2}{xy-y^2}$

15. $\dfrac{x^2-3x}{3x^2-x-2} \div \dfrac{x^3-9x}{x^2+2x-3}$

16. $\dfrac{x^2+x-2}{6x^2-x-1} \times \dfrac{3x^2+13x+4}{2x^2+3x-2} \div \dfrac{x^2+3x+4}{4x^2-4x+1}$

17. $\frac{1}{2a}\left(\frac{1}{x-a} - \frac{1}{x+a}\right)$

18. $\left(1 + \frac{2}{x-2}\right) \div \left(1 - \frac{1}{x+1}\right)$

19. $\left(\frac{1}{x^2 - 4x + 3} - \frac{1}{x^2 + 4x - 5}\right) \times \left(x - \frac{15}{x+2}\right)$

20. $\frac{1}{\frac{1}{x} + \frac{1}{y}} \times \left(\frac{x}{y} - \frac{y}{x}\right)$

Factors

The previous section gives plenty of practice at simple factorization! Here, we draw attention to two particular ideas, with which you are already familiar.

(a) *Difference of Two squares.*

$$x^2 - y^2 = (x - y)(x + y)$$

The "x" and "y" could be replaced by any algebraical expression. Sometimes we shall try to make this stand out by putting the expressions in different-shaped "boxes." You may or may not find this a help; it sometimes makes things clearer to people (Fig. 1).

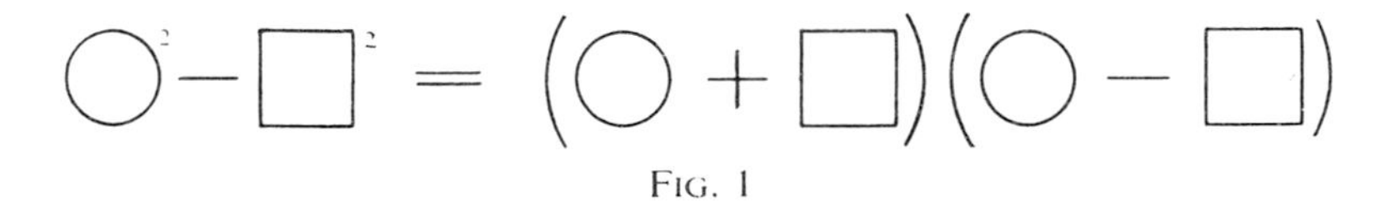

FIG. 1

(b) *Factorization by Grouping.*

e.g. $ax + ay - bx - by$
$= a(x + y) - b(x + y)$
$= (x + y)(a - b)$

This depends on what is known as the "Distributive Law," that

$$ap + bp = p(a + b).$$

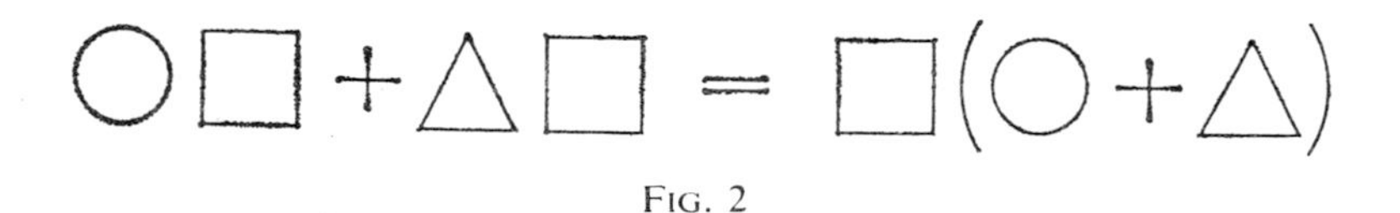

FIG. 2

Again, we may write any expression we like in our boxes (Fig. 2).

Here are some harder examples, based mainly on these two ideas.

Example 5. Factorize the following expressions as far as possible.

(i) $2x^3 - 3x^2 + 2x - 3$

(ii) $2x^3 - x^2 - 8x + 4$

(iii) $a^2 - 6ab + 9b^2 - 2a + 6b$

(iv) $4p^2 - 25q^2 - 6p - 15q$

(v) $x^4 - 17x^2 + 16$

(vi) $x^2 - 4(y - z)^2$

(vii) $2(r - 2s)^2 - 18(2r - s)^2$

(viii) $(c + d)^2 - c^2 + d^2$

In each case we will write a normal statement of the factorization, but will add additional steps where they may help to clear up difficulties.

(i) $\quad 2x^3 - 3x^2 + 2x - 3$

$= x^2(2x - 3) + (2x - 3)$

$$\left[\bigcirc\!\!\!\!\!\!x^2\;\boxed{2x-3} + \triangle\!\!\!\!\!1\;\;\boxed{2x-3}\right]$$

$= (2x - 3)(x^2 + 1)$

(ii) $\quad 2x^3 - x^2 - 8x + 4$

$= x^2(2x - 1) - 4(2x - 1)$

$$\left[\bigcirc\!\!\!\!\!\!x^2\;\boxed{2x-1} - \triangle\!\!\!\!\!4\;\;\boxed{2x-1}\right]$$

$= (2x - 1)(x^2 - 4)$

$$\left[= \boxed{2x-1}\left\{\bigcirc\!\!\!\!\!\!x^2 - \bigcirc\!\!\!\!\!\!2^2\right\}\right]$$

$= (2x - 1)(x - 2)(x + 2)$

(iii) $\quad a^2 - 6ab + 9b^2 - 2a + 6b$

$= (a^2 - 6ab + 9b^2) + (-2a + 6b)$

$= (a - 3b)^2 - 2(a - 3b)$

$$\left[\left(a-3b\right)\;\boxed{a-3b} - \triangle\!\!\!\!\!2\;\;\boxed{a-3b}\right]$$

$= (a - 3b)(a - 3b - 2)$

$$\left[\boxed{a-3b}\left\{\left(a-3b\right) - \triangle\!\!\!\!\!2\;\right\}\right]$$

(iv) $\quad 4p^2 - 25q^2 - 6p - 15q$

$= (4p^2 - 25q^2) - 3(2p + 5q)$

$= (2p - 5q)(2p + 5q) - 3(2p + 5q)$

$= (2p + 5q)(2p - 5q - 3)$

(v) $\quad x^4 - 17x^2 + 16$

$= (x^2 - 1)(x^2 - 16)$

$= (x - 1)(x + 1)(x - 4)(x + 4)$

(vi) $x^2 - 4(y - z)^2$
$= x^2 - \{2(y - z)\}^2$
$= \{x - 2(y - z)\}\{x + 2(y - z)\}$
$= (x - 2y + 2z)(x + 2y - 2z)$

(vii) $2(r - 2s)^2 - 18(2r - s)^2$
$= 2\{(r - 2s)^2 - 9(2r - s)^2\}$
(Always take out common factors first where possible.)
$= 2\{(r - 2s) - 3(2r - s)\}\{(r - 2s) + 3(2r - s)\}$

(since we have $\boxed{r - 2s}^2 - \boxed{3(2r - s)}^2$)

$= 2(r - 2s - 6r + 3s)(r - 2s + 6r - 3s)$
$= 2(s - 5r)(7r - 5s)$

Notice that in this case we could have multiplied out:

$$2\{(r - 2s)^2 - 9(2r - s)^2\}$$
$$= 2\{(r^2 - 4rs + 4s^2) - 9(4r^2 - 4rs + s^2)\}$$
$$= 2(r^2 - 4rs + 4s^2 - 36r^2 + 36rs - 9s^2)$$
$$= 2(-35r^2 + 32rs - 5s^2)$$
$$= -2(35r^2 - 32rs + 5s^2)$$
$$= -2(5r - s)(7r - 5s)$$
$$= 2(s - 5r)(7r - 5s)$$

This, however, is not nearly as neat as the previous method.

EXERCISE 14B

Factorize the following expressions as far as possible:

1. $x^3 + x^2 - 4x - 4$
2. $8x^3 + 12x^2 - 2x - 3$
3. $x^3 - x^2 - x + 1$
4. $x^3 + 3x^2 - 9x - 27$
5. $(3x - 4y)^2 - 15x + 20y$
6. $(2x - y)^2 + (4x - 2y)$
7. $p^2 + 2pq + q^2 + 2p + 2q$
8. $x^2 - y^2 + 2x + 2y$
9. $9m^2 - 49n^2 - 12m + 28n$
10. $4x^3 - 8x^2 - 9x + 18$
11. $x^4 - 13x^2 + 36$
12. $x^4 - 1$
13. $4a^2 - 25(b + c)^2$
14. $16(p + q)^2 - 9q^2$
15. $(x - y)^2 - 4(x + y)^2$
16. $3x^2 - 12(x + 2y)^2$

The Factor Theorem

Consider the function $x^2 + 3x - 4$ ("y" for short).

If $x = 1$, $y = 1 + 3 - 4 = 0$.

If $x = -4$, $y = (-4)^2 + 3(-4) - 4 = 16 - 12 - 4 = 0$.

The two values of x which we have chosen both make $y = 0$. This is hardly surprising, since $x^2 + 3x - 4 = (x - 1)(x + 4)$, and we have chosen the values of x which make the factors zero!

Obviously, any value of x which makes a factor zero, makes the whole expression zero. We have used this fact many times in solving quadratic equations.

Here is another example:

$$\begin{aligned}(x+1)(2x-1)(x-2) &= (x+1)(2x^2-5x+2)\\ &= x(2x^2-5x+2)+1(2x^2-5x+2)\\ &= 2x^3-5x^2+2x+2x^2-5x+2\\ &= 2x^3-3x^2-3x+2\end{aligned}$$

i.e. $2x^3-3x^2-3x+2\,(=y\text{, say}) = (x+1)(2x-1)(x-2)$

The values of x which make the factors zero are -1, $\frac{1}{2}$ and 2. When x has any one of these values, the product of the factors is zero. Confirm this by direct substitution in the left-hand side:

$$\begin{aligned}\text{When } x=-1,\ y &= 2(-1)^3-3(-1)^2-3(-1)+2\\ &= 2(-1)-3(+1)+3+2\\ &= -2-3+3+2\\ &= 0\end{aligned}$$

Try the others for yourself.

Again, any value of x which makes a factor zero, makes the value of the function zero.

Does this work the other way round? Remember that we are thinking only of functions such as x^2-3x-4, $2x^3-3x^2-3x+2$, x^4+x^2-8 and so on, in which all the powers of x are positive whole numbers. They are called "polynomials in x." If a polynomial is zero when x has some particular value, say $x=k$, is $x-k$ *necessarily* a factor?

First, consider the statement "$27 \div 6 = 4$, remainder 3" (4 is the "quotient").

Another way of writing it is "$27 = (6 \times 4) + 3$."

Now, take an algebraical example:

$$\begin{array}{r l} x-2)\,2x^3-\ x^2-4x-3\,(2x^2+3x+2 & \\ \underline{2x^3-4x^2} & \\ 3x^2-4x & \\ \underline{3x^2-6x} & \\ 2x-3 & \\ \underline{2x-4} & \\ \underline{1} & \end{array}$$

The quotient is $2x^2+3x+2$, the remainder is 1.

We can write this as

$$\text{“}2x^3-x^2-4x-3=(x-2)(2x^2+3x+2)+1\text{”}$$

If you multiply out and collect up the terms on the right-hand side, you will see that this is correct. Remember that this is an identity; the two sides are the *same algebraic expression;* they are equal when x has *any* particular value.

For example, when $x = 2$, the right-hand side is $0 + 1 = 1$ (which was the remainder in the division); so the left-hand side must be 1, also. Substitution verifies this: $2(2^3) - 2^2 - 4(2) - 3 = 16 - 4 - 8 - 3 = 1$.

Now we will go back to the general result that we are trying to prove. If we divide our polynomial—which we will call "y" for short—by $x - k$, we can always go on dividing, as in the above example, until we have a *constant* remainder, R, say. Writing the result as an identity, as we did before, we shall have

$$y = (x - k)\,(\text{some quotient}) + R$$

Now, $y = 0$ when $x = k$ (this was our starting-point); so, since the two sides are always equal,

$$\begin{aligned} 0 &= 0 \times (\text{value of quotient}) + R \\ &= 0 + R \\ &= R \end{aligned}$$

The remainder is 0, which means that $x - k$ is a factor of y. We have proved what we suspected:

If a polynomial in x is zero when $x = k$,
then $x - k$ is a factor of the expression.

This is the "Factor Theorem." It is often useful in finding factors when the "grouping" method breaks down.

Example 6. Find the factors of (i) $3x^3 + 4x^2 - 17x - 6$, (ii) $x^3 + 1$, (iii) $x^3 - 1$.

(i) Let $y = 3x^3 + 4x^2 - 17x - 6$.
Can we find a value of x which makes $y = 0$?

Try 1: when $x = 1$, $y = 3 + 4 - 17 - 6 = -16$.
Try -1: when $x = -1$, $y = 3(-1) + 4(1) - 17(-1) - 6 = 12$.
Try 2: when $x = 2$, $y = 3.8 + 4.4 - 17.2 - 6 = 24 + 16 - 34 - 6 = 0$.

So $x - 2$ is a factor.

How can we find the other factor or factors?
Method 1: By long division.

$$\begin{array}{r} x - 2)\,3x^3 + 4x^2 - 17x - 6\,(3x^2 + 10x + 3 \\ \underline{3x^3 - 6x^2} \qquad\qquad\qquad\qquad \\ 10x^2 - 17x \qquad\qquad \\ \underline{10x^2 - 20x} \qquad\qquad \\ 3x - 6 \qquad \\ \underline{3x - 6} \qquad \end{array}$$

$$\begin{aligned} \text{So } y &= (x - 2)(3x^2 + 10x + 3) \\ &= (x - 2)(3x + 1)(x + 3) \end{aligned}$$

Method 2: By inspection. (This may seem complicated at first, as we shall have to write down much that you would do mentally. However, it is quicker when you are used to it.)

We find what we must multiply by $x - 2$ to give y.

$$3x^3 + 4x^2 - 17x - 6 = (x - 2)(\quad ? \quad)$$

Obviously, we must start with $3x^2$ (since $x.3x^2 = x^3$) and finish with $+ 3$ $\{$since $(- 2)(+ 3) = - 6\}$. What "x" term must we put in between?

$$3x^3 + 4x^2 - 17x - 6 = (x - 2)(3x^2 + ?x + 3)$$

The curves indicate the pairs of terms which, when multiplied together, must make up the $+ 4x^2$. Now $(- 2)(3x^2) = - 6x^2$; so $(x)(?x)$ must be $+ 10x^2$. Our ? must be 10.

$$3x^3 + 4x^2 - 17x - 6 = (x - 2)(3x^2 + 10x + 3)$$

We have chosen terms to make the x^3, x^2 and constant terms in the product correct. We can check by considering the "x" term:

$(- 2)(10x) = - 20x$; $(x)(3) = 3x$; sum, $- 17x$, as required.

(ii) Let $y = x^3 + 1$. It is obvious that $y = 0$ when $x = - 1$, so $x - (- 1)$, i.e. $x + 1$, must be a factor.

We will find the other factor by inspection, without much explanation. If you find this difficult to follow, use long division.

$$x^3 + 1 = (x + 1)(x^2 + ?x + 1)$$

The left-hand side has $0x^2$; $(+ 1)(x^2) = 1x^2$, so $(x)(?x)$ must be $- 1x^2$. The ? must be $- 1$.

$$x^3 + 1 = (x + 1)(x^2 - x + 1)$$ (We cannot factorize further in this case.)

(iii) $x^3 - 1$. Try this for yourself. (The result is given in a footnote.)*

***Example* 7.** Show that $2x - 1$ is a factor of $4x^3 - 13x + 6$, and find the remaining factors.

Note: Our proof of the Factor Theorem referred only to a factor $1x - k$. The same argument applies to any linear factor. In this case, the value of x which makes $2x - 1 = 0$ is $\frac{1}{2}$; we have to show that our function $= 0$ when $x = \frac{1}{2}$.

When $x = \frac{1}{2}$, $4x^3 - 13x + 6 = 4(\frac{1}{8}) - 13(\frac{1}{2}) + 6 = \frac{1}{2} - 6\frac{1}{2} + 6 = 0$; so $2x - 1$ is a factor.

(Try to find the other factor before reading on.)

By inspection, $4x^3 - 13x + 6 = (2x - 1)(2x^2 + x - 6)$

$$= (2x - 1)(2x - 3)(x + 2)$$

*$x^3 - 1 = (x - 1)(x^2 + x + 1)$.

Example 8. Find a and b if $x + 1$ and $x - 2$ are factors of $x^3 + ax^2 + bx - 6$; then find the remaining factor.

Since $x + 1$ and $x - 2$ are factors, the function must be zero when $x = -1$ and when $x = 2$.

$$\begin{aligned} &\text{So} \quad -1 + a - b - 6 = 0 \\ &\text{and} \quad 8 + 4a + 2b - 6 = 0 \\ &\text{Hence} \qquad a - b = 7 \\ &\text{and} \qquad 4a + 2b = -2 \end{aligned}$$

Solving these simultaneous equations, you will find $a = 2, b = -5$.

$$\begin{aligned} x^3 + 2x^2 - 5x - 6 &= (x + 1)(x - 2)(\ ?\ ) \\ &= (x^2 - x - 2)(\ ?\ ) \\ &= (x^2 - x - 2)(x + 3) \quad \text{(by inspection)} \end{aligned}$$

The remaining factor is $x + 3$.

Sum and Difference of Cubes

You know that $x^2 - y^2 = (x - y)(x + y)$, and that $x^2 + y^2$ has no factors. We will now use the factor theorem to find the factors of $x^3 + y^3$ and $x^3 - y^3$.

When $x = -y$, $x^3 + y^3 = (-y^3) + y^3 = -y^3 + y^3 = 0$; so $x + y$ is a factor. Similarly, $x - y$ is a factor of $x^3 - y^3$.

By inspection, $x^3 + y^3 = (x + y)(x^2 - xy + y^2)$

and $x^3 - y^3 = (x - y)(x^2 + xy + y^2)$

N.B.: Neither $x^2 - xy + y^2$ nor $x^2 + xy + y^2$ can be factorized further.

Notice that $x^3 + 1$ and $x^3 - 1$, which we factorized in Example 6, are particular cases of these ($x^3 + 1^3$ and $x^3 - 1^3$).

Example 9. Factorize (i) $8a^3 + 27b^3$, (ii) $1 - 1000k^6$.

$$\begin{aligned} \text{(i)}\ 8a^3 + 27b^3 &= (2a)^3 + (3b)^3 \\ &= (2a + 3b)\{(2a)^2 - (2a)(3b) + (3b)^2\} \quad \text{(replacing "}x\text{" by } 2a\text{, "}y\text{" by } 3b) \\ &= (2a + 3b)(4a^2 - 6ab + 9b^2) \\ \text{(ii)}\ 1 - 1000k^6 &= 1^3 - (10k^2)^3 \\ &= (1 - 10k^2)(1 + 10k^2 + 100k^4) \quad \text{(replacing "}x\text{" by } 1\text{, "}y\text{" by } 10k^2) \end{aligned}$$

EXERCISE 14C

1. Find the factors of (i) $x^3 + x^2 - 3x + 1$, (ii) $2x^3 - 3x^2 - 3x + 2$, (iii) $6x^3 - 17x^2 - 4x + 3$.

(In each case, there is at least one factor which you should be able to find by the factor theorem. You might try $x = 1, -1, 2, -2$, etc., in turn. The remaining factor may or may not factorize further.)

2, Find k so that $x^3 + x^2 - 4x + k$ shall be divisible by $x + 2$. If k has this value, factorize the expression completely.

3. Find the value of p if $8x^3 + 18x^2 + px + 3$ is divisible by $2x - 1$; then find the remaining factors.

4. Find a and b if $x - 1$ and $2x - 1$ are both factors of $2x^3 + x^2 + ax + b$. Find the remaining factor.

5. Find the values of c and d if $3x^3 + cx^2 + dx + 4$ is divisible by $3x^2 + 11x - 4$. Find the remaining factor.

[Since $3x^2 + 11x - 4 = (x + 4)(3x - 1)$, both $x + 4$ and $3x - 1$ must be factors.]

6. Show that $x = -2$ is a root of the equation

$$12x^3 + 31x^2 + 2x - 24 = 0,$$

and find the other roots.

7. Find p if $x = 3$ is a root of the equation $x^3 - 3x^2 - x + p = 0$. Find the other roots of the equation.

8. Show that $x - 2$ and $x + 1$ are factors of the expression

$$x^4 - 2x^3 - 3x^2 + 4x + 4.$$

Factorize the expression completely, and hence find its square root.

9. Factorize (i) $8x^3 - 1$, (ii) $64y^3 + 125z^3$, (iii) $x^6 + y^6$.

10. Solve for x the equation $p(x - p^2) = q(x - q^2)$.

CHAPTER 15

SERIES; ARITHMETIC AND GEOMETRIC PROGRESSIONS

(i) 5, 8, 11, 14, 17, ...
(ii) 2, 6, 18, 54, 162, ...
(iii) 2, 8, 18, 32, 50, ...
(iv) 0, 7, 26, 63, 124, ...
(v) 2, 6, 12, 20, 30, ...

Can you go on with each of the above series of numbers? In other words, can you recognize the pattern, the way in which each number is found when the one before it is known? (This is a favourite question in TV quiz shows and "Eleven-Plus" examination papers.)

Study each of them for a few minutes to see if you can hit on the solution.

Deducing a Formula. We shall call the numbers in each series the "terms" of the series. In each case, we will say how the given terms were formed, study the "rule of formation," and so deduce a *formula* which we can use to find any term we wish. We shall refer to the "nth" term, meaning the term coming nth in order from the beginning. For the first term, $n = 1$, for the second term, $n = 2$, and so on.

Series (i) is 5, $5 + 3$, $5 + 3 + 3$, $5 + 3 + 3 + 3$, ...
that is, 5, $5 + 3$, $5 + 2.3$, $5 + 3.3$, ...

We add 3 to each term to form the next. In other words, the *difference* between successive terms (any term minus the previous one) is always 3.

The first term is 5;
the *second* term is $5 +$ *one* 3;
the *third* term is $5 +$ *two* 3's;
the *fourth* term is $5 +$ *three* 3's;
the *fifth* term will be $5 +$ *four* 3's; and so on.
The nth term will be $5 + (n - 1)3$
Thus the 100th term is $5 + 99.3$
$= 5 + 297 = 302$

With each of the other series, even if you were unable to see how the terms were formed, try to write down the nth term after seeing the explanation, without looking at what is printed.

Series (ii) is 2, 2.3, 2.3.3, 2.3.3.3, ...
that is, 2, 2.3, 2.3^2, 2.3^3, ...

We multiply each term by 3 to form the next. In other words, the *ratio* of each term to the preceding one is 3.

The first term is 2;
the *second* term is $2.3^{\underline{1}}$;
the *third* term is $2.3^{\underline{2}}$;
the *fourth* term is $2.3^{\underline{3}}$;
the *fifth* term will be $2.3^{\underline{4}}$; and so on.
The nth term will be 2.3^{n-1}.

Thus the tenth term is 2.3^9—which you may work out if you wish!

Series (iii) is 2.1^2, 2.2^2, 2.3^2, 2.4^2, . . . , and so on.
The nth term is $2n^2$.

Series (iv) is $1^3 - 1$, $2^3 - 1$, $3^3 - 1$, $4^3 - 1$, . . . , and so on.
The nth term is $n^3 - 1$.

Series (v) is 1.2, 2.3, 3.4, 4.5, ... and so on.
The nth term is $n(n + 1)$.

If we know the formula for the nth term of a series, we can, of course, write down as many terms of the series as we wish.

Example 1. Write down the first four terms, and the 50th term, of the series whose nth terms are:

(i) $4 - (n - 1)2$; (ii) $6.(-\frac{1}{3})^{n-1}$; (iii) $n^4 - n$; (iv) $(n - 1)(n + 2)$.

Putting $n = 1, 2, 3, 4, 50$, successively in each case, we obtain

(i) $4 - 0$, $4 - 2$, $4 - 4$, $4 - 6$, $4 - 98$;
i.e. 4, 2, 0, -2, -94.

(ii) $6(-\frac{1}{3})^0$, $6(-\frac{1}{3})^1$, $6(-\frac{1}{3})^2$, $6(-\frac{1}{3})^3$, $6(-\frac{1}{3})^{49}$;
i.e. 6.1, $6(-\frac{1}{3})$, $6(+\frac{1}{9})$, $6(-\frac{1}{27})$, $6(-\frac{1}{3^{49}})$;
i.e. 6, -2, $\frac{2}{3}$, $-\frac{2}{9}$, $-\frac{2}{3^{48}}$.

(iii) $1^4 - 1$, $2^4 - 2$, $3^4 - 3$, $4^4 - 4$, $50^4 - 50$;
i.e. $1 - 1$, $16 - 2$, $81 - 3$, $256 - 4$, $6{,}250{,}000 - 50$;
i.e. 0, 14, 78, 252, 6,249,950.

(iv) 0.3, 1.4, 2.5, 3.6, 49.52;
i.e. 0, 4, 10, 18, 2,548.

Series (i) and (ii) are examples of two particular types of series which we shall study in this chapter.

Series like (i) (also (i) of Example 1), in which the *difference* between successive terms is constant, are called "*arithmetic progressions*" or "A.P."

Series like (ii) (also (ii) of Example 1), in which the *ratio* of successive terms is constant, are called "*geometric progressions*" ("G.P.").

We have met these series before. For example, in Chapter 3, in introducing fractional and negative indices and the theory of logarithms, we studied

x	1	2	3	4	5
2^x	2	4	8	16	32

The values of x form an arithmetical progression (common difference 1), those of 2^x a geometrical progression (common ratio 2). In fact, in using logs., one is really multiplying (or dividing) the terms of a G.P. by adding (or subtracting) the corresponding terms of an A.P.

Arithmetic Progressions

Notation. We shall call the first term of the series a, and the "common difference" d. The series is then

$$a, \quad a + d, \quad a + 2d, \quad a + 3d, \; \ldots\ldots\ldots\ldots$$

The nth term is $$a + (n - 1)d \quad \ldots\ldots\ldots\ldots(1)$$

Arithmetic Mean. If three numbers are in A.P., the middle one is called the "arithmetic mean" of the other two.

Calling the numbers a, x, b, we have $x - a = b - x$

$$\therefore 2x = a + b$$

$$\therefore \quad x = \frac{a + b}{2}$$

So the "*arithmetic mean*" of two numbers is what is commonly called their "*average*."

Sum of Series. What is the sum of the integers (whole numbers) from 1 to 10? If you add them up you should find that they come to 55. Can we get this result without adding the numbers one by one? Call the sum S.

$$S = 1 + 2 + 3 + 4 + 5 + 6 + 7 + 8 + 9 + 10$$

Starting from the other end, we could write

$$S = 10 + 9 + 8 + 7 + 6 + 5 + 4 + 3 + 2 + 1$$

Adding the pairs of corresponding numbers in the two lines,

$$\begin{aligned} 2S &= 11 + 11 + 11 + 11 + 11 + 11 + 11 + 11 + 11 + 11 \\ &= 11.10 \\ &= 110 \\ \therefore S &= 55 \end{aligned}$$

This suggests a way of finding a formula for the sum of n terms of an A.P.

We will call the nth term l; the previous ones will then be $l - d$, $l - 2d$, $l - 3d$ and so on.

Using S for the sum of n terms,

$$S = a + (a + d) + (a + 2d) + (a + 3d) + \dots \dots + (l - 2d) + (l - d) + l.$$

Also,

$$S = l + (l - d) + (l - 2d) + (l - 3d) + \dots \dots + (a + 2d) + (a + d) + a.$$

Adding,

$$2S = (a + l) + (a + l) + (a + l) + (a + l) + \dots \dots + (a + l) + (a + l) + (a + l) \quad (n \text{ terms})$$

$$= n(a + l).$$

$$\text{So } S = \frac{n}{2}(a + l) \dots\dots (2)$$

To give S directly in terms of a, d and n, without having to work out l, we use formula (1), which gives $l = a + (n - 1)d$.

$$\text{Hence } S = \frac{n}{2}\{a + a + (n - 1)d\}$$

$$\text{i.e. } S = \frac{n}{2}\{2a + (n - 1)d\} \dots\dots (3)$$

These formulae, (1), (2) and (3) should be learnt. We will use the same notation throughout our worked examples.

Example 2. (i) Show that $2\frac{1}{4}$, $\frac{3}{4}$, $-\frac{3}{4}$ are in arithmetic progression; then find (ii) the tenth term, and (iii) the sum of ten terms of the series of which they are the first three.

(i) (We have to show that 2nd term − 1st term = 3rd term − 2nd term.)

$$\left.\begin{array}{r} \frac{3}{4} - 2\frac{1}{4} = -1\frac{1}{2} \\ (-\frac{3}{4}) - \frac{3}{4} = -1\frac{1}{2} \end{array}\right\}$$ The differences are the same, so the numbers are in A.P.

(ii) With the above notation, $a = 2\frac{1}{4}$, $d = -1\frac{1}{2}$

$$\begin{aligned} \text{Tenth term} &= 2\tfrac{1}{4} + 9(-1\tfrac{1}{2}) \quad \{\text{formula (1)}\} \\ &= 2\tfrac{1}{4} - 13\tfrac{1}{2} \\ &= -11\tfrac{1}{4} \end{aligned}$$

(iii)

$$\begin{aligned} \text{Sum of ten terms} &= \tfrac{10}{2}\{2\tfrac{1}{4} + (-11\tfrac{1}{4})\} \quad \{\text{formula (2)}\} \\ &= 5(-9) \\ &= -45 \end{aligned}$$

Example 3. The thirteenth term of an arithmetic progression is three times the fourth; the sum of the first eight terms is 80. Find the first term and the common difference, and give the first five terms of the series.

$$a + 12d = 3(a + 3d) \quad \{\text{formula (1)}\}$$

$$\text{i.e. } a + 12d = 3a + 9d$$

$$\therefore 3d = 2a \dots\dots (i)$$

$$\text{Also, } \tfrac{8}{2}(2a + 7d) = 80 \quad \{\text{formula (3)}\}$$

$$\text{i.e. } 4(2a + 7d) = 80$$

$$\therefore 2a + 7d = 20 \dots\dots (ii) \quad (\text{dividing both sides by 4})$$

Using equation (i),

$$3d + 7d = 20$$
$$\text{i.e. } 10d = 20$$
$$\therefore d = 2$$

Substituting in equation (i),

$$2a = 6$$
$$\therefore a = 3$$

The series is 3, 5, 7, 9, 11, ...

Example 4.

(i) Find the sum of all the multiples of 7 between 100 and 200.

(ii) For how many of these multiples of 7, starting from the smallest, is the sum 735?

(i) $100 \div 7 = 14$, remainder 2; so the first multiple of 7 is 105 ($= 7 \times 15$).
$200 \div 7 = 28$, remainder 4; so the last multiple of 7 is 196 ($= 7 \times 28$).

We have to find the sum of the A.P.

$105 + 112 + 119 + \ldots\ldots\ldots\ldots + 182 + 189 + 196.$

There are 14 terms (since $196 - 105 = 91$, and $91 \div 7 = 13$; this means that 13 lots of 7 are added between the first term and the last, making 14 terms in all).

$$\text{Hence the sum is } \tfrac{14}{2}(105 + 196) \quad \{\text{formula (2)}\}$$
$$= 7(301)$$
$$= 2107$$

(ii) The series is $105 + 112 + 119 + \ldots\ldots\ldots\ldots$

Let the number of terms whose sum is 735 be n; then

$$\frac{n}{2}\{210 + (n - 1)7\} = 735 \quad \{\text{formula (3)}\}$$
$$\therefore n(210 + 7n - 7) = 1470$$
$$\therefore n(203 + 7n) = 1470$$
$$\therefore 7n^2 + 203n - 1470 = 0$$
$$\therefore n^2 + 29n - 210 = 0 \text{ (dividing both sides by 7)}$$
$$\therefore (n - 6)(n + 35) = 0$$
$$\therefore n - 6 = 0 \text{ or } n + 35 = 0$$
$$\therefore n = 6 \text{ or } -35$$

Hence *the number of terms is* 6. (It cannot be negative.)

Example 5. (This requires careful study.)

The sum of the first n terms of an A.P. is $2n^2 + 4n$, for all values of n. Find the first 3 terms and the nth term.

$$\text{Putting } n = 1$$
$$\text{sum of 1 term} = 6$$
$$\textit{i.e.} \text{ first term} = 6$$

$$\text{Putting } n = 2, \text{ sum of first 2 terms} = 2 \cdot 2^2 + 4.2$$
$$= 16$$
$$\text{first term} = 6$$
$$\therefore \text{ second term} = 10$$
$$\text{Putting } n = 3, \text{ sum of first 3 terms} = 2.3^2 + 4 \cdot 3$$
$$= 30$$
$$\text{Sum of first 2 terms} = 16$$
$$\therefore \text{ third term} = 14$$
$$n\text{th term} = 6 + (n - 1)4 = 4n + 2$$

Note: The nth term could be found directly in this way:

$$\text{Sum of first } n \text{ terms} = 2n^2 + 4n$$
$$\text{Sum of first } n - 1 \text{ terms} = 2(n - 1)^2 + 4(n - 1)$$
$$= 2(n^2 - 2n + 1) + 4n - 4$$
$$= 2n^2 - 4n + 2 + 4n - 4$$
$$= 2n^2 - 2$$
$$\text{Hence the } n\text{th term} = (2n^2 + 4n) - (2n^2 - 2)$$
$$= 4n + 2$$

EXERCISE 15A

1. Find the sums of the following arithmetic progressions:

(i) $7 + 3 + (-1) + (-5) + \ldots\ldots\ldots\ldots$ to 10 terms.

(ii) $2 + 5 + 8 + \ldots\ldots\ldots\ldots + 38$.

(iii) A series with 16 terms of which the 15th and 16th are $1\frac{1}{2}$, -1, respectively.

2. The sum of the terms of an A.P. is 72. The first and last terms are -5 and $+17$ respectively. Find the number of terms and the common difference.

3. The ninth term of an A.P. is twice the third; show that the twelfth is three times the second.

If the seventh term is 15, find the first term and the common difference.

4. Find the sum of all the multiples of 3 between 500 and 1,000.

5. The sum of the fifth and seventh terms of an A.P. is 20, and that of the first ten terms is 115. Find the first term.

6. The sum of five numbers in A.P. is 85, and the last is 20 more than the first.

Find the five numbers.

7. The first term of an A.P. is $(x - 1)^2$, the second is $x^2 + 1$. The sum of eight terms is 200. Find the possible values of x.

8. The sum of n terms of an A.P. is $4n^2 - n$ for all values of n. Find the first three terms and the nth term.

Geometric Progressions

Notation. We shall call the first term of the series a, and the "common ratio" r.

The series is then $\quad a, ar, ar^2, ar^3, \ldots\ldots\ldots\ldots$
The nth term is $\quad ar^{n-1} \ldots\ldots\ldots\ldots\ldots\ldots\ldots\ldots\ldots\ldots$(4)

Geometric Mean. If three numbers are in geometric progression, the middle one is called the "geometric mean" of the other two.

Calling the numbers a, x, b, we have

$$\frac{x}{a} = \frac{b}{x}$$
$$\therefore x^2 = ab$$
$$\therefore x = \sqrt{ab}$$

Sum of Series. What is the sum of the first 10 powers of 2, starting from 2 itself?

That is, $2 + 4 + 8 +$ *** ?

If you care to work them out and add them up, you will find that the sum is 2046; but if you try the short cut that we used for the arithmetic progression, you will find that it does not help.

Can we find another one?

Call the sum S.

$$S = 2 + 4 + 8 + 16 + 32 + 64 + 128 + 256 + 512 + 1024$$
Now, $$2S = 4 + 8 + 16 + 32 + 64 + 128 + 256 + 512 + 1024 + 2048$$

(Since each term is half the next one, each becomes *equal* to the next when we multiply by 2. In doing this, we have moved each term one space to the right. It then becomes clear that if we subtract, all the terms disappear except the 2 and the 2048.)

Subtracting the upper line from the lower,

$$S = 2048 - 2$$
$$= 2046$$

This suggests a method of finding a formula for the sum (S) of n terms of a G.P.

$$S = a + ar + ar^2 + \ldots\ldots\ldots\ldots + ar^{n-3} + ar^{n-2} + ar^{n-1}$$
$$\therefore rS = ar + ar^2 + \ldots\ldots\ldots\ldots + ar^{n-3} + ar^{n-2} + ar^{n-1} + ar^n$$

Subtracting,

$$S - rS = a - ar^n$$
$$i.e.\ S(1 - r) = a(1 - r^n)$$
$$\therefore S = \frac{a(1 - r^n)}{1 - r} \ldots\ldots\ldots\ldots\ldots \text{(5a)}$$

If $r > 1$, it is more convenient to subtract the upper line from the lower, as we did in our first example. This gives

$$rS - S = ar^n - a$$
$$\text{i.e. } S(r - 1) = a(r^n - 1)$$
$$\therefore S = \frac{a(r^n - 1)}{r - 1} \quad \ldots\ldots\ldots\ldots\ldots\ldots(5b)$$

(The expressions in 5a and 5b are, of course, equal; either form can be turned into the other by multiplying numerator and denominator by -1.)

Example 6. Show that 12, -6, 3, are in G.P. If they are the first three terms of a series, write down the 20th term and the sum of the first 20 terms, leaving your answers in factors.

$\frac{-6}{12} = -\frac{1}{2}$; $\frac{3}{-6} = -\frac{1}{2}$; so the three terms form a G.P. with common ratio $-\frac{1}{2}$.

(Note that if the common ratio is negative, the terms will be alternately positive and negative.)

First term $= 12$; $\therefore$ 20th term $= 12.(-\frac{1}{2})^{19}$ {formula (4)

$$= 2^2.3\left(-\frac{1}{2^{19}}\right)$$
$$= -\frac{3}{2^{17}}$$

Sum of first 20 terms $= \dfrac{12\{1 - (-\frac{1}{2})^{20}\}}{1 - (-\frac{1}{2})}$

$$= \frac{12\left(1 - \frac{1}{2^{20}}\right)}{1\frac{1}{2}}$$
$$= 8\left(1 - \frac{1}{2^{20}}\right)$$

Example 7. The difference between the second and third terms of a G.P. (in which the terms increase) is 18; that between the third and fourth is 72. Find the first 3 terms and the sum of 5 terms.

With our usual notation,

$$ar^2 - ar = 18 \quad \ldots\ldots\ldots\ldots\ldots\ldots(1)$$
$$ar^3 - ar^2 = 72 \quad \ldots\ldots\ldots\ldots\ldots\ldots(2)$$
$$\text{i.e. } ar(r - 1) = 18 \quad \ldots\ldots\ldots\ldots\ldots\ldots(3)$$
$$ar^2(r - 1) = 72 \quad \ldots\ldots\ldots\ldots\ldots\ldots(4)$$
$$\therefore \frac{ar^2(r - 1)}{ar(r - 1)} = \tfrac{72}{18}$$
$$\text{i.e. } r = 4$$

N.B: Eliminating an unknown by *dividing*, in this way, is often useful in problems on G.P.

Substituting in (3), $a \cdot 4 \cdot 3 = 18$

$\therefore a = 1\frac{1}{2}$

Hence the first 3 terms are $1\frac{1}{2}$, 6, 24

The sum of 5 terms is $\dfrac{1\frac{1}{2}(4^5 - 1)}{4 - 1}$

$= \frac{1}{2}(4^5 - 1)$

Example 8. The second, fifth and seventh terms of an A.P. are in G.P.; the ninth term of the A.P. is 1. Find the first 7 terms of both the A.P. and the G.P.

We have $\dfrac{a + 4d}{a + d} = \dfrac{a + 6d}{a + 4d}$

Cross-multiplying,

$$(a + 4d)^2 = (a + d)(a + 6d)$$

i.e. $a^2 + 8ad + 16d^2 = a^2 + 7ad + 6d^2$

$\therefore ad + 10d^2 = 0$

i.e. $d(a + 10d) = 0$

$\therefore a + 10d = 0$........(1) ($d \neq 0$, or there would be no series).

Also, $a + 8d = 1$........(2)

Subtracting, $2d = -1$

$\therefore d = -\frac{1}{2}$

Substituting in (1),

$a + 10(-\frac{1}{2}) = 0$

$\therefore a = 5$

The A.P. is 5, $4\frac{1}{2}$, 4, $3\frac{1}{2}$, 3, $2\frac{1}{2}$, 2, ...

The G.P. is $4\frac{1}{2}$, 3, 2, $\frac{4}{3}$, $\frac{8}{9}$, $\frac{16}{27}$, $\frac{32}{81}$, ... (common ratio $\frac{2}{3}$).

EXERCISE 15B

1. Find the 8th term, and the sum of the first 8 terms, of the following G.P's:

(i) $2\frac{1}{2}$, 5, 10, 20, ...

(ii) 1, -3, 9, ...

(iii) 36, 24, 16, ...

2. The product of three numbers in G.P. is 8; the third is 4 more than the second. Find the three numbers.

Hint: If you call the numbers $\frac{a}{r}$, a, ar, your first equation will contain "a" only.)

3. The second and third terms of a G.P. are $\frac{3}{4}$ and $-\frac{1}{2}$ respectively. Find the first term, and the sum of the first 6 terms.

4. The second and fifth terms of a G.P. are 24 and $10\frac{1}{8}$ respectively. Find the common ratio and the first, third and fourth terms.

5. The product of the second and sixth terms of a G.P. is 4; the product of the third and seventh is 9. Show that there are two possible values of the common ratio and two possible values of the first term.

If the common ratio and the first term are both negative, find the sum of the first four terms.

6. The difference between the second and fourth terms of a G.P. is $107\frac{1}{4}$; that between the third and fifth is 1287. Find the sum of the first three terms. (All the terms are positive, and the common ratio greater than 1.)

7. Find a number x such that $2\frac{1}{2} + x$, $8 + x$, $19 + x$ are in G.P.

Find the sum of the first 5 terms of the series.

8. If the first term of a G.P. is x and the *sum* of the first two terms is y, show that the sum of the first three is $x - y + \dfrac{y^2}{x}$.

REVISION SUMMARY

ALGEBRA AND THE CALCULUS

(**A** = *Syllabus A;* **B** = *Syllabus B*)

(A & B) TRINOMIALS AND QUADRATIC EQUATIONS

Page

An expression containing *three* terms is called a *trinomial.* It is generally impossible to factorize a trinomial without special advanced techniques, but many elementary examples can be factorized by intelligent guesswork.

Thus, in the trinomial $3a^2 - 7a - 6$, the term $3a^2$ can arise as $3a \times a$, and 6 can arise as 3×2 or 6×1. Trial of the possible combinations finally gives the factors $(3a + 2)(a - 3)$.

Rules of Signs.

Trinomial		*Factors*		*Example*
+	+	+	+	$a^2 + 3a + 2 = (a + 2)(a + 1)$
−	+	−	−	$a^2 - 2a + 2 = (a - 2)(a - 1)$
+ or −	−	+	−	$a^2 - 2a - 3 = (a + 3)(a - 1)$

Factorize $a^2 + 4a + 3$ 114

$4b^2 + 16b - 9$ 115

***Quadratic Equations.* These are usually solved by use of the fact that if the product of two expressions is zero, one or other of the expressions must be zero.**

If $(x - 2)(y + 3) = 0$,

then either $x - 2 = 0$

or $y + 3 = 0$,

that is

$x = 2$ or $y = -3$.

Solve $x(y - 3) = 0$

$(a - 2)(a + 6) = 0$ 118

Any equation which can be thus put in *zero form* (i.e. R.H.S. zero) can be solved in this way.

Thus $2x^2 = 5x + 3$ can be written $2x^2 - 5x - 3 = 0$ *(zero form)*

$$(2x + 1)(x - 3) = 0$$

Either $2x + 1 = 0$ or $x - 3 = 0$,

so $x = -\frac{1}{2}$ or $x = 3$.

Solve $x^2 = 3x + 4$

$x = 6x^2 - 2$ 119

Page

Graphical solutions. **Having drawn the graph of y = (a function of x) we can solve any equation of the form:**

(that function of x) = (a number)

Draw the graph of $y = 4 + 2x - x^2$ and hence solve $x^2 - 2x = 2$. 123

Problems. **Quadratic equations arise from problems quite naturally. They cannot be anticipated and there is no special technique.**

A photograph is mounted on a piece of card 8 in. long and 4 in. wide, leaving a border of constant width all round. The area of this border is 22 sq. in. Find its width. 125

(A & B) SIMPLE FRACTIONS

Fractions in algebra are treated by the same processes as those used in arithmetic.

Cancelling. **Only common factors of the top and bottom can be cancelled. Always put the expression into factors first.**

$$\frac{a+3}{3a+9} = \frac{(a+3)}{3(a+3)} = \frac{1}{3}$$

$$\frac{b^2-4b}{b^2} = \frac{b(b-4)}{b \times b} = \frac{b-4}{b}$$

Cancel $\dfrac{3a+6}{9b-3}$, $\dfrac{2x-6}{x-3}$. 128

Multiplication and Division. **Factorize and cancel where possible: for division, turn the divisor upside down and multiply.**

$$\frac{2}{d-2} \div \frac{5}{2d-4} = \frac{2}{d-2} \times \frac{2(d-2)}{5} = \frac{4}{5}$$

Multiply $\dfrac{4}{c-2}$ by $\dfrac{3c-6}{8}$. 129

Addition and Subtraction. **Each fraction must be brought to the same denominator.**

$$\frac{2}{x-3} - \frac{5}{x} = \frac{2x}{x(x-3)} - \frac{5(x-3)}{x(x-3)}$$

$$= \frac{2x-5x+15}{x(x-3)}$$

$$= \frac{15-3x}{x(x-3)}$$

Simplify: $\dfrac{2}{3} - \dfrac{5}{6(b+1)}$. 130

Page

Equations. **Multiply each term of the equation by the L.C.M. of the denominators.**

If $\frac{20}{x} - \frac{15}{x+1} = 2$

is multiplied throughout by $x(x+1)$
it gives

$$20(x+1) - 15x = 2x(x+1),$$

which reduces to an easy quadratic.

Solve: $\frac{2}{x-1} - \frac{3}{x+4} = \frac{4}{7}$. 132

Problems. **A table showing the given facts greatly helps the solution.**

Example: **A platoon of soldiers took two hours less to cover 15 miles than the rival platoon took to cover 20 miles. The rival platoon marched at a rate of 1 m.p.h. slower than the first. What was its marching speed?**

	Fast platoon	***Slow platoon***	
Speed	$x+1$	x	**m.p.h.**
Distance	**15**	**20**	**miles**
Time	$\frac{15}{x+1}$	$\frac{20}{x}$	**hours**

$$\frac{20}{x} - \frac{15}{x+1} = 2, \text{ etc.}$$

The price of a fountain pen was increased by 3s. As a result, a shopkeeper found that he could buy two fewer pens for £9 than had previously been possible. Find the previous price. 135

Long division. **The process is similar to the corresponding arithmetic process.**

$$\begin{array}{rll} & x - 2 & \\ x - 1 \,\big)\! & x^2 - 3x - 6 & \\ & x^2 - x & ((x-1) \times x) \\ & \quad - 2x - 6 & (\textit{by subtraction}) \\ & \quad - 2x + 2 & ((x-1) \times (-2)) \\ & \qquad - 8 & (\textit{by subtraction}) \end{array}$$

Answer: $x - 2$**: remainder** -8**.**

Divide $a^3 + 3a^2 - 2a + 20$ by $a + 2$. 137

Page

INDICES AND LOGARITHMS

(A & B) ***Indices.*** **$a \times a \times a \times a \times \ldots$ (n a's multiplied together) is written a^n (read as "a to the nth"). n is the *index* or *power*.**

Thus $a \times a \times a \times a = a^4$, and so on.

Roots. **If $a^n = b$, a is called the "nth *root of b*" (written $\sqrt[n]{b}$).**

Thus $2^5 = 32$,
so 2 is the 5th root of 32 ($\sqrt[5]{32}$).

(A & B) ***Laws of Indices.***

To *multiply* powers of a number, *add* the indices

$$a^m \times a^n = a^{m+n}$$

To *divide* powers of a number, *subtract* the indices

$$a^m \div a^n = a^{m-n}$$

To find a *power of a power* of a number, *multiply* the indices

$$(a^m)^n = a^{mn}$$

(A & B) ***Zero, Negative and Fractional Indices.***

According to the above definition of an index, expressions such as a^0, a^{-1}, $a^{\frac{1}{2}}$ have no meaning. We give them meanings which fit in with the laws of indices:

If "a" is any positive number

(i) a^0 is always 1;

(ii) a^{-n} means $\dfrac{1}{a^n}$

(thus $a^{-1} = \dfrac{1}{a}$, $a^{-2} = \dfrac{1}{a^2}$, etc.);

(iii) $a^{\frac{1}{n}}$ means $\sqrt[n]{a}$

(thus $a^{\frac{1}{2}} = \sqrt[2]{a}$, $a^{\frac{1}{3}} = \sqrt[3]{a}$, etc.);

(iv) In any fractional index, the denominator (bottom) of the fraction is a *root*, the numerator (top) is a power (either may be taken first).

Thus we can say either,

$$8^{\frac{2}{3}} = (\sqrt[3]{8})^2 = 2^2 = 4$$
$$\text{or } 8^{\frac{2}{3}} = \sqrt[3]{8^2} = \sqrt[3]{64} = 4.$$

What are the values of the following:

$16^{\frac{1}{4}}$, $27^{\frac{2}{3}}$, 10^0, 6^{-2}, $25^{-\frac{1}{2}}$, $(\frac{2}{5})^{-2}$? 140

Page

Express $\dfrac{x^{m+n} \times x^{m-n}}{x^{m}}$ as a power of x. 142

Express $\sqrt[3]{\cdot 01}$ as a power of 10. 142

(A) Simplify $\left(\dfrac{64x^6}{y^3}\right)^{\frac{1}{3}} \times \left(\dfrac{y}{2x}\right)^{-1}$ 143

Logarithms. **If N $= a^x$, x is called the "Logarithm of N to base a" (written $\log_a N$).**

(A) ***Laws of Logarithms.***

(i) $\log_a pq = \log_a p + \log_a q$.

(To find the log of the product of two numbers, add the logs of the numbers.)

(ii) $\log_a \dfrac{p}{q} = \log_a p - \log_a q$.

(The log of the quotient of two numbers is the difference of their logs.)

(iii) $\log_a (p^n) = n \log_a p$.

(To find the log of a power of a number, multiply the log of the number by the power.)

Since roots may be expressed as powers, finding the logs of square roots cube roots, etc., is covered by this rule.

Thus $\log_a(\sqrt{p}) = \log_a(p^{\frac{1}{2}}) = \frac{1}{2} \log_a p$.

Note also that, since $a^0 = 1$, log 1 = 0 *whatever the base.*

The following examples deal with logs to base 10:

Express as powers of 10:

(i) 3,
(ii) $5{\cdot}61 \times 10^7$,
(iii) 0·836. 145

Given that $\log_{10} 2 = 0{\cdot}30103$, $\log_{10} 3 = 0{\cdot}47712$, find, *without using tables*:

(i) $\log_{10} 12$
(ii) $\log_{10} \sqrt{6}$
(iii) $\log_{10} 5$
(iv) $\log_{10} 0{\cdot}54$. 145

Use four-figure tables to find the values of

(i) $2^{\frac{3}{4}}$
(ii) x, where $x^3 = 8{\cdot}16 \times 10^{-7}$. 146

Page

(A & B) ***Large and Small Numbers.*** **In scientific work, very large and very small numbers are usually expressed as $a \times 10^n$, where "a" is a number between 1 and 10 and "n" is a whole number.**

$$\text{Thus } 236{,}000{,}000 = 2{\cdot}36 \times 10^8$$
$$0{\cdot}00000517 = 5{\cdot}17 \times 10^{-6}$$

N.B. **When a number is expressed in this way, the whole number part of its log, is the power of 10.**

$$\text{Thus } \log 236{,}000{,}000 = \underline{\underline{8}}{\cdot}3729$$
$$\log 0{\cdot}00000517 = \underline{\underline{\bar{6}}}{\cdot}7135$$

The unit normally used for distances to stars is the "light year," that is, the distance travelled by light in a year. How many miles is this? (The speed of light is 186,000 miles per second.) 148

(A & B) LINEAR AND QUADRATIC FUNCTIONS

Functions and Graphs. **Consider the formula $y = 2x - 3$. If we *choose* a particular value of x, we can always find *one*, definite, corresponding value of y.**

When this condition holds, we say that "*y is a function of x*" x is called the *independent variable*, y the *dependent variable.*

In elementary work, there is always a formula giving y in terms of x (other letters may be used, of course), but the idea of a function does not depend on this.

You should be able, from the formula, to tell the general shape of the graph of a function, to sketch it roughly without accurate plotting.

We shall usually assume that we can choose any value for x, but it is important to realize that in a practical problem only some values may be possible.

For example, if y ft. is the amount by which a 30-ft. beam sags at a distance x ft. from one end, x can only take values from 0 to 30.

Parts of a formula separated by + or − are called *terms*, the number multiplying a power of x is called its *coefficient*; a number on its own is called a *constant term.*

Thus in $x^2 + 5x - 2$ there are three terms;

the coefficient of x^2 is 1,
the coefficient of x is 5,
the constant term is − 2.

Page

Linear Functions. **Any function of the type $mx + c$, where m and c are constants, is called a *linear function*, since its graph is a straight line.**

If we take any two points on a line, then

$$\frac{\text{the difference in } y}{\text{the difference in } x}$$

is called the *gradient* of the line.

It is the tangent of the angle between the line and the positive direction of the x-axis.

The graph $y = mx + c$ has gradient m, and cuts the y-axis where $y = c$.

An equation "$y =$ a constant" represents a line parallel to the x-axis (zero gradient).

An equation "$x =$ a constant" represents a line parallel to the y-axis (infinite gradient).

Sketch the graphs:

(i) $y = 2x - 1$

(ii) $y = 5 - \frac{1}{2}x$ 153

showing where they cross the axes and stating their gradients.

Quadratic Functions. **Any function of the type $ax^2 + bx + c$, where a, b and c are constants, is called a *quadratic function*. (b, or c, or both, may be zero, of course; that is, there need not be an x term or a constant term.)**

The graph of any such function is a *parabola*, with one maximum or one minimum point called the *vertex*.

If the coefficient of x^2 is positive, the vertex is the lowest ("minimum") point.

If the coefficient of x^2 is negative, the vertex is the highest ("maximum") point.

Sketch the graphs:

(i) $y = x^2 - 4x + 3$

(ii) $y = 4x - x^2$

showing where they cross the axes. 161

Page

(B) GRADIENTS AND RATES OF CHANGE

Gradient of a Line. **The gradient of a straight line graph represents the rate at which one variable changes relative to the other.**

Thus if we graph the number of units consumed by an electric fire, against the time for which it is switched on, the gradient represents the rate of consumption of electricity (so many units per hour, say).

If we graph the distance covered by a body moving at a steady speed, against the time, the gradient represents the rate at which the distance increases, that is, the speed (so many miles per hour, say).

If we graph the perimeter of a square against the length of its side, the gradient represents the "rate" at which the perimeter changes relative to the side (so many inches increase in perimeter per inch increase in length of side, say).

Sketch rough graphs illustrating these examples. 164

Gradient of a Curve. **"The gradient of a curve at any point" means the gradient of the tangent at that point.**

The gradient of a space-time graph at any point represents the speed at that particular time.

A body moves in a straight line, starting from a point A, so that, t seconds later, its distance from A is s feet, where $s = t^2$.
Find, *from first principles*:
(i) the speed of the body after 3 seconds,
(ii) a formula giving the speed after t seconds.

Similarly, the gradient of a speed-time graph at any point represents the rate at which the speed is changing, *i.e.* the "acceleration" (so many m.p.h. per second, say).

Again, if we graph the temperature of hot water as it cools, against the time, the gradient at any point represents the rate of cooling (so many degrees per minute, say).

Sketch rough graphs illustrating these examples. 170

Generally, the gradient at a point of a graph gives the rate at which, at that particular point, the "y" is changing relative to the "x."

Page

(B) DIFFERENTIATION

Derived Functions. **Given a function of x, we can find a formula giving the gradient of the tangent at any point on the graph of the given function.**

This gradient formula is called the *derived function* or *derivative.*

We use "y" to stand for the given function, $\frac{dy}{dx}$ for the derived function.

The process of finding the derived function is called *differentiation.*

If $y = x^2$, find $\frac{dy}{dx}$ from first principles. Calculate the values of the gradient when $x = 3, 2, 1, 0, -1, -2, -3$ and illustrate the meaning of the results by sketching the tangents at the corresponding points of the graph $y = x^2$. 173

Find $\frac{dy}{dx}$ from first principles in the following cases:

(i) $y = 5x^2$ 174
(ii) $y = mx + c$ 175
(iii) $y = x^2 - 4x + 3$ 176
(iv) $y = x^3$ 178
(v) $y = \frac{1}{x}$ 179

We arrive at the following:

y	$\frac{dy}{dx}$
x^3	$3x^2$
x^2	$2x$ (i.e. $2x^1$)
x (i.e. x^1)	1 (i.e. $1x^0$)
1 (i.e. x^0)	0
$\frac{1}{x}$ (i.e. x^{-1})	$-\frac{1}{x^2}$ (i.e. $-1.x^{-2}$)
$\frac{1}{x^2}$ (i.e. x^{-2})	$-\frac{2}{x^3}$ (i.e. $-2.x^{-3}$)

Summary of Results:

(i) If $y = x^n$, $\frac{dy}{dx} = nx^{n-1}$ (the above table shows examples of this, with $n = 3, 2, 1, 0, -1$ and -2).

(ii) Multiplying y by a number multiplies $\frac{dy}{dx}$ by that number (thus if $y = 5x^3$, $\frac{dy}{dx} = 5.3x^2 = 15x^2$).

(iii) If y has more than one term, $\frac{dy}{dx}$ is made up of the derivatives of the separate terms (thus if $y = 8x^3 - \frac{3}{x}$, $\frac{dy}{dx} = 16x^2 + \frac{3}{x^2}$).

These may be used to *write down* the derivatives of simple functions without going through the process of differentiation from first principles.

Write down $\frac{dy}{dx}$ in the following cases:

(i) $y = 4x^3 - 3x + 2$

(ii) $y = x^2 + \frac{1}{x}$

(iii) $y = \frac{1}{2}x^2 - 8 - \frac{1}{2x^2}$

(iv) $y = \frac{1}{3}x^3 - x^2 - \frac{6}{x}$ 181

(B) MAXIMUM AND MINIMUM VALUES

Suppose that y is a function of x.
If, when x has a particular value—call it "c"—the value of y is greater than it is for all other values of x close to c, we say that "y has a maximum value when $x = c$."
If, when $x = c$, the value of y is less than it is for all other values of x close to c, we say that "y has a minimum value when $x = c$."

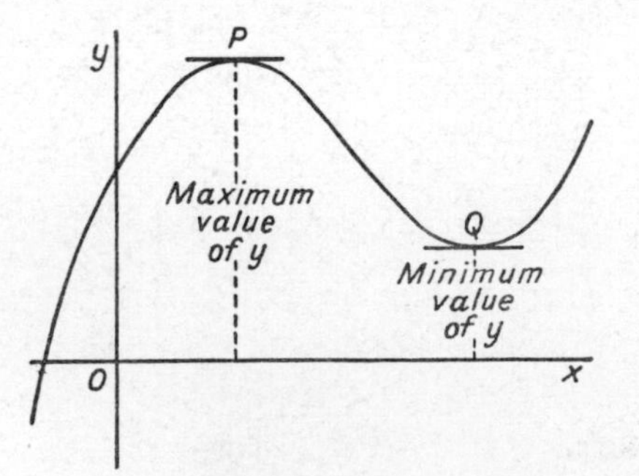

The corresponding points on the graph of y are called *turning points*; in this diagram P is a maximum point, Q is a minimum point.

Page

(B) ***Tests for Maximum and Minimum Values.***

y has a *maximum* value when $x = c$ if

(i) $\frac{dy}{dx} = 0$ when $x = c$, and

(ii) $\frac{dy}{dx}$ changes from positive to negative as x increases through the value c.

y has a *minimum* value when $x = c$ if

(i) $\frac{dy}{dx} = 0$ when $x = c$, and

(ii) $\frac{dy}{dx}$ changes from negative to positive as x increases through the value c.

Show that the function $x^2 - 5x + 6$ has a minimum value when $x = 2\frac{1}{2}$; calculate this minimum value; sketch the graph $y = x^2 - 5x + 6$. 185

Find the maximum and minimum values of the function $x^3 - 3x^2 + 5$, distinguishing between them. 186

(B) ***Problems of Maximum and Minimum Values.***

1. Choose a letter (x, say) to stand for one of the variable quantities in the problem.

2. Choose a letter (y, say) to stand for the quantity whose maximum or minimum value is required.

3. Find a formula giving y in terms of x.

4. Find the maximum or minimum value of y as above.

5. Make a correct statement of the solution of the problem.

Divide 12 into two parts so that the sum of their squares is as small as possible. 188

A length of thin metal sheeting 20 in. wide is to be bent up at each side to form an open rectangular gutter. What is the greatest possible area of the cross-section of the gutter? 189

Page

(A & B) FURTHER FUNCTIONS AND THEIR GRAPHS

Cubic Functions. **By a "cubic function" of x we mean one whose formula contains x^3, but no higher powers of x (and no negative powers). The graph of a cubic function cannot have more than two turning points.**

Draw the graph $y = x^3$ for values of x from -3 to $+3$. 192

Draw the graph of the function $x^3 - 3x^2 + 5$ for values of x from -2 to $+4$. 193

Sketch the graph of the function $(x + 1)(2 - x)(x - 3)$. 194

Find the gradient of the graph $y = x^3 - 2x^2 + x$ at the origin; show that the curve touches the x-axis where $x = 1$; find the other point on the curve at which the tangent is parallel to the tangent at the origin; sketch the graph. 195

Hyperbolic Functions. **Division by zero is impossible; the graph of function $\frac{1}{x}$ has a break in it when $x = 0$.**

(Similarly, the graph of any function has a break if x takes a value which makes the denominator of a fraction zero.) On the other hand, the closer x is to 0, the larger is $\frac{1}{x}$ (positive or negative according to the sign of x).

Draw the graph $y = \frac{1}{x}$ for values of x from -4 to $-\frac{1}{4}$ and from $+\frac{1}{4}$ to $+4$. 198

Curve Sketching.

Some points helpful in making rough sketches of graphs are:

1. Is it a "standard" curve?

2. What is y when $x = 0$?

3. For what values of x is $y = 0$?

4. Are there any "breaks" in the curve?

5. What happens when x is numerically large (+ or −)?

6. Are there any maximum or minimum points?

Sketch the graph $y = x + \frac{1}{x}$. 199

(B) INTEGRATION

Integration is the reverse process to differentiation: given a derived function ($\frac{dy}{dx}$), to find the original function.

Whenever we integrate, the function we find always includes an *arbitrary constant*. Thus if $\frac{dy}{dx} = 2x$, $y = x^2 + c$, where c is *any* constant.

We may have further information that tells us what the constant must be in a particular case. Thus, in the above example, if we know that $y = 10$ when $x = 0$, we find by substituting these values for x and y that $c = 10$; so $y = x^2 + 10$.

Rules for Integrating.

If $\frac{dy}{dx} = x^n$, $y = \frac{x^{n+1}}{n+1} + c$, where c is an arbitrary constant.

Thus if $\frac{dy}{dx} = x^2$, $y = \frac{1}{3}x^3 + c$;

if $\frac{dy}{dx} = 5x$, $y = \frac{5x^2}{2} + c$;

if $\frac{dy}{dx} = \frac{1}{x^3}$ (i.e. x^{-3}), $y = -\frac{1}{2x^2} + c$ (i.e. $\frac{x^{-2}}{-2} + c$); and so on.

"To integrate, increase the power by 1, and divide by the new power."

Find functions of x of which the derived functions are

(i) $6x^2 - 4x + 3$

(ii) $5 - \frac{2}{x^2}$ — 205

y is a function of x such that $\frac{dy}{dx} = 1 - 3x^2$. When $x = 2$, $y = 0$. Express y in terms of x, and find the value of y when $x = 3$. — 205

The gradient of a curve is given by the function $4 - 2x$. The curve passes through the origin. Find

(i) the equation of the curve;

(ii) the point other than the origin at which it crosses the x-axis;

(iii) the point where the gradient is 0.

Sketch the curve. — 205

Page

(B) DISTANCES, VELOCITIES AND ACCELERATIONS

***Velocity*. Suppose that a body is moving in a straight line, so that after t sec. its distance from a fixed point in the line is s ft., and its velocity is v ft./sec. Then if s is known as a function of t, v is given by the derived function; that is, $v = \frac{ds}{dt}$.**

Graphically, this means that if P is any point on the space-time graph, representing where the body is at a particular time, the gradient of the tangent at P represents the velocity at that time.

A stone is thrown vertically upwards at 80 ft./sec.; t sec. later its height above the ground is s ft., where $s = 80t - 16t^2$.
Find
(i) the velocity after 1, 2, 3, 4, 5 seconds, interpreting the results,
(ii) when the stone stops rising, and the greatest height it reaches,
(iii) how long it is in the air. 208

***Acceleration*. Suppose that a body is moving in a straight line so that, t sec. after starting, it has a velocity of v ft./sec. and an acceleration of "a" ft./sec./sec., then $a = \frac{dv}{dt}$.**

Graphically, this means that if P is any point on the velocity-time graph, representing the velocity of the body at a particular time, the gradient of the tangent at P represents the acceleration of the body at that time.

A body moves in a straight line so that, t sec. after it passes a fixed point A, its distance from A is s ft., where $s = 12t - t^2$.
Find formulae for the velocity and acceleration after t sec.; sketch and interpret the space-time, velocity-time and acceleration-time graphs. 208

If v (that is, $\frac{ds}{dt}$) is known and s to be found, or if "a" (that is, $\frac{dv}{dt}$) is known and v to be found, the problem is one of integration.

A marble rolls down a groove in a sloping board, starting from rest at a point 1 ft. from the top, and moving with a constant acceleration of 2 ft./sec./sec.
Find
(i) how fast the marble is moving after $1\frac{1}{2}$ sec,
(ii) how far from the top of the board it then is,
(iii) how long it takes to roll down the groove if the board is 10 ft. long. 213

Page

(B) AREAS AND VOLUMES

Area Under a Curve. **To find the area "under" a curve (area *DHKE* in the diagram) consider any point *P* (x, y) on the curve between *D* and**

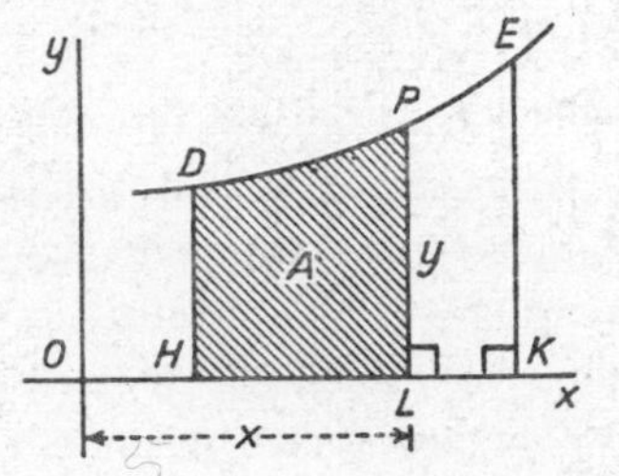

***E.* Call the (variable) area *DHLP*, "*A*"; then *A* is a function of *x*, and $\frac{dA}{dx} = y$.**

If we know the formula for *y* in terms of *x*, we can integrate to find a formula for *A*.

Thus, to find the area under $y = x^2 + 1$ from $x = 0$ to $x = 3$, we have $\frac{dA}{dx} = x^2 + 1$.

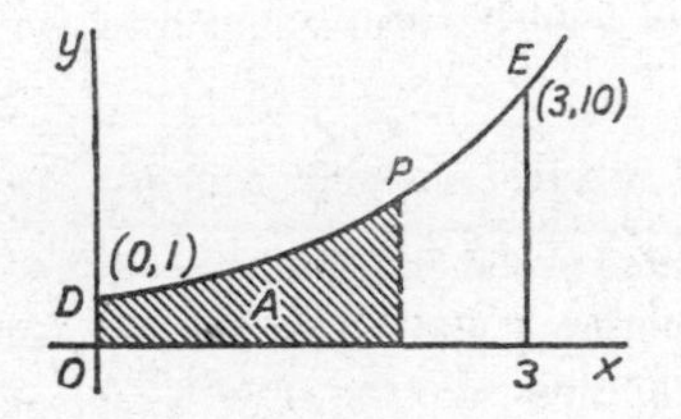

This gives $A = \frac{1}{3}x^3 + x + c$.

When $x = 0$, $A = 0$, so $c = 0$, and $A = \frac{1}{3}x^3 + x$.

We can now find the required area by substituting $x = 3$.

Find the area enclosed between the curve $y = x^2 - 4x + 3$ and the x-axis. 219

Find the area enclosed between the curve $y = 4x - x^2$ and the line $y = x$. 220

Page

Volumes of Solids of Revolution. **To find the volume formed by rotating an area under a curve (area *DHKE* above) through 360° about the x-axis, consider any point P (x, y) as before, and call the (variable) volume formed by rotating area *DHLP*, "V." Then V is a function of x, and $\frac{dV}{dx} = \pi y^2$.**

Use this formula in the same way as the one for areas, above.

The area enclosed by the curve $y = x^2 + 1$, the x-axis, the line $x = 1$ and the line $x = 3$, is rotated through 360° about the x-axis. Find the volume of the resulting solid of revolution. 222

A barrel is 4 ft. high, 4 ft. in diameter at its widest part, 3 ft. in diameter at the ends. The barrel can be thought of as formed by

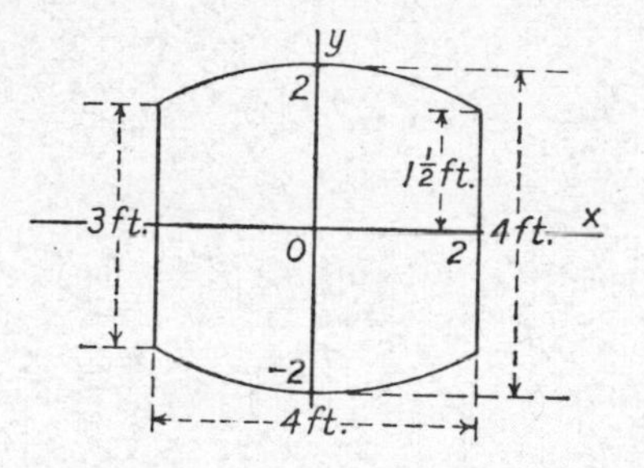

rotating a curve with equation $y = a - bx^2$ about the x-axis. Find "a" and "b," and the capacity of the barrel to the nearest $\frac{1}{10}$ cu. ft. 223

FURTHER WORK ON EQUATIONS: IDENTITIES

(A & B) ***Quadratic Equations.*** **Solution by completing the square: Make one side of the equation a perfect square [the constant term must be (half coefficient of x)^2]; then take the square root of both sides.**

Thus, if $x^2 + 6x + 4 = 0$,
$x^2 + 6x + 9 = 5$, i.e. $(x + 3)^2 = 5$,
$\therefore x + 3 = \pm\sqrt{5}$.
This gives two values for x.

Use this method to solve the equation $x^2 - 3 = 10x$, giving the roots correct to one place of decimals. 228

N.B. To use this method, you must first make the coefficient of x^2 equal to 1, by division if necessary.

Page

Solution by formula:

If $ax^2 + bx + c = 0$, $$x = \frac{-b \pm \sqrt{b^2 - 4ac}}{2a}.$$

Use this formula to solve the equations

(i) $x^2 + 5x + 2 = 0$,

(ii) $5x = 2 + \frac{6}{x}$. 229

(A & B) *Graphical Solution of Equations.*

Suppose that we draw a graph "y = a function of x." Then we can solve any equation which can be put in the form "that function of x = a constant." (Find where on the graph y = that constant, and read off the corresponding value of x.)

Further, if the graphs of two functions of x meet at a point, the x-co-ordinate of this point is a root of the equation formed by putting the two functions equal.

Draw the graph $y = 5x^2 - 2x - 6$ for values of x between -2 and $+2$. 231

Using this graph:

(i) solve the equation $5x^2 - 2x - 6 = 0$, and state the range of values of x for which $5x^2 - 2x - 6 < 0$; 231

(ii) solve the equation $4x - 10x^2 + 9 = 0$. 232

Using the same axes, draw the straight line $y = 9 - 3x$.

(iii) For what range of values of x is $5x^2 - 2x - 6 < 9 - 3x$? 232

(iv) What equation in x can be solved by considering the points of intersection of the two graphs? Read off the roots of this equation as accurately as you can. 233

Using the same scales and axes, draw the graph

$$y = \frac{8}{x+2} \text{ and } y = \frac{1}{2}(11 - 3x)$$

from $x = -1$ to $x = 4$. 234

Explain how

(i) the roots of the equation $3x^2 - 5x - 6 = 0$,

(ii) the range of values of x for which $3x^2 - 5x - 6 < 0$, may be found from these graphs, and solve the equation. 234

Page

(A) ***Further Simultaneous Equations (One linear, one quadratic).*** **Use the linear equation to find one unknown in terms of the other, then substitute in the quadratic equation.**

Solve the equations

$$(a)\ x^2 + y^2 + 6y = 4, \quad 2x - y = 7.$$ 237

$$(b)\ x^2 + xy - 2y^2 = 4, \quad 2x + 3y = 7.$$ 238

(A & B) ***Equations With Letters.***
The principles employed in solving equations are always the same—add equal amounts to, or subtract equal amounts from, both sides; multiply or divide both sides by the same amount.

Solve for x the following equations:

$$\text{(i) } \frac{a}{x} = \frac{b}{c},$$

$$\text{(ii) } px - a = b - qx,$$

$$\text{(iii) } \frac{x-a}{b} = \frac{x-b}{a}.$$ 239

Solve for x and y the simultaneous equations

$$bx + ay = a^2 + b^2$$
$$ax - by = a^2 + b^2$$

and solve for x the equation $x^2 + ab = ax + bx$. 240

(A & B) ***Transformation of Formulae.*** **To change the subject of a formula, proceed as in solving an equation.**

Make r the subject of the formula $V = \frac{1}{3}\pi r^2 h$ (that is, express the formula as "$r = \ldots$"); also, make g the subject of $T = 2\pi\sqrt{\frac{l}{g}}$. 241

In each of the following cases, make the letter in brackets the subject of the formula:

$$\text{(i) } s = ut + \frac{1}{2}ft^2\ (f),$$

$$\text{(ii) } A = P + \frac{PRT}{100}\ (P),$$

$$\text{(iii) } E = \frac{wa}{(w+W)b}\ (w).$$ 242

Page

(A & B) ***Identities.*** **If a statement that two expressions involving x are equal, is true for all values of x, the statement is called an "Identity." (This means that the expressions must in fact be the same.)**

One of the following three statements is an equation, one is an identity, and one is not true for any value of x. Find out which is which, and solve the equation.

(i) $x(x+1)(x+2)-(x-1)x(x+1)=3x^2+3x$;

(ii) $x(x+1)(x+2)-(x-1)x(x+1)=6$;

(iii) $x(x+1)(x+2)-(x-1)x(x+1)=3x^2+3x+1$. 244

Find constants a and b such that
$2x+7=a(x-1)+b(x+2)$ for all values of x. 244

If $x^3=ax+bx(x-1)+cx(x-1)(x-2)$ for all values of x, find the constants a, b and c. 244

Find constants a and b such that
$8x-2x^2-11=a-2(x+b)^2$.
Hence find the maximum value of the expression. 244

VARIATION

(A & B) ***Direct Variation.*** **The phrases "y varies directly as x" or "y is directly proportional to x" (denoted by "$y \propto x$") mean that, as x and y vary, the ratio $\frac{y}{x}$ is constant, $= k$, say; in other words, $y = kx$. Similarly, if n is any given power of x, "y varies as x^n," or "y is proportional to x^n" (written "$y \propto x^n$"), mean that as x and y vary, $y = kx^n$. (The word "directly" is often omitted.)**

If $y \propto x^2$, and $y = 40$ when $x = 4$, find:

(i) An equation connecting x and y;

(ii) The value of y when $x = 3$;

(iii) The value of x when $y = 250$. 248

Show that the weight of a solid sphere of given material varies as the cube of its radius. If the weight of such a sphere of radius 1 cm. is 297 gm., find, to the nearest 10 gm., the weight of one of radius 2 cm. 249

Page

(A & B) ***Inverse Variation.*** **"y varies inversely as x" or "y is inversely proportional to x" mean that, as x and y vary, the product yx is constant, $= k$, say; in other words,**

$$y = \frac{k}{x}.$$

This may be written $y = k.\frac{1}{x}$, so the inverse proportion relationship is sometimes denoted by $y \propto \frac{1}{x}$.

Similarly "y varies inversely as x^n" means $y = \frac{k}{x^n}$.

If y is inversely proportional to the cube root of x, and $y = 5$ when $x = 27$, find:

(i) The formula connecting x and y.

(ii) The value of x when $y = 3$. 250

(A & B) ***Joint Variation.***

A statement such as "p varies directly as x and as the cube of y, and inversely as the square root of z" means that, as x, y, z and p vary,

$$p = \frac{kxy^3}{\sqrt{z}}.$$

(If x varies while y and z are kept constant, $p \propto x$;
if y varies while z and x are kept constant, $p \propto y^3$;
if z varies while x and y are kept constant, $p \propto \frac{1}{\sqrt{z}}$.)

The electrical resistance of a wire of given material varies directly as its length and inversely as the square of its diameter. The resistance of a piece of copper wire of diameter $\frac{1}{20}$ in. and length 1 yd. is $\frac{1}{60}$ ohm. Find the resistance of a similar wire 10 ft. long and $\frac{1}{25}$ in. diameter. 252

Partial Variation.

If a formula giving one quantity (y, say) in terms of another (x) contains two or more terms, y will not vary either directly or inversely as any power of x, but the separate terms may do so.

y varies partly as x and partly inversely as x^2. When $x = 1$, $y = 7$; when $x = 2$, $y = 7$. Find the value of y when $x = 4$. 252

The resistance to the motion of a car is partly constant and partly varies as the square of the velocity. At 20 m.p.h. the resistance is 46 lb. wt., at 40 m.p.h. the resistance is 94 lb. wt. Find the resistance at 60 m.p.h. 253

Page

FRACTIONS AND FACTORS

Fractions. **Algebraical fractions are dealt with in the same way as numerical ones. The essential principle is that the value of a fraction is unchanged if the numerator and denominator are multiplied or divided by the same factor. To see what will "cancel," always factorize.**

Simplify

$$\text{(i)}\ \frac{x^2 - 3x}{x^2 - 9},$$

$$\text{(ii)}\ \frac{2x^3 - 5x^2 + 2x}{x^3 - 2x^2 + x - 2},$$

$$\text{(iii)}\ \frac{x^3 - x^2 - 2x}{12x^2 - 3x^4}.$$

254

In addition and subtraction, find the lowest common denominator, which must contain all the factors of each separate denominator.

Simplify

$$\text{(i)}\ \frac{x + 1}{x^2 - 4} - \frac{1}{x + 2},$$

$$\text{(ii)}\ \frac{1}{2x + 1} - \frac{2}{x - 3} + \frac{5x - 1}{2x^2 - 5x - 3}.$$

255

In multiplying or dividing, first (if necessary) get rid of "fractions within fractions." (See (ii) below.)

Simplify

$$\text{(i)}\ \frac{x^2 - 2x}{2x^2 + x - 1} \times \frac{x + 1}{x^3 - 4x},$$

$$\text{(ii)}\ \left(\frac{1}{b^2} - \frac{1}{a^2}\right) \div \left(\frac{1}{a} + \frac{1}{b}\right).$$

257

(A & B) ***Factors.*** **Here are some harder examples involving**

(a) **difference of two squares:**

$$x^2 - y^2 = (x - y)(x + y),$$

(b) **factorization by grouping, e.g.:**

$$ax + ay - bx - by = a(x + y) - b(x + y) = (x + y)(a - b).$$

Factorize as far as possible

(i) $2x^3 - x^2 - 8x + 4$,

(ii) $a^2 - 6ab + 9b^2 - 2a + 6b$,

(iii) $x^4 - 17x^2 + 16$.

260

Page

(A) *The Factor Theorem*

If a polynomial in x is zero when $x = k$, then $x - k$ is a factor of the expression. For example,

$$2x^3 - 3x^2 - 3x + 2 = 0 \text{ when } x = 2 \text{ (try it);}$$
$$\text{so } x - 2 \text{ is a factor.}$$

The expression $= 0$ also when $x = -1$; so $x + 1$ is a factor. When one factor has been found in this way, the remaining factor can be found by inspection or by long division.

Find the factors of

(i) $3x^3 + 4x^2 - 17x - 6$,
(ii) $x^3 + 1$. 263

Show that $2x - 1$ is a factor of $4x^3 - 13x + 6$, and find the remaining factors. 264

Find a and b if $x + 1$ and $x - 2$ are factors of $x^3 + ax^2 + bx - 6$; then find the remaining factor. 265

(A & B) *Sum and Difference of Cubes.*

$$x^3 + y^3 = (x + y)(x^2 - xy + y^2)$$
$$x^3 - y^3 = (x - y)(x^2 + xy + y^2).$$

Factorize:

(i) $8a^3 + 27b^3$,
(ii) $1 - 1000k^6$. 265

Page

(A) ARITHMETIC AND GEOMETRIC PROGRESSIONS

Arithmetic Progressions. An A.P. is a series of numbers in which the difference between successive terms is constant.

Call the first term of the series, "a," the common difference, "d."

The series is then

$$a, \quad a + d, \quad a + 2d, \quad a + 3d. \ldots$$

The nth term is

$$a + (n - 1)d.$$

The sum to n terms is

$$\frac{n}{2}(a + l),$$

where "l" stands for the nth term, or

$$\frac{n}{2}\left\{2a + (n - 1)d\right\}.$$

The "Arithmetic Mean" of two numbers is a number between the two such that the three form an A.P. If the given numbers are a, b the mean is $\frac{a + b}{2}$.

Show that $2\frac{1}{4}$, $\frac{3}{4}$, $-\frac{3}{4}$ are in arithmetic progression; then find the tenth term and the sum of ten terms of the series of which they are the first three. 270

The thirteenth term of an A.P. is three times the fourth; the sum of the first eight terms is 80. Find the first term and the common difference, and give the first five terms of the series. 270

Find the sum of all the multiples of 7 between 100 and 200. For how many of these multiples of 7, starting from the smallest, is the sum 735? 271

The sum of the first n terms of an A.P. is $2n^2 + 4n$, for all values of n. Find the first three terms and the nth term. 271

Geometric Progressions. A G.P. is a series of numbers in which the ratio of successive terms is constant.

Call the first term, "a," the common ratio, "r."

The series is then a, ar, ar^2, ar^3. . . .

The nth term is ar^{n-1}.

The sum to n terms is $\frac{a(1 - r^n)}{1 - r}$ or $\frac{a(r^n - 1)}{r - 1}$.

Page

The "Geometric Mean" of two numbers is a number between the two such that the three form a G.P. If the given numbers are a, b, the mean is $\sqrt{ab}$.

Show that 12, −6, 3 are in G.P. If they are the first three terms of a series, write down the 20th term and the sum of the first 20 terms, leaving your answers in factors. 274

The difference between the second and third terms of a G.P. (in which the terms increase) is 18; that between the third and fourth is 72. Find the first three terms and the sum of five terms. 274

The second, fifth and seventh terms of an A.P. are in G.P.; the ninth term of the A.P. is 1. Find the first seven terms of both the A.P. and the G.P. 275

GEOMETRY

CHAPTER 1

SIMILAR FIGURES

THE FIRST stage in making a new building is to prepare a number of plans or drawings. The drawings show exactly what shape and size each part of the building is to be; they are drawn to scale.

What does "drawing to scale" mean? It means that each length in the drawing is in the same proportion to the corresponding length in the building itself. On the plans there will be a note: 1 inch to 4 feet, or perhaps 1 : 50.

There are a great many details to think out before building even the simplest kind of house, and every one of them must be drawn first. After the work begins you can see, laid out on the ground, the outline of the walls, perhaps one brick high, looking like a gigantic copy of the drawing from which it was made.

To get it right, the builders have to measure a good number of lengths, but this is not enough; they must measure angles, too. You may think that the only important angles are right-angles, but this is not true.

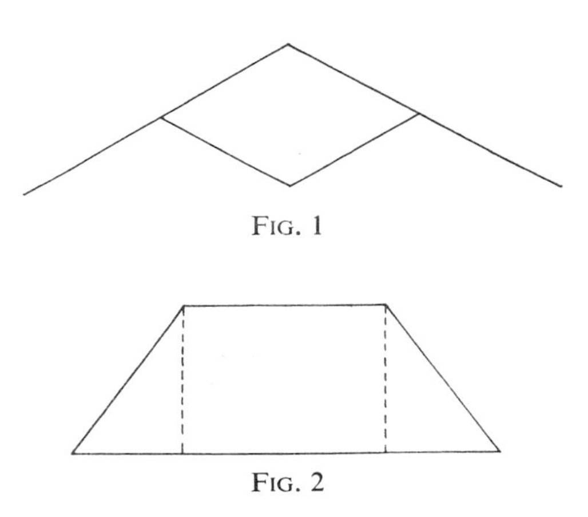

FIG. 1

FIG. 2

Here is a simplified drawing of roof beams (Fig. 1). A copy of this, with each length fifty times as large, will be exactly the same shape. Figure 2 is the plan of a bay window; to make a copy of this you must get the angles correct.

This need not be done by measuring the angles with a protractor; a better way is to use "offsets," shown by the dotted lines.

The figure and the copy will then be similar. This word does not mean "rather like each other," but "exactly the same shape."

Designs for a piece of machinery may be more complicated. All kinds of queer shapes are needed, and the exact angles have to be made for such things as cutting edges, teeth on gear wheels and so on. Many parts of machines are curved, and these curves must be precise. Besides, the dimensions of a building are large, and an error of an inch in the building itself may not be serious; but machine parts must be correct to a thousandth of an inch.

The only indispensable tools for accurate drawing are a ruler and a pair of compasses; the others, which save time, are effective because they are based on the theorems of pure geometry.

To Draw Two Similar Figures

Any drawing made of straight lines can be copied as follows:

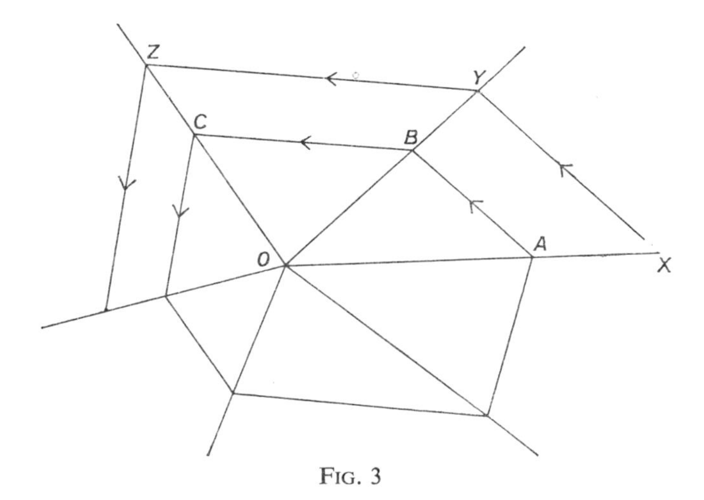

FIG. 3

Draw lines (rays) from a point O, one ray through each corner (vertex). On the ray through A mark a point X; then draw XY parallel to AB, ending on the ray through B. Continue in this way till you arrive again at X. The new figure $XYZ\ldots$ has the same set of angles as $ABC\ldots$, and its sides are in proportion to the sides of $ABC\ldots$ In Fig. 3, the ratio $\frac{OX}{OA}$ is $\frac{3}{2}$, and the ratio $\frac{XY}{AB}$ is also $\frac{3}{2}$. So the two figures are similar, and the position of X can be chosen so as to regulate the scale of $XYZ\ldots$

Notice that to make this drawing we divided up the original figure into triangles. The proof of this construction depends on the fact that the area of a triangle $= \frac{1}{2}$ (base) $\times$ perpendicular height.

These two triangles have the same perpendicular height; call it h, the dotted line in Fig. 4.

$$\frac{\text{area } OAB}{\text{area } XAB} = \frac{\frac{1}{2}h.OA}{\frac{1}{2}h.AX} = \frac{OA}{AX}$$

It is true also that

$$\frac{\text{area } OAB}{\text{area } OXB} = \frac{OA}{OX}\left(\frac{\frac{1}{2}h.OA}{\frac{1}{2}h.OX}\right)$$

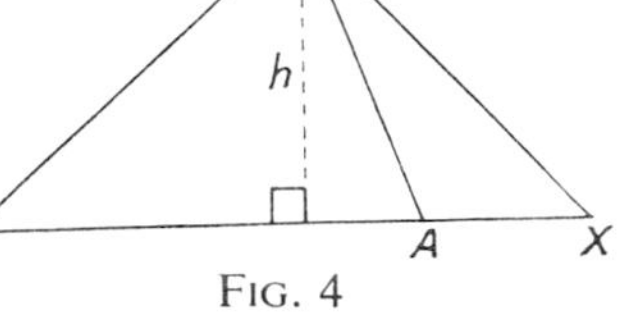

FIG. 4

(Theorem 1 is the key theorem on similar figures.)

Theorem 1:

Given: A triangle OXY, and a line AB parallel to XY, which cuts OX at A and OY at B (Fig. 5).

To prove: (1) $\frac{OA}{AX} = \frac{OB}{BY}$

(2) $\frac{OA}{OX} = \frac{OB}{OY}$

(3) $\frac{OB}{OY} = \frac{AB}{XY}$

Construction: Join BX

$$\frac{OA}{AX} = \frac{\triangle OAB}{\triangle XAB} \text{ (as in Fig. 4)}$$

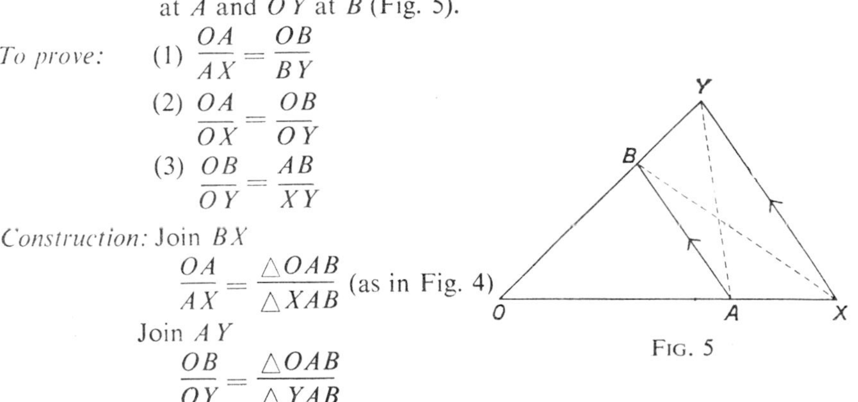

FIG. 5

Join AY

$$\frac{OB}{OY} = \frac{\triangle OAB}{\triangle YAB}$$

But $\triangle XAB = \triangle YAB$, since they are on the same base AB and have equal perpendicular heights (XY is parallel to AB).

Therefore the two ratios are equal:

$$\frac{OA}{AX} = \frac{OB}{BY} \quad \ldots\ldots\ldots\ldots\ldots (1)$$

To prove $\frac{OA}{OX} = \frac{OB}{OY}$. This can be shown at once from the previous result; see No. 1 (2) in Exercise 1A. Or, directly from the figure,

$$\triangle OXB = \triangle OAB + \triangle AXB$$
$$\triangle OYA = \triangle OAB + \triangle AYB$$
$$\therefore \triangle OXB = \triangle OYA$$

Since $\frac{OA}{OX} = \frac{\triangle OAB}{\triangle OXB}$ and $\frac{OB}{OY} = \frac{\triangle OAB}{\triangle OYA}$, these two ratios are equal:

$$\frac{OA}{OX}=\frac{OB}{OY}\;\ldots\ldots\ldots\ldots\ldots\ldots\ldots\ldots(2)$$

Draw $BC \parallel OX$ to meet XY at C (Fig. 6).

Then, as in (1), $\frac{OB}{BY}=\frac{XC}{CY}$

So that $\frac{OB}{OY}=\frac{XC}{XY}$ (if this is not obvious, see Questions 1 and 2 in Exercise 1A).

But $XC=AB$, since $ABCX$ is a parallelogram.

$$\frac{OB}{OY}=\frac{AB}{XY}\;\ldots\ldots\ldots\ldots\ldots\ldots\ldots\ldots(3)$$

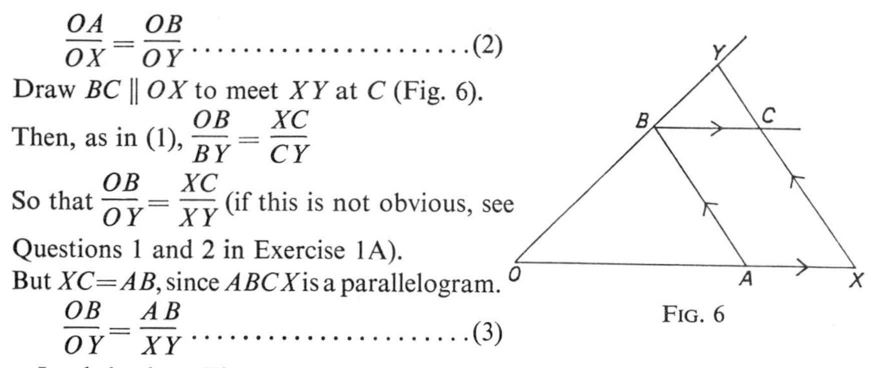

FIG. 6

Look back at Fig. 3, and you see that the method of drawing is indeed based on this theorem.

EXERCISE 1A

Nos. 1-6 are on Simple Ratio.

1. If $\frac{AB}{BC}=\frac{3}{2}$ (Fig. 6*a*), write down the ratios of $\frac{AB}{AC}$, $\frac{BC}{AC}$ and $\frac{BC}{AB}$.

Also if $\frac{AB}{BC}=\frac{h}{k}$.

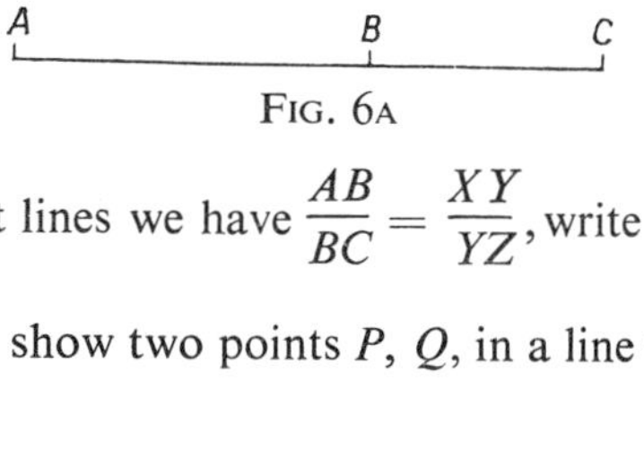

A B C

FIG. 6A

2. If on two straight lines we have $\frac{AB}{BC}=\frac{XY}{YZ}$, write down five other pairs of equal ratios.

3. Make a sketch to show two points P, Q, in a line with A and B, so that $\frac{AP}{PB}=\frac{2}{1}$ and $\frac{AQ}{BQ}=\frac{2}{1}$.

4. In Fig. 6*b*, O is the mid-point of AB, and $\frac{AP}{PB}=\frac{AQ}{BQ}$.

Show that $\frac{OA}{OP}=\frac{OQ}{OA}$. and that $(OA)^2=OP.OQ$.

(*Hint:* $AP=OA+OP$; treat the other lengths the same way.)

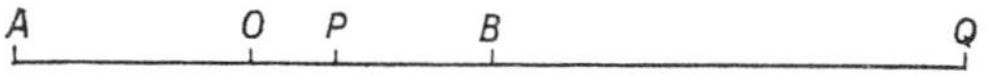

A O P B Q

FIG. 6B

5. If $\frac{a}{b}=\frac{x}{y}$, let each ratio $=R$. Then $a=b.R$, $x=y.R$.

Use this to show that (i) $ay=bx$; (ii) $\frac{a+b}{a-b}=\frac{x+y}{x-y}$; (iii) $\frac{a}{b}=\frac{a+x}{b+y}$.

6. In No. 4, show that $OP = \frac{1}{2}(AP - PB)$, $OQ = \frac{1}{2}(AQ + BQ)$. What lengths in the sketch are equal to $\frac{1}{2}(AP + PB)$, $\frac{1}{2}(AQ - BQ)$?

Nos. 7-10 *are on Theorem* 1.

(*Note:* If $\frac{a}{b} = R$, then $a = b.R$.)

7. Notice that the theorem is true in these three cases (Fig. 7):

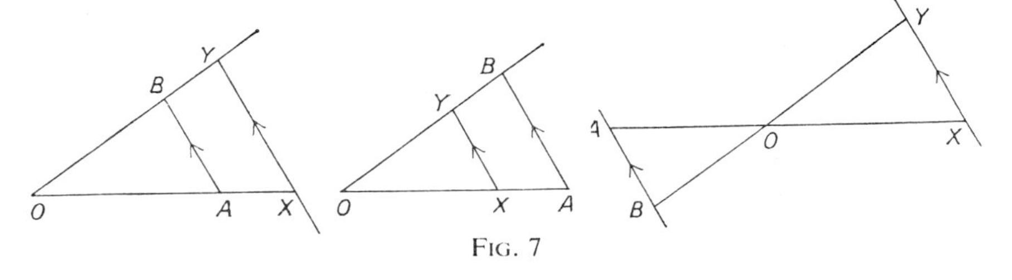

FIG. 7

In each case, $\frac{OA}{AX} = \frac{OB}{BY}$, and $\frac{OA}{OX} = \frac{OB}{OY} = \frac{AB}{XY}$. Draw each figure, and use exactly the same proof each time.

8. Show that if $\frac{OA}{AX} = \frac{3}{5}$, then $\frac{OA}{OX} = \frac{3}{8}$, and that the area OAB is $\frac{3}{8}$ of $\triangle OBX$, which is itself $\frac{3}{8}$ of $\triangle OXY$.

9. Prove the converse theorem: If A, B, are points on the lines OX, OY, and $\frac{OA}{OX} = \frac{OB}{OY}$, then AB will be parallel to XY.

10. In Fig. 8 $\hat{M}$ and $\hat{N}$ are right-angles.

$\frac{OM}{ON} = \frac{OA}{OB}$ because $AM \parallel BN$. Write instead $\frac{OM}{OA} = \frac{ON}{OB}$. This ratio is called the cosine of the angle O ($\cos \hat{O}$).

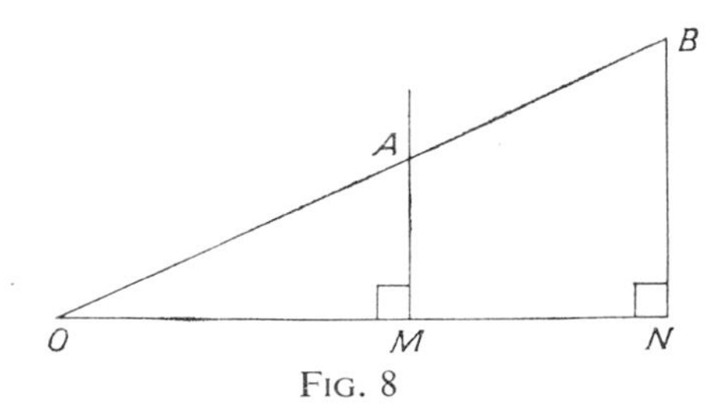

FIG. 8

Wherever the point A is marked, OM will be the same fraction of OA. $OM = OA.(\cos \hat{O})$.

It is also true that $AM = OA.(\cos \hat{A})$.

Nos. 11-14 *are exercises on Fig.* 6

11. $YC = 4$ in., $CX = 6$ in., $YB = 5$ in.; find the length of OB.

12. $YB = YC = 3$ in., $BC = 4$ in., $OX = 10$ in.; find CX.

13. Y is a right-angle. $BY = 4$ cm., $YC = 3$ cm., and $OB = 8$ cm. Find OX.

14. BC is $\frac{1}{3}$ of OX; find the ratio $\dfrac{YC}{CX}$

15. In Fig. 7 (which one?), $OX = 2.OA$, and XY is 3 in. longer than AB. How long is AB?

16. In *two* of the diagrams in Fig. 7, AB is 8 in., XY is 12 in., BY is 15 in. Find OB in each case.

Constructions

(*Note:* Parallel lines and right-angles are drawn here with ruler and set-square.)

17. To inscribe in a given triangle: (i) a square with one side along the base; (ii) a semicircle with diameter parallel to the base.

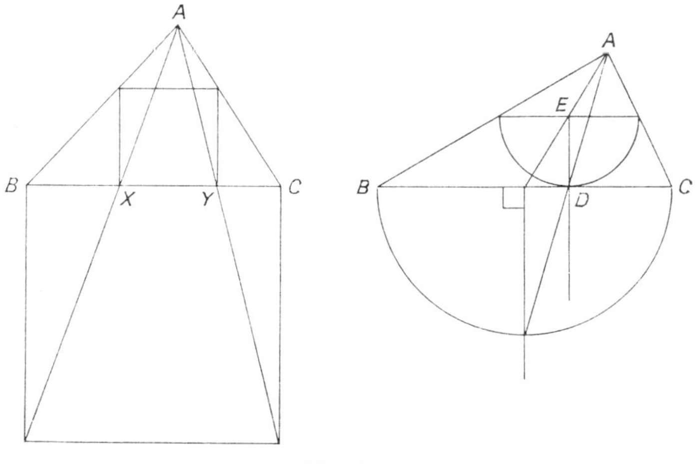

FIG. 9

18. To divide a line in a given ratio; or into a number of equal parts.

AB is the line. Draw AP, BQ parallel, but in opposite senses (opposite directions). Use compasses—not a ruler—to mark off lengths, all equal, from A towards P and from B towards Q. In the figure, AM is 4 units, MP 3 units (Fig. 10).

Prove: $MN \parallel BP$, $\dfrac{AO}{OB} = \dfrac{4}{3}$

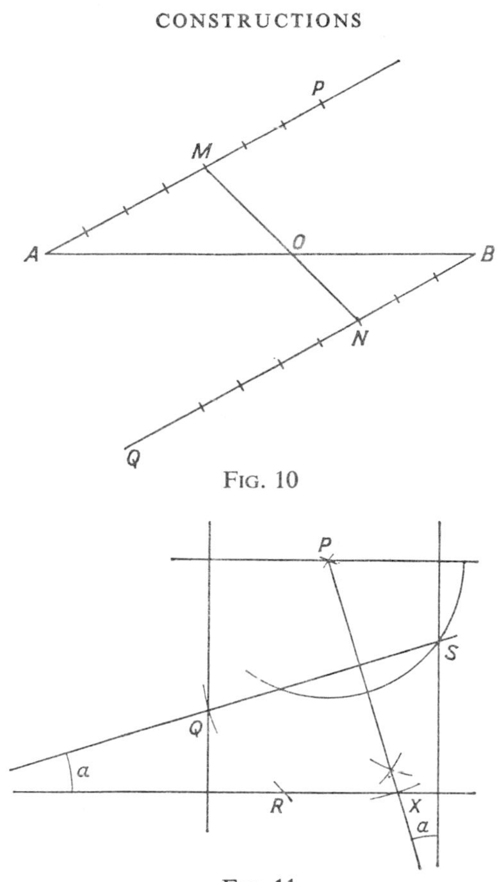

FIG. 10

FIG. 11

19. This makes use of the cosine.

Given four points, to draw a square with one of its sides passing through each of the points. The four points are P, Q, R, S put down anywhere at random.

Draw PX at right-angles to QS and equal to QS. Draw the line through R, X. Draw perpendiculars to this through Q and S, and a parallel through P.

This makes a rectangle; to prove that it is a square.

If QS makes an angle "a" with RX, then PX will make an equal angle a with the side of the rectangle which passes through S. Therefore the sides of the rectangle are $QS.\cos a$ and $PX.\cos a$.

But QS was drawn equal to PX; so the rectangle is a square.

(*N.B.:* In this drawing, use compasses to make PX at right-angles to QS; this gives a better result than using a set-square.)

20. Given an angle $A\hat{O}B$ and a point M inside it. Construct a straight line through M to cut OA at X, OB at Y, so that $\frac{XM}{MY} = \frac{1}{2}$.

21. Given two triangles ABC, XYZ. Inscribe in the triangle ABC another triangle whose sides are parallel to those of $\triangle XYZ$.

(One vertex of this triangle is to be on each side of $\triangle ABC$.)

22. Inscribe a square in a semicircle, with one side along the diameter.

Theorem II

If two triangles are equi-angular, then their corresponding sides are in the same ratio: that is,

Given: $\triangle ABC$, $\triangle XYZ$, with $\hat{A} = \hat{X}$, $\hat{B} = \hat{Y}$, $\hat{C} = \hat{Z}$

Prove: $\frac{YZ}{BC} = \frac{XZ}{AC} = \frac{XY}{AB}$

(In Fig. 12 XY is shorter than AB; but the proof would need no altering if XY were longer than AB.)

Construction: On AB cut off $AH = XY$
on AC cut off $AK = XZ$

Then $\triangle AHK \equiv \triangle XYZ$ (SAS)

Since $A\hat{H}K = \hat{Y}$, and this $= \hat{B}$

Therefore $HK \parallel BC$

and by Theorem I, $\frac{AH}{AB} = \frac{AK}{AC} = \frac{HK}{BC}$

$\therefore \frac{XY}{AB} = \frac{XZ}{AC} = \frac{YZ}{BC}$

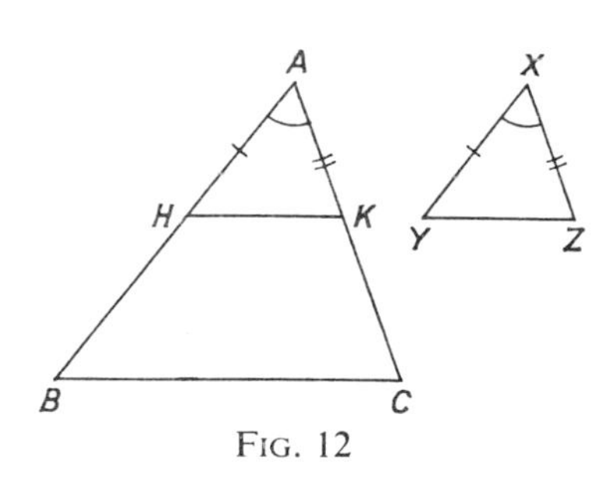

FIG. 12

Theorem III (*converse of Theorem II*)

If the sides of two triangles are in proportion, then the triangles are equi-angular.

Given: $\triangle ABC$, $\triangle XYZ$, with $\frac{YZ}{BC} = \frac{XZ}{AC} = \frac{XY}{AB}$

Prove: $\hat{A} = \hat{X}$, $\hat{B} = \hat{Y}$, $\hat{C} = \hat{Z}$.

Construction: On AB cut off $AH = XY$.
On AC cut off $AK = XZ$. Join HK.

Then $\frac{AH}{AB} = \frac{AK}{AC}$

$\therefore HK \parallel BC$, and each of these two ratios $= \frac{HK}{BC}$.

$\therefore HK = YZ$, and $\triangle AHK \equiv \triangle XYZ$ (S S S)

$\therefore \hat{X} = A\hat{H}K$
$= \hat{B}$; and likewise for the other angles.

Note: When writing down the names of two similar triangles, it is worth while to show the equal angles in the same positions, thus:

If $\triangle ABC$, $\triangle PQR$ have $\hat{A} = \hat{Q}$, $\hat{B} = \hat{R}$, $\hat{C} = \hat{P}$,

write $\dfrac{\triangle ABC}{\triangle QRP}$ are similar.

This makes certain of putting down the correct ratios. Mistakes are sometimes made by reading them off the figure, but here you need only read them as they are written:

$$\frac{\triangle ABC}{\triangle QRP} \qquad \frac{AB}{QR} = \frac{AC}{QP} = \frac{BC}{RP}$$

Note how this works in No. 1 and 3 of Exercise 1B.

EXERCISE 1B

1. Pythagoras' Theorem.

Given: $\triangle ABC$, with a right-angle at $\hat{A}$.

Prove: $BC^2 = AB^2 + AC^2$.

Draw AD, the perpendicular on BC. (Fig. 13)

$D\hat{A}B = \hat{C}$, and $A\hat{B}D$ is $\hat{B}$ (of $\triangle ABC$).

So, the left-hand triangle and the $\triangle ABC$ have equal angles: write

$\dfrac{\triangle ABC}{\triangle DBA}$ are similar.

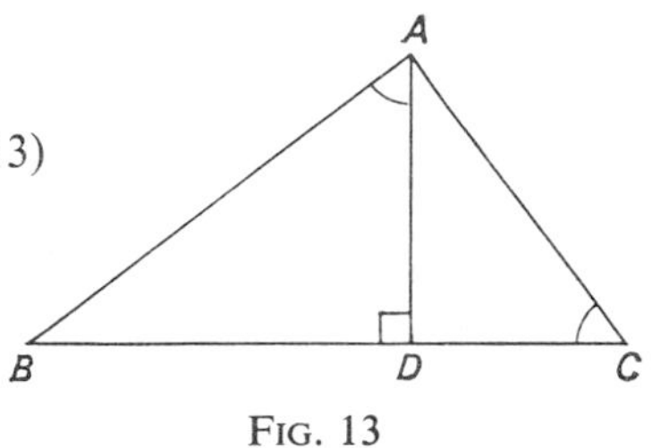

FIG. 13

By Theorem II, $\dfrac{AB}{DB} = \dfrac{BC}{BA}$ $\qquad AB^2 = BC.DB$

Likewise,

$\dfrac{\triangle ABC}{\triangle DAC}$ give $\dfrac{AC}{DC} = \dfrac{BC}{AC}$ $\qquad AC^2 = BC.DC$

Add together and you have $AB^2 + AC^2 = BC(DB + DC)$

$$= BC^2$$

2. In the example above, we said nothing about AD; what we needed were lengths along the sides of $\triangle ABC$.

Prove that $AD^2 = BD.DC$.

3. Two chords of a circle, AB and CD, cross at X. Show that $\triangle XAC$ and $\triangle XDB$ are similar (Fig. 14).

X may be either inside or outside the circle. Notice that in either case $\hat{A} = \hat{D}$, $\hat{C} = \hat{B}$, so we have written $X\hat{A}C$, $X\hat{D}B$ in that order. Draw two figures, and supply the reasons.

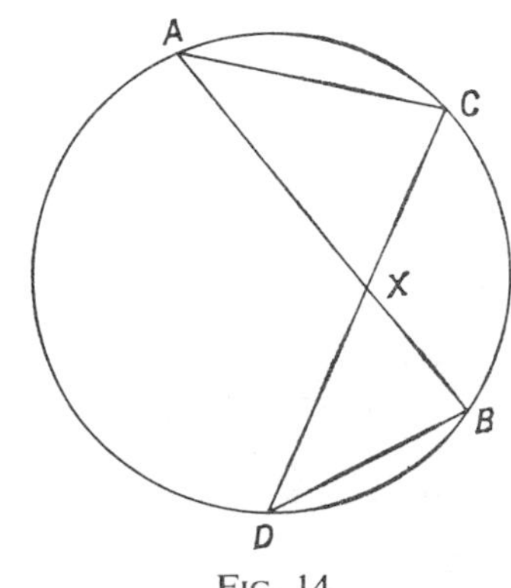

FIG. 14

4. Again in Fig. 14, prove that $AX.XB = CX.XD$, and if O is the centre of the circle, prove that $AX.XB = OA^2 - OX^2$.

(If X is outside the circle, $AX.XB = OX^2 - OA^2$.)

5. The first part of No. 4 is not hard. The result $AX.XB = CX.XD$ is true for any two chords which meet at X; very well, then, pick out one special chord. In the left-hand figure below, CD is at right-angles to OX, so X must be the mid-point of CD.

$AX.XB = CX.XD$, but this time it equals CX^2.

$\triangle OCX$ has a right-angle at X, therefore $CX^2 = OA^2 - OX^2$ $(OC = OA)$.

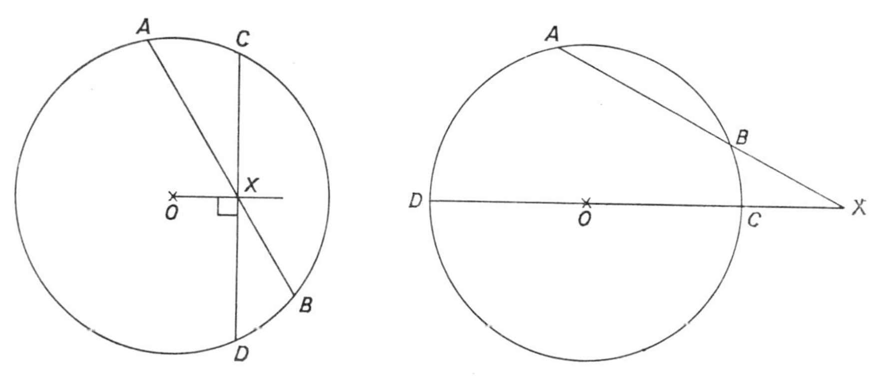

FIG. 15

In the right-hand figure, the chord picked out actually goes through the centre; $CX = OX - OC$, $XD = OX + OD$. Write x for the length of OX, r for the radius, then

$$AX.XB = CX.XD = (x - r)(x + r)$$
$$= x^2 - r^2$$

Nos. 6-8 *make use of the Mean Proportional.*

6. If $\frac{a}{x} = \frac{x}{b}$, x is the mean proportional between a, b. To construct the mean proportional between two given lengths: mark these lengths AX, XB along a straight line. Draw *any* circle through A, B. Now complete the figure, like that in Fig. 15, left. CX is the "mean."

7. Question No. 2 shows the same thing more neatly. If BD, DC are given lengths, how do you construct the rest? Oh, yes; the angle in a semicircle is a right-angle.

This construction is often needed. First bisect BC; draw a semicircle on BC as diameter; construct DA at right-angles to BC.

Note: The square drawn on DA is equal in area to the rectangle $BDEF$, which has $DE = DC$. (Compare this with No. 2.)

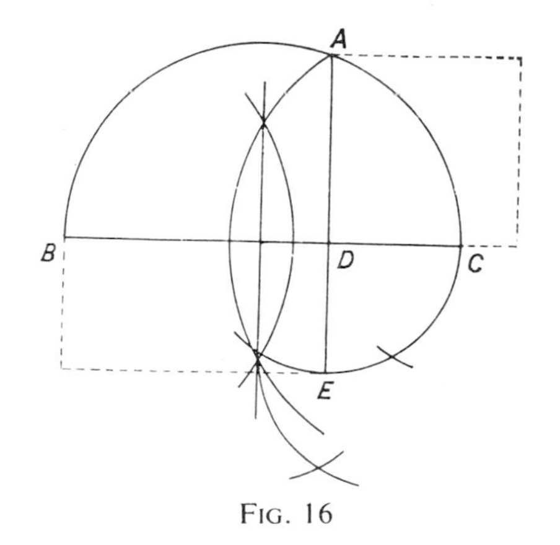

FIG. 16

8. Make this construction, and prove that it is correct (Fig. 16).

The given lengths are BD, DC. Draw the semicircle on BD as diameter; mark C between B and D, with DC the right length. Construct CZ at right-angles to BD, to meet the semicircle at Z. Then DZ is the mean proportional to BD, DC.

Similar Figures in Perspective

The method of Fig. 3 (page 302) is good enough for making a copy on a different scale, if the drawing is made up of straight lines. But curves, too, may be similar; how can a curve be copied?

You can make a set of straight lines, joining points on the curve, and "magnify" them. This does not produce an exact copy of the curve, but merely a kind of skeleton (Fig. 17).

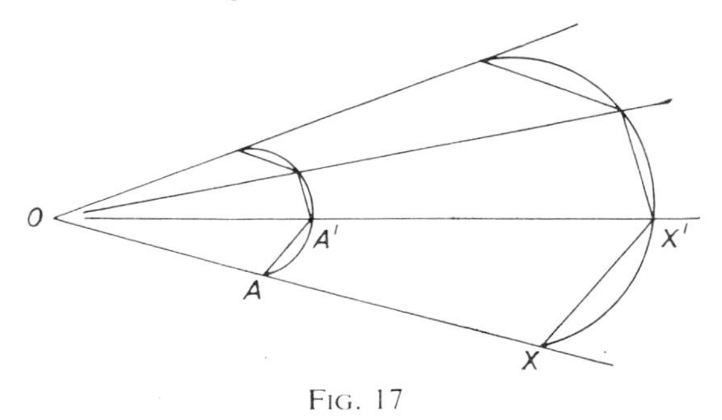

FIG. 17

To make an exact copy, you can use a simple instrument made of four bars hinged together. In this linkage OB, BX are of equal length and OC, CA are equal; also $BD = AC$. There is a pin at O; fix this to the paper, and make A trace out the original curve. Then X will trace out a copy of it.

Smooth pivots at the points C, D can be adjusted in any positions, but see that $ACBD$ is a parallelogram (Fig. 18).

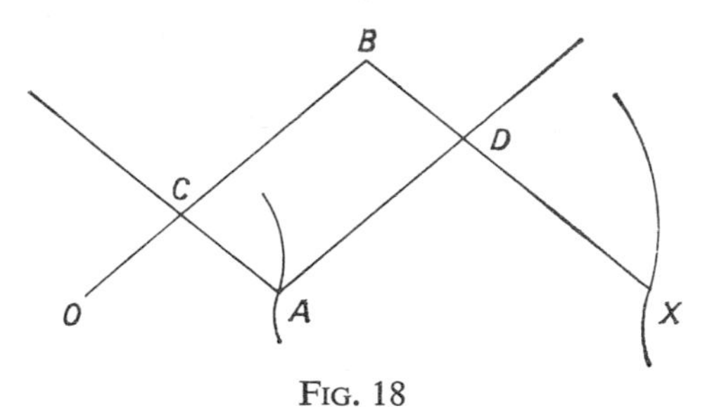

FIG. 18

Since OCA and OBX are isosceles triangles, the angles $O\hat{A}C$, $O\hat{X}B$ will be equal, and O, A, X will always be in a straight line. So O is a centre of perspective, and lines AA', XX' joining points which correspond are always in the same ratio, for this ratio is $\dfrac{OA}{OX}$ which equals $\dfrac{OC}{OB}$.

The instrument is called a pantograph. Unlike other "drawing-office" instruments, it is easy to make; four perforated strips from a construction set, two thin pencils at A and X, and a sharp point to put at O.

Two Circles

Any two circles are similar, and are in perspective. If their centres are A, B and radii a, b, draw the straight line through AB. Draw two parallel radii, AH and BK. H, K are corresponding points. Draw the line HK, to meet AB at a point S.

By Theorem I, $\dfrac{AS}{BS} = \dfrac{AH}{BK}$

$= \dfrac{a}{b}$, the ratio of the two radii.

So, wherever H is, S will be a fixed point; every line like HK must pass through S, so it is a centre of perspective for the two circles (Fig. 19).

EXERCISE 1C

1. In Fig. 19 prove that $AH' \parallel BK'$, $HH' \parallel KK'$, and $\dfrac{HH'}{KK'} = \dfrac{a}{b}$.

2. In the figure, AH, BK point the same way; they are in the *same sense*. Draw a figure with AH, BK parallel but in opposite senses, and find another centre of perspective S', *between* the two circles.

3. Where are the points S, S' in these cases? Make a drawing for each.

(i) Two equal circles;

(ii) Two circles which cross in two points;
(iii) Two circles touching;
(iv) One circle inside the other;
(v) Two circles with the same centre.

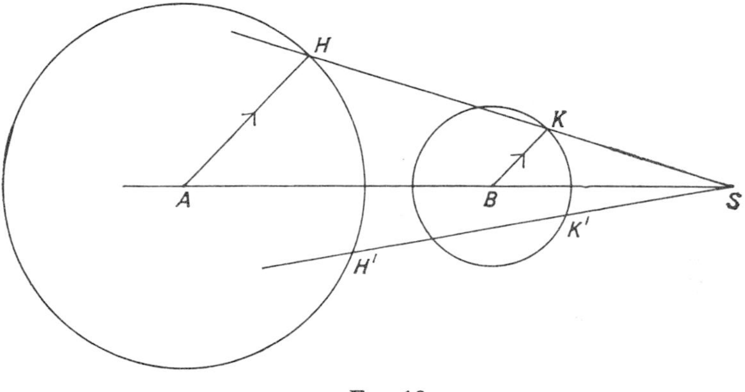

FIG. 19

4. Given two unequal circles, as in Fig. 19, make this construction:

Find the point S, and on AS as diameter construct a semicircle, to cut the left-hand circle at X. Draw the straight line SX.

Theorem IV

If *two* sides of a triangle are proportional to two sides of another triangle, and the included angles are equal, then the triangles are similar.

Given: $\triangle ABC$, $\triangle XYZ$ with $\dfrac{XY}{AB} = \dfrac{XZ}{AC}$

$\hat{A} = \hat{X}$ (Fig. 20)

Prove: $\hat{B} = \hat{Y}$, $\hat{C} = \hat{Z}$

Construction:

On AB cut off $AH = XY$.

On AC cut off $AK = XZ$.

Then $\triangle AHK \equiv \triangle XYZ$ (S A S).

Also $\dfrac{AH}{AB} = \dfrac{AK}{AC}$

$\therefore HK \parallel BC$,

by Theorem I (Converse)

$\therefore \hat{B} = \hat{H}$ and $\hat{C} = \hat{K}$

$= \hat{Y}$ $\quad = \hat{Z}$

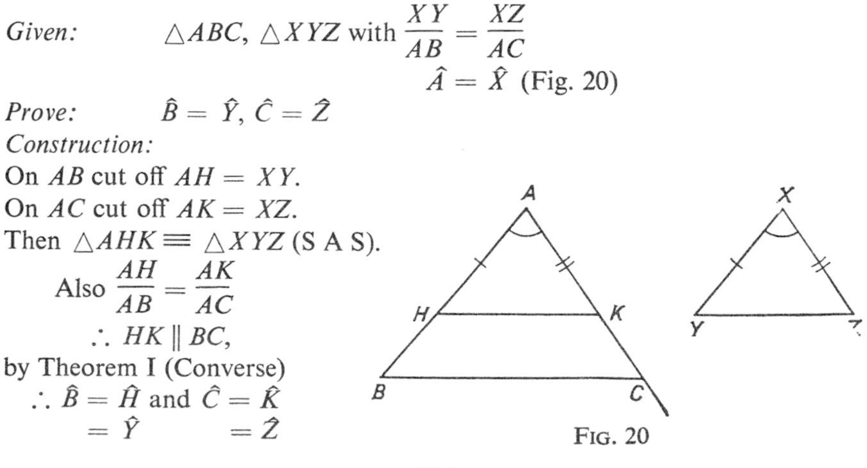

FIG. 20

Note: The proofs of Theorems II, III, IV, are all alike. The same construction is used each time, then $\triangle AHK$ is proved congruent to $\triangle XYZ$. They all depend on Theorem I quite simply.

Compare these theorems with those on congruent triangles.

	Similar	*Congruent*	*Reference*
II.	Two pairs of equal angles. (The third pair will also be equal.)	Two pairs of equal angles, and one pair of equal sides.	S A A
III.	Three pairs of sides proportional.	Three pairs of sides equal.	S S S
IV.	Two pairs of sides proportional, and the angles between them equal.	Two pairs of sides equal and the angles between them equal.	S A S

EXERCISE 1D

1. In Fig. 21, given $\dfrac{OA}{OH} = \dfrac{OB}{OK}$, prove that A, B, H, K, lie on a circle.

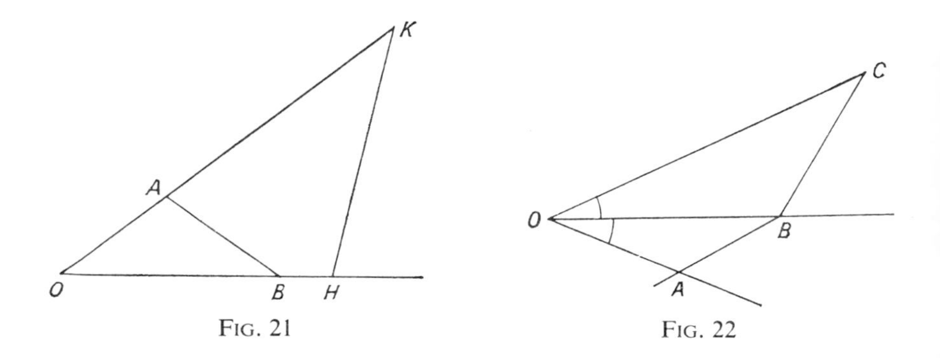

FIG. 21

FIG. 22

2. O is the centre of a circle of radius r. OPQ is a straight line, and $OP.OQ = r^2$. Prove that for every point X on the circle, $\triangle OPX$, $\triangle OXQ$ are similar, and that $\dfrac{PX}{XQ}$ is constant in value.

3. In Fig. 22, OB bisects $A\hat{O}C$, and $\dfrac{OA}{OB} = \dfrac{OB}{OC}$.

Prove that $\left(\dfrac{AB}{BC}\right)^2 = \dfrac{OA}{OC}$

4. In the same figure, is it possible for O, A, B, C to lie on a circle?

Theorem V (*the bisector of an angle*)

Given: AH bisects $B\hat{A}C$ and meets BC at H.

Prove: $\dfrac{BH}{HC} = \dfrac{BA}{AC}$

Construction: Draw $CY \parallel AB$, to cut the line AH at Y (Fig. 23).

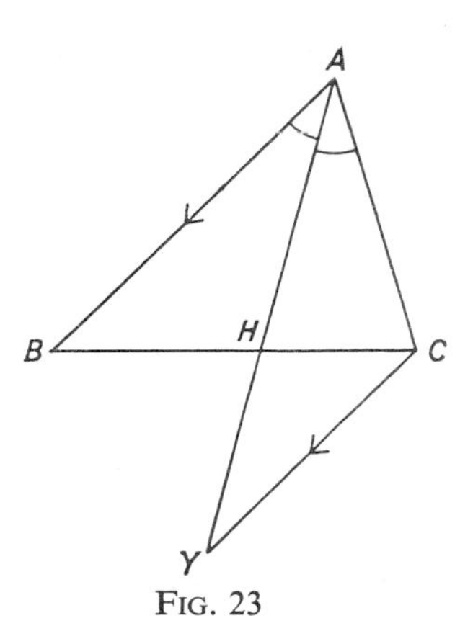

FIG. 23

Then by Theorem I, $\dfrac{BH}{HC} = \dfrac{BA}{YC}$

Also by parallels, $\hat{Y} = B\hat{A}H$

$= C\hat{A}H$

$\therefore\ YC = AC$

$\therefore\ \dfrac{BH}{HC} = \dfrac{BA}{AC}$

This proof uses Theorem I only.

Bisector of an Exterior Angle

Given: $C\hat{A}E$ is an exterior angle for $\triangle ABC$; AK bisects this exterior angle and meets the line BC at K.

Prove: $\dfrac{BK}{CK} = \dfrac{BA}{AC}$

Construction: The same line as before is needed, through C parallel to AB. Let it cut AK at Z (Fig. 24).

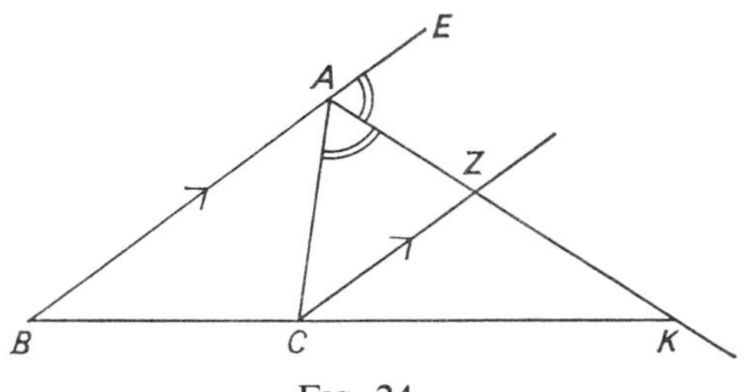

FIG. 24

Then by Theorem I, $\dfrac{BK}{CK} = \dfrac{BA}{CZ}$

And by parallels, $CZA = Z\hat{A}E = Z\hat{A}C$

$\therefore\ CZ = AC$

$\therefore\ \dfrac{BK}{CK} = \dfrac{BA}{AC}$

There is no need to use even the key theorem. Both parts of Theorem V can be proved by using simply areas.

Draw $HP \perp BA$, $HQ \perp AC$ (Fig. 25).
$\triangle AHP \equiv \triangle AHQ$ (S A A)
$\therefore HP = HQ$
Now the area of $\triangle AHB = \frac{1}{2}BA.HP$
and the area of $\triangle AHC = \frac{1}{2}AC.HQ$
Therefore the ratio of these areas is $\frac{BA}{AC}$.

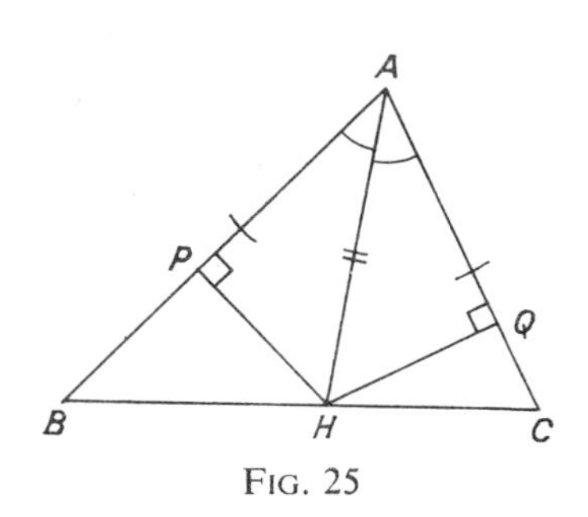

FIG. 25

But these two triangles stand on bases BH, HC, and they have the same perpendicular height from A to BC.

The ratio of the areas is then $\frac{BH}{HC} \therefore \frac{BH}{HC} = \frac{BA}{AC}$

This theorem is often stated as follows:

The internal and external bisectors of one angle of a triangle divide the base, internally and externally, in the ratio of the two sides.

EXERCISE 1E

1. Prove the theorem for the external bisector AK, using areas only.

2. Converse of Theorem V.

Prove that, if H is a point on BC and $\frac{BH}{HC} = \frac{BA}{AC}$, then AH bisects $B\hat{A}C$.

3. Given $\triangle ABC$, inscribed in a circle; AD bisects $\hat{A}$, meets the circle at D, and meets BC at X (Fig. 26).

Show that $\triangle AXC$, $\triangle BXD$ are similar, and hence that $AX.XD = BX.XC$.

Also show that $\triangle AXC$, $\triangle ABD$ are similar, hence that $AX.AD = AB.AC$.

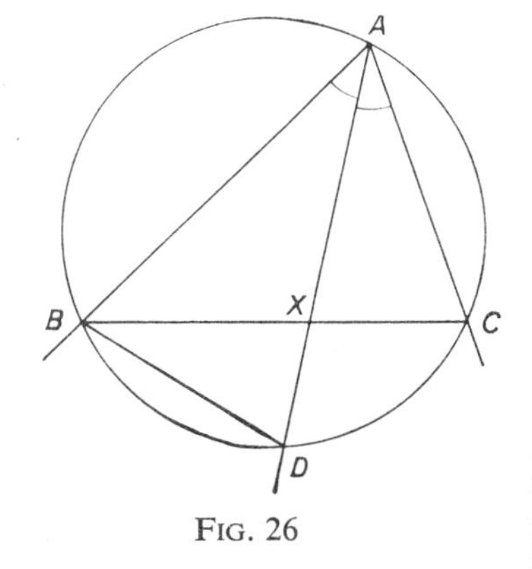

FIG. 26

4. Use these two results to calculate the length of AX:

(i) If $AB = 45$ in., $AC = 20$ in., $BC = 39$ in.

(ii) If $AB = 4$ in., $AC = 2$ in., $BC = 3$ in.

Areas of Similar Figures

Two squares are certainly similar. If their sides are a inches, b inches, then their areas are a^2 sq. in., b^2 sq. in.

So the ratio of the areas is $\frac{a^2}{b^2}$, the square of the ratio of their sides. This is true of all similar figures. It is enough to prove the fact for two triangles, since any two similar figures with straight sides can be divided up into sets of triangles, each pair of triangles being similar.

Theorem VI

The ratio of the areas of two similar triangles is the square of the ratio of corresponding sides.

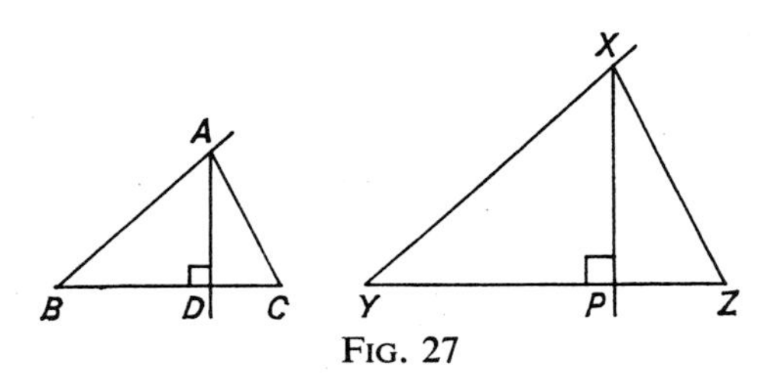

FIG. 27

Given: $\triangle ABC$, $\triangle XYZ$ are similar.

Draw $AD \perp BC$, $XP \perp YZ$.

Then $\triangle ABD$, $\triangle XYP$ are similar (three angles).

$$\therefore \frac{AD}{XP} = \frac{AB}{XY}$$
$$= \frac{BC}{YZ}$$

The areas of $\triangle ABC$, $\triangle XYZ$ are $\frac{1}{2}.BC.AD$ and $\frac{1}{2}.YZ.XP$.

So the ratio of the areas is $\frac{BC}{YZ}\cdot\frac{AD}{XP} = \left(\frac{BC}{YZ}\right)^2$

It can be shown that the areas of similar figures with curved outlines obey the same rule. They may not have "sides" at all, but they will have straight lines which correspond, as in Fig. 17.

Everyone uses the formula for the area of a circle, $A = \pi r^2$; but perhaps does not stop to think where it comes from.

One part of it comes from the fact that all circles are similar, and so the ratio of the areas of two circles is the *square* of the ratio of corresponding lengths. Their radii are certainly corresponding lengths. As for the other part, the number π, there must *be* a definite number.

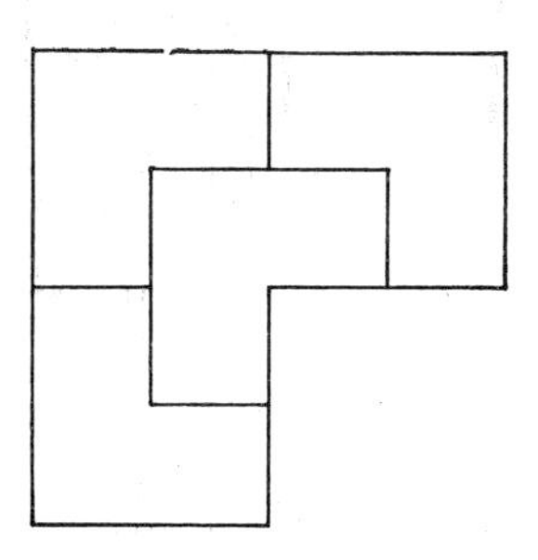

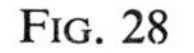

FIG. 28

If $\frac{A}{A'} = \frac{(r)^2}{(r')^2}$, then A must equal $k.r^2$, and A' must equal $k.r'^2$, with the same multiplier k each time. This constant number has to be calculated; its value depends on the shape of the figures.

For squares, $k = 1$. For equilateral triangles, $k = \frac{1}{2}.\sqrt{3}$, and for other triangles k is found from the angles (see Chapter 5). For circles $k = \pi$, that curious number.

To come back to rectilinear figures (those with straight sides). An old puzzle runs like this:

> *A man left to his four sons three-fourths of a square piece of land, to be divided equally between them, in four pieces of the same shape.*

The answer is shown in Fig. 28. Here you can see similar figures of two sizes. The corresponding lengths are in the ratio $\frac{1}{2}$ and the areas, $\frac{1}{4}$.

It is all very well to learn that the ratio of areas, etc., is the square of the ratio of lengths. It is also possible to forget this important fact. The simple shapes in Fig. 29 illustrate it; you can actually count the pieces, and see that a "double size" contains 4 pieces, and a triple size, 9 pieces.

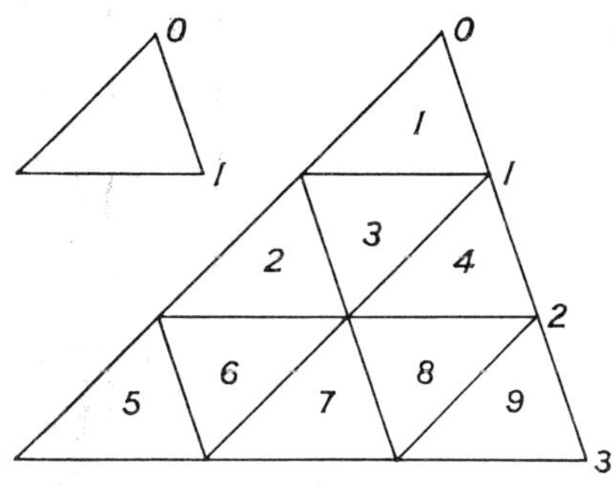

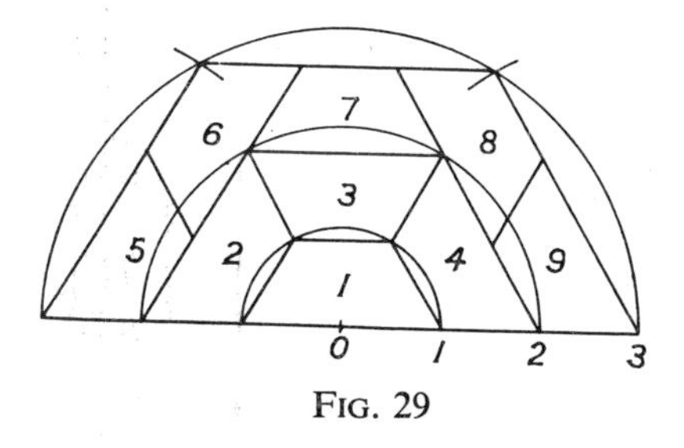

FIG. 29

Volumes of Similar Figures, in Three Dimensions

Begin with a 1-in. cube. To build up cubes with edges 2 in., 3 in., you would need 8 small cubes for the 2-in. cube, and 27 for the 3-in. one. The ratio of the volumes is:

$$\frac{8 \text{ cu. in.}}{27 \text{ cu. in.}} = \left(\frac{2}{3}\right)^3; \text{ the cube of the ratio of the lengths.}$$

This is true for similar solid figures of any shape. A model train or ship driven by steam may work well; but amateur engineers have often found that when they make a bigger one it won't work at all. Steam exerts a certain pressure per square inch on the head of a piston. If you increase the scale in the ratio $\frac{10}{1}$, the area of the piston-head will be increased 100 times, and so will the steam pressure. But the volume, and therefore the weight of the machine will be 1,000 times as big, so the steam will not be able to drive it.

Whatever the motive power, it must be made 1,000 times more effective, if it has to drive a weight 1,000 times as great.

A bird depends on the area of its wings to travel quickly, and indeed to keep itself up in the air. So quite apart from its shape, streamlined so as to present the least possible area to wind resistance, its weight is vitally important. No bird can be as big as a large animal, even though it is made of lighter material.

There is a natural limit to the size of an animal. A creature twice as tall, twice as wide and twice as long as the usual size, must somehow have eight times as much muscle; this means thick stumpy legs, and large flat feet to hold up its weight and to push it along. Altogether, it is most unlikely that animals, or birds, or even machines of different sizes can be similar in shape.

EXERCISE 1F

Constructions

1. To make a figure similar to a given figure and twice its area.

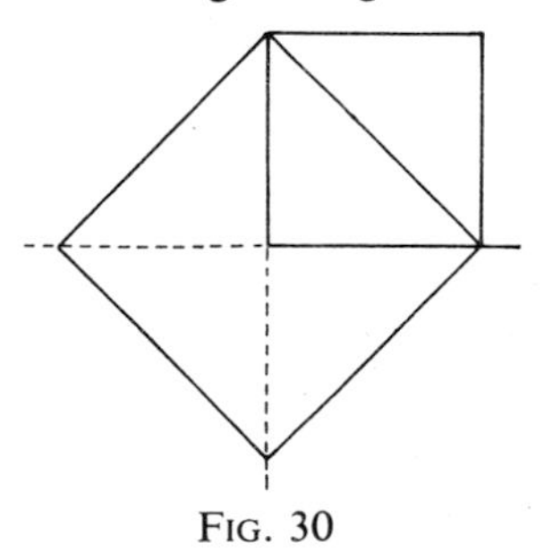

FIG. 30

The ratio of the areas is $\frac{2}{1}$, so the ratio of corresponding lengths must be $\frac{\sqrt{2}}{1}$. This is so in Fig. 30. The large square is *seen* to be twice the area of the small one.

Hence the construction for a triangle. ABC is any triangle (Fig. 31, overleaf). The construction makes AZ the diagonal of a square; then makes $AX = AZ = AB.\sqrt{2}$. XY is parallel to BC, and $\triangle AXY$ is twice the area of $\triangle ABC$.

2. Construct a square equal in area to a given triangle.

3. To construct a mean proportional between any two lengths. In Fig. 32 the lengths are 4, 5 units $BM^2 = AB.BC$.

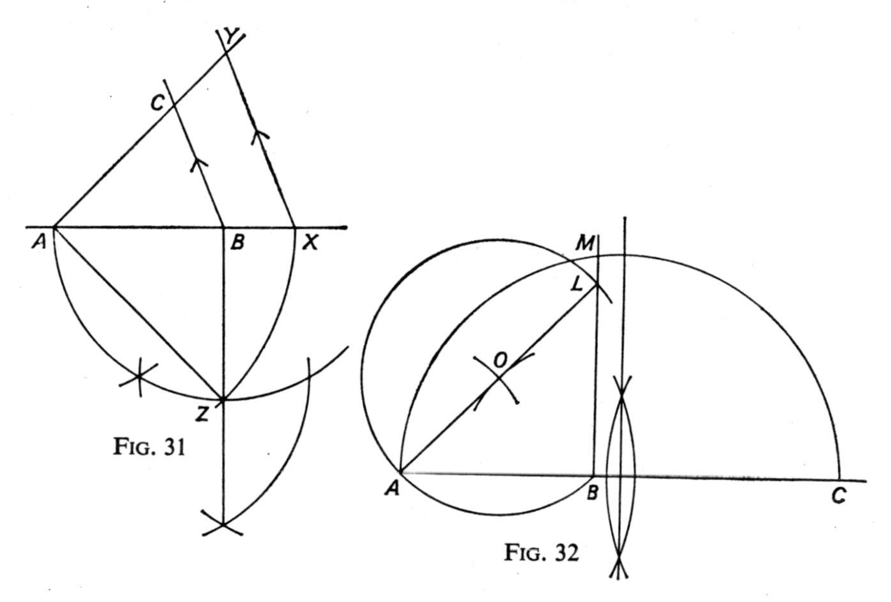

FIG. 31

FIG. 32

4. Given a length AB, to construct a length XY so that $\left(\frac{XY}{AB}\right)^2 = \frac{5}{3}$.

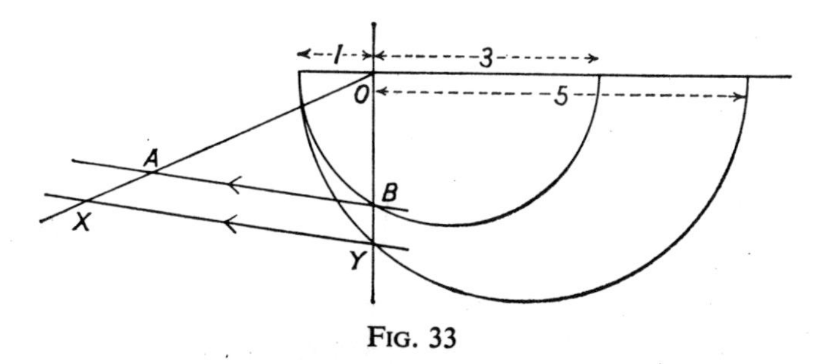

FIG. 33

5. To draw a triangle of given shape, with a given area. This requires several steps: draw a $\triangle ABC$ of the given shape, then:

(i) To draw a rectangle equal in area to the triangle; join the mid-points of AB, AC and complete the rectangle with BC as one side.

(ii) Construct CM, the mean proportional between the two sides of this rectangle.

(iii) Let the given area be a square; make CN, in the line CM, equal to the side of this square.

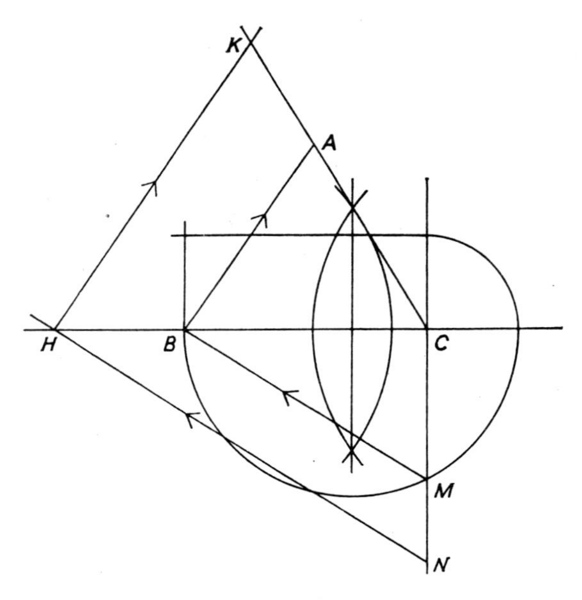

FIG. 34

(iv) Draw $NH \parallel MB$ to meet the line CB at H; $HK \parallel BA$ to meet the line CA at K.

$$\frac{HK^2}{AB^2} = \frac{CN^2}{CM^2}$$

$$\frac{\triangle CHK}{\triangle ABC} = \frac{CN^2}{CM^2}$$

Since $CM^2 = \triangle ABC$, then $\triangle CHK = CN^2$, the given area (Fig. 34).

CHAPTER 2

ANGLES AND TANGENTS

BEFORE TRYING to collect any facts about tangents to a circle, you must define exactly what a tangent is. In this chapter, and afterwards, remember that "line," or "straight line," means a straight line of unlimited length; "AB" is written for "the piece of straight line between A and B": for the whole line we shall generally write "the line through A, B," or just "line AB."

A line, then, will cut a circle at two points, one point, or no point at all. The correct definition of a tangent is: *A line which cuts a circle at one point only.*

It is usual to say that a tangent "touches" a circle; never use the word "touch" for any other kind of line. In Fig. 1 to 5, following, the line BC does not touch the circle; it cuts the circle, at two points.

Key Theorem

Chapter 8 in Book I contained several theorems about circles: the one we need just now is:

Angles in the same segment of a circle are equal: $A\hat{B}D = A\hat{C}D$.

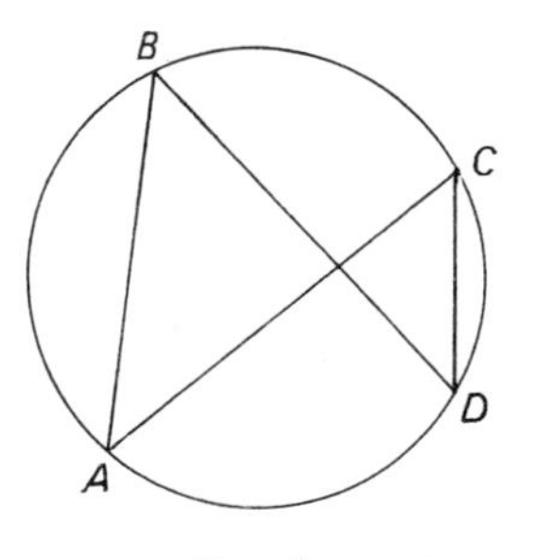

FIG. 1

We shall also say that the arc AD subtends an angle ($A\hat{B}D$) at the point B, and subtends other angles at other points; and if these points are on the other part of the circle, the angles subtended are all equal.

Consequences

1. A cyclic quadrilateral $ABCD$ (Fig. 2).

If AD is produced to E, then $C\hat{D}E$ is exterior to $\triangle\ ACD$ (join AC)

$$= \hat{1} + \hat{2}$$

Now join BD (Fig. 3).

$$\hat{1} = C\hat{B}D \text{ (in the same segment)}$$
$$\hat{2} = A\hat{B}D, \text{ likewise.}$$
$$\text{So } \hat{1} + \hat{2} = A\hat{B}C$$

Therefore $C\hat{D}E$, exterior to the cyclic quadrilateral $ABCD$, is equal to $A\hat{B}C$ at the opposite vertex.

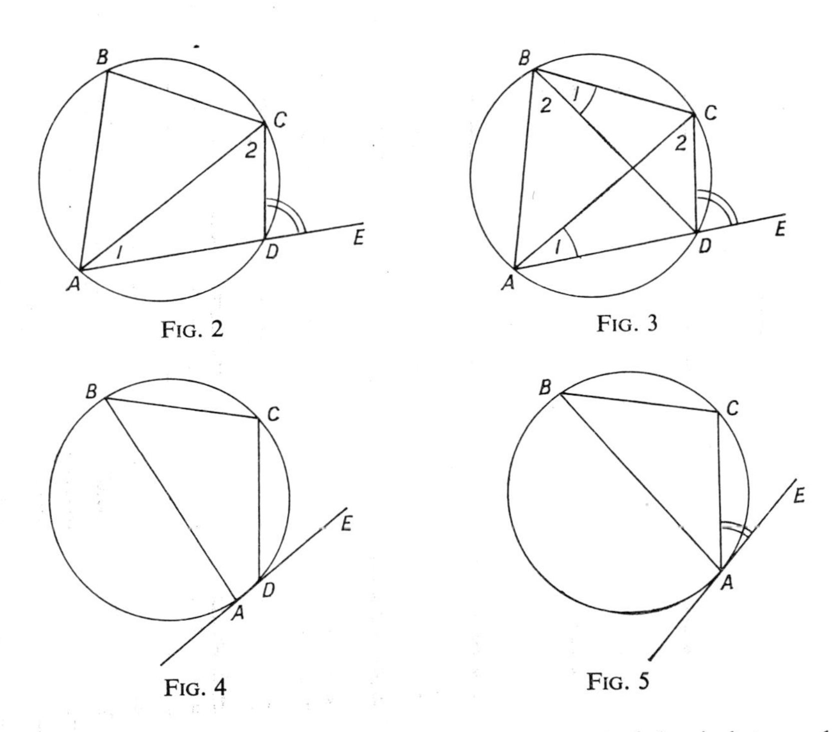

FIG. 2 FIG. 3

FIG. 4 FIG. 5

2. The tangent at D. Suppose the point A to move round the circle towards D (Fig. 4); what becomes of the line AE?

It becomes a tangent; $A\hat{B}C$ is still equal to $C\hat{D}E$; but when A reaches D, this latter angle becomes the angle between the tangent (at A) and the chord AC (Fig. 5).

This proves that the angle between the tangent at A to a circle and the chord AC is equal to the angle subtended by that chord at any point of the circle on the other side of AC.

Rather an awkward description? Could you say "any angle in the segment on the other side of AC"? You could, but it is briefer to use a technical term: "The angle in the alternate segment."

Here we have proved a useful theorem for circles and tangents: quite a different proof will be seen in Theorem X, later on. Note, in every proof, how one theorem leads to another; in fact, they are like a family tree, you can trace out the various "ancestors" of each.

The present proof (2) contains a new idea; not content with studying the drawing as it is, with the point A fastened to one place, we imagined this point to travel round the circle. On the way, it must pass through the point D, and at that moment the line AD swings into a special position—usually called a "limiting position"—at that moment the line is a tangent. This is how we define tangents to curves of any kind, not only circles; a straight line may cut a curve in several points, and if two of these run together into one point, the line will be a tangent at that point (Fig. 6).

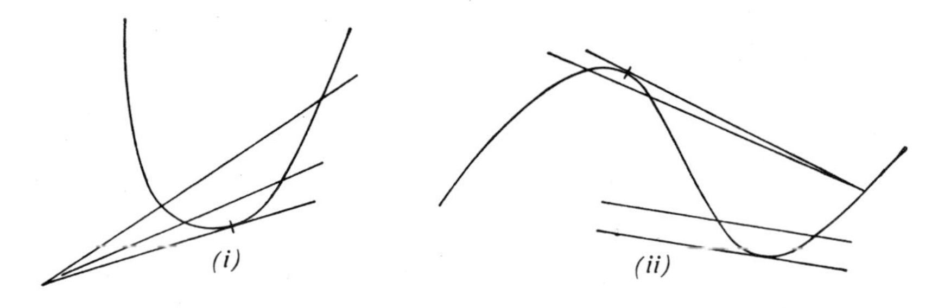

FIG. 6

Not "one point," but "two points in the same place"?

Theorem VII

Given: A circle, centre O. AO is a radius, and AB is a straight line perpendicular to OA.

Prove: AB is a tangent (i.e. does not cut the circle again).

Proof: To prove this, you must pretend that AB does cut the circle again, and see what would happen then.

If AB cut the circle again at X, then $OA = OX$ (radii of a circle).

$\therefore O\hat{X}A = O\hat{A}X$, which is a right-angle (given).

So, if X existed, we should have a triangle with two of its angles right-angles. This is not possible: there is no such point X, and AB meets the circle at A only.

(Or you could put it this way: here is a queer triangle with a right-angle at A, and a right-angle at X; the third angle $A\hat{O}X$ must be zero, and OX must be the same line as OA—must "coincide with OA." Then we say, not "there is no X," but "X is the same point as A".)

This shows that AB does not cut the circle again; and here is another proof (known as Euclid's).

If X is any other point on AB, then in $\triangle AOX$, $\hat{A}$ is a right-angle. Therefore $\hat{X}$ must be less than a right-angle (Fig. 7).

$\therefore$ OX opposite the larger angle is longer than OA.

$\therefore$ X is outside the circle, so AB does not meet the circle again.

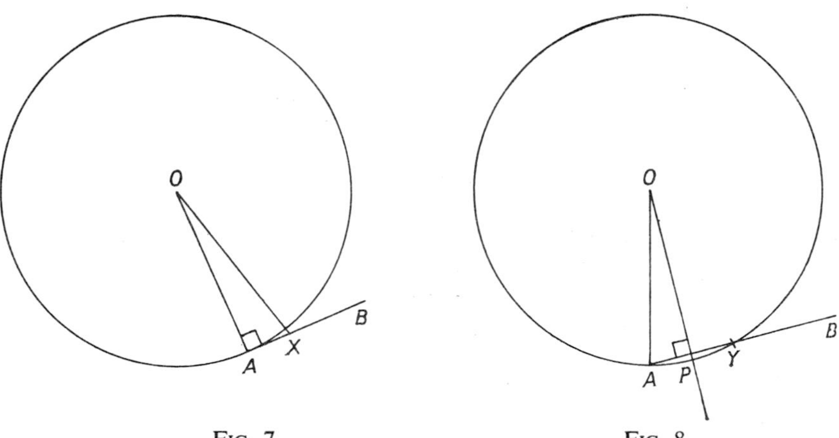

FIG. 7 FIG. 8

Theorem VIII (Converse of Theorem VII)

Given: The line AB touches a circle at A; the centre of the circle is O.

Prove: $AB \perp OA$.

Proof: If $O\hat{A}B$ is not a right-angle, perhaps it is acute.
If so, there must be another point Y on AB, such that

$$O\hat{Y}A = O\hat{A}B.$$

Construction: To find this point, draw $OP \perp AB$.
On the line AB, make $PY = AP$ (Fig. 8).
Then $\triangle OPY \equiv \triangle OPA$ (S A S)
$\therefore$ $OY = OA$. $\therefore$ Y is on the circle.

Therefore, if AB is not $\perp OA$, it must cut the circle twice.
But this is not so, since it is a tangent.
Hence AB must be $\perp OA$.

EXERCISE 2A

1. Show, in the same way, that it is impossible for the tangent AB to make an obtuse angle with OA.

2. Construct the tangent at a point A on the circle.

3. Draw two tangents from a point B outside the circle, by guess; and if they touch the circle at P, Q, prove that $BP = BQ$.

4. O is the centre of the circle; prove that $PQ \perp OB$.

5. OB cuts PQ at C; show that $\triangle\ OCP$, $\triangle\ OPB$, are similar.

Note: Two circles touch at a point when they have the same tangent at that point; they do not meet anywhere else.

Theorem IX

Given: Two circles with centres A, B, which touch at a point C.
Prove: That AB passes through C.
Construction: Draw CT, the common tangent to the circles at C.
Proof: $CT \perp AC$, $CT \perp CB$ by Theorem VIII.
A, B lie on the line through C perpendicular to CT.

EXERCISE 2B

1. Euclid's proof, once again, makes you think. It is like the reasoning in a good detective story; we examine all the likely answers, and then reject all of them that we can show to be impossible. Here we say: "C is either on the line AB or it is not." If it is not, draw the line AB, and we have a triangle ABC; also AB must cut the circles at two points (X, Y).

Then Fig. 9*a* $AC + CB$ is greater than AB.

But $AC = AX$ (radii) and $CB = YB$.

So $AC + CB$ is less than AB, by the amount XY.

It is impossible for both these statements to be true, so we reject "C not on AB."

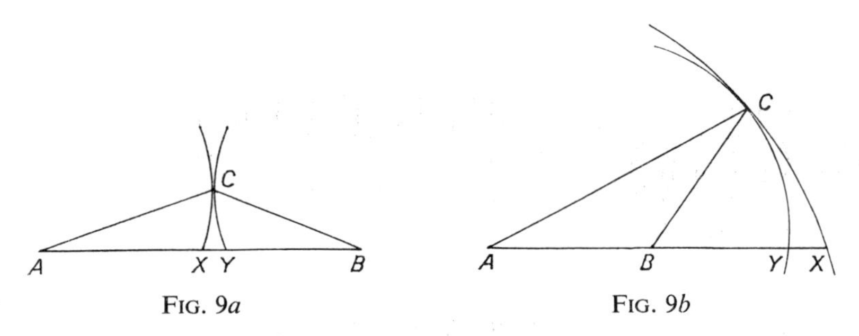

FIG. 9*a* FIG. 9*b*

2. In Fig. 9*b*, one circle is inside the other; how can you adapt the proof above to this figure?

3. Two circles have radii 3 in., 4 in., and touch at A. Find the distance between their centres.

4. In Fig. 10, O is the centre of the large semicircle; the small circle touches all three semicircles. $OA = 3$ in.; show that the radius of the small circle is 1 in. (*Clue:* Let its radius be x; $OC = 3 - x$.)

5. In Fig. 11, there are two lines at right-angles, OC and OD. A circle, radius 2 in. touches both. Another circle touches OC, OD and the first circle. Calculate its radius.

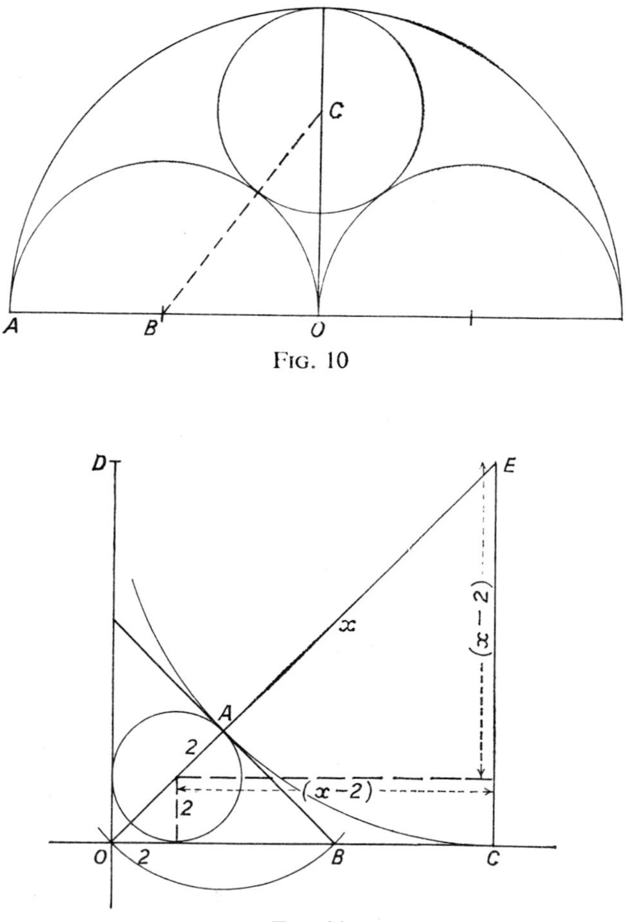

FIG. 10

FIG. 11

6. Three circles are drawn; each touches both the others. The points of contact are A, B, C. Show that the common tangents meet in a point O, and that O is the centre of the circle through A, B, C.

7. Four circles are drawn inside a square. Each circle touches two other circles, and also touches two sides of the square. Prove that there are two pairs of equal circles.

Theorem X ("Alternate segment theorem")

This is the second proof, using Theorem VII and the key theorem.

Given: A tangent AT and a chord AB of a circle.

Prove: $T\hat{A}B$ is equal to every angle in the alternate segment (on the side of AB farther from T).

It is enough to prove $T\hat{A}B$ equal to one angle in this segment; we choose one that helps us with an extra fact.

Construction: Draw the diameter AC.
Join BC.

Proof: $T\hat{A}C$ is a right-angle (Theorem VIII).
$A\hat{B}C$ is a right-angle (in a semicircle).

$$\therefore \quad A\hat{C}B = 90^\circ - B\hat{A}C$$
$$= T\hat{A}B.$$

Also $A\hat{C}B =$ every other angle in this segment.

EXERCISE 2C

1. In Fig. 12, mark a point V, to the left of A, on the line TA; and a point D on the smaller arc (AB) of the circle. Prove that $V\hat{A}B = A\hat{D}B$, by using the same construction.

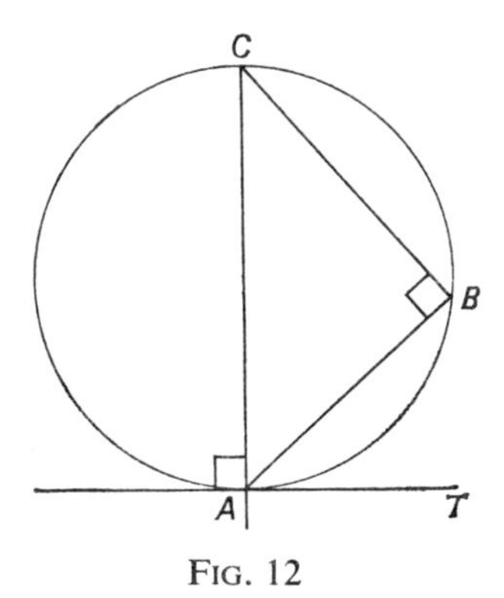

FIG. 12

2. Given a chord AB, and C any other point on the circle, show that if $B\hat{A}X$ is drawn equal to $B\hat{C}A$, then AX is a tangent.

3. There is another position for AX, to cut the circle in a point Z. Sketch this, and find any properties of this figure.

4. In a given circle, to inscribe a triangle with angles 40°, 60°, 80°. Draw a tangent at some point A on the circle. Study Fig. 13 and explain the method.

5. Two circles touch at X; a line through X cuts the circles at P, Q; a second line through X cuts them at M, N. Prove that MP is parallel to NQ.

6. The tangent at A is parallel to the chord BC. Prove $AB = AC$.

7. LM is a chord of a circle, centre O. The tangents at L, M meet at a point T, and OT cuts the circle at N. Prove that MN bisects $L\hat{M}T$.

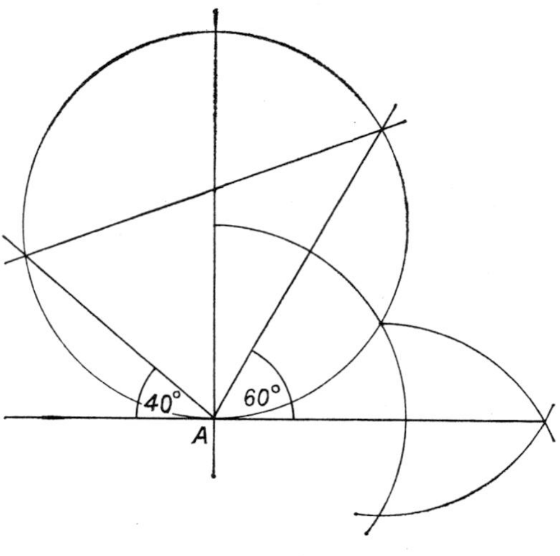

FIG. 13

Theorem XI

Given: TA touches a circle at A; the line TBC cuts the circle at B, C.

Prove: $TA^2 = TB.TC$

For this kind of result, we need two equal ratios, so we look for two similar triangles.

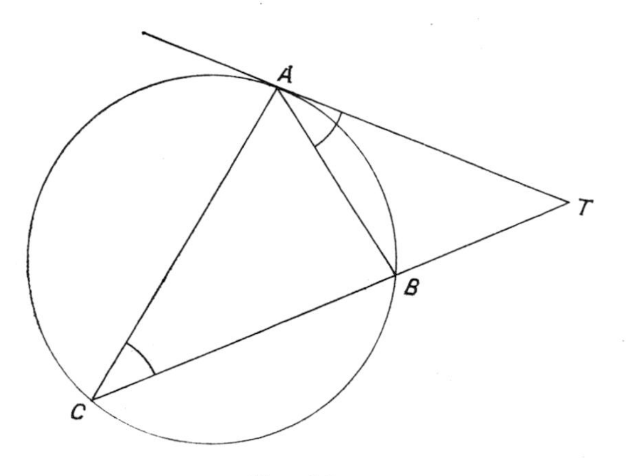

FIG. 14

Construction: Join AB, AC.

Proof: $\triangle TAB$, $\triangle TCA$ are similar (A A A) because $A\hat{T}B$ is an angle of each triangle.

$T\hat{A}B = T\hat{C}A$, in the alternate segment.

$\therefore$ The third angles are equal.

$$\therefore \frac{TA}{TC} = \frac{TB}{TA}$$

$$\therefore TA^2 = TB.TC$$

EXERCISE 2D

1. In Fig. 14, if $TB = 4$ in., $TA = 6$ in., calculate TC.

2. If $TA = 4$ in., $BC = 6$ in., calculate TB.

3. O is the centre of the circle, $OM \perp BC$. Prove that $TM^2 - MB^2 = TA^2$.

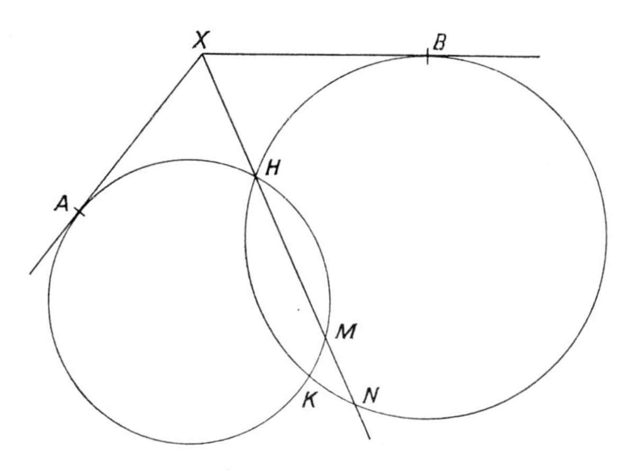

FIG. 15

4. Two unequal circles cut at points H, K. X is any point on the line HK, but outside both circles. Prove that the tangents from X to the two circles are equal . . .

5. . . . but if X does *not* lie on the line HK, the two tangents will not be equal. In Fig. 15, XA touches one circle at A, and XB touches the other at B. X is not on the line HK, so XH cuts the circles at two different points M, N.

Then by Theorem XI,

$$XA^2 = XH.XM$$
$$XB^2 = XH.XN$$

These two products are not equal, because XM does not equal XN.

$\therefore$ XA does not equal XB.

6. Put No. 4 and 5 together, and what do they amount to? Not only are tangents from a point to one circle equal, but you can find many points so that the tangents from each of them to two circles are equal; and *all* these points are on a straight line (HK).

This line is the locus of these points (see Chapter 6).

Theorem XII (*Converse of Theorem XI*)

Given: Two straight lines through T; on one line are points B, C; on the other, a point A. Also $TA^2 = TB.TC$.

Prove: That TA touches the circle through A, B, C.

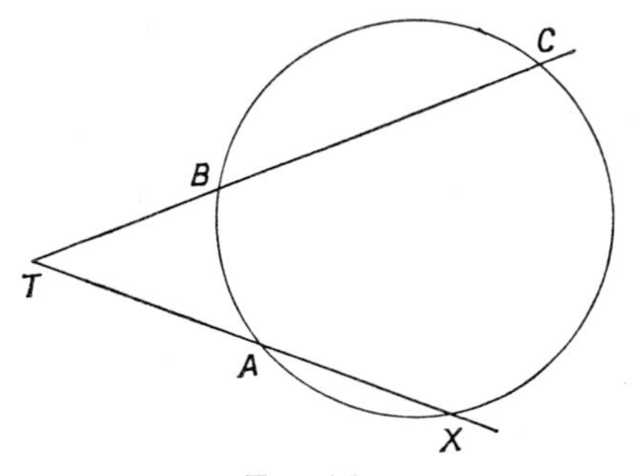

FIG. 16

Construction: Draw the circle A, B, C.

Proof: If TA is not a tangent, then it will cut the circle again at a point X (Fig. 16).

$TB.TC = TA.TX$..........Exercise 1B, No. 4

Also $TB.TC = TA^2$ ....Given

Therefore $TX = TA$

So that X can only be at A, and TA cuts the circle once only—it is the tangent at A.

Constructions

Chapter 3 gives a full account of the construction of geometrical figures, but this is an appropriate place to describe two constructions for tangents to a circle.

(1) *To Construct a Tangent* from *a Given Point,* to *a Given Circle*

What's wrong with just taking a ruler and drawing the tangent? If the "circle" were a wheel and the "straight line" were an iron bar, just lay the bar against the edge of the wheel, and there you are. But a wheel is not an exact circle, and a bar is never an exact straight line; it may touch the wheel, but you can't see exactly where, to within an inch or so.

This is not good enough for an exact circle. The exact point of contact can be found, and this is how to find it.

The centre of the circle is O, the point is A — outside the circle, of course; you could not draw a tangent from an inside point. If the tangent is drawn, and touches the circle at X, then $A\hat{X}O$ will be a right-angle (Theorem VIII). But you can't tell beforehand where X is; so you must find every point where OA subtends a right-angle.

Draw a semicircle with diameter OA; this diameter subtends a right-angle at every point on the semicircle, and nowhere else.

Now look at the original circle: O is inside, A is outside, and if we complete the circle that is half drawn, the whole circle will cut the first one in two points, X, Y (Fig. 17).

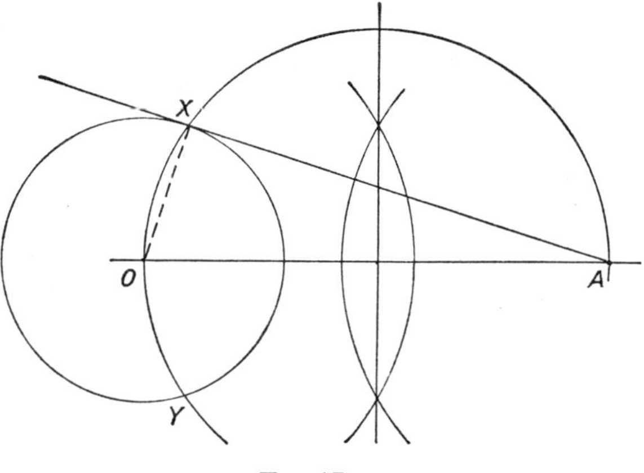

FIG. 17

$AX \perp$ the radius OX.

$\therefore$ AX is a tangent.

AY is also a tangent, for the same reason.

Another method: OA must cut the given circle; let B be the point where it does so.

Draw a circle with the same centre O, and radius OA.

Construct $BX \perp OA$, to cut the outer circle at X.

Join OX, to cut the given circle at Y; then join AY.

Make this drawing, and prove that AY is a tangent. ($\triangle OYA \equiv \triangle OBX$, because . . .)

(2) *To Construct a Line to Touch Two Given Circles* (*A Common Tangent*)

Two methods are described here; they are both correct in theory, but the first one is a little awkward in practice, while the second is simpler to draw and usually gives a better result.

Method 1: Given two circles with centres A, B. Take the first circle to be the bigger one. Suppose first that the tangent has been drawn, and touches the circles at M, N; then AM, BN are $\perp$ MN. You could now draw $BK \parallel NM$, to meet AM at K.

$B\hat{K}A$ would be a right-angle, and AK equal to the difference between the two radii. So, to find K:

Draw a circle with centre A, and radius equal to the difference of the given radii. Construct tangents from B to this circle (BK is one of them); draw the line AK, to cut the outer circle at M; draw $MN \parallel KB$. MN is a common tangent. An improvement is to draw a radius $BN \perp BK$.

Note: There can be four of these common tangents, as in Fig. 18. This method, so far, has drawn two of them; they are usually called "direct common tangents." To draw the other two, "transverse," begin with a circle, centre A, and radius equal to the sum of the radii.

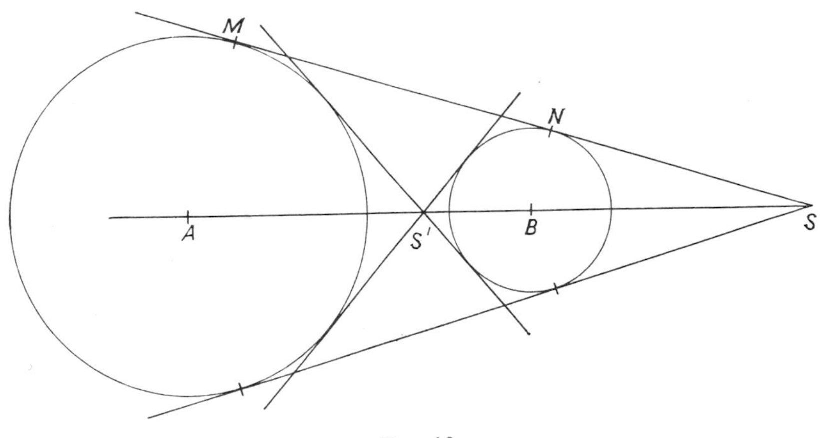

FIG. 18

EXERCISE 2E

1. Draw two unequal circles, and construct the direct common tangents by Method 1; make AB 5 units, and the radii 2, $1\frac{1}{2}$ units. (Choose your own units, not too small.)

2. Make a separate drawing, and construct two transverse common tangents.

3. For two equal circles: (i) Draw radii AX, $BY \perp AB$; join XY. (ii) If each radius is of length r, construct the circle on AB as diameter; let O be its centre. Cut off chords AP, AQ, each $= 2r$. They cut the circle "A" at X, Y. Draw the lines through XO, YO.

In Fig. 18, each pair of tangents meets on the line AB. The meeting points are S, S'; they are centres of perspective. (See Chapter 1, Fig. 19.)

Method 2*:* Find the centres of perspective first.

Draw two parallel diameters HAK, LBM, in the same sense; draw the line through A, B. Draw KM, to meet AB at S, and construct the tangents from S to the larger circle. They will touch the smaller one too.

Draw HM, to meet AB at S'; construct the tangents from S', again to the larger circle. These are the transverse common tangents.

Fig. 19(i) and (ii) show one common tangent, drawn by both methods. Method 1 requires seven steps, and three more to get a second tangent. Method 2 needs only five, and one more. (See note on next page.)

The real advantage of the second method is that it begins with a large circle; if there is a slight error in the position of X, it will be reduced at the other point of contact. The first way, however, begins with a small circle, through K; if AK is not absolutely perfect, the error will be magnified twice over, as the drawing shows (Fig. 19 (i)).

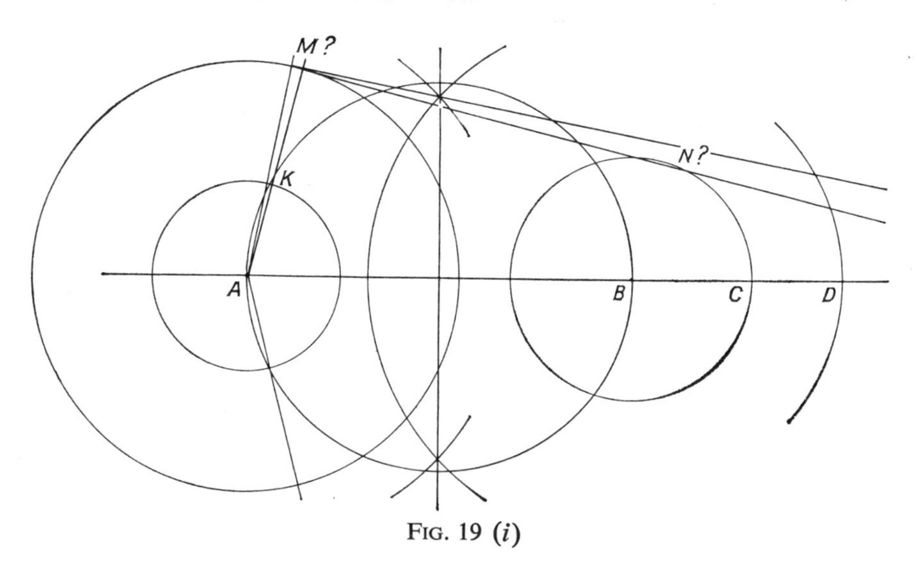

FIG. 19 (*i*)

Try this for yourself; see if you can make a perfect drawing, either way. The advantage is still with Method 2 when constructing the transverse tangents (Fig. 19 (ii)).

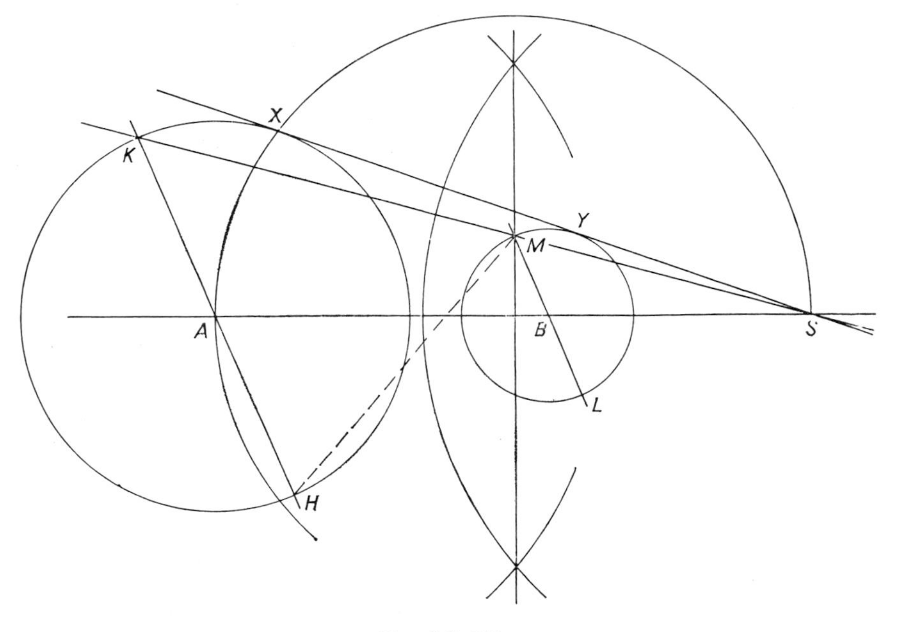

FIG. 19 (*ii*)

Note: The steps are:

1. Set off *CD*, difference of radii,
   draw circle, radius *AK*,
   bisect *AB*,
   circle, *AKB*,
   line *AKM*,
   line *BK*,
   MN ∥ *BK*,
   or *BN* ⊥ *BK* (four more arcs
   to draw).
2. Draw parallels,
   join *KM*,
   bisect *AS*,
   circle, *AXS*,
   line *SX*.

CHAPTER 3

METHODS OF CONSTRUCTION

WHEN YOU are faced with a "problem," or a "construction," it sometimes seems difficult to make a start. How can you break it down, so as to be sure of your method?

First pick out the separate items; then consider what theorem, or what method out of your stock, you can use for each item. Here is an example:

Given: A circle (centre O, radius r) and a point A which is not on the circle.

Construct: A chord of given length ($= XY$) to pass through A.

The items are (1) Lines through A.
(2) Equal chords.

Try (1); is it any use to draw a lot of lines through A? You might get one on which the circle cut off a piece of just the right length, but it would be a sheer fluke, and you could not prove it was right. In fact, you have no theorem handy about a set of lines through a point.

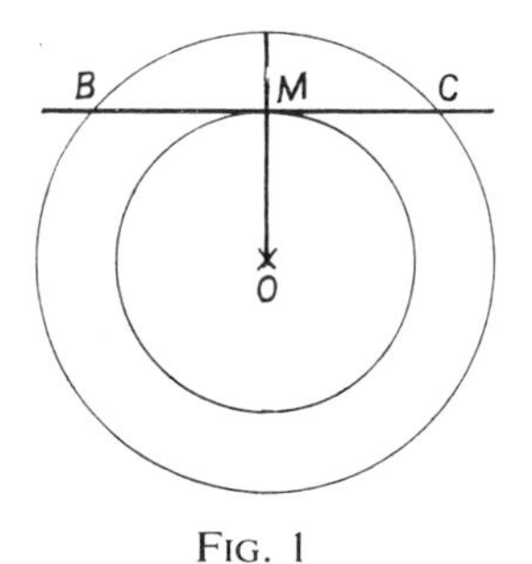

FIG. 1

Try (2); there *is* a theorem about equal chords. They are at equal (perpendicular) distances from the centre. So if you draw one chord $BC = XY$, and draw $OM \perp BC$, you have what? The *length* of OM is fixed; that is, if BC were moved into all possible positions, and M moved with it, M would move round a circle, centre O, and BC would be a tangent to this circle (Fig. 1). So you draw this circle, and construct a tangent to it which goes through A (Fig. 2).

The problem is now solved, and you use ruler and compasses to make the construction.

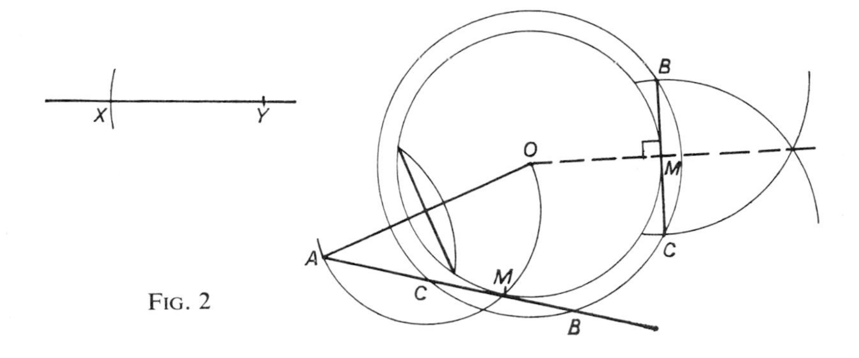

FIG. 2

What is Your Stock of Methods?

To Copy a Length or an Angle: Use compasses; in the example above, the first step is to take the length XY on your compasses, and with centre at B, any point on the circle, draw an arc to cross the circle at C.

For an angle, you copy two lengths. $P\hat{O}Q$ is given; to make a copy on the line XY, first you draw an arc with centre O, and with centre X draw an arc of equal radius to cut XY at H; then take length PQ for radius, and draw an arc with centre H. This cuts the previous arc at K, and $H\hat{X}K = P\hat{O}Q$ (Fig. 3).

How do you know? By this theorem: $\triangle HXK \equiv \triangle POQ$ (S S S).

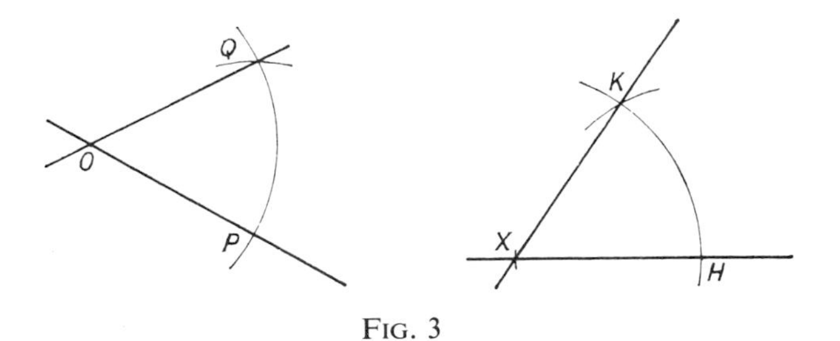

FIG. 3

To Draw a Right-angle: What theorems are there about right-angles? The first one that occurs to you may be: the angles in a semicircle are right-angles. Then there is the definition: when a line meets another line and the two adjacent angles are equal, they are right-angles. Constructions which use this usually mean that you make two congruent triangles side by side. (Fig. 4.)

From A to BC, or at D, a point on BC.

You make $AX = AY$ or $DX = DY$, and by means of equal arcs, draw AZ.

(Theorem) $\triangle AXZ \equiv \triangle AYZ$ (S S S), $\triangle AXO \equiv \triangle AYO$ (S A S)-

For a perpendicular at D to BC, this is neat:

Mark E any other point on BC; draw equal arcs with centres D, E to cross at F.

Draw the circle with centre F, through D, E.

Draw the diameter EFG, join DG.

(Theorem) The angle in a semicircle is a right-angle.

For points at which BC subtends a right-angle, construct a circle with BC as diameter. This was used to construct a tangent to a circle from a point outside.

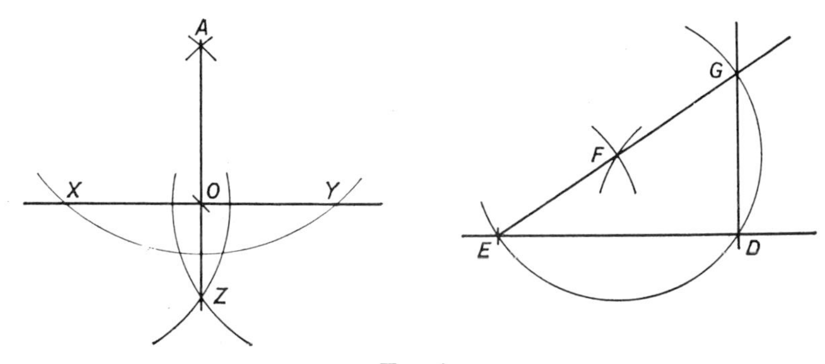

FIG. 4

To Bisect a Line, an Arc or an Angle: This, too, is done by making two congruent triangles. The two points at the ends of the arc or line are known.

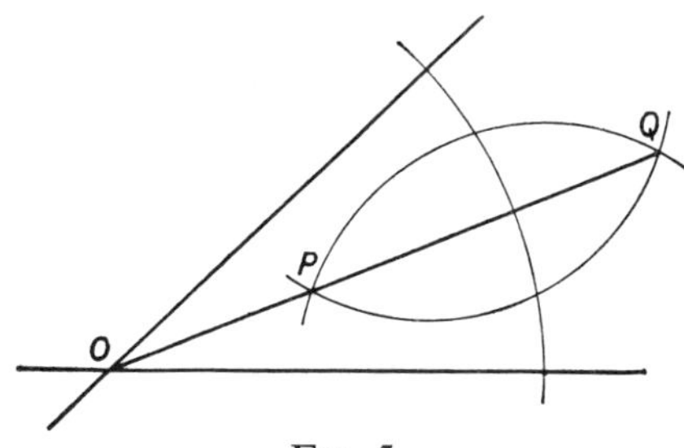

FIG. 5

For an angle, we have to make the two points at equal distances from the vertex.

Note: In Fig. 5, the *three* points O, P, Q, should be in line; this checks the accuracy of the drawing.

Equal Lengths on the Same Line: Constructions for these depend on (i) two congruent triangles; (ii) a parallelogram; (iii) the mid-point theorem.

Examples:

1. Given a $\triangle ABC$, and a point D on the line BC; construct a line DEF to cut AC, AB at E, F, so that $DE = EF$.

Using a parallelogram: draw $DX \parallel AB$ to cut the line AC at X. On AB, make $AF = DX$; join DF, to cut AC at E.

$AFXD$ is a parallelogram, and AX, DF its diagonals (Fig. 6a).

Using the mid-point theorem: on BC make $CH = CD$; draw $HF \parallel CA$ to cut AB at F; join DF to cut AC at E.

In $\triangle DHF$, C is mid-point of DH, $CE \parallel HF$; therefore E is the mid-point of DF (Fig. 6b).

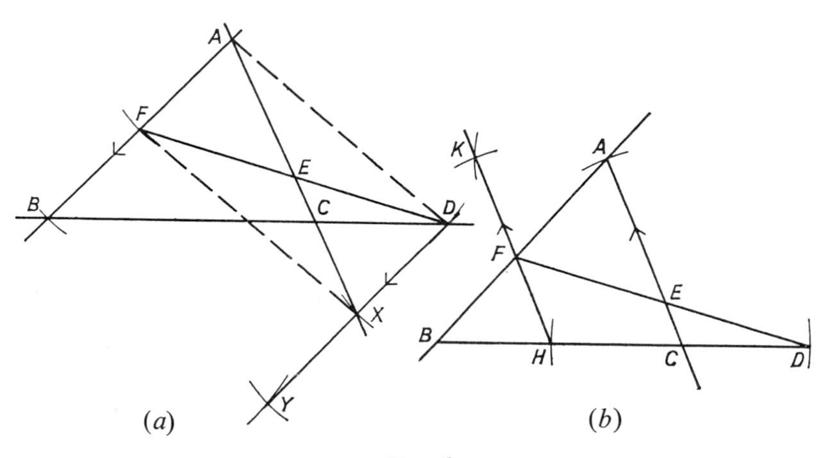

FIG. 6

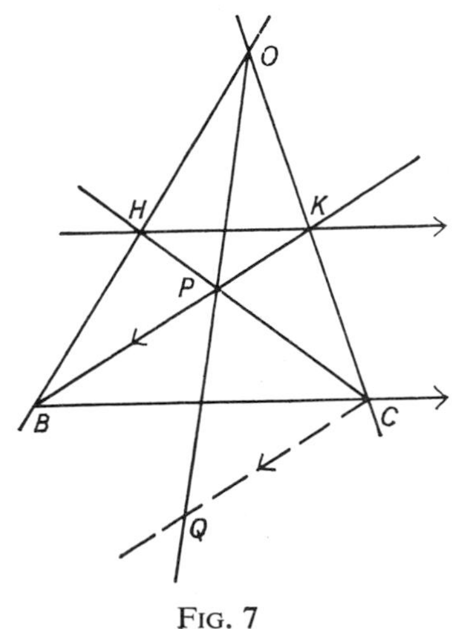

FIG. 7

2. If you are given two parallel lines, and a length BC on one of them, you can bisect BC by drawing nothing but straight lines.

Join B and C to any point O, so that OB, OC cut the given parallel at H, K.

Join BK, CH to cross at P.

The line through OP will bisect BC.

Proof: Draw $CQ \parallel KB$, to cut the line OP at Q; then $\frac{OP}{OQ} = \frac{OK}{OC}$ by parallels, and this $= \frac{OH}{OB}$.

$\therefore$ $BQ \parallel HP$, and $BPCQ$ is a parallelogram (Fig. 7).

Parallels, and Regular Figures

In so many constructions, you need to draw parallel lines. The draughtsman, working with drawing-board and T-square, can simply slide a set-square along into any position he wants, or use a "parallel ruler" mounted on wheels. You can follow the same method, i.e. use a set-square and a ruler.

But all the drawings you need to make—except drawing an angle of, say, 35 degrees—can be made with ruler and compasses only. To draw a line through a given point, parallel to a given line, you have to copy an angle; or, as in Fig. 6, to make two congruent triangles. Look again at Fig. 6: in the left-hand figure, an arc with centre D and radius $= AB$ crosses an arc with centre B, radius $= AD$, at the point Y, and so $DY \parallel AB$. In the right-hand figure likewise, $HK = CA$, $AK = CH$. This construction, of course, makes a parallelogram ($CHKA$) by making each pair of opposite lengths equal.

Note on the equilateral triangle: The essence of this construction is a pair of equal circles with centres A, B and radii equal to AB. This certainly gives an equilateral $\triangle ABC$. But there are many more such triangles to be found. In Fig. 8 (ii), CX and CY pass through the centres; $\triangle CXY$ is equilateral, and XY passes through D. In (iii) and (iv), XY is just any line through C, and $\triangle DXY$ is equilateral. For in each of these two figures, since $C\hat{A}D$ is 120°, the angle at $\hat{X}$ is half as big, 60°. In (iii) $C\hat{Y}D - C\hat{A}D$ in the same segment, $= 120°$, and in (iv) $\hat{Y} = 60°$.

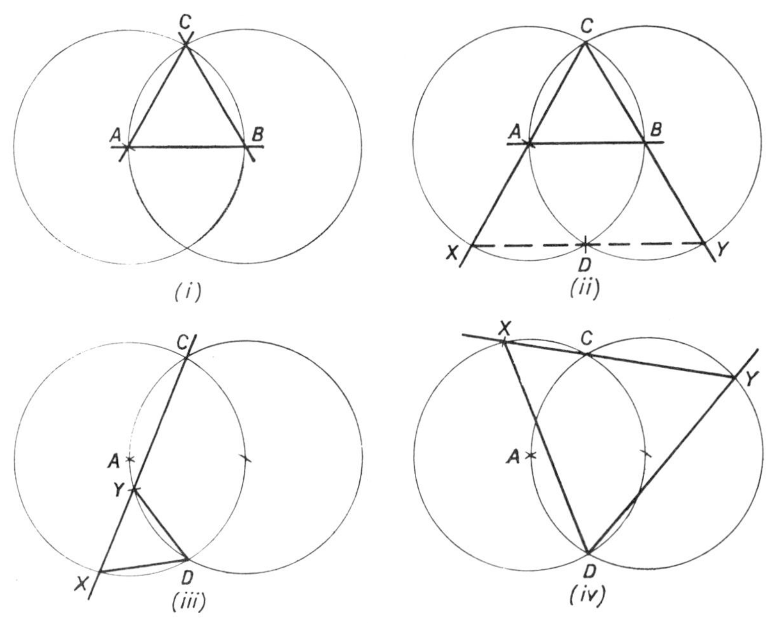

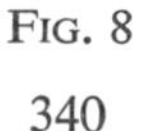

FIG. 8

On (i) it is easy to draw a regular hexagon, and by bisecting $A\hat{B}C$, to make a regular figure with 12 sides, and so on.

Square and Octagon: Fig. 9 shows a square with a given side, also a square and an octagon inscribed in a circle.

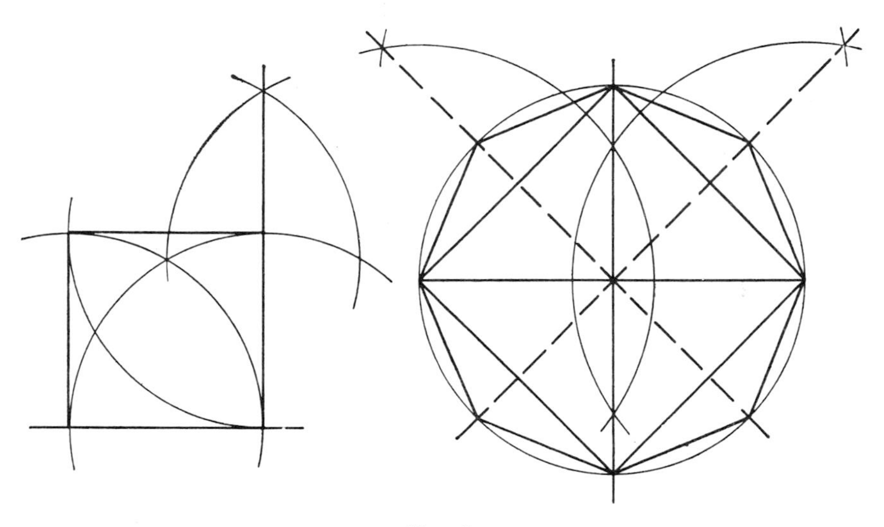

FIG. 9

Regular Pentagon: Here is a neat and exact method to construct a regular five-sided figure inscribed in a circle (Fig. 10).

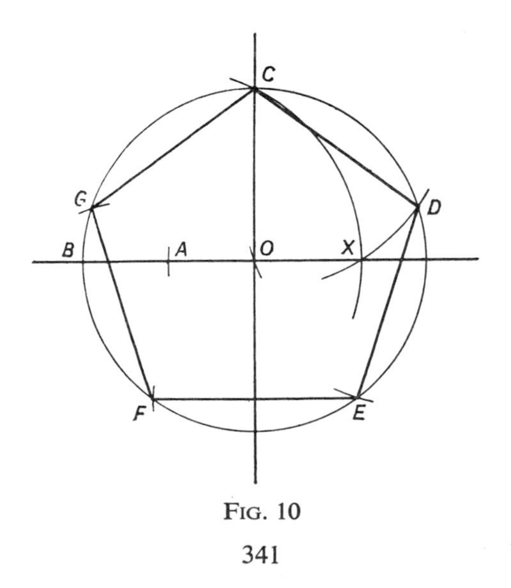

FIG. 10

O is the centre, OC and OB are perpendicular diameters.
A is the mid-point of OB.

(1) Make $AX = AC$.

(2) Make $CD = CX$.

(3) Make DE, EF, FG each equal to CD.

Then $CDEFG$ is an exact regular pentagon.
The proof is not quite so simple; see "The Golden Section" in this chapter.

Examples on Equal Areas

(1) *To draw a triangle of area equal to* $\triangle ABC$, *with one side* $= PQ$

(i) On the same base BC. The new triangle must have the same perpendicular height; draw through A a line parallel to BC. With Centre B and radius $= PQ$, draw an arc to cut this parallel at X, Y (Fig. 11 (i)). Each of the triangles BXC, BYC is correct.

(This cannot be done if PQ is less than the perpendicular height.)

(ii) On the line BC, cut off $BD = PQ$. Join AD; draw $CX \parallel DA$. Make X the point where this parallel meets the line BA; $\triangle BDX$ is equal to $\triangle ABC$, for each triangle is made up of two pieces; $\triangle ADX$, $\triangle ADC$ are on the same base AD and between parallels DA, CX; $\triangle ABD$ belongs to each area (Fig. 11 (ii)).

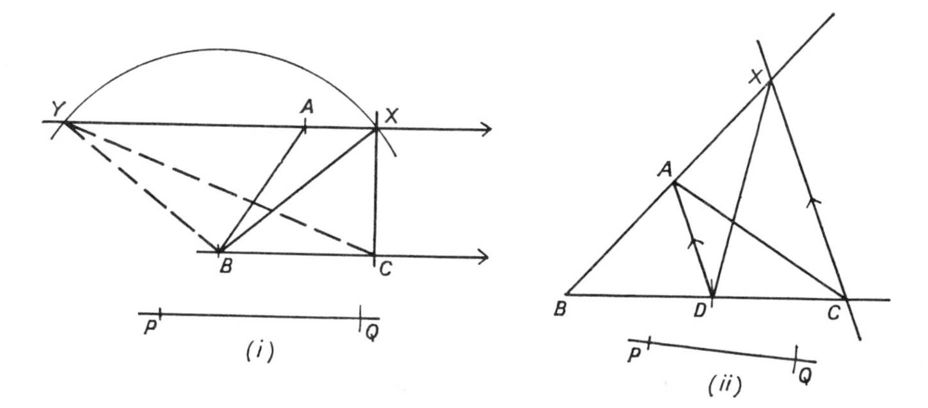

FIG. 11

(2) *To draw a rectangle equal to a given rectangle* $ABCD$, *with one side* $= PQ$

(i) If PQ is not less than AB, the shorter side, draw arcs with centres B, C and each radius $= PQ$, to cut the line AD at X, Y; then the parallelogram $BCYX$ is equal to the rectangle. Draw XH, $BK \perp CY$.

(ii) Or, produce BC to E, making $CE = PQ$. Draw the line ED, to meet BA at X. On the line CD (produced) make $DF = AX$, and on AD produced make $DG = CE$. The lines EG, XF meet at Y, and $DGYF$ is a rectangle equal to the given rectangle.

(Theorem) If D lies on a diagonal of a rectangle, or parallelogram, and lines are drawn through D parallel to the two sides, they cut off two equal rectangles (parallelograms), as shown in Fig. 12.

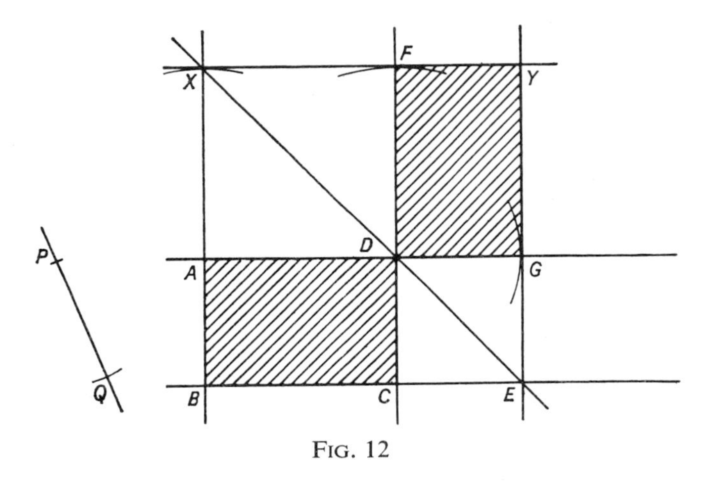

FIG. 12

(3) "*Triangles on the same base and between parallels are of equal area*"

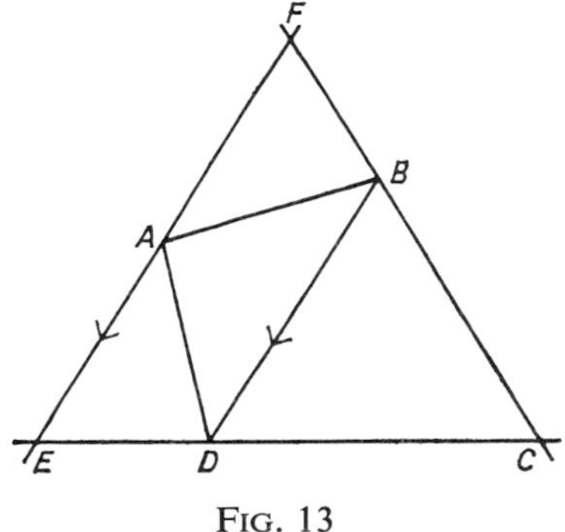

FIG. 13

An exercise on this is to construct a triangle equal to a given quadrilateral $ABCD$. Through A a line is drawn parallel to BD; it cuts the lines CD, CB at E, F. $\triangle DEB$, $\triangle DFB$ are equal to $\triangle DAB$, so $\triangle BEC$, $\triangle DFC$ are equal to the quadrilateral (Fig. 13).

(4) *Another exercise*

P is a point on the side AB of $\triangle ABC$; to draw a line through P which cuts the triangle in half. Mark M, the mid-point of AC; join PM, and draw $BQ \parallel PM$, to meet AC at Q. Then PQ cuts the triangle in half.

For $\triangle PMQ = \triangle PMB$; add to each the $\triangle APM$ and we have $\triangle APQ = \triangle ABM$, which is half the area of $\triangle ABC$ (Fig. 14).

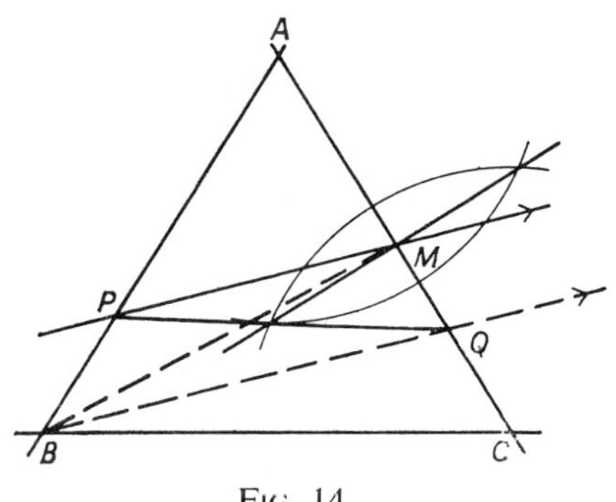

FIG. 14

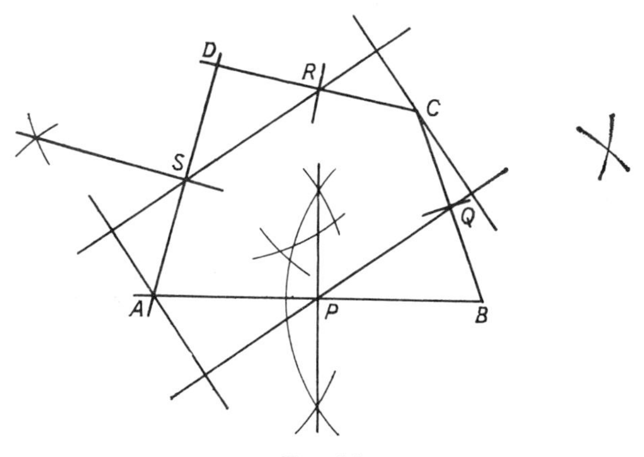

FIG. 15

(5) *To draw a rectangle equal to a given triangle or quadrilateral*

For a triangle, a rectangle on the same base, and half the perpendicular height. For a quadrilateral, this is most rapidly drawn thus: quadrilateral $ABCD$; bisect all the sides (at P, Q, R, S); then PQ and RS are parallel to AC. Draw perpendiculars on PQ, RS from A and from C (Fig. 15).

(6) *To make a square equal to a given area*

It is possible to make a triangle or a rectangle of area equal to that of any polygon, by the methods of No. 4 and 5.

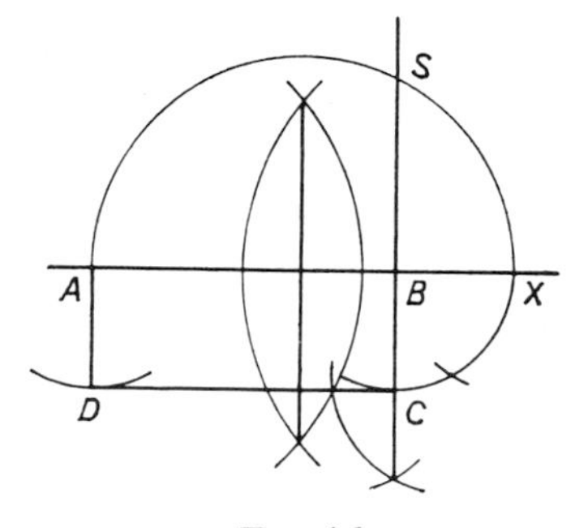

FIG. 16

But to make a square equal to a given area, you must use a circle construction. Example 2 (page 343) cannot be modified so as to give a square. To make a square equal to a given rectangle $ABCD$, make $BX = BC$, in line with AB; construct a semicircle on diameter AX. The line CB cuts the semicircle at S; then $BS^2 = AB.BC$ (Fig. 16).

Constructing a Circle

The facts to remember are:

If a circle is to pass through A, B, its centre must lie on the line which bisects AB at right-angles.

If it is to touch two given lines AOM, BON, its centre must lie on *one* of the lines which bisect the angles at O.

If it is to touch a given circle, the line joining the centres must pass through the point of contact (Theorem IX); i.e. if O is the given centre, and A the point of contact, the centre of the new circle must lie somewhere on the line OA. Also both circles must touch the same straight line at A—this is often useful; see Example 1 below.

In each of these three cases, many circles can be drawn; to satisfy two conditions. One of these many circles can be picked out to satisfy a third condition as well. Sometimes more than one.

Example 1. Given a circle, centre O, and a straight line which cuts the circle. How could you draw circles to touch both circle and line?

(i) Draw OP perpendicular on the given line, to meet the circle at A; bisect AP at M. OM passes through A; MP is perpendicular to the given line, and $MP = MA$. So centre M and radius MA gives one of many possible circles.

(ii) This one is to touch the given circle at a marked point B. Draw OB, to cut the given line at Q; the centre will not be the mid-point of QB, but it must be on QB, and the required circle must touch the tangent at B ($\perp OB$). It must therefore touch two lines (BX, QX). So bisect $B\hat{X}Q$, and the centre is at C, where this bisector crosses QB.

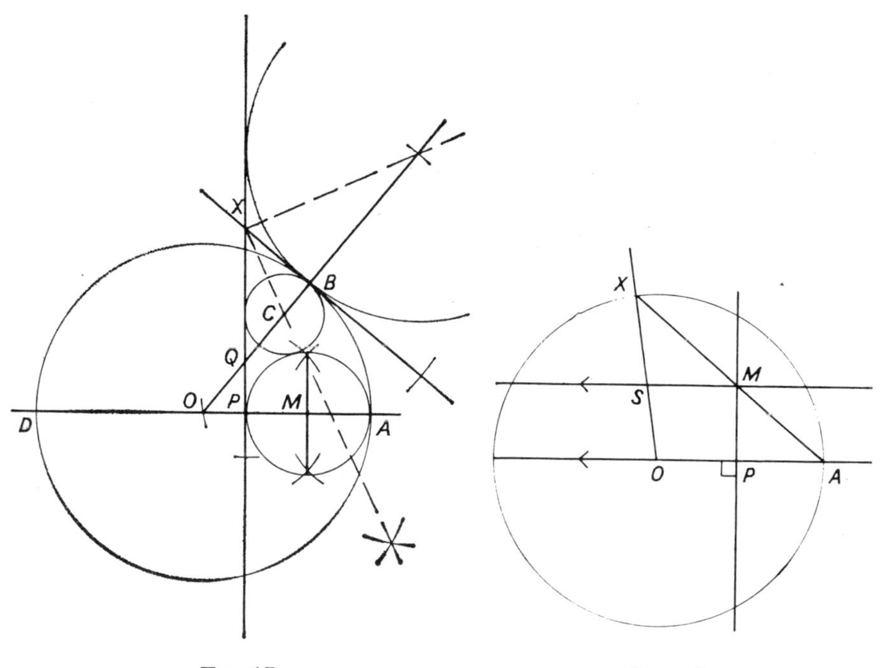

FIG. 17

FIG. 18

(iii) There are other circles to the left of the given line (bisect PD, for instance) and still more on the outside; one of these is shown on Fig. 17.

(iv) Can you draw one to touch the *line* at a marked point? In Fig. 17, Q is not the point of contact. In Fig. 18 mark a point M on the given line PM. The centres of the required circle must be on the line through $M \perp PM$; if the circles touch at X, then O, S, X must be in a straight line. Also $SX = SM$, and $OX = OA$. So, first draw the diameter AOD perpendicular to the given line; draw the line AM to cut the circle at X, then draw OX. Finally, draw MS perpendicular to PM to cut OX at S.

S is the required centre, and SM the radius (Fig. 18).

For $OA = OX$ (radii)

$S\hat{M}X = O\hat{A}X$, by parallels

$= \hat{X}$; therefore $SM = SX$.

Note: For practice in drawing, carry out these constructions in a figure where the given line is *outside* the given circle.

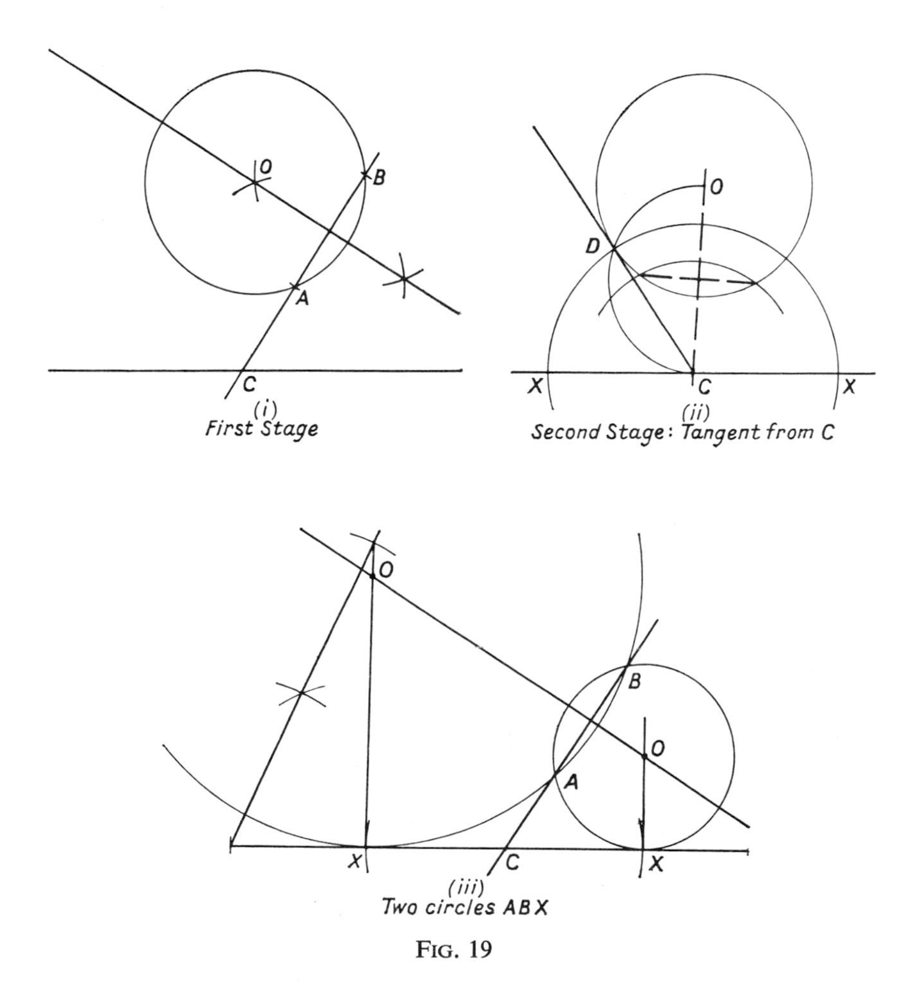

FIG. 19

Example 2. Construct a circle through two given points *A*, *B*, to touch a given line. First draw the perpendicular bisector of *AB*; the centre must be on this line (Fig. 19 (i)). There are two entirely different methods:

(i) Depends on Theorems XI, XII. Draw the line *AB*, to cut the given line at *C*. Draw any circle through *A*, *B*, and construct a tangent to it from *C*, to touch it at *D* (Fig. 19 (ii)). On the given line, mark off $CX = CD$. Then $CX^2 = CA.CB$, and *CX* touches at *X* a circle through *A*, *B*.

The centre is on the line through *X* perpendicular to the given line, and also on the perpendicular bisector of *AB* (Fig. 19 (iii)).

(ii) *N.B.:* This method was invented by a boy at school! The idea is to make two circles in perspective; an idea frequently used in Chapter 1 for figures of various shapes.

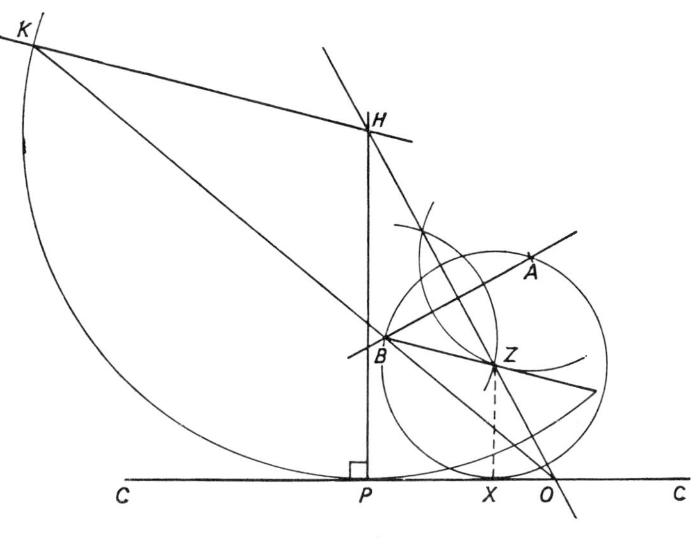

FIG. 20

Call the given line CC; the perpendicular bisector of AB meets CC at O. From any point H on the perpendicular bisector, draw $HP \perp$ on CC; and take care to make HP large, so as to draw a large circle with centre H and radius HP. Then you can reduce this to a circle which fits.

Draw OB, to cut the circle at K. Draw $BZ \parallel KH$, to meet OH at Z. Z is the required centre, and ZB the radius (Fig. 20).

Proof: Draw $ZX \perp CC$.

$$\frac{ZX}{HP} = \frac{ZO}{HO} \text{ (key theorem on ratios)}$$

$$= \frac{ZB}{HK} \text{ (same theorem for } \triangle OHK)$$

$$HP = HK, \text{ radii of a circle}$$

$$\therefore ZX = ZB$$

Notes: Two different circles can be drawn; in (i) CX can be marked on the left instead of the right. Do this, and complete the drawing. The resulting circle is a big one, and you may not be able to show all of it. In (ii) the line OB cuts the first circle at a second point L. If you join LH and draw $BY \parallel LH$, to cut OH at Y, then draw the circle with centre Y, radius YB, this will touch the given line CC.

If $AB \parallel CC$, the construction is much simpler, and only one circle can be drawn. This is also the case if B is actually on the line CC. If AB is at right-angles to CC, Fig. 21 shows a neat method, which begins with M the mid-point of AB (radius $BC = OM$).

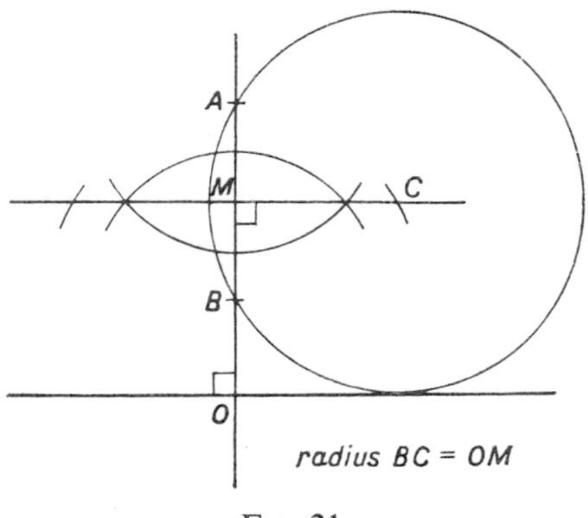

FIG. 21

Example 3. Construct a triangle similar to a given triangle, and with sides all touching a given circle.

Method: Draw three radii, perpendicular to the three sides of the triangle, and construct the tangents at the ends of these radii.

Example 4. Draw three circles, with centres A, B, C, so that each circle touches both the others.

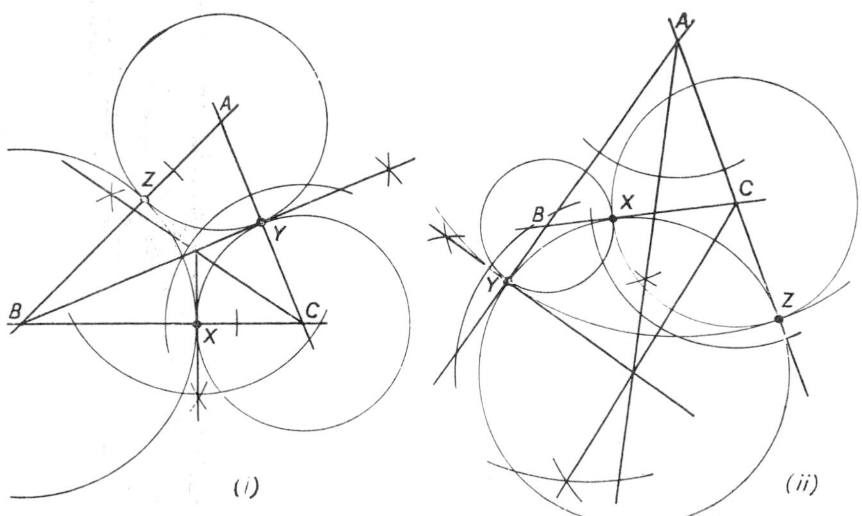

FIG. 22

The points where they touch must be on the lines AB, BC, CA; let them be X, Y, Z as in Fig. 22. Then $CX = CY$, $BX = BZ$ and $AY = AZ$. This can be ensured by constructing the circle XYZ to touch the three sides of $\triangle ABC$; then the lengths just mentioned will be pairs of tangents.

(This problem has four answers; four circles can be drawn to touch the three sides of $\triangle ABC$. To find their centres, bisect exterior angles as in (ii).)

Example 5. Given $\triangle ABC$, construct three circles, one through each vertex, and all three to meet in a point.

This is a "swindle"; draw any circle through A, and it cuts AB at P, AC at Q. Draw any circle through B, P; it will cut BC at some point R. Now draw the circle through C, Q, R. These three circles will all meet at one point—you can't go wrong!

(Proof in Chapter 4, page 367.)

Example 6. Find a point S inside $\triangle ABC$, so that the sides of the triangle subtend equal angles at S.

For the angles to be equal, they must be 120° each. Construct two equilateral triangles, ABX and ACY, outside the $\triangle ABC$ and draw circles ABX, ACY; they will cross at a point S inside $\triangle ABC$, making two angles of 120° each, $A\hat{S}B$ and $A\hat{S}C$; the third angle $B\hat{S}C$ will also be 120° (Fig. 23).

Fig. 23 looks remarkably simple. Where are the two equilateral triangles, and where are the two circles? There is no need to draw them; if the circle ACY cuts the straight line BY at S, then $Y\hat{S}C = Y\hat{A}C$ in the same segment $= 60°$. Therefore $B\hat{S}C$ is 120°.

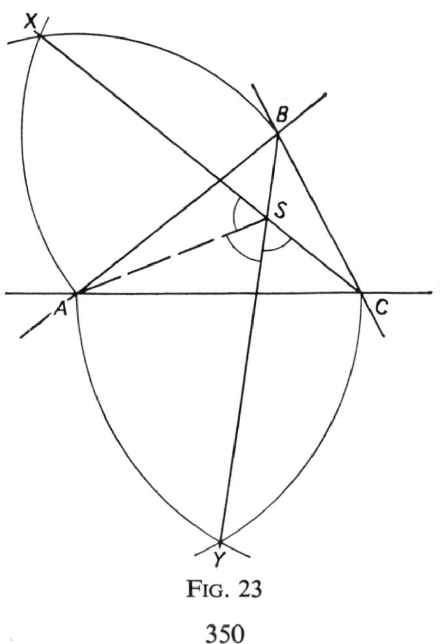

FIG. 23

Also $A\hat{S}Y = A\hat{C}Y = 60°$; so . . . $A\hat{S}C$ is 120°; S is the point required.

Finally, $A\hat{S}Y = A\hat{X}B$, since each is 60°, therefore $ASBX$ lie on a circle ($A\hat{S}Y$ is an exterior angle to $ASBX$) so that $A\hat{S}X$, too, equals 60°, and C, S, X are in a straight line (180°).

The construction, then, is simply to mark X, Y and to draw the lines BY, CX.

In Fig. 22 (i) it was not necessary to draw the circle XYZ; only the point X is needed (the circle, in fact, would only get in the way). So, after finding the centre, a perpendicular was constructed from it to BC, to find X; two of the required circles, centres B and C, each go through X, and we found that $AY = AZ$, as expected.

Drawing Figures in Practice

"Practice" is the word; every figure in these chapters must be drawn, not once, but many times, until you can produce a really good and exact figure, which is a pleasure to look at. The regular pentagon (Fig. 10) is a good one to draw; it is not too difficult, and when you do get it right, you can *see* that it is right.

The simplest part of a drawing is to draw a straight line joining two

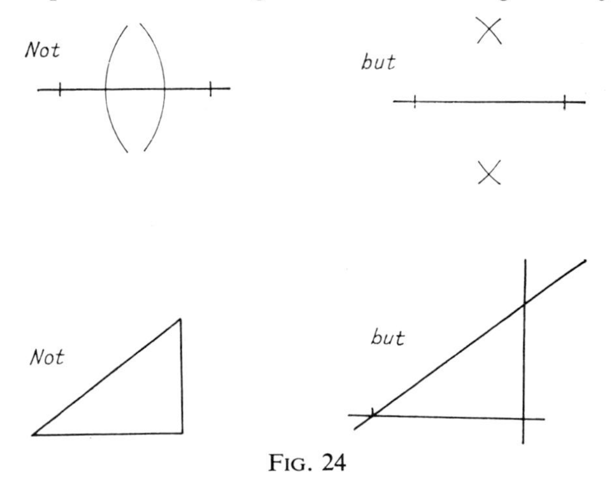

FIG. 24

points. Very well; all points in a drawing should be "marked with an X," maybe the X is made by two circles crossing, or two lines; draw them right through the point, to show clearly where the point is (Fig. 24). If you begin with a measured length on a straight line, draw a short cross line at each end.

For an exact construction, must you always do everything with compasses and ruler? Not at all; the construction of Fig. 19 would require fourteen or fifteen different circles or arcs, if you allowed it to.

Often, in an examination, you are ordered to make a construction with ruler and compasses only. In that case, you must do so. But otherwise, it is much more convenient, and quite as exact, to use a 60/30° set-square when parallels or perpendiculars are needed. For perpendiculars especially, use the long edge, as in Fig. 25. You turn the set-square round its own right-angle, against a ruler; slide it into the position you want; the perpendicular to BC is to be drawn through X. Do not make the edge of the set-square run exactly through X, but allow room for the pencil point; it is attention to details of this sort that leads to a perfect drawing—and needs a good deal of practice.

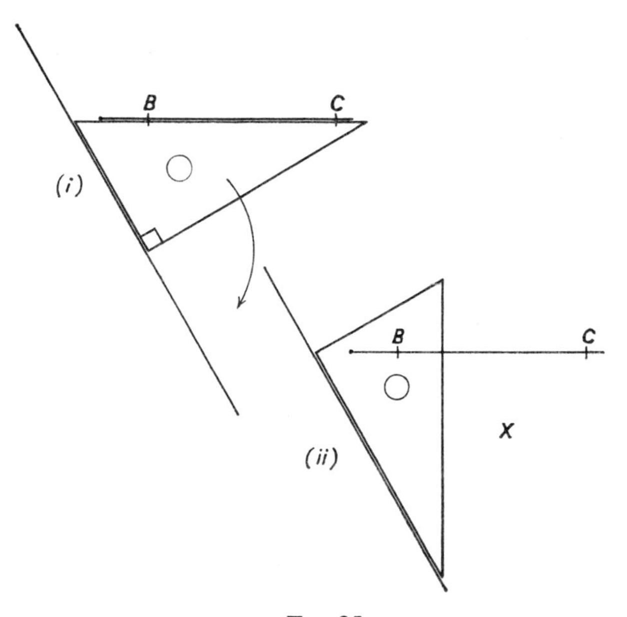

FIG. 25

A measured line must be made with a ruler; but to copy it, do not measure again; take the length with compasses. To copy an angle, too, do not use a protractor, or make a second measurement; for it is not so easy to adjust this correctly, and a very slight difference in measurement may ruin a drawing. Unless you can use parallels, always copy an angle with compasses.

Try to use instruments economically; for instance, do not alter the setting of compasses unless you need to. In the first stage of Fig. 19, you draw "any circle through A, B." You have just bisected AB by drawing two equal arcs crossing; since *any* circle will do, use the same radius for it. In the second stage you bisect OC; no need to alter the compasses and draw two new arcs; use the same radius again and draw one arc with centre C, as the figure shows. After that, you must alter the radius to draw the circle CDO.

Criticize Fig. 2 in this way. No one wants a drawing to look like a maze; the fewer lines one can manage with, the better. A good deal of labour can be saved if you think of the details a little before making a final drawing.

The Golden Section

On a straight line BC, to find a point D so that $\frac{BD}{DC} = \frac{BC}{BD}$, or $BC.CD = BD^2$. This may be written $\frac{DC}{BD} = \frac{BD}{BC}$; BD, one part of the line, is the mean proportional between the whole line and the other part.

1. Draw a line through B perpendicular to BC; on this line, mark BM equal to $\frac{1}{2}BC$. With centre M and radius MC, draw an arc to cut this line at X. (M, X must be on opposite sides of BC.)

On BC, make $BD = BX$.

2. This is really the same construction, done with fewer lines.

Draw $CN \perp BC$ and equal to $\frac{1}{2}BC$; join BN. On BN make NY equal to NC, then on BC make $BD = BY$ (Fig. 26).

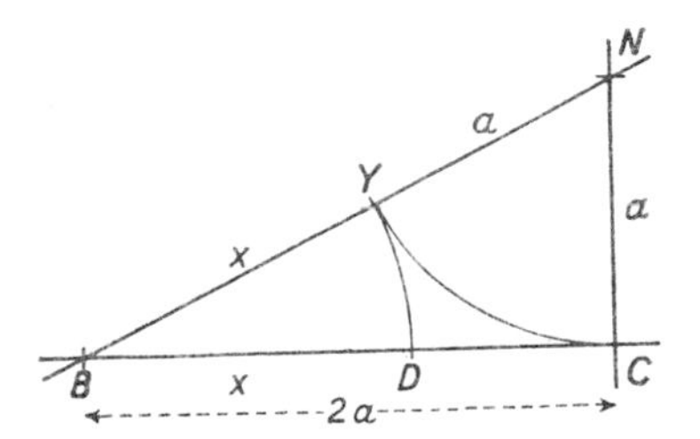

FIG. 26

To prove $BC.CD = BD^2$.

Let $CN = a$, $BC = 2a$; $BD = BY = x$.

$$\begin{aligned} \text{Then } CD &= 2a - x, \text{ and } BN = x + a. \\ BN^2 &= BC^2 + CN^2 (\text{rt.-angled } \triangle) \\ (x + a)^2 &= 4a^2 + a^2 \\ x^2 + 2ax &= 4a^2 \\ x^2 &= 4a^2 - 2ax \\ &= 2a(2a - x) \\ \text{i.e. } BD^2 &= BC.CD \end{aligned}$$

EXERCISE 3A

1. Now make the drawing by Method 1 (above), and prove the result $BD^2 = BC.CD$ in the same way.
2. Next, show that $BN = a.\sqrt{5}$, and that $BD = a(\sqrt{5} - 1)$.

Why is this called "the Golden Section"? Look at the front of a handsome building, where the proportions are "just right"; the heights of the ground floor and the first floor are almost sure to be in the ratio of BD to DC in the figure.

This ratio has been used by builders and designers for centuries. Why it looks right is hard to say; but ask ten people to draw a line, and mark a point on it in the place where it looks best. Perhaps three of them will put it exactly in the middle; the rest will mark it almost exactly in the position D, either to the right or to the left.

What has this to do with a regular pentagon?

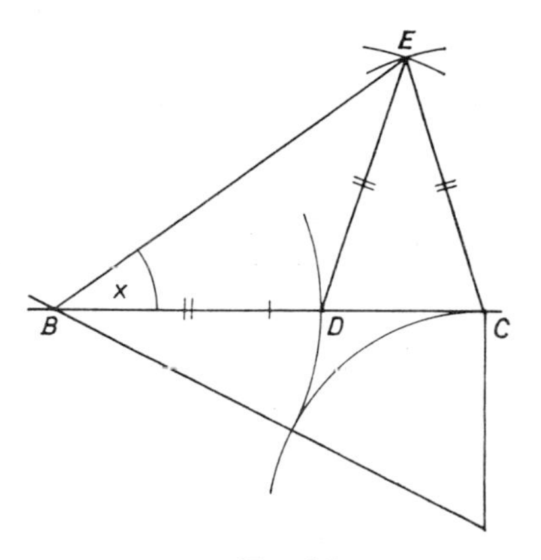

FIG. 27

In Fig. 27, $BC.CD = BD^2$, and DE, EC are drawn each equal to BD.

Then $\hat{B}$ is exactly 36°, and $B\hat{D}E$ is exactly 108°, which is one angle of a regular pentagon.

Proof: $\dfrac{BC}{BD} = \dfrac{BD}{CD}$, $\dfrac{BC}{CE} = \dfrac{CE}{CD}$

These lines are sides of two triangles, $\triangle BCE$ and $\triangle CED$.

Each triangle has $\hat{C}$ for one of its angles.

So, they are similar (S A S, Theorem IV).

Mark $\hat{B}$ "x," then $D\hat{E}C = x$.

Also $D\hat{E}B = x \quad (BD = DE)$

and $E\hat{D}C = 2x$ (exterior to $\triangle BDE$)

$= \hat{C} \quad (DE = EC)$

The angles of $\triangle EDC$ are x, $2x$, $2x$, and they add up to 180°.

Hence $5x = 180°$, and $x = 36°$.

Notice that $BC = BE$, and verify that $B\hat{D}E$ is 108°.

Constructing two Regular Figures: Five-sided and Ten-sided (a Decagon)

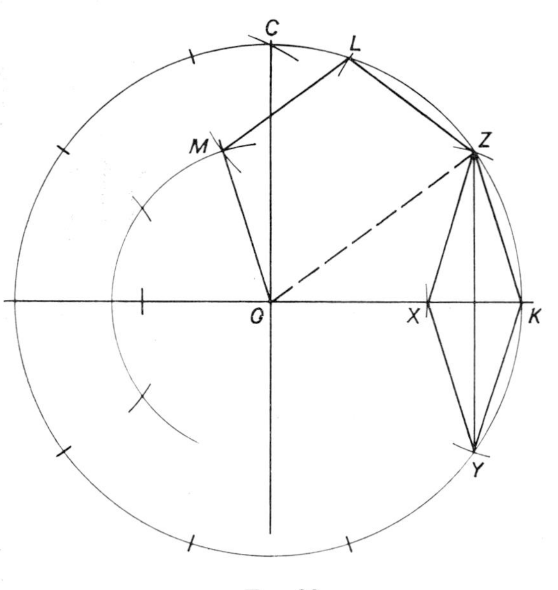

FIG. 28

In Fig. 28, OK and OC are perpendicular radii, and X has been marked so that $OX^2 = OK.KX$. XZ, ZK are each equal to OX, and $OZ = OK$ exactly as in the previous figure.

Verify that it is really the same; it is deliberately drawn the other way up; and we have used different letters.

You have done this? Well, then, Z is a point on the circle, $K\hat{O}Z = 36°$. Ten of these make 360°, so you can draw ten equal lines, which go right round the circle (Y, K, Z, L, etc.).

All this is done with one radius $= OX$. With the same radius I have constructed a small pentagon; and YZ is one side of a larger pentagon, inscribed in the circle.

Proof of the construction in Fig. 10

Figure 10 is repeated in Fig. 29. It is easy to prove that the construction puts X in the right place; i.e. that

$$OX^2 = OK.KX$$

To show that CX is the right length for the pentagon is not so easy; we have to prove that $CX = YZ$. You must start as shown on page 356.

Given: $OX^2 = OK.KX$

Prove: $CX = YZ$

The proof is really a calculation. Write r for the radius, OK or OC; and x for the length OX.

Given $x^2 = r(r - x)$, or $r^2 = x^2 + xr$................(Equation I)

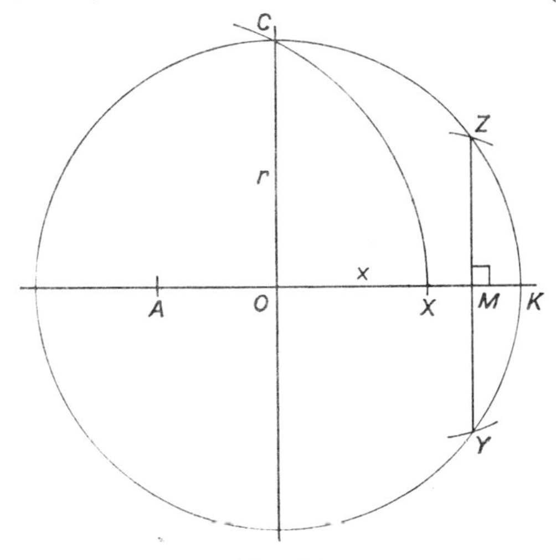

FIG. 29

To calculate YZ; it cuts OK at M, which is the mid-point of XK. And at right angles. Why? Because $ZKYX$ has four equal sides.

Then $OZ = r$

$OM = \frac{1}{2}(x + r)$

$OZ^2 = OM^2 + MZ^2$, that is $r^2 = \left(\frac{x+r}{2}\right)^2 + \left(\frac{YZ}{2}\right)^2$

$(x + r)^2 + YZ^2 = 4r^2$ ....(Equation II)

CX is simpler; $CX^2 = r^2 + x^2$

$(x + r)^2 + CX^2 = x^2 + 2xr + r^2 + x^2 + r^2$

$= 2x^2 + 2xr + 2r^2$

by Equation I, this $= 2r^2 + 2r^2$

$(x + r)^2 + CX^2 = 4r^2$ ....(Equation III)

From Equations II, III, $CX^2 = YZ^2$

so CX does equal YZ, one side of a regular pentagon.

Note on Quadratic Equations

The simplest of all quadratic equations is solved by Fig. 16. If AB is 5 units and BX 1 unit, then $SB^2 = 5$; so this drawing will show the answer to an equation like $x^2 = a$.

You can show on a diagram both answers to $x^2 + ax = b$, in several ways.

Here (Fig. 30) O is the centre of a circle; $BX = b$, $XC = 1$, $OM \perp BC = \frac{1}{2}a$, and $PXQ \perp BC$.

PX gives one answer, for $PX.XQ = BX.XC$.

Let $PX = x$, then $x(x + a) = b$ (the other answer is $- QX$!).

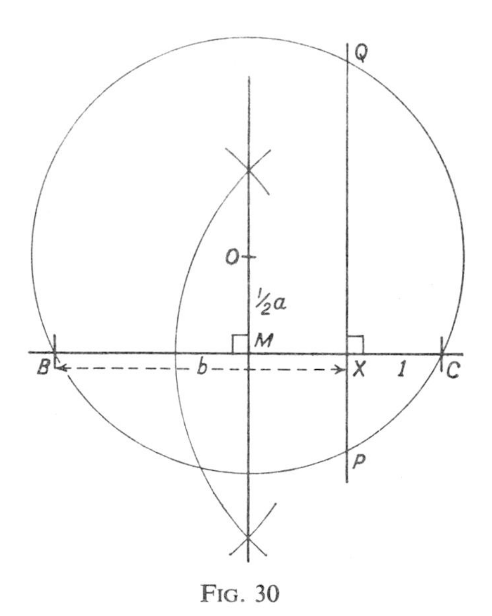

FIG. 30

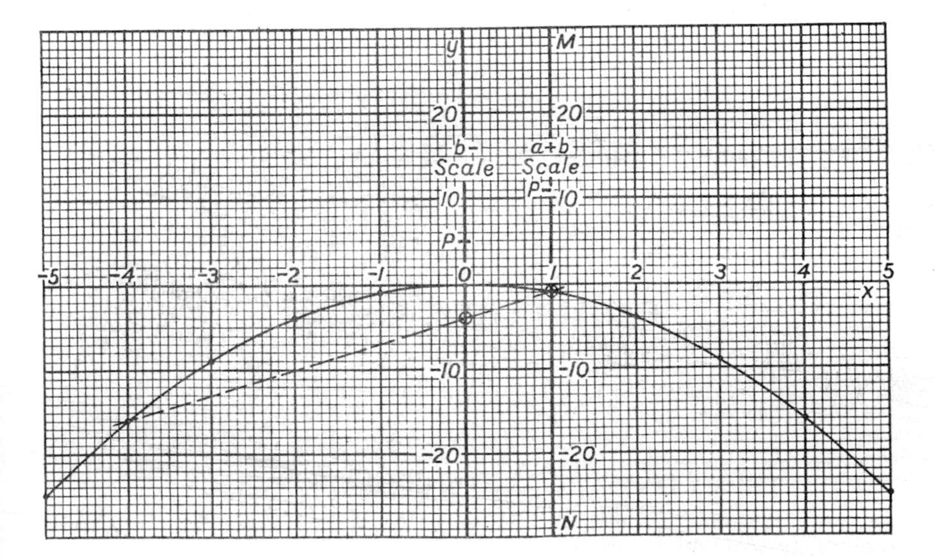

FIG. 31

A more wholesale attempt, to make a single drawing which will show answers to many different quadratic equations, is shown in Fig. 31. It is a kind of graph; the curve is the graph of $y = -x^2$. On Oy is marked the "b-scale," and on MN is the "$(a + b)$ scale."

Suppose the equation is $x^2 + 3x - 4 = O$
compare this with $x^2 + ax + b = O$

Find b (-4) on its scale, and $a + b$ (-1) on the other scale; join these two points, and you have the line $y = 3x - 4$. This crosses the curve $y = -x^2$ at two points, where $-x^2 = 3x - 4$.

Look at the values of x at these points; they are $+1$ and -4; these are the two answers.

Once you have made this diagram, you can use it again and again, for many values of a and b. But if you do this, do not draw the cross-lines, but put the edge of a ruler through the two points (P, P in the diagram are marked for $a = 6$, $b = 5$); you can still read off the answers.

CHAPTER 4

HOW TO SOLVE RIDERS

IN A "rider," just as in a theorem, you are given some figure, and have to prove something extra. As a rule, there is no need to spend a lot of time drawing the figure very carefully; and you can never prove anything by taking measurements.

It is good practice to examine a drawing, and guess new facts in it, such as a pair of equal angles, four points on a circle, a right-angle, and so on. How do you make sure that the things you have guessed are true, or false, or mere accidents?

When you examine a figure you have drawn, you may very well have made a right-angle in it by accident; two lines may look equal which are not really so. Some things may be true for one sort of triangle, but not for another sort.

If you suspect, for instance, that two lines are equal, but cannot find any reason why they should be, take the hint and sketch the figure differently.

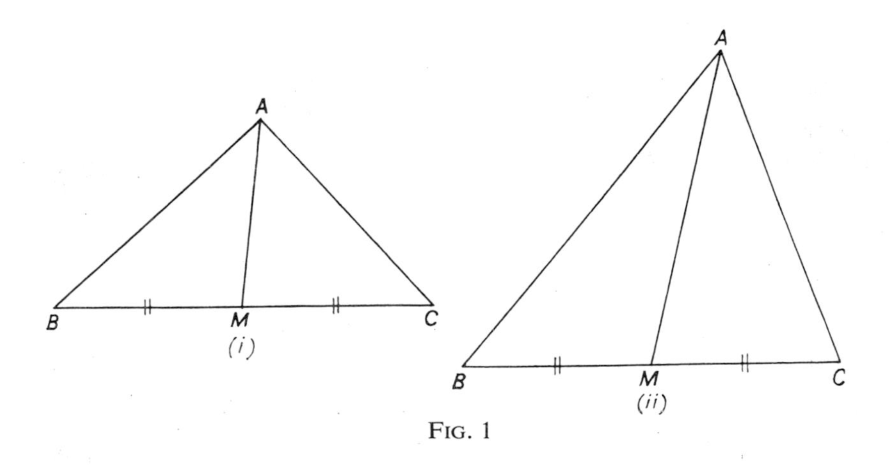

FIG. 1

In Fig. 1 (i) you see $\triangle ABC$, with M the mid-point of BC. It looks as though $MC = AM$, but is there any reason why?

Sketch the figure again with A in a different place. This time (ii) MC is certainly not equal to AM; this is not true for every triangle.

There must be something extra in the first sketch; what is it? (It is . . . a right-angle at A.)

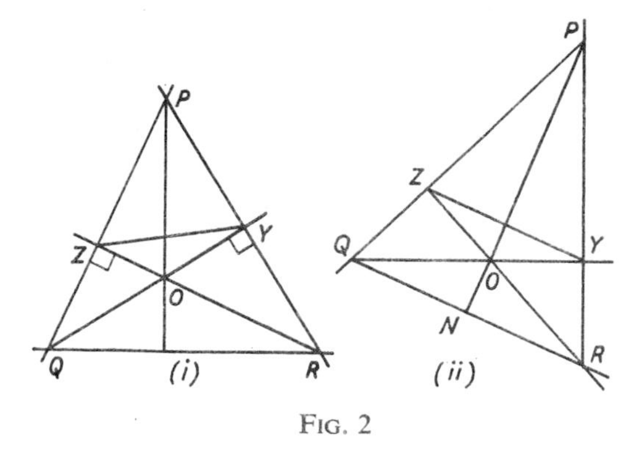

FIG. 2

In Fig. 2 (i), $QY \perp PR$, and $RZ \perp PQ$; they cross at O. It looks as though $PO \perp QR$.

Draw $\triangle PQR$ a completely different shape (ii); PO still looks perpendicular to QR. Well, perhaps there is a reason for this.

Since $O\hat{Y}P$, $O\hat{Z}P$ are right-angles, O, Y, P, Z lie on a circle.

$O\hat{P}Y = O\hat{Z}Y$ (in the same segment). Likewise for Q, R, Y, Z; this time it is a semicircle.

$R\hat{Z}Y = R\hat{Q}Y$; but these angles are $O\hat{Z}Y$, $O\hat{Q}R$. Therefore $O\hat{P}Y = O\hat{Q}R$.

OP meets QR at N; re-christen these angles, $N\hat{P}Y = N\hat{Q}Y$ so that N, Q, P, Y, lie on yet another circle.

$\therefore P\hat{N}Q = P\hat{Y}Q$, which is a right-angle.

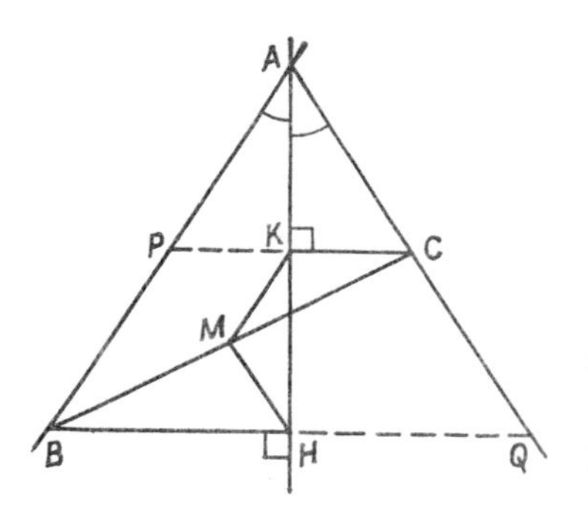

FIG. 3

In Fig. 3, ABC is a triangle of no special shape; M is the mid-point of BC, and BH, CK are perpendicular on the line AKH, which bisects the angle $\hat{A}$.

Does $MK = MH$? It looks parallel to BA? Produce CK to meet BA at P. Why, of course! K is the mid-point of CP, and M is the mid-point of CB; $MK = \frac{1}{2}BP$.

Now for MH . . . $MH = \frac{1}{2}CQ$. (Can you supply the reasons?)

Also $BP = CQ$. (Why?)

$\therefore MK = MH$.

Knowing Which Theorems Suit the Figure

In this proof we used the results of several theorems. Evidently you need to have the right sort of results in your mind; you must know which theorems will suit the figure. Can you make a system for this?

Well, you can try; here is one way:

In the Figure	*What Follows?*
1. Two parallel lines	Equal angles . . . equal ratios.
	Equal areas . . . perhaps a parallelogram.
2. Equal lines $AB = AC$	$\triangle ABC$ has $\hat{B} = \hat{C}$.
	A is the centre of a circle through B, C.
	If A is on the line BC, this line is one diagonal of a parallelogram.
. . . and $AM \perp$ on BC ..	M is the mid-point of BC.
	If X is any point on AM, $XB = XC$.

In this way you can go over the various theorems, till you can say to yourself: "Here are the facts; they suggest these theorems which I know."

In the example here, the facts are mid-points; you have to prove two lines are parallel. Is there a parallelogram? Can you put one in? This is how you think out a "construction."

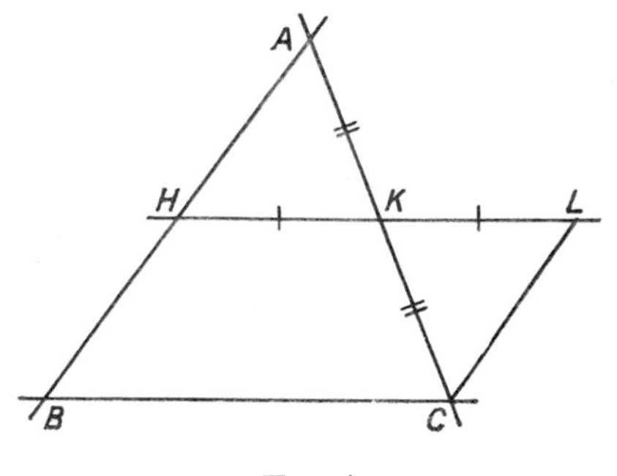

FIG. 4

Given: $\triangle ABC$; H, K mid-points of AB, AC.

Prove: HK is parallel to BC.

Construction: Make a parallelogram; produce HK to L so that $KL = HK$, then HL, AC bisect each other (Fig. 4).

$\therefore$ $AHCL$ is a parallelogram.

$\therefore$ CL is equal and parallel to AH, which $= HB$ (given).

$\therefore$ $CL = HB$ and is parallel to HB.

$\therefore$ $CLHB$ is a parallelogram, and $HL \parallel BC$.

Always look to see what else there is; not only is $HK \parallel BC$, but HK is half HL, therefore HK is half BC.

A Harder Example

Given: A quadrilateral $ABCD$, with $AB = CD$, and M, N the mid-points of BC, AD.

What can you prove? Take care! You cannot prove that $ABCD$ is a parallelogram; there are not enough facts; nothing but one pair of equal sides, opposite to each other. So you make a sketch, and put in these two equal lines, askew; you may by accident make something like (i) in Fig. 5. Here BC and AD are parallel, and you can prove all sorts of things. But why should they be parallel? That is not given either.

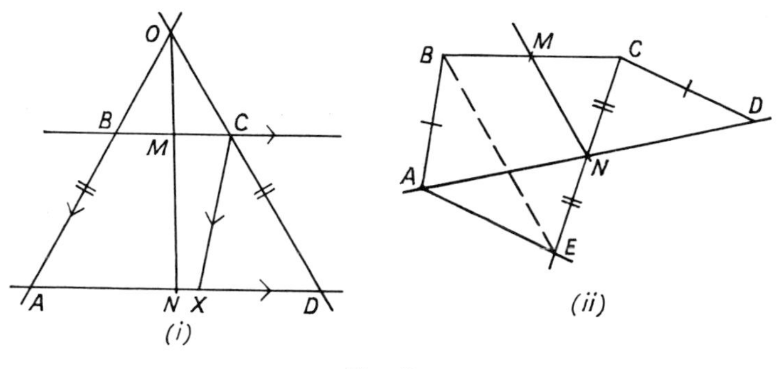

FIG. 5

Fig. (ii) is all you can be certain of; $AB = CD$, M and N are mid-points, and nothing else is any special size, or in any special direction.

In each figure, the line MN is drawn. Look at (i) first. It is easy to show that angles at A, D are equal, also angles at B, C: that AB, DC meet on the line MN; and make equal angles with MN; that $MN \perp AD$. One way to do all this is to draw $CX \parallel AB$, to meet AD at X; you then have a parallelogram, and you can find two isosceles triangles (OAD, OBC). But everything depends on BC being parallel to AD.

In Fig. (ii), which tells the truth, and nothing but the truth, none of these results seems to happen. But those mid-points are still there, and we shall prove: AB, CD make equal angles with the line MN.

Construction: As in Fig. 4, produce CN to E, so that $NE = CN$. Join BE. This gives two results at once.

$BE \parallel MN$ (joining two mid-points).

$AEDC$ is a parallelogram (its diagonals bisect each other).

Thus $AE = CD = AB$ (given).

$\therefore$ $\triangle ABE$ is isosceles; AB, AE make equal angles with BE.

$\therefore$ They make equal angles with MN. Also $AE \parallel CD$.

$\therefore$ AB, CD make equal angles with MN.

These two examples show that it helps to have a set of theorems in your mind, but that you may have to help out the facts given, by putting in some extra line. How do you think of such things? Do you have to make a lucky guess?

Not really. The facts given may remind you of certain theorems; but it is even more useful to examine the result you want to prove, and to think: what kind of evidence will prove this?

The Kind of Evidence Needed

You can do this, too, on a system. For example, if you need to prove that two lines AB, PQ are parallel; what kind of evidence will prove it?

1. Can you see a parallelogram? Or make one?
2. Are there two equal areas? ($\triangle APQ$, $\triangle BPQ$)
3. Any equal ratios? (Fig. 6, Chapter 1.)
4. Are there two equal angles, alternate or corresponding?
5. Any other ideas?

The evidence you need may be part of the given facts, or you may have to provide an extra fact. You go over in your mind the "possibles," and find one that is there already, or one you can construct. The detectives in fiction often find bits of evidence which other people didn't notice, because they know what they are looking for. In Fig. 5, the secret of success is exactly that: we did know what we were looking for: (a) parallelograms; (b) isosceles triangles . . . and so we found them.

Do this on a system. Make a list in writing to show what kind of evidence will prove:

1. $A\hat{B}C$ is a right-angle. (Six possible answers.)
2. Angles X, Y are equal.
3. Two areas are equal.
4. Two ratios equal.
5. Three points lie on a straight line.
6. Three lines meet in a point.
7. $ABCD$ is a parallelogram.
8. Four points lie on a circle.
9. Anything about a square.

By working at this, you soon have the right answers at your fingertips. You could put in more items; the clues to these nine are printed at the end of this chapter.

In the examples which follow, you will see this system at work. The proofs seem rather long, because the first stage, taking the thing to pieces, is written out in full. When you write out a proof, you think this part, and do not write it down. The first example shows what you do write down as "Proof."

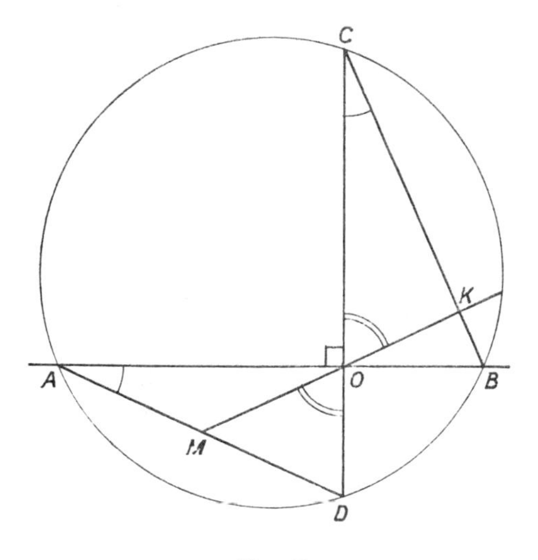

FIG. 6

Given: AB, CD are chords of a circle; they meet at O, at right-angles.
M is the mid-point of AD, and MO cuts BC at K (Fig. 6).
Prove: MK is perpendicular to BC.

Thinking it out: There are right-angles in the figure.
Can we prove $O\hat{K}C = C\hat{O}B$? Or $= D\hat{O}A$?
K belongs to a $\triangle OKC$; how about its other angles?
At once, $\hat{C} = \hat{A}$, in the same segment.
As for $K\hat{O}C$, it does equal $M\hat{O}D$, vertically opposite.
If this one were equal to $\hat{D}$, we should have two similar triangles, $\triangle DOA$, $\triangle KOC$, and so $O\hat{K}C$ would equal $A\hat{O}D$, a right-angle.
What does "right-angle" suggest? An angle in a semicircle; oh, yes, AD for the diameter, and one fact has not been used yet. M is the mid-point of AD, and therefore the centre of this semicircle.
So, $MO = MD$, $\therefore$ $M\hat{O}D$ does equal $\hat{D}$.
This is all we need. How do you write out the proof?

Proof: (There is no "Construction.")
In triangles DOA, OKC:
$\hat{A} = \hat{C}$ in the same segment.
M is the mid-point of AD, and $A\hat{O}D$ is a right-angle (given).
$\therefore$ M is the centre of a circle through AOD.

$\hat{D} = M\hat{O}D$ ($MO = MD$, radii).
$= K\hat{O}C$ (vertically opposite).
$\therefore$ $\triangle DOA$, $\triangle OKC$ are similar.
$\therefore$ $O\hat{K}C = D\hat{O}A$, a right-angle.

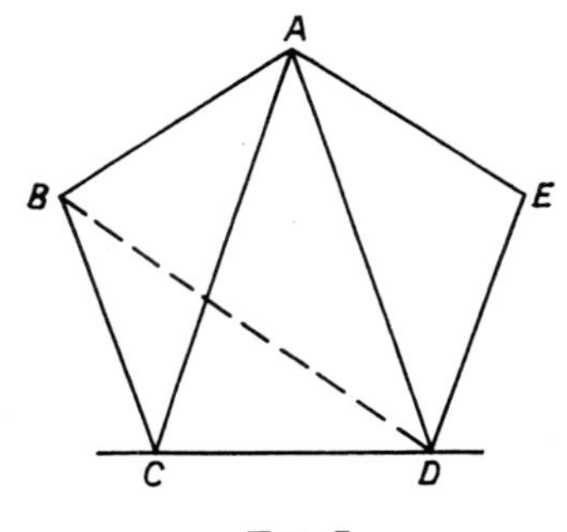

FIG. 7

Given: $ABCDE$, a regular pentagon
AC, AD, diagonals.
Prove: The three angles at A are all equal.

The facts given are not set out completely; they are:
all the sides AB, BC, etc. are equal, and
all the complete angles at A, B, etc. are equal.

Can you prove $\triangle BAC \equiv \triangle DAE$? That will give two equal angles at A, to begin with.

$$\left.\begin{array}{r} AB = AE \\ BC = ED \\ A\hat{B}C = D\hat{E}A \end{array}\right\} \text{(all given) (S A S).} \therefore B\hat{A}C = D\hat{A}E$$

There is no triangle like DAC, so make one; join BD (Fig. 7). $\triangle DAC \equiv \triangle BDA$, easily. $D\hat{A}C = B\hat{D}A$ is not much use; nothing else is known about $B\hat{D}A$, so you bring in another fact about congruent triangles —they are equal in area; these two are also on the same base AD.

$$\therefore BC \parallel AD.$$
$$\therefore D\hat{A}C = A\hat{C}B$$
$$= B\hat{A}C \; (BA = BC).$$

Calculating an Angle or a Length

A question often asked is, "Calculate an angle or a length." This rider is easily done by calculation, if you know, or prove, that each angle of the pentagon is 108°. For then the other two angles of $\triangle ABC$ are 36° each, and $D\hat{A}C$ is 108° minus twice 36°.

Another way: the five points named are on a circle and BC, CD, DE, are equal chords, so they subtend equal angles at A. (Is it obvious from the facts, that $ABCDE$ are on a circle? If not, how do you prove it?)

Given: $ABCD$ is a parallelogram; X is on AD, Y on BC, and $DX = BY$.
AY, CX cut BD at P, Q (Fig. 8).

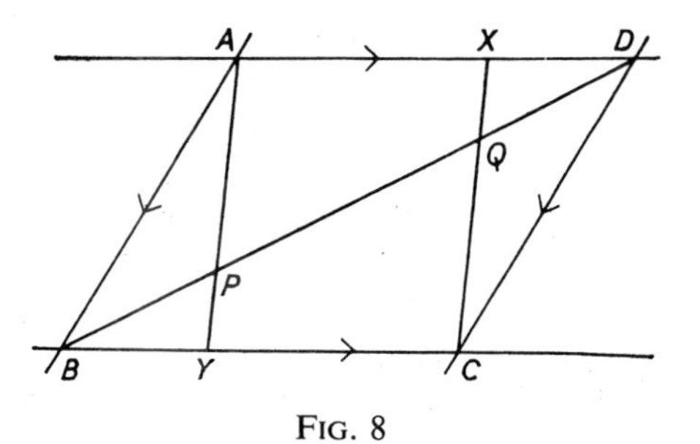

FIG. 8

Prove: $\triangle ABP \equiv \triangle CDQ$

We have two equal sides, $AB = CD$. No good looking for other equal lengths, but equal angles are "given away."

$$A\hat{B}P = C\hat{D}Q \text{ by parallels.}$$

And surely $AY \parallel CX$, because AX, YC are equal and parallel. (Why?)
$\therefore$ $A\hat{P}B = C\hat{Q}D$ (alternate angles!).

EXERCISE 4A

1. If X, Y are the mid-points, what more can be proved?

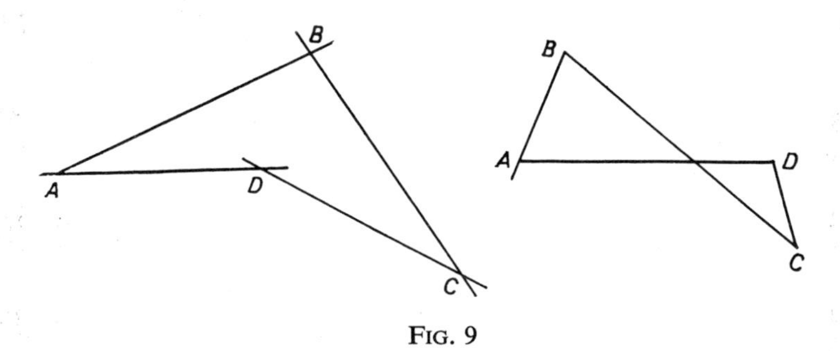

FIG. 9

2. Given a quadrilateral, with each side a different length. The mid-points of the four sides are joined. Prove that this makes a parallelogram and its two diagonals.

3. Is this still true of these two quadrilaterals? (Fig. 9.)

Not in the Same Segment

Given: Two chords of a circle, AB and AC (they are not equal). M, N the mid-points of the arcs AB, AC. The line MN crosses AB at X, AC at Y.
Prove: $AX = AY$.

It *must* be done by angles, and the angles at X, Y are in mid-air; we need angles at the circle, in the same segment if possible.

Two such angles can be made by joining AM and CN; $\hat{M} = \hat{C}$. Now you can bring in $A\hat{X}Y$, as the exterior angle to $\triangle AXM$. So far, we have not used the fact that N is in the middle of the arc AC; this proves that the lines AN, NC are equal, so join AN (Fig. 10).

Then $Y\hat{A}N = \hat{C} = \hat{M}$. Likewise $A\hat{N}M$ (or $A\hat{N}Y$) $= A\hat{B}M = X\hat{A}M$.

So $A\hat{X}Y$ is the sum of two angles, and $A\hat{Y}X$ is the sum of two other angles equal to those two. Therefore $\triangle AXY$ is isosceles.

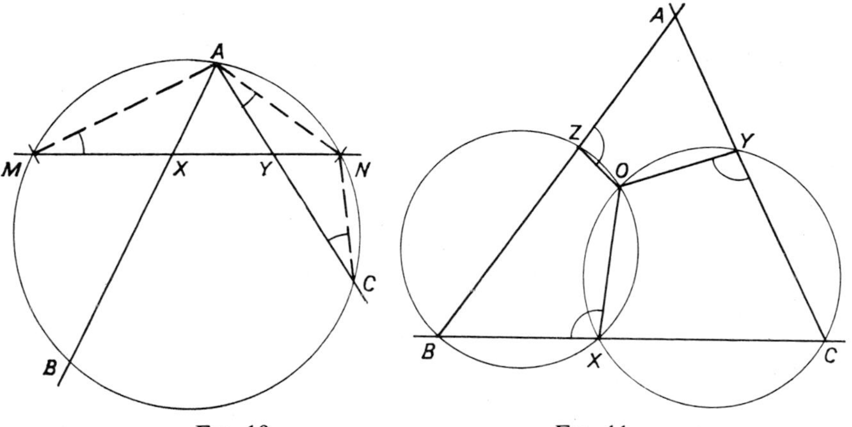

FIG. 10 FIG. 11

Given: $\triangle ABC$, $\left.\begin{matrix}X\\Y\\Z\end{matrix}\right\}$ any points on $\left\{\begin{matrix}BC\\CA\\AB\end{matrix}\right.$

Prove: The circles through BCX, CAY, ABZ meet in a point.

The idea is to draw *two* circles BXZ, CXY, which cross again at O, and prove that O lies on the third circle.

Construction: Join OX, OY, OZ (Fig. 11). To prove that O, Y, A, Z are on one circle we must show that the exterior $O\hat{Y}C = O\hat{Z}A$.
$O\hat{Z}A$ does equal $O\hat{X}B$ ($OXBZ$ is cyclic, constr.)
$O\hat{X}B = O\hat{Y}C$, likewise. And that is all.

Note: There is a special case; circles BXZ, CYX might accidentally touch at X, and would not cross again. Draw the figure like this, and supply the proof that A, Y, X, Z lie on a circle.

EXERCISE 4B

Three examples on tangents. (Tangents from a point to a circle are equal in length.)

1. $\triangle ABC$ has $AB = AC$. A circle touches AB and AC; BZ, CZ are also tangents, and meet at Z. Prove $BZ = CZ$.

2. O is the centre of a circle. Tangents are drawn at two fixed points on the circle, M and N; any other tangent cuts these two at A, B. Prove that AB subtends at the centre an angle of definite size.

(*Hint:* If $M\hat{O}N$ is 100°, $A\hat{O}B$ is either 50° or 130°.)

3. AB is a diameter of a circle; AP, PQ, QB are tangents. Show that the area of $APQB$ is $\frac{1}{2}AB.PQ$.

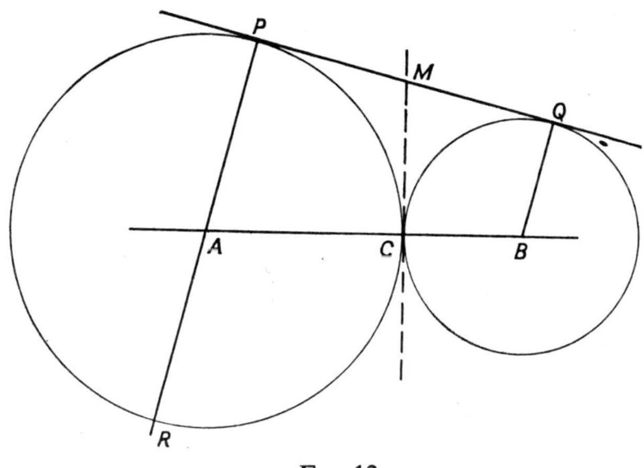

FIG. 12

4. In Fig. 12, the circles touch at C; PQ is a common tangent, and the centres are A, B. See how many other facts you can discover—and prove.

Note: Draw the tangent at C.

A Tangent Proof

Given: AB is a diameter of a semicircle, $AYXB$, centre M. Y, X any two points on the semicircle (notice the order $AYXB$), and AY, BX cross at C. L is the centre of the circle through CXY.

Prove: That LX, LY touch the first circle.

To prove that LX is a tangent, we have three possible ways:

Can we show that $L\hat{X}Y = X\hat{A}Y$

or $L\hat{X}A = X\hat{B}A$

or prove $L\hat{X}M$ a right-angle?

The semicircle can supply a right-angle, $A\hat{X}B$, so join AX. Notice that $X\hat{L}Y$, at the centre L, is twice $\hat{C}$, and that $\triangle ACX$ is a right-angled triangle. Can you cut $X\hat{L}Y$ in half, so as to have an angle at L equal to $\hat{C}$? Yes, you have only to join the two centres L, M (Fig. 13).

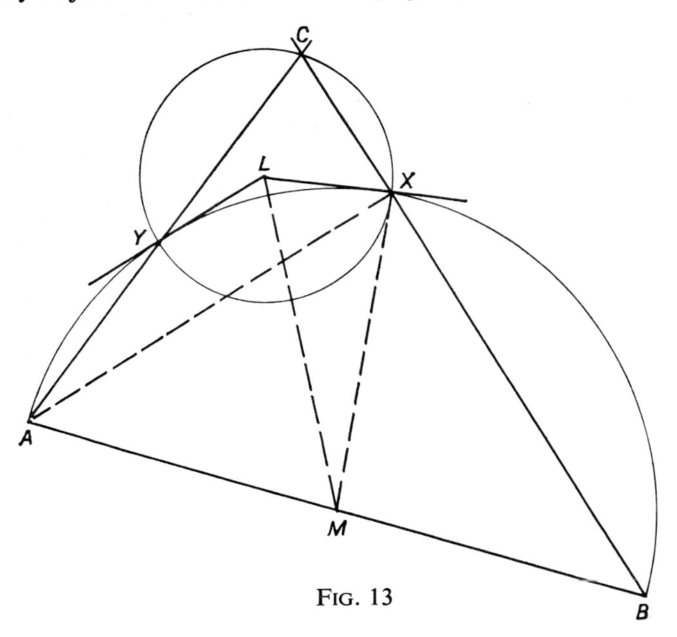

FIG. 13

$\triangle LXM \equiv \triangle LYM$ (S S S).
Then $\triangle LXM$ has the angle at $\hat{L}$ equal to $\hat{C}$, which is an angle of $\triangle ACX$.
And it has the angle at $M = X\hat{A}Y$ (reasons?).
Therefore $\triangle LXM$, $\triangle XCA$ are similar. $\therefore$ $L\hat{X}M = C\hat{X}A$, a right-angle.

EXERCISE 4C

1. If O is the point where AX crosses BY, prove that CO goes through L.

2. Draw the figure as it is given; instead of the method just used, join LO, XY and prove $L\hat{X}O = X\hat{B}A$ (via O and Y).

Two Circles

Given: Two (unequal) circles cross at A, B. Lines from a point C are drawn through A, B. The line CA cuts the circles at P, X and CB cuts them at Q, Y (Fig. 14).

Prove: That PQ is parallel to XY: (i) If C is outside both circles; (ii) If C is inside one of them.

In (i) what evidence do you need? $C\hat{X}Y$, $C\hat{P}Q$ are corresponding angles and if they are equal . . . this angle at X is exterior to a quadrilateral in one circle (consider one circle at a time), and equals one of the angles at B, and that one is exterior to . . .

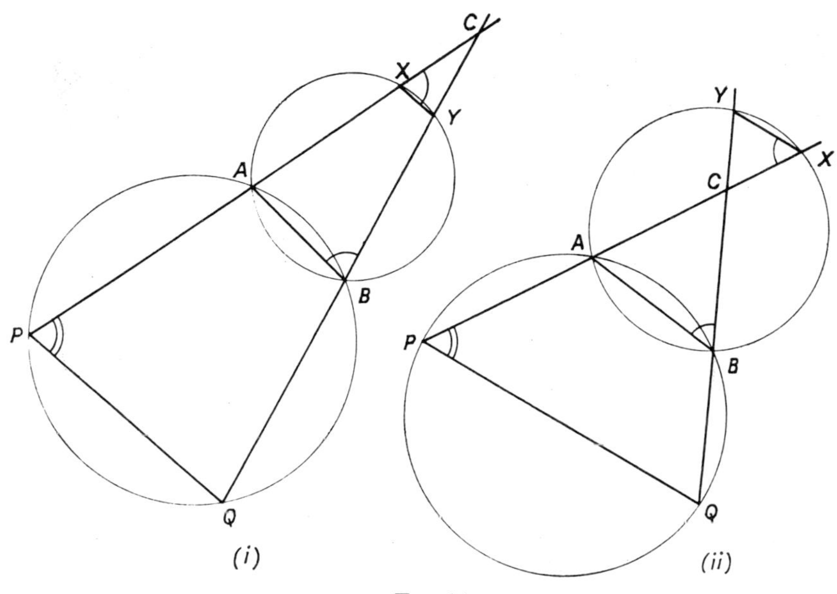

FIG. 14

In (ii) the angles at P and X are alternate angles; $\hat{X}$ is in the same segment as $Y\hat{B}A$, and this is exterior to the quadrilateral in the other circle, so it equals $\hat{P}$. $\therefore\ \hat{X} = \hat{P}$, and $XY \parallel PQ$.

What happens if C is actually *on* one of the circles?

Another Right-Angle

Given: A circle with centre O; another circle crosses the first at A, B (Fig. 15). X is any point on the first circle; XA, XB cut the other circle at C, D.

Prove: $CD \perp XO$.

This alleged right-angle is hard to get at. There are no semicircles, no tangents, no congruent triangles and no other right-angle to compare with it.

If Y is the point where CD cuts OX, the point Y appears to be right off the map. You can do something with angles at a circle, or angles at a centre, but where are they?

As soon as we ask this question, we can see $\triangle CXY$, with one vertex on each circle, and one of its angles is the one we want. If the angles at X and C add up to a right-angle? Look at the left-hand circle first; O is its centre.

Therefore $A\hat{X}Y$ is half $A\hat{O}Z$.

If only the angle C will oblige by being half $A\hat{O}X$, we shall know that their sum is half of two right-angles.

There is an angle that is half $A\hat{O}X$, the angle $A\hat{B}X$.

Now look at the other circle, and re-name this last angle $A\hat{B}D$.

$A\hat{B}D$ is in the same segment as $A\hat{C}D$. They are equal.

$\triangle XCY$ has $X + Y =$ half of $(A\hat{O}X + A\hat{O}Z)$
$=$ half of two right-angles;
the angle at Y is the other half (Sum of angles of a $\triangle$).

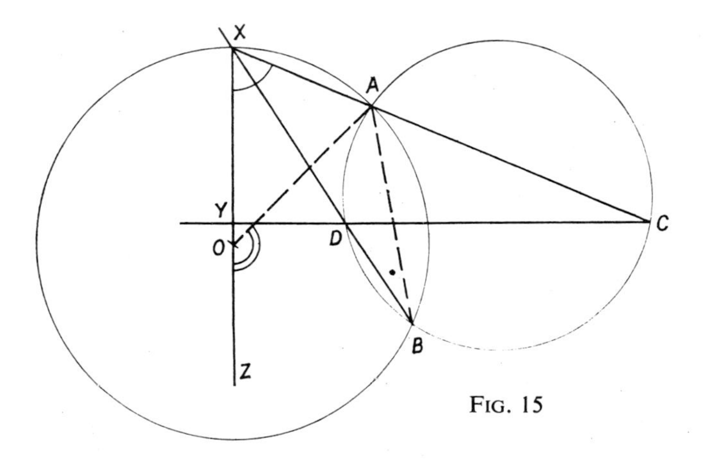

FIG. 15

Given: Two circles which do not meet; AB, CD are any diameters, one for each circle. P, Q are mid-points of the semicircles between these lines. The line PQ cuts the circles again at X, Y.

Prove: That the lines through XB, XA, YC, YD, form a square.

There are right-angles at X, Y.

Two equal arcs PA, PB make $P\hat{X}A = P\hat{X}B$, and each is $45°$.

To prove the figure is a square we have to show that all its sides are equal and *one* of its angles is a right-angle. But now you can see two isosceles triangles, and they are congruent.

A Square Through Four Points

Here is a solution to the problem: construct a square with one side through each of four given points (Fig. 16). This was done by a different method in Fig. 11, Chapter 1. (And a simpler one. Try drawing Fig. 16 and see how queerly it may come out.)

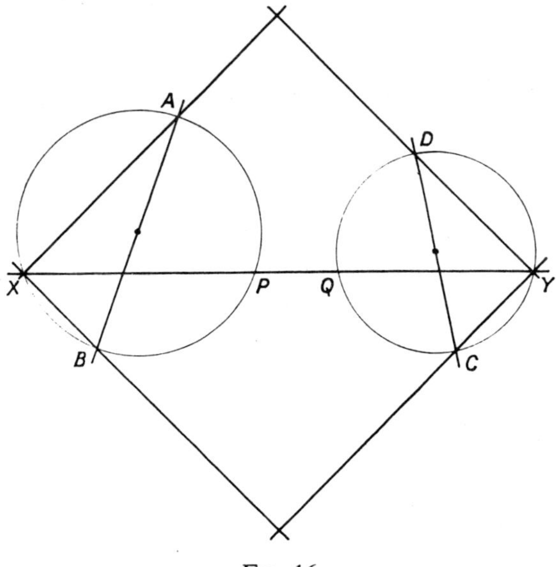

FIG. 16

Given: Two circles cross at A, B. The tangents at A cut the circles again at X, Y.
Prove: $AB^2 = BX.BY$ (Fig. 17).

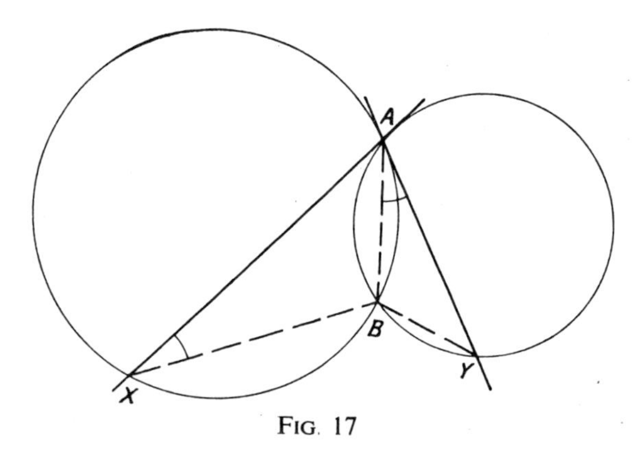

FIG. 17

There should be equal angles somewhere; you can't do anything with the vertically opposite angles at A, which have nothing to do with tangents anyhow.

Alternate segment! Join BX, BY.

$B\hat{A}Y = A\hat{X}B$ ($B\hat{X}A$ is better; why?).
$A\hat{Y}B = X\hat{A}B$.

To prove $AB^2 = BX.BY$; this is the same thing as $\frac{AB}{BX} = \frac{BY}{AB}$; and we have two similar triangles BAY, BXA which show these ratios to be equal.

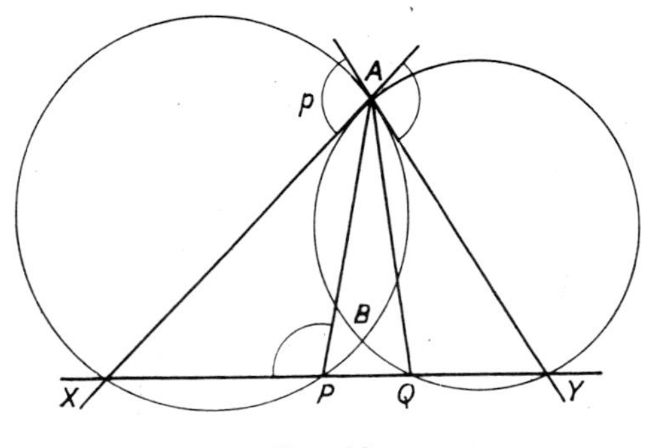

FIG. 18

Given: The same figure; XY cuts the circles again at P, Q (in this order, $XPQY$).

Prove: $AP = AQ$.

We can prove this by showing that $\triangle APQ$ has two equal angles (Fig. 18). Don't look at both circles at once; look first at the left-hand one.

$A\hat{P}X =$ the angle between AX and the tangent AY (marked). This time, vertically opposite angles are useful; looking at the right-hand circle, the other marked angle $= A\hat{Q}Y$.

$\therefore$ $\triangle APQ$ has equal angles at P, Q. $\therefore$ $AP = AQ$.

When proving these various riders, we had to allow several theorems to take their turn. Two especially useful theorems, as you have seen, are:

(1) Exterior angle, of a triangle or of a cyclic quadrilateral.

(2) The mid-point theorem for a triangle.

Hardly ever useful are: the actual sizes of angle, 45°, 60° or what not. Or: the sum of this and that is 180°. However, we will give each of them a turn, in the next two examples.

Given: An equilateral $\triangle ABC$, inscribed in a circle. P, any point on the minor arc BC.

Prove: $PA = PB + PC$

When you have to show that one quantity is the sum of two others, cut a piece out of it equal to one of the others, and examine the piece you have left.

Construction: On PA, make $PX = PC$ (Fig. 19).

Join CX. (PA, PB, PC are there already.)

Does $AX = PB$? $\triangle AXC$ looks as if it might $\equiv$ $\triangle PBA$, or $\triangle PBC$.

The last one looks better, for the two angles marked are equal, and also $AC = BC$ (given).

One more fact is needed; and you have not made use of $PX = PC$ yet.

$\triangle PXC$ has $PX = PC$, and $\hat{P}$ is $60°$. (In the same segment as $A\hat{B}C$.)

The other two angles are equal, and their sum is $120°$ ($180°$ for the three). So $A\hat{X}C$ is $120°$. $B\hat{P}C$ is made up of two $60°$ angles, so it is also $120°$.

$\therefore \triangle AXC \equiv \triangle BPC$, therefore $XA = PB$.

$PA = PX + XA = PB + PC$.

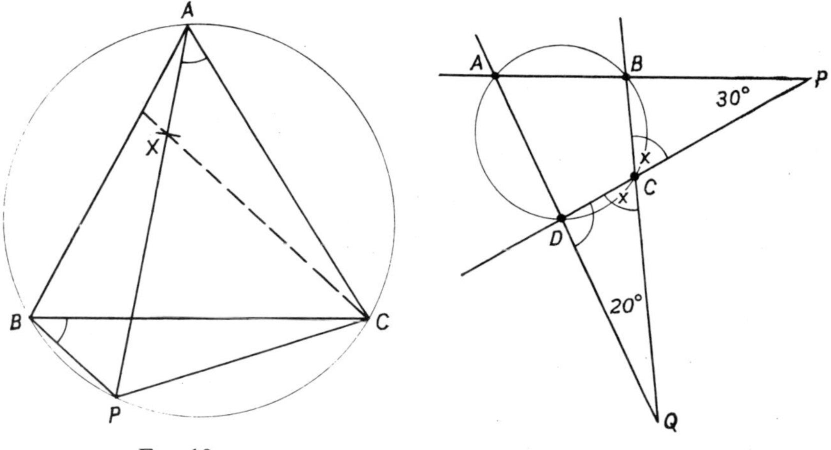

FIG. 19

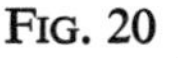
FIG. 20

In Fig. 20, calculate the angle x.

$A\hat{B}C$, exterior to $\triangle BCP$, $= (x + 30)°$.

$Q\hat{D}C$, exterior to the cyclic quadrilateral, $= A\hat{B}C$.

The sum of the angles of $\triangle QDC$ is $180°$, and these angles are: x, 20, $x + 30$ degrees.

$$\therefore 2x + 50 = 180$$
$$x = 65°$$

Clues to the Evidence (page 363)

1. $A\hat{B}C$ a right-angle — Angle of a square or rectangle.
   Two adjacent angles equal, usually by congruent triangles.
   Angle in a semicircle.
   Tangent perpendicular to radius.
   $\triangle ABC \equiv \triangle XYZ$, when $\hat{Y}$ is given a right-angle.
   In calculations, Pythagoras' Theorem.

2. Equal angles ..	$\triangle ABC$; if $AB = AC$, $\hat{B} = \hat{C}$. Parallel lines. Vertically opposite angles. In congruent triangles, or similar triangles. In the same segment. Exterior angle, cyclic quadrilateral. Tangent and chord, alternate segment. Subtended by equal arcs at another point on the circle (or in two equal circles).
3. Equal areas ..	Triangles, if congruent. Triangles, parallelograms on the same or on equal bases, and between parallels (or of equal perpendicular height). In the form $a.x = b.y$, by similar triangles.
4. Equal ratios ..	$\triangle A\hat{B}C$ with $HK \parallel BC$. Similar triangles. Triangle with one angle bisected.
5. Three points on a line ABC	Join BC, BA, show $A\hat{B}C$ = two right-angles. $X\hat{B}C$, $X\hat{B}A$ right-angles. Angles $X\hat{A}B$, $X\hat{A}C$ equal.
6. Three lines meet ..	In general, two of them meet at O; prove O is on the third line. Two pairs of parallels.
7. $ABCD$ a parallelogram	$AB = CD$ *and* $\parallel CD$. Diagonals bisect each other. $AB = CD$ *and* $AC = BD$. $\hat{A} = \hat{C}$ *and* $\hat{B} = \hat{D}$.
8. Four points $PQRS$ lie on a circle in that order	$P\hat{Q}S = P\hat{R}S$. Exterior angle at $S = P\hat{Q}R$. $OP.OQ = OR.OS$, or (diagonals) $PK.KR = QK.KS$. Two right-angles opposite, or $P\hat{Q}R$, $P\hat{S}R$ or $P\hat{Q}S$, $P\hat{R}S$ right-angles.
9. Squares	Four sides equal and *one* right-angle. Four right-angles and two adjacent sides equal. Diagonals equal and perpendicular *and* bisect each other. For anything about squares, Pythagoras' Theorem or ratios equal: $\frac{a}{x} = \frac{x}{b}$

CHAPTER 5

TRIANGLES AND CIRCLES

The Sides of a Triangle: To draw a triangle with sides of given lengths (call them a, b, c inches), first draw XY, a in. long; then with centre X and radius b in., and centre Y, radius c in., draw two circles.

If they cross, you have a triangle XYZ; they will not cross unless $b + c$ is greater than a; so one indisputable fact about every triangle is:

The sum of any two sides is greater than the third side.

Sides and Angles

1. If a triangle has two equal angles, it must have two equal sides.
2. If $\triangle XYZ$ has $\hat{Z}$ greater than $\hat{Y}$ (write $\hat{Z} > \hat{Y}$), then $XY > XZ$.

"The greater side is opposite the greater angle." This is "obvious," perhaps; but see how it can be accounted for:

Theorem I

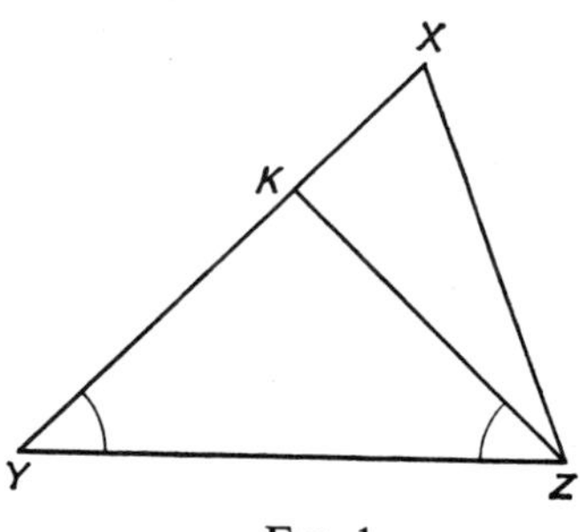

FIG. 1

Given: $\triangle XYZ$, with $\hat{Z} > \hat{Y}$.

Prove: $XY > XZ$.

Construction: Since $\hat{Z}$ is the greater angle, a line ZK can be drawn *inside* the $\hat{Z}$, so that $Y\hat{Z}K = \hat{Y}$ (Fig. 1).

Draw this line; it meets XY at K, a point between X and Y.

Proof: $\triangle YKZ$ has two equal angles. $\therefore$ $YK = KZ$

$XY = YK + KX$

$= KZ + KX$, two sides of $\triangle XKZ > XZ$

The simplest theorems deal with two equal lines—or angles—or areas. The next stage, to show which of two quantities is greater, is also important.

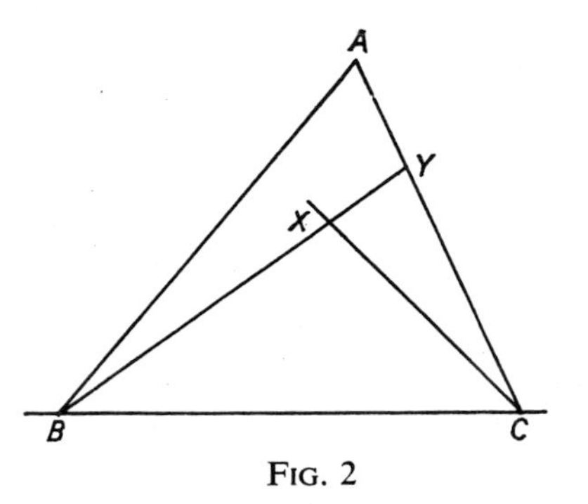

FIG. 2

(1) *Given:* X a point inside $\triangle ABC$.
Prove: $BA + AC > BX + XC$.

Each of these sums is greater than BC; but that does not help; like so many things in a geometrical figure, the fact is easy to see, but not so easy to put into words. It will not help either to join AX.

Construction: Produce BX, to cut AC at Y (Fig. 2).

Proof: $BA + AC = BA + AY + YC$
and $BA + AY > BY$ (see first paragraph above).
$\therefore BA + AC > BY + YC$
i.e. $> BX + XY + YC$
also $XY + YC > XC$ ($\triangle XYC$)
$\therefore BA + AC > BX + XC$.

(2) The sum of the sides of a quadrilateral is greater than the sum of the diagonals, but less than twice this sum.

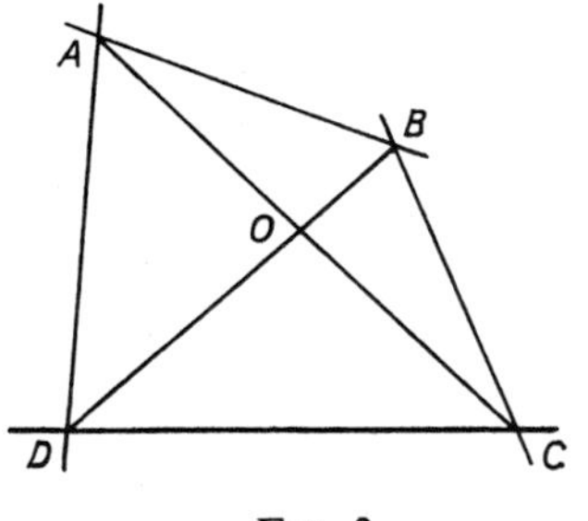

FIG. 3

Given: A quadrilateral $ABCD$.
Prove: $2(AC + BD) > AB+BC+CD+DA$ and the latter sum $> AC + BD$.

Proof: Let O be the point where the diagonals cross; look at the four triangles which meet at O (Fig. 3).

$AO + OB > AB$, and $DO + OC > CD$

By adding these, $AC + BD > AB + CD$ (one pair of sides).

Likewise $AC + BD > BC + DA$.

$\therefore 2(AC + BD) >$ the sum of all four sides.

To prove the second part, consider the triangles ABC, ACD.

$AB + BC > AC$, and $CD + DA > AC$.

$\therefore$ The sum of the sides $> 2.AC$.

AC was chosen as the longer diagonal (Fig. 3).

The sum of the sides $> AC + BD$.

If the diagonals happen to be equal, this is still true.

EXERCISE 5A

1. M is a point inside a circle with centre O, and $BMOA$ is a diameter. P is any other point on the circle; prove that $MA > MP$.

2. In the same figure, prove that $MP > MB$, and hence that MA is the longest, and MB the shortest line from M to the circumference.

3. Prove that the sum of the diagonals of a parallelogram is greater than twice the longer side of the parallelogram.

4. A point A is joined by straight lines to various points on a given straight line a; prove that the shortest of these joins is the one perpendicular to a.

5. $\triangle PQR$ has $PQ = PR$, and X is any point on the side QR. Prove that PX is less than PQ ($PX < PQ$).

The Path of a Ray of Light, Reflected in a Mirror

In Fig. 4, the light is at the point A, the mirror is represented by the line PQ; one ray is reflected through the point B.

It must take the shortest possible path. To find this, mark the point C which is the "image" of B; that is, draw $BMC \perp PQ$ and make $MC = BM$.

If the ray went from A to X, from X to B, the length of its path would be $AX + XB$, and this equals $AX + XC$.

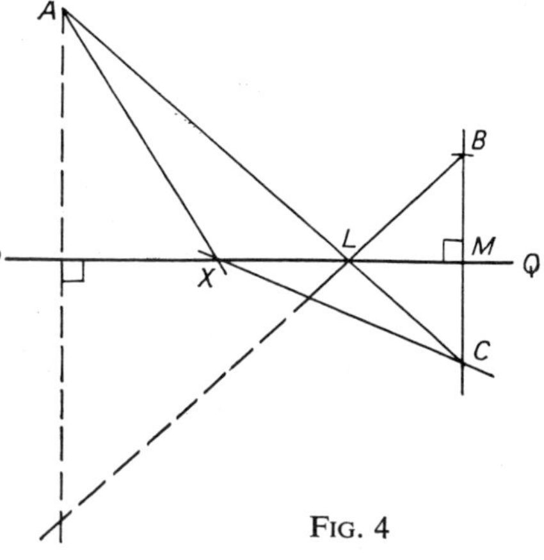

FIG. 4

This is longer than the straight line AC; draw this line, to cut PQ at L:

$$AL + LB \text{ is the shortest path } (= AC).$$

For $AX + XC$, two sides of a triangle, cannot be as short as the third side AC.

The two parts of the ray of light make equal angles with the mirror.

The Maximum Area

Rectangles are drawn, each with the same perimeter; which one has the maximum area? The sides are a in., b in., which can be altered, so long as the perimeter, $2a + 2b = 4k$. Since the area is $a.b$ sq. in., and $a + b = 2k$, let $a = k + x$, $b = k - x$.

Then the area $= (k + x)(k - x)$ sq. in.
$= k^2 - x^2$.

This is maximum if $x = 0$; each side is k in. and the figure is a square.

Another way (Fig. 5):

$AXYZ$ is a square,
$ABCD$ is a rectangle with the same perimeter.
Thus $YO = OC$
and $DO > OX$.
$\therefore$ The top rectangle $DOYZ$ is greater than the side one $XOCB$.
$\therefore$ The square $AXYZ$ is greater than the rectangle $ABCD$.

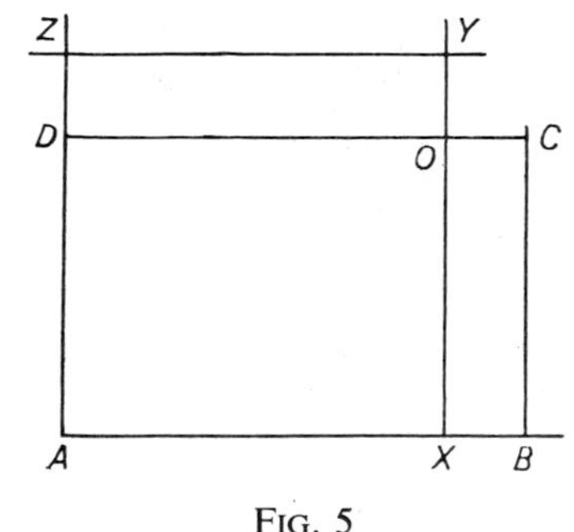

FIG. 5

EXERCISE 5B

1. What is the maximum area of a rectangle, given only that its diagonal is 4 in. long?

2. A rectangle has two sides along the sides BA, BC of a $\triangle\ ABC$, with a right-angle at B; the other two sides meet on AC. Where is the greatest rectangle? Compare its area with that of the triangle.

3. A farmer makes a rectangular sheep pen, using a stone wall for one side, and 16 hurdles, each 4 ft. long, for the others. What shape does he make it to enclose the maximum area, and what is this area?

4. Triangles are inscribed in a circle, with a given chord BC as base. Find the triangle of maximum area.

5. Can you prove that the greatest possible triangle inscribed in a fixed circle will be equilateral?

6. Two sides of a triangle are 5 in., 6 in. Construct the triangle with the maximum area. What is this area?

7. The diagonals of a quadrilateral are 10 in., 8 in. Show that its area is not greater than 40 sq. in.

The Sine of an Angle

After saying "these sides are equal," and "this side is greater than that one," there is a third stage: to compare two sides of a triangle exactly. What is the ratio of two sides? This, too, depends on the angles.

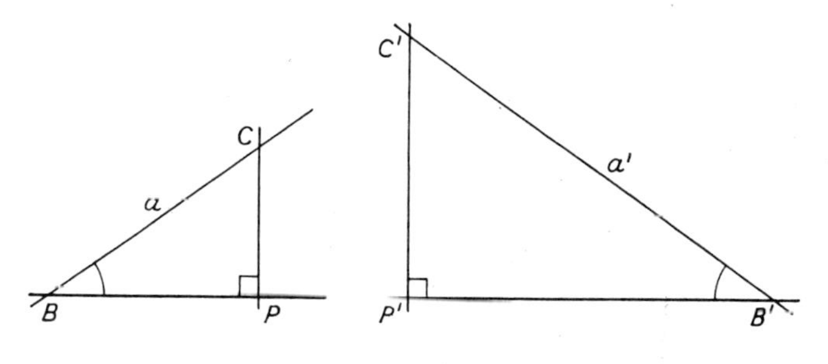

FIG. 6

Begin with a right-angled triangle (Fig. 6). a is the longest side of $\triangle BPC$; $\hat{P}$ is the right-angle.

$$\frac{CP}{a} \text{ is a fraction less than 1.}$$

The other triangle in Fig. 6 has $\hat{B}' = \hat{B}$, and a right-angle at P'.

$$\text{Then } \frac{C'P'}{a'} = \frac{CP}{a} \text{ (the triangles are similar).}$$

So the fraction depends on the size of $\hat{B}$ only. It is the sine of B, usually written sin B.

The values of the sines of angles from 0 to 90° range from 0 to 1. Look through the table of natural sines (page 476), and you see that they do not go up steadily; at 30° the sine is already halfway there, but after that it increases more and more slowly. And how about angles of more than 90°? We shall come to that presently.

To Compare Two Sides of a Triangle of Any Shape

In Fig. 7, the first sketch shows simply a $\triangle$ ABC, with each side and each angle labelled; for convenience, we write simply $\hat{A}$ for "the angle BAC," and a for the side BC, opposite to A. In the other sketch, $AN \perp BC$, and the two parts of the triangle are drawn separately.

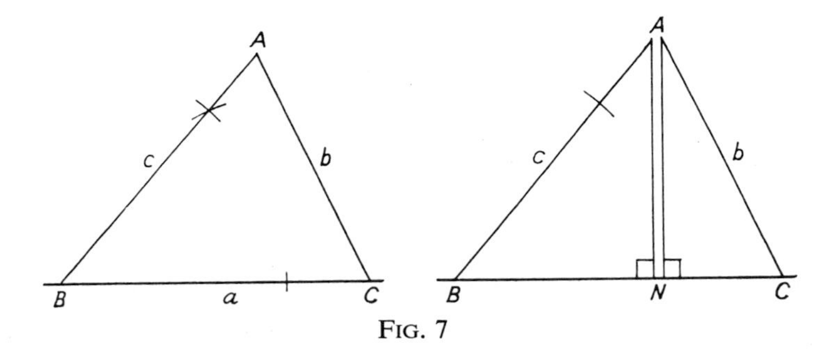

FIG. 7

$\frac{AN}{AB}$ is the sine of $\hat{B}$, so $AN = c.\sin \hat{B}$

$\frac{AN}{AC} = \sin \hat{C} \quad \therefore \quad AN = b.\sin \hat{C}$

$\therefore c.\sin \hat{B} = b.\sin \hat{C} \quad \therefore \frac{c}{\sin \hat{C}} = \frac{b}{\sin \hat{B}}$

Two sides are proportional to the sines of the angles opposite. This "sine rule" is the most useful of all in calculating distances or angles; see Arithmetic, Chapter 7, page 70.

Make a sketch which shows that $a.\sin \hat{B} = b.\sin \hat{A}$.

We have three equal ratios now: $\frac{a}{\sin \hat{A}} = \frac{b}{\sin \hat{B}} = \frac{c}{\sin \hat{C}}$

Each of them is equal to a definite length, in fact to the diameter of the circle through A, B, C. Draw this circle, and a diameter, CD.

$$C\hat{D}B = \hat{A} \text{ (in the same segment)}$$
$$D\hat{B}C \text{ is a right-angle (in semicircle)}$$
$$\therefore a = CD.\sin C\hat{D}B,$$
$$\text{i.e. } a = 2R.\sin \hat{A} \text{ (} R \text{ is the radius).}$$

Formulae for the Area of a Triangle: The area, usually written as $\triangle$, is equal to half the base multiplied by the perpendicular height.

$$\triangle = \tfrac{1}{2}a.AN = \tfrac{1}{2}a.b.\sin \hat{C}$$

$$\text{Since } c = 2R.\sin \hat{C},\ \sin \hat{C} = \frac{c}{2R}$$

$$\therefore \text{The area } \triangle = \frac{a.b.c}{4.R}$$

Another formula is:

$$\triangle = \tfrac{1}{2}(2R.\sin \hat{A})(2R.\sin \hat{B}).\sin \hat{C}$$
$$= 2R^2.\sin \hat{A}.\sin \hat{B}.\sin \hat{C}$$

We may say that the angles $\hat{A}$, $\hat{B}$, $\hat{C}$ tell us the shape, and the radius R tells the size of the triangle. This last formula includes the shape and the size in a tabloid form.

Triangle and Circle

O is the centre of a circle (Fig. 8), and ABC is a triangle inscribed in the circle.

Draw $OL \perp$ on BC; then L is the mid-point of BC ($\triangle OLB \equiv \triangle OLC$).

This fact can be stated in three ways:

(1) OL, the perpendicular on BC, bisects BC.

(2) If O is joined to the mid-point of BC, the line so drawn is perpendicular to BC.

(3) The perpendicular bisector of BC passes through O.

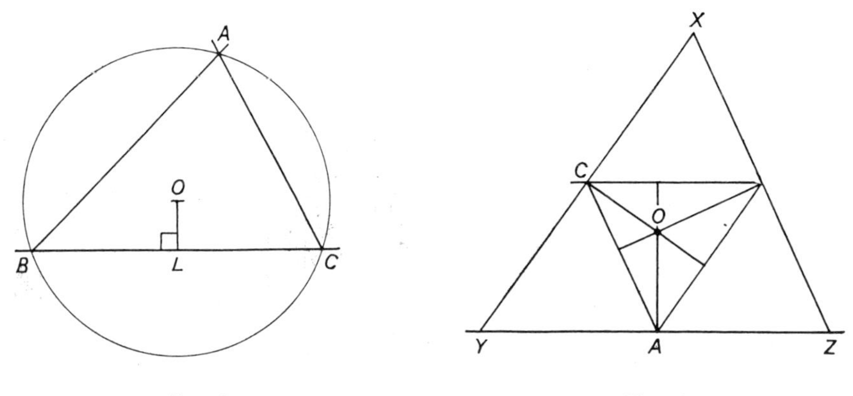

FIG. 8

FIG. 9

EXERCISE 5C

1. Prove (2) and (3) without using (1).

Perpendicular Bisectors and Altitudes

It follows that the perpendicular bisectors of the three sides of any triangle must meet in a point, which is the centre of the circle through the three vertices.

In Fig. 9, A, B, C, are the mid-points of YZ, ZX, XY.

$\therefore BC \parallel YZ$.

So AO, the perpendicular bisector of YZ, is also perpendicular to BC; it is one of the altitudes of $\triangle ABC$.

The perpendicular bisectors of the sides of $\triangle XYZ$ meet in the point O; and these three lines are the altitudes of $\triangle ABC$.

The altitudes of a triangle meet in a point.

Fig. 10 shows a $\triangle$ *ABC* inscribed in a circle; *AP*, *BQ* are two altitudes and cross at *H*; the line *AP* cuts the circle at *K*.

To prove that $HP = PK$.

$H\ Q\ C\ P$ lie on a circle (diameter HC)

$\therefore\ C\hat{H}P = C\hat{Q}P$ (same segment)

$P\ Q\ A\ B$ lie on a circle (diameter AB)

$\therefore\ C\hat{Q}P = \hat{B}$ (exterior angle theorem).

Finally $\hat{B} = C\hat{K}P$ (same segment of circle ABC).

This completes a string of equal angles, and now:

$\triangle HPC \equiv \triangle KPC$ (S A A)

because $\begin{cases} C\hat{H}P = \hat{K}, \text{ just proved.} \\ \text{angles at } P \text{ are equal (right angles).} \\ PC \text{ is a common side.} \end{cases}$

Therefore the lines *HP*, *PK* are equal.

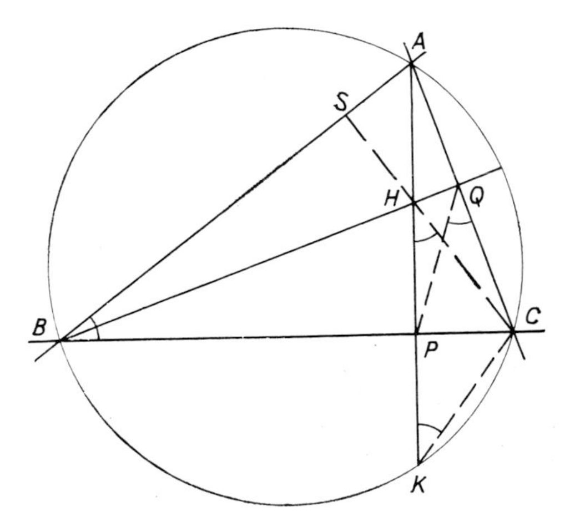

FIG. 10

In case we didn't know it already, we can prove again that *CH* is $\perp AB$. For, $\triangle HCP$, $\triangle BCS$ have $C\hat{H}P = \hat{B}$, and each has the angle $H\hat{C}P$; their third angles are equal:

$C\hat{S}B = C\hat{P}H$, which is a right-angle.

The circle through $P\ Q\ S$ is in perspective with the circle $A\ B\ C$; H is the centre of perspective, and $P\ Q\ S$ are "halfway" to the outer circle. The radius of the circle $P\ Q\ S$ is therefore half the radius of the circle $A\ B\ C$.

Draw a figure to show the two circles.

The Nine-point Circle

Fig. 11 shows the three altitudes of $\triangle ABC$, meeting at H. AD is a diameter.
$A\hat{C}D$ is a right-angle, and $= A\hat{Q}B$.
$\therefore CD \parallel QB$.
$A\hat{B}D = A\hat{S}C$ (right-angles) $\therefore DB \parallel CS$.
$\therefore$ The figure $BDCH$ is a parallelogram; and HD, BC bisect each other (at X).

We can now have six lines drawn from H to meet the circle; their mid-points are P, Q, S, the feet of the three altitudes; X, Y, Z, the mid-points of the three sides. These six points lie on a circle which is in perspective with the circle ABC; so do the mid-points of HA, HB, HC.

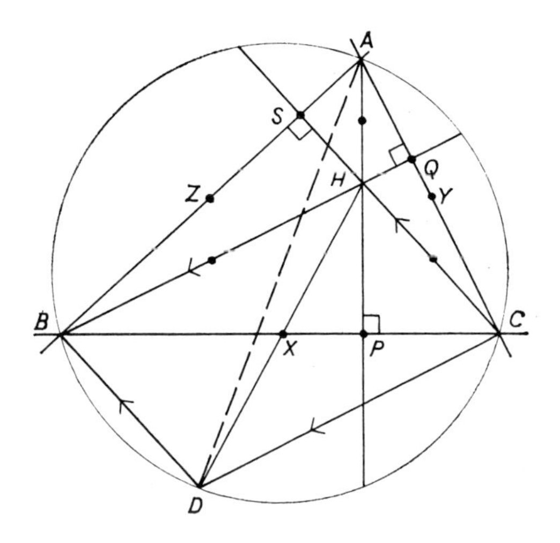

FIG. 11

These are the nine special points which lie on a circle; its radius is $\frac{1}{2}R$, and its centre is halfway between H and the centre of the circle ABC.

EXERCISE 5D

1. Draw a careful figure, given $\triangle ABC$; AP, BQ and CS are perpendiculars (altitudes) meeting at H. Mark X, the mid-point of BC, and E, the mid-point of AH. Find angles equal to $E\hat{Q}A$ and to $X\hat{Q}C$; hence prove that $E\hat{Q}X$ is a right-angle. (Use the fact that $A\ Q\ H\ S$ lie on a circle.)

2. If Y is the mid-point of AC, prove that $E\hat{Y}X$ is a right-angle.

3. Prove that EX is a diameter of the nine-point circle.

Calculations: In Fig. 12, AD is a diameter, and $BDCH$ is a parallelogram, so that $BH = CD$.

$A\hat{D}C = \hat{B}$ (same segment).

R is the radius of the circle.

$\therefore BH = CD = 2R.\cos\hat{B}$.

Likewise $AH = 2R.\cos\hat{A}$,

$CH = 2R.\cos\hat{C}$.

For the length of AP, show that $\triangle APC$, $\triangle ABD$ are similar;

$$\therefore \frac{AP}{AB} = \frac{AC}{AD}, \text{ so that}$$

$$AP = \frac{bc}{2R}$$

Compare this with the formula for the area, $\frac{abc,}{4R}$ and show that they agree.

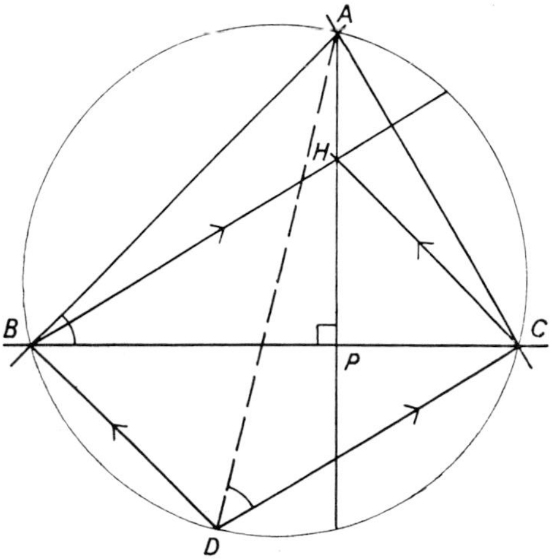

FIG. 12

EXERCISE 5E

In Fig. 13 R is the radius of the circle; AP is perpendicular to BC, and cuts the circle at K, and AD is a diameter.

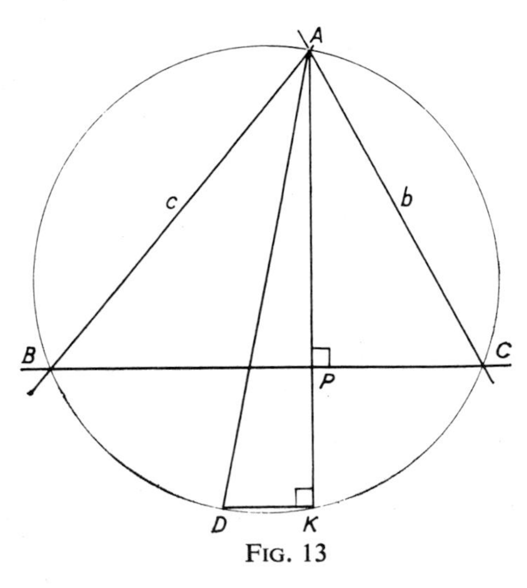

FIG. 13

1. Prove that $KD \parallel BC$.

2. If B is $40°$ and C is $63°$, show that $K\hat{A}C = D\hat{A}B$, and calculate $D\hat{A}K$.

3. Whatever sizes the angles are, prove that $D\hat{A}K = \hat{C} - \hat{B}$, and that $DK = 2R.\sin(\hat{C} - \hat{B})$.

4. Show that

$$DK = BP - PC = \frac{c^2 - b^2}{a}$$

5. $BC = 2R.\sin\hat{A}$; use the previous results to show that:

$$\frac{c^2 - b^2}{a^2} = \frac{\sin(\hat{C} - \hat{B})}{\sin\hat{A}}$$

More About Altitudes

The three altitudes of a triangle—or are there six?

Given: AX, BY, CZ are the altitudes of $\triangle ABC$, and that they meet in a point H (Fig. 14).

H is the "orthocentre" of $\triangle ABC$.

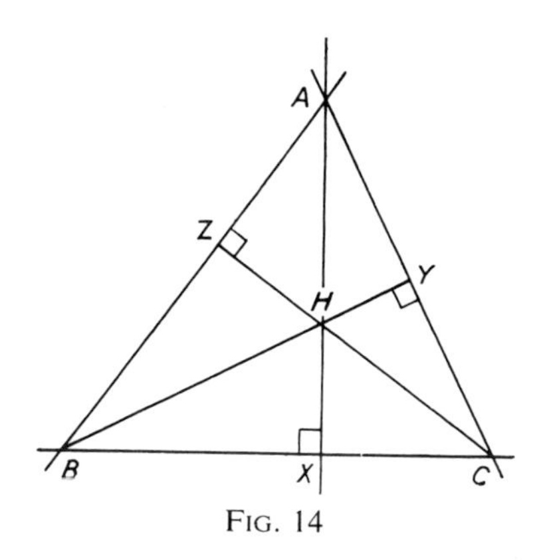

FIG. 14

Now look at the $\triangle$ HBC, which has an angle at H greater than a right-angle. The altitudes of this triangle are HA, BA, CA, and two of them are right outside the $\triangle HBC$; so A is now the orthocentre, and it is outside its triangle.

Here is a figure made of four points A B C H, joined by six lines. Take any three of the lines as "the triangle," then the other three are the perpendiculars; or take any three of the points as the triangle, the fourth one is its orthocentre.

The four points are on a completely equal footing; if you change any two of them over, it makes no difference.

EXERCISE 5F

1. In Fig. 10, prove that $\triangle HBC$, $\triangle KBC$ are congruent. From this fact, deduce another property of the four points A B C H: the four circles drawn through any three of them are all equal.

2. In Fig. 10, draw the line PS, and prove that no fewer than four angles are all equal: $Q\hat{C}H$, $Q\hat{P}H$, $H\hat{B}S$, $H\hat{P}S$. Hence, PH bisects the angle QPS. Now you can prove that H is the centre of the circle that touches the sides of $\triangle PQS$.

3. There are in fact four circles that touch these three lines; their centres are H, A, B, C. As a drawing exercise, construct these four circles.

Theorem II—Simson's Line

And who was Simson? Robert Simson was Professor of Mathematics at Edinburgh, and just over two hundred years ago he published the first really good book in English on Geometry. Most English geometry books are still based on this; and here is one of his theorems:

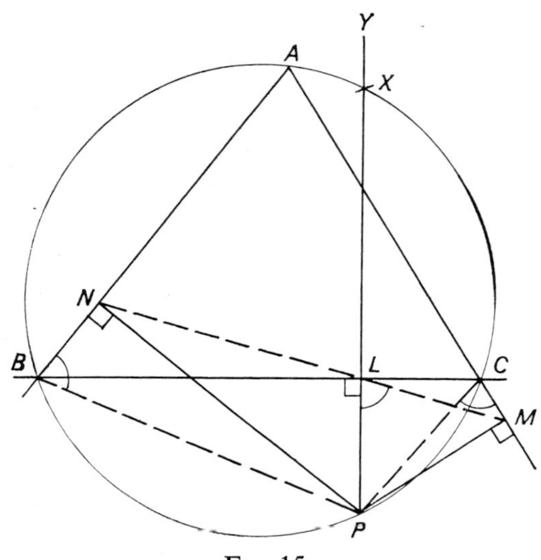

FIG. 15

Given: $\triangle ABC$, P any point on the circle through A, B, C.
PL, PM, PN are perpendiculars on the sides of the triangle.

Prove: L, M, N, lie on a straight line.

Construction: Join LM, LN, PB, PC (Fig. 15).

Proof: $P\,L\,C\,M$ lie on a circle (right-angles at L and M).

$\therefore P\hat{L}M = P\hat{C}M$

$= P\hat{B}A$ ($A\,B\,P\,C$ cyclic)

$P\,L\,N\,B$ lie on a circle.

$\therefore P\hat{L}N + P\hat{B}A = 180°$

$\therefore P\hat{L}N + P\hat{L}M = 180°$

and LMN is a straight line.

Another way is to produce PL to a point X, and prove by using the same cyclic quadrilaterals ($PMCL$ and $PLNB$) that $P\hat{L}M = P\hat{C}M$

$= P\hat{B}A$

$= N\hat{L}X$

Then, since two vertically opposite angles at L are equal, NLM is straight.

EXERCISE 5G

1. Write out in full the proof just suggested for Theorem II.

2. In Fig. 15, X is the point where the line PL meets the circle. Prove that AX is parallel to MLN.

In- and Ex-circles

Fig. 16 is the in-circle figure. To construct it, draw AI to bisect the angle $\hat{A}$, BI to bisect the angle $\hat{B}$. IX, IY, IZ are perpendiculars on BC, CA, AB.

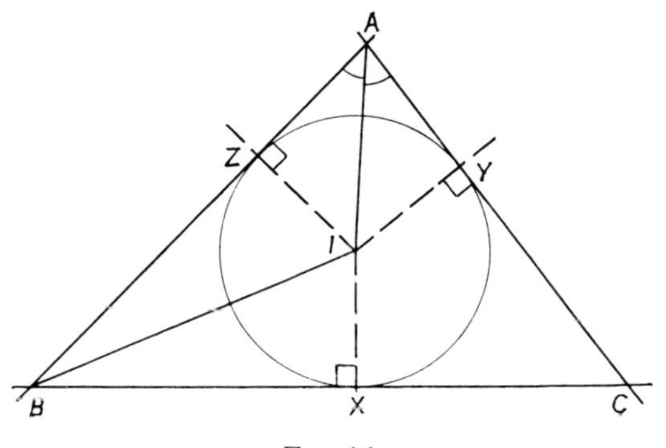

FIG. 16

$$\triangle AIY \equiv \triangle AIZ \text{ (S A A)}.$$
$$\therefore IY = IZ, \text{ and likewise } = IX.$$

I is the centre of the circle that touches the three sides of $\triangle ABC$. Notice another set of three lines which meet at a point; for

$$\triangle ICY \equiv \triangle ICX, \text{ so } CI \text{ bisects the angle } \hat{C}.$$

The bisectors of the three angles of a triangle meet at a point.

IX is the radius of the circle; call this r.

The area of the $\triangle ABC = \triangle IBC + \triangle ICA + \triangle IAB$

$$= r.\tfrac{1}{2}a + r.\tfrac{1}{2}b + r.\tfrac{1}{2}c$$
$$= r.\left(\frac{a+b+c}{2}\right)$$

This is generally written $r.s$; s is the "semi-perimeter."

Four circles touch the sides of a triangle. Fig. 17 shows one of the "ex-circles"; its centre is found by drawing AI to bisect the angle $\hat{A}$, and BL to bisect the external angle at B, $C\hat{B}X$; they cut at L, the centre of this circle. N, M are centres of two other circles, each of them touching the lines BC, CA, AB.

Notice that $BL \perp BM$ (why?), and that I, L, M, N, form the same figure as Fig. 14, a triangle and its orthocentre.

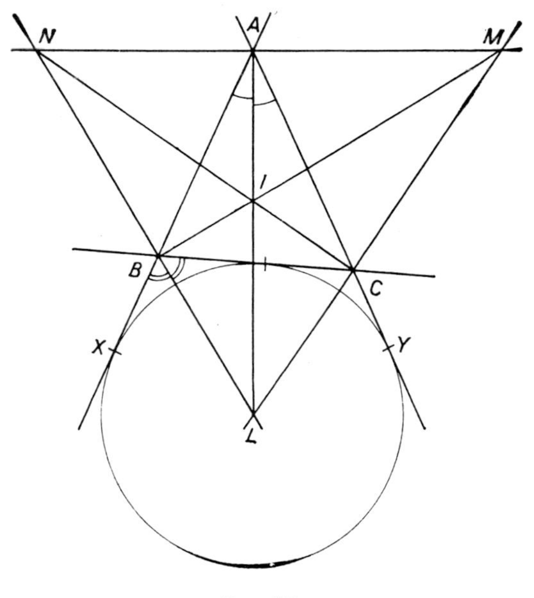

FIG. 17

EXERCISE 5H

1. Show that $A\hat{L}B = \frac{1}{2}\hat{C}$.

2. Show that AX, AY, tangents, each $= s$, and that the radius of the ex-circle $= \dfrac{\triangle}{s - a}$

3. If MN is parallel to BC, prove that $AB = AC$.

A Calculation

The sides of a triangle are 13, 14, 15 in. How can you calculate the angles? Draw $AP \perp BC$; call BP x in., PC y in., and AP h in. (Fig. 18).

Then first, $x + y = 14$

$$\text{Also } \left.\begin{aligned} x^2 + h^2 &= 15^2 \\ y^2 + h^2 &= 13^2 \end{aligned}\right\} \therefore\ x^2 - y^2 = 15^2 - 13^2 = 56$$

Since $x^2 - y^2 = (x + y)(x - y)$,

we have $x + y = 14$

$x - y = 4$

$\therefore x = 9,\ y = 5$

Look at the right-angled $\triangle ABP$.

$$\text{Cos } \hat{B} = \frac{x}{15} = \cdot 6.$$

$\triangle APC$ shows that $\cos \hat{C} = \dfrac{y}{13} = \dfrac{5}{13} = \cdot 3846$

The table of natural cosines gives $\hat{B} = 53° \, 8'$, $\hat{C} = 67° \, 23'$; $\hat{A} = 59° \, 29'$.

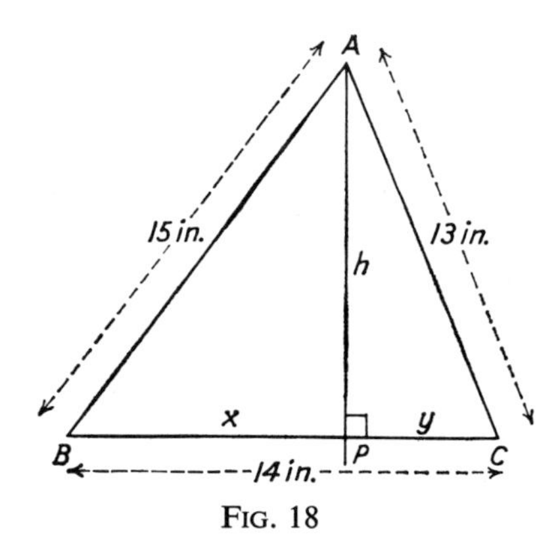

FIG. 18

EXERCISE 5J

1. Repeat this calculation for a triangle with sides 8, 7, 5 in. (make $BC =$ 8 in.).

2. Take $BC = 33$ in., the other sides 65 and 56 in.

3. Make the sides 7, 13, 17 in. (Here you had better use logs.)

4. Suppose that $BC = 5$ in., $c = 12$ in., $b = 8$ in., and we press on as before.

$$x^2 - y^2 = 80$$
$$x + y = 5$$
$$\text{then } x - y = 16$$

This gives the curious result, $x = 10\frac{1}{2}$, $y = -5\frac{1}{2}$

which leads to $\cos \hat{B} = \dfrac{10\frac{1}{2}}{12}$, $\cos \hat{C} = \dfrac{-5\frac{1}{2}}{8}$. Does this make sense?

On making the drawing, you find that $\hat{C}$ of the triangle is obtuse. So in order to talk about obtuse angles, you have to realize that the cosine of an obtuse angle is a negative number. You could, of course, work out from the drawing the cosine of the outside angle at C, and then take this away from 180°; but it is often necessary to use cosines and sines of obtuse angles, and the fact is that $\cos X = -\cos(180° - X)$.

You will find, in the section on Trigonometry, that the sine of an obtuse angle is positive. Here we give two illustrations of this:

In Fig. 7 (page 381), the perpendicular $AN = c . \sin \hat{B} = b . \sin \hat{C}$.

In Fig. 19 you are "seeing double." Each of the lengths AC, $AC' = c$, and each of the triangles ABC, ABC' has the same perpendicular height AN; it does not matter whether you call AN $c.\sin A\hat{C}B$ or $c.\sin A\hat{C}'B$ (obtuse).

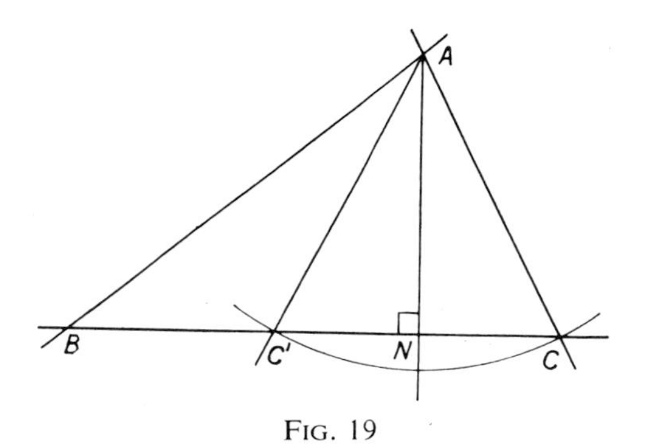

FIG. 19

Fig. 20 illustrates the formula $a = 2R.\sin \hat{A}$. The point A' is on the opposite arc of the circle, and the angle $\hat{A}' = 180° - \hat{A}$. If the angle $\hat{A}'$ is

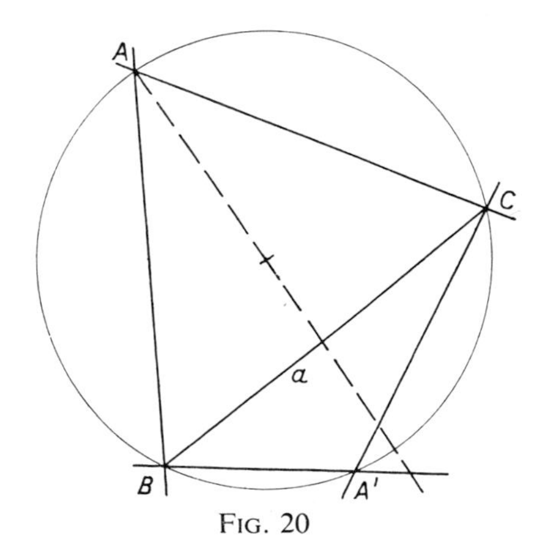

FIG. 20

to have a sine, the only statement that will make sense is $a = 2R.\sin \hat{A}'$, and again $\sin \hat{A}' = \sin(180° - \hat{A}) = \sin \hat{A}$.

Three Lines Which Meet in a Point

So far we have had:

1. The perpendicular bisectors of three sides of a triangle.
2. The lines bisecting the angles.

3. The medians, joining each vertex to the mid-point of the opposite side.
4. The perpendiculars, or altitudes.

Each is a set of three lines meeting in a point; No. 1 is a case by itself, but in 2, 3 and 4 the lines are drawn from the corners of the triangle. They are all "special cases," for you can draw three such lines in all kinds of positions.

Here is a general theorem about this, and another one about three points which lie on a straight line.

Theorem III—Ceva's Theorem

Given: $\triangle ABC$; AX, BY, CZ meet in a point S, and meet the opposite sides at X, Y, Z (Fig. 21).

Prove: $\dfrac{BX}{XC}\cdot\dfrac{CY}{YA}\cdot\dfrac{AZ}{ZB} = 1$

This seems an odd thing to prove, and hardly to be expected; but there are two quite simple ways of proving it, and it turns out that the result combines in one all the cases 2, 3, 4, and indeed many others.

Proof: There are three triangles BSC, CSA, ASB; we want their areas.

(1) Draw BH, CK perpendicular, on the line AS.

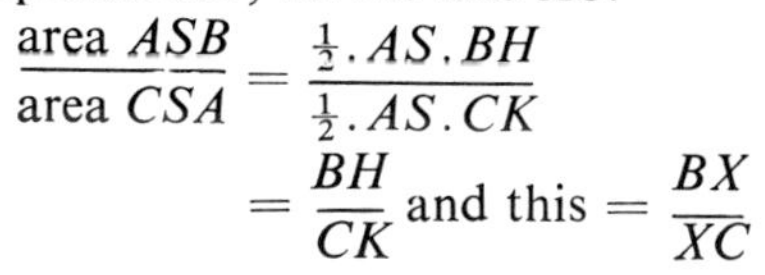

$$\frac{\text{area } ASB}{\text{area } CSA} = \frac{\frac{1}{2}.AS.BH}{\frac{1}{2}.AS.CK}$$

$$= \frac{BH}{CK} \text{ and this } = \frac{BX}{XC}$$

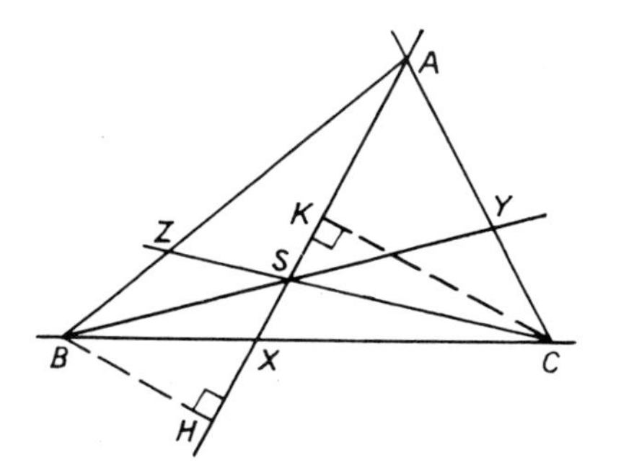

FIG. 21

because $\triangle BHX$, $\triangle CKX$ are similar.

Likewise $$\frac{\text{area } CSA}{\text{area } BSC} = \frac{AZ}{ZB}$$

$$\frac{\text{area } BSC}{\text{area } ASB} = \frac{CY}{YA}$$

Multiply these three ratios together, and you have the result:

$$1 - \frac{BX}{XC} \cdot \frac{CY}{YA} \cdot \frac{AZ}{ZB}$$

See how this looks in the special cases:

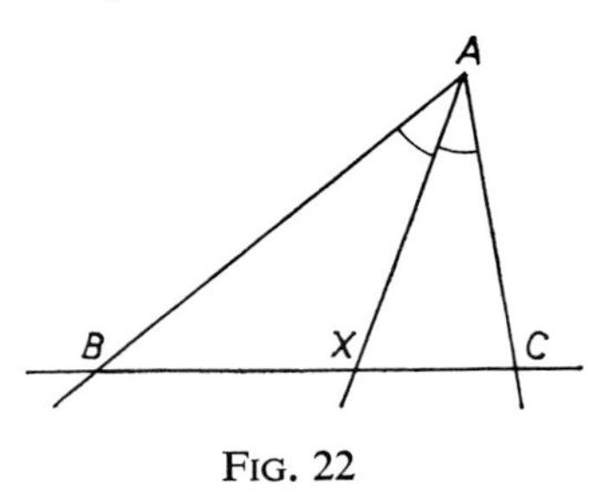

FIG. 22

(2) AX bisects the angle $\hat{A}$ etc. then $\dfrac{BX}{XC} = \dfrac{c}{b}$ (Fig. 22):

Now the product $\dfrac{BX}{XC} \cdot \dfrac{CY}{YA} \cdot \dfrac{AZ}{ZB} = \dfrac{c}{b} \cdot \dfrac{b}{a} \cdot \dfrac{a}{c}$

and this is certainly equal to 1.

(3) $AX \perp BC$, etc.

This time $BX = c.\cos \hat{B}$, $XC = b.\cos \hat{C}$ and

$$\frac{BX}{XC} \cdot \frac{CY}{YA} \cdot \frac{AZ}{ZB} = \frac{c.\cos \hat{B}}{b.\cos \hat{C}} \cdot \frac{a.\cos \hat{C}}{c.\cos \hat{A}} \cdot \frac{b.\cos \hat{A}}{a.\cos \hat{B}}$$
$$= 1.$$

(4) X, Y, Z, the mid-points of the sides.

Here, of course, $\dfrac{BX}{XC} = 1$, and so do the other two ratios.

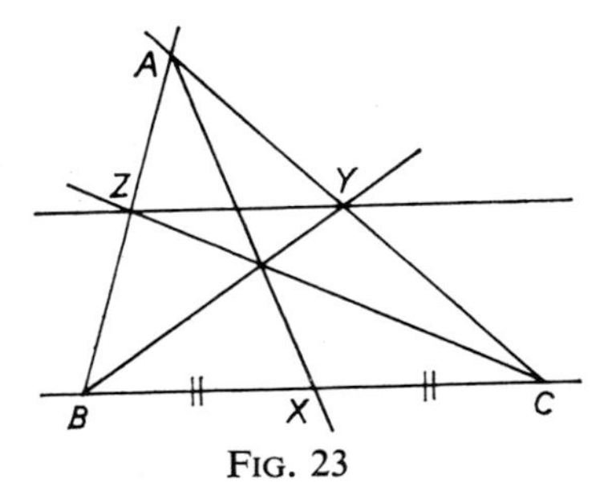

FIG. 23

Here is a nice example; given a line BC, and its mid-point X, draw XA in any direction and join AB, AC; then, as in Fig. 23, draw BY, CZ through any point on XA, to meet the opposite sides of $\triangle ABC$ at Y, Z.

YZ is parallel to BC; for $\dfrac{CY}{YA}\cdot\dfrac{AZ}{ZB}\cdot\dfrac{BX}{XC} = 1$, and $BX = XC$

$$\therefore \frac{AY}{YC} = \frac{AZ}{ZB} \therefore YZ \parallel BC.$$

This makes it possible to draw parallel lines, at any distance apart, using a straight edge only. The "ruler" must have two marks on its edge, so that you can make $BX = XC$; mark a point Y in any position you like, and complete a figure like Fig. 23.

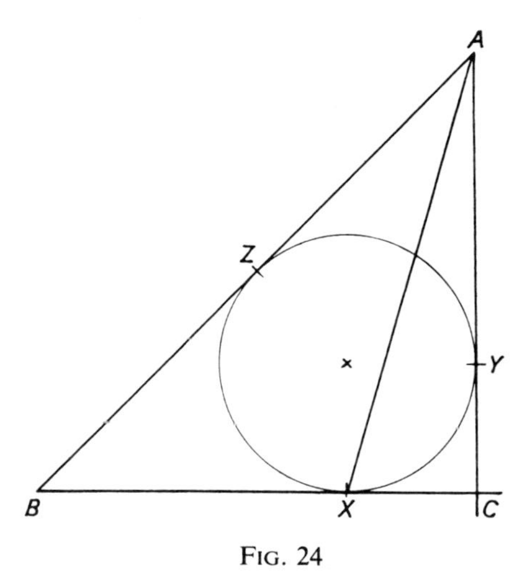

FIG. 24

Given: $\triangle ABC$; a circle touching the sides of the triangle at X, Y, Z (Fig. 24).
Prove: AX, BY, CZ meet at a point.
Proof: $BX = ZB$ (tangents)

$XC = CY$, and $YA = AZ$

So the product $\dfrac{BX}{XC}$ etc. does $= 1$.

This seems to agree with Theorem III; but the facts are the wrong way round.

Can we prove:

Theorem IV (*Converse of Theorem III*)

Given: $\triangle ABC$, points X, Y, Z on the sides, and $\dfrac{BX}{XC}\cdot\dfrac{CY}{YA}\cdot\dfrac{AZ}{ZB} = 1$

Prove: AX, BY, CZ meet at a point.

Proof: Let O be the point where AX meets BY, and suppose the line CO to meet AB at K. By Theorem III, $\dfrac{BX}{XC}\cdot\dfrac{CY}{YA}\cdot\dfrac{AK}{KB} = 1$

$$\frac{AZ}{ZB}=\frac{AK}{KB}$$

So, if Z, K are both between A and B (or both outside AB) then Z is the same point as K.

All right so far—but there is another answer; AX and BY may not meet at all, they may be parallel. If so, then CZ will be parallel to each of them.

An Easier Method

This kind of proof is not so simple. There is a method which is rather easier, for both theorems.

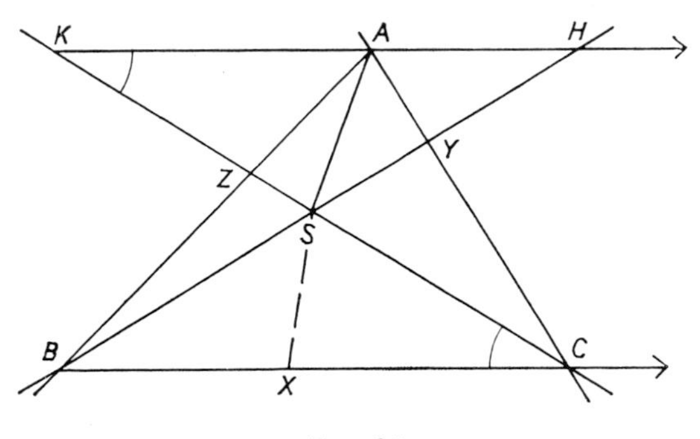

FIG. 25

Study Fig. 25; in this figure, we find a single ratio,

$$\frac{AK}{AH}, \text{ which is equal to } \frac{CY}{YA}\cdot\frac{AZ}{ZB}$$

Begin with $\triangle ABC$, and straight lines BY, CZ crossing at S.

Draw the line HAK through A, parallel to BC, to cut BY at H, and CZ at K. This is the construction used in the two proofs below.

$$\frac{CY}{YA}=\frac{BC}{AH} \text{ and } \frac{AZ}{ZB}=\frac{AK}{BC}, \text{ by parallels.}$$

Multiply these together:

$$\frac{CY}{YA}\cdot\frac{AZ}{ZB}=\frac{AK}{AH}$$

For Theorem III

Given: . . . AS cuts BC at X.

Prove: $\frac{BX}{XC}\cdot\frac{CY}{YA}\cdot\frac{AZ}{ZB}=1$

Construction: As in Fig. 25.

Proof: We have only to prove that $\frac{BX}{XC} = \frac{AH}{AK}$

But $\frac{BX}{AH} = \frac{SX}{AS}$ by parallels; or, because $\triangle BXS$, $\triangle HAS$ are similar. And this $= \frac{XC}{AK}$ by parallels; or, because $\triangle XSC$, $\triangle ASK$ are similar.

$\frac{BX}{XC}$ does $= \frac{AH}{AK}$, and the product of the other two ratios $= \frac{AK}{AH}$

For Theorem IV

Given: $\ldots \frac{BX}{XC} \cdot \frac{CY}{YA} \cdot \frac{AZ}{ZB} = 1.$

Prove: That AX, BY, CZ meet in a point.

Construction: As in Fig. 25.

Proof: We have to prove that AX passes through S. What will prove this? Since CSK is a straight line, it will be enough to show either that $A\hat{S}K = C\hat{S}X$,
or that $K\hat{A}S = S\hat{X}C$.

These statements are both true if $\triangle ASK$, $\triangle XSC$ are similar.

But $\frac{BX}{XC} = \frac{AH}{AK}$,

because $\frac{CY}{YA} \cdot \frac{AZ}{ZB} = \frac{AK}{AH}$

$\therefore \frac{BC}{XC} = \frac{HK}{AK}$

$\therefore \frac{XC}{AK} = \frac{BC}{HK} = \frac{SC}{KS}$ ($\triangle BSC$, $\triangle HSK$).

Also $S\hat{C}X = S\hat{K}A$ by parallels.

$\therefore$ $\triangle XSC$, $\triangle ASK$ are similar (S A S).

Three Points Which Lie on a Straight Line

Theorem V (*Menelaus' Theorem*)

Given: $\triangle ABC$; a straight line cuts BC at P, CA at Q and AB at R.

Prove: $\frac{BP}{PC} \cdot \frac{CQ}{QA} \cdot \frac{AR}{RB} = -1$

Why must this be -1?

Look at a single line through points B, C. Is there a point on it, P such that $\frac{BP}{PC} = \frac{3}{2}$?

Yes, but unluckily there are two of them (Fig. 26a).

To tell one from the other, we count lengths in one direction, BP, PC, BP_1 as plus, and lengths in the opposite direction, P_1C for instance, as minus, and write:

$$\frac{BP}{PC} = +\frac{3}{2} \qquad \frac{BP_1}{P_1C} = -\frac{3}{2}$$

In Fig. 26b, the point P is outside BC; and wherever the line PQR is drawn, it will cut one of the lines BC, CA, AB at an outside point, so we write one of the ratios with a minus sign.

It may cut all three at outside points; so, in every position, the product of the three ratios is minus.

Construction: Draw $BX \parallel CA$, to cut the line PQR at X.

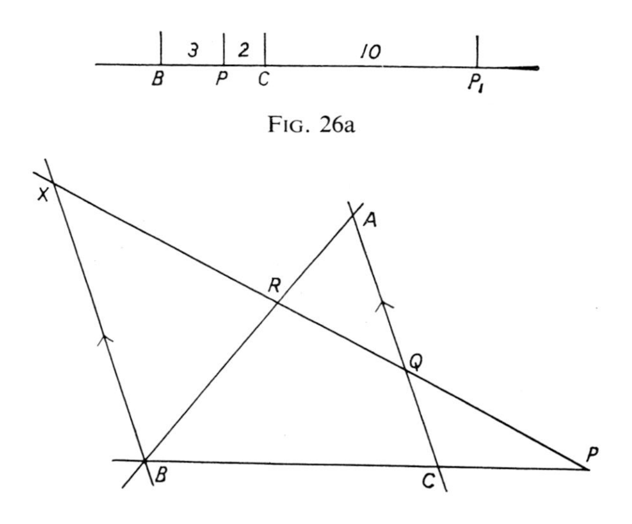

FIG. 26a

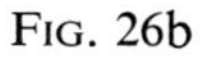

FIG. 26b

Proof: By parallels, $\dfrac{BP}{CP} = \dfrac{BX}{CQ}, \dfrac{AR}{RB} = \dfrac{QA}{BX}$

$$\frac{BP}{CP}\cdot\frac{CQ}{QA}\cdot\frac{AR}{RB} = \frac{BX}{CQ}\cdot\frac{CQ}{QA}\cdot\frac{QA}{BX} = 1$$

$$\text{Or, } \frac{BP}{PC}\cdot\frac{CQ}{QA}\cdot\frac{AR}{RB} = -\mathbf{1}.$$

OCL/M2—2B

CHAPTER 6

LOCUS: THE PATH OF A MOVING POINT

ONE WAY to learn Geometry is to study the drawings and arguments that are printed in a book. This is all very well, but it is not enough. You need to draw the figures yourself; then you see the point of the pencil moving, along a straight line, a circle, or some other curve.

What you draw depends on how you control the pencil. Let your arm swing freely, without trying to guide the movement at all, and you will probably make a curve like Fig. 1; it is not likely to be part of a circle, in fact it will be part of the curve in Fig. 2, which you can also draw "freehand." It can be drawn exactly as a graph. This curve is the path, or "locus," of a ball thrown up in the air, at an angle.

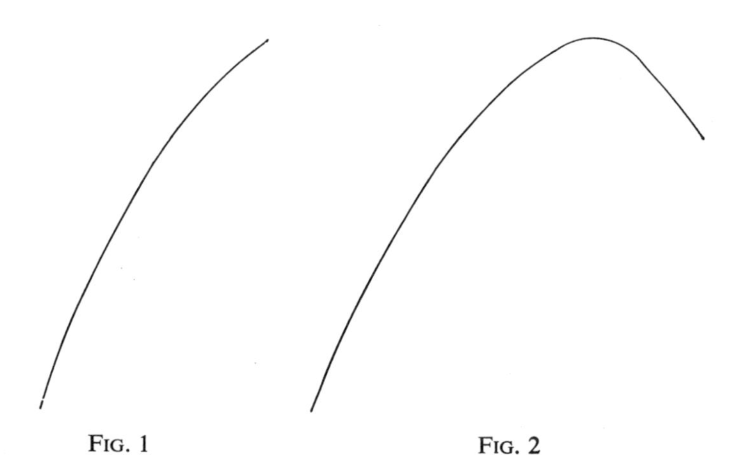

FIG. 1 FIG. 2

EXERCISE 6A

To Draw a Locus on Paper

1. O is a fixed point, and $OP = 2$ in. P can move round a circle with centre O and radius 2 in. You would naturally control its movement by using compasses, but you could do so just as well with a shapeless piece of cardboard with two small holes in it, by sticking a pin through one hole, to fix its position on the paper, and a pencil-point through the other. All that matters is to keep P at a constant distance from O; you can even draw a fairly good circle in the soil, with two pegs and a piece of string.

Is this circle the complete locus of P? Yes, if P must be on the paper. No, if P can move in space; the complete locus is the surface of a sphere, with O at the centre.

2. If OP is to be *not more than* 2 in., the locus of P is quite different; P can move about anywhere inside the circle, and its locus is the area bounded by the circle. (In space, it is the whole volume enclosed by the sphere.)

3. A, B are two fixed points, and $PA = PB$. Draw the line which bisects AB at right-angles (MN in Fig. 3). If P is any point on this bisector, $PA = PB$. But if not?

Take P somewhere else; suppose that P, A are on the same side of MN, then PB will cross MN at a point X. $AX = XB$.

But $PB = PX + AX$
$> PA$ (Two sides of $\triangle APX$ are PX, AX.)

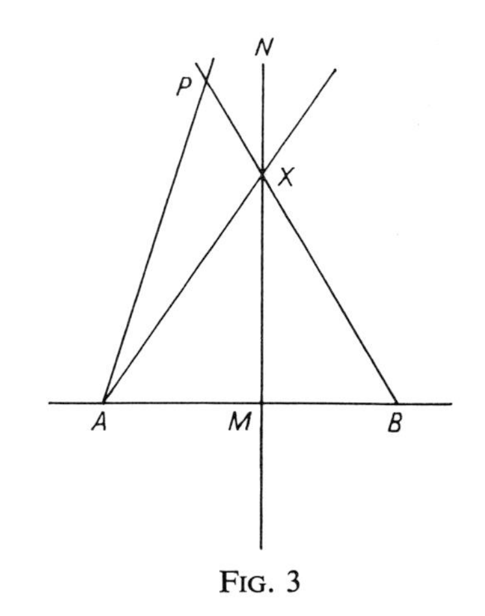

FIG. 3

So, the perpendicular bisector of AB is the complete locus; if P is on the line through M, N then PA is equal to PB, and if P is not on this line, PA is not equal to PB.

When you think you have found a locus, always look again to make sure that there isn't any more of it—as in the following examples.

4. AB is part of an endless straight line. P moves so that its distance from the nearest point of this line is 2 in. This means the perpendicular distance, and P can move along a line parallel to AB. But this is not all of its path; there are two lines, each parallel to AB and 2 in. distant; so the locus of P is a pair of lines.

5. If P can move in three dimensions, what is the locus in No. 3 and No. 4?

We shall not be concerned with movement in space, but only in the plane of the paper; but it is always worth while to think out the "Three-D" locus.

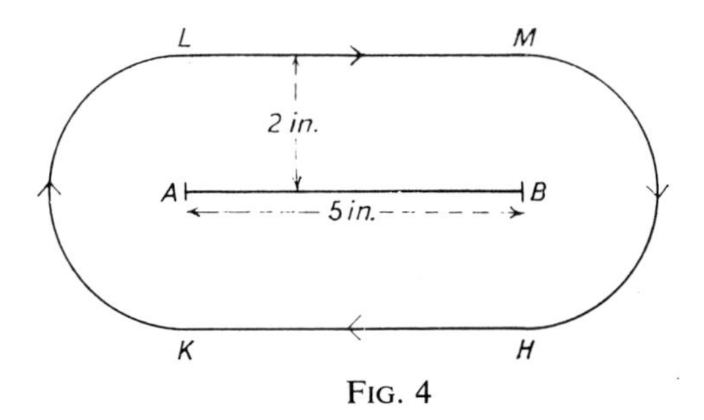

FIG. 4

6. Suppose that AB is a straight line 5 in. long, and P is to be 2 in. from the nearest point of AB. Part of P's path is the pair of lines HK, LM (Fig. 4), but this is not the whole path. P moves from H to K, and then, in order to keep 2 in. from the *nearest* point of AB, it must go round a semicircle, centre A and radius 2 in., till it reaches L. It will travel right round the curve shown in the figure.

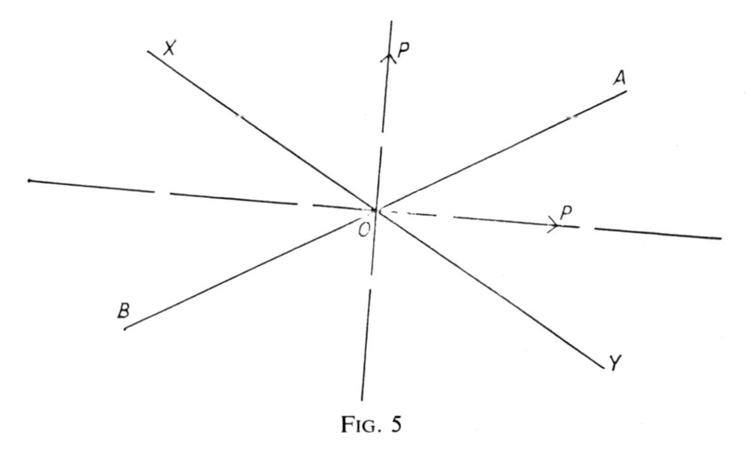

FIG. 5

7. A, B are fixed and the angles $P\hat{A}B$, $P\hat{B}A$ are equal. Surely this will give the same locus for P as in No. 3? Not if you allow "zero angles."

8. ABC is a fixed triangle with $AB = AC$, and P moves so that $A\hat{P}B = A\hat{P}C$. The same locus again? No, there are four parts to the locus of P (and no zero angles this time).

9. Two fixed lines AOB, XOY cross at O. P is equidistant from the two lines; that is, the perpendiculars from P on the two lines are equal (Fig. 5).

Then OP will bisect the angle at O. But which angle? There are four angles at O, and two straight lines bisect them. P can move anywhere on these two lines. (And nowhere else?)

Making Constructions

To draw a triangle is easy; you are not bound by any measurements, you simply draw three straight lines, but make sure that they all cross.

To draw a triangle with one side 3 in. does limit you a little; one side must be drawn to the right length, but the third vertex can be anywhere.

If one side AB has to be 3 in., and another AC to be 4 in., you draw AB first, and then C must be 4 in. from A—in what direction? It doesn't matter; but C must be somewhere on a circle with centre A and radius 4 in. C has a locus, then.

If AB is 3 in., and $B\hat{A}C$ is 30°, C can be as far away as you like, but it is limited to one straight line from A, on either side of AB, making an angle 30° with AB.

These two lines are, this time, the locus of C.

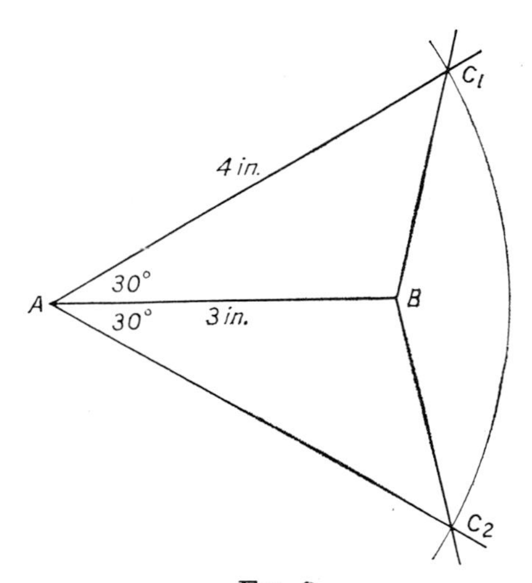

FIG. 6

To draw $\triangle ABC$, with AB 3 in., AC 4 in., and $B\hat{A}C$ 30°, the first step is to draw AB the right length. Then draw the two paths, and C is the point where they cross. Notice that there are two triangles possible; they are exactly alike, though one of them is upside down (Fig. 6).

In every construction you have to locate one point, or more than one. The measurements given will limit the point to a certain path, and if the figure can be drawn exactly, there will be two measurements, each of them limiting a point to move on a certain locus. So part of every construction is to draw two loci, and find where they cross.

EXERCISE 6B

1. Draw $\triangle ABC$, with $\hat{A}$ 30°, AB 4 in., and BC (opposite $\hat{A}$) $2\frac{1}{2}$ in.

In Fig. 7, one locus for C is the line AX, the other locus is a circle, centre B, radius $2\frac{1}{2}$ in. These two loci cross twice; there are two possible triangles, not exactly alike, $\triangle ABC_1$ and $\triangle ABC_2$ (Fig. 7).

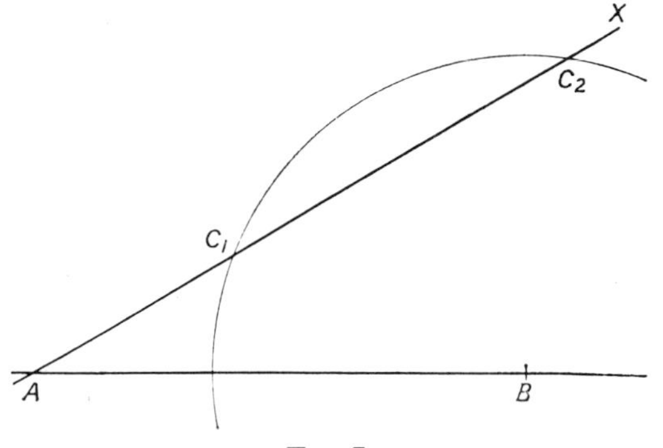

FIG. 7

2. What loci need be drawn to make a square with sides each 2 in.?

3. How many positions can be found for a point, so that its shortest distance from the (endless) line through A, B is 2 in., and its distance from A is 3 in.?

4. PQ is a given line, and $P\hat{X}Q$ is 30°. Show that X can move on part of a circle, whose centre is at a point R, and that $\triangle PQR$ is equilateral.

Why can X not move right round the circle? How much of the circle is "out of bounds"? Sketch the complete locus.

5. P is equidistant from the lines AB, AC, which are not equal; and is also equidistant from the points B, C. Draw two loci, and find the point P.

Prove that P lies on the circle through A, B, C.

Theorem I

Given: A fixed line AB. $A\hat{X}B$ is a given size (call it x).

Prove: The locus of X consists of two arcs of circles.

The idea that floats into your mind is "angles in the same segment," and so:

Construction: Draw $BC \perp AB$; make $B\hat{A}C = 90° - x$; then $A\hat{C}B = x$, so C is a point on the locus. Construct the circle through A, B, C (its centre is the mid-point of AC, Fig. 8).

Compare Fig. 4, Chapter 3.

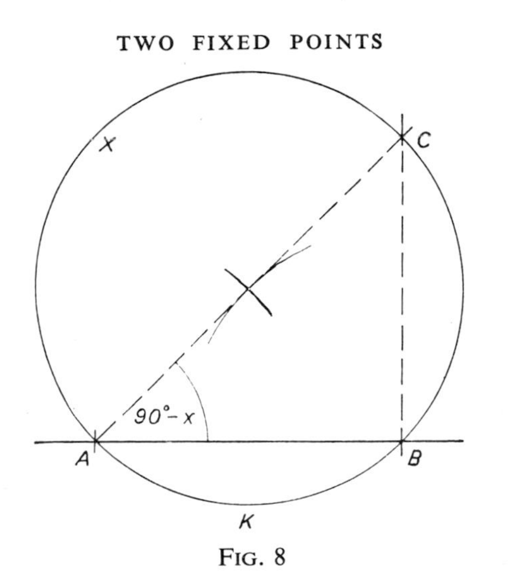

FIG. 8

Proof: Let X be any point on the arc ACB of this circle.

$$A\hat{X}B = A\hat{C}B \text{ in the same segment}$$
$$= x.$$

$\therefore$ X may move anywhere on this arc; but not on the other arc AKB, since $A\hat{K}B = 180° - x$.

The complete locus consists of this arc and another arc exactly like it, on the opposite side of AB (its "image" in AB).

EXERCISE 6C

1. What is the locus of X, if $A\hat{X}B$ is a right-angle?

2. Draw BC, $2\frac{1}{2}$ in. Construct an arc of a circle through B, C, so that BC subtends an angle of 30° at all points on the arc. Find two points on the arc which are 4 in. from B.

(Compare this with Exercise 6A, No. 8.)

3. Construct a quadrilateral $PQRS$, with PQ 3 in., PS $2\frac{1}{2}$ in., PR 4 in., $Q\hat{P}S$ 60°, $Q\hat{R}S$ 60°.

(R is the point where two loci cross.)

Two Fixed Points

A, B are fixed, and P can move in a limited way. We know the locus of P if $PA = PB$; but what happens if $PA = 2.PB$?

Theorem II

Given: Two points A, B; $PA = 2.PB$.

Prove: The locus of P is a circle!

Where is its centre, and what is its radius? Begin by marking a few points;

in Fig. 9, AB is 3 in.; by drawing pairs of arcs, you can make PA 4 in., PB 2 in.; PA 3 in., PB $1\frac{1}{2}$ in., and so on. Each time you get two positions for P, above AB and below it. It seems as if P moves round an oval curve.

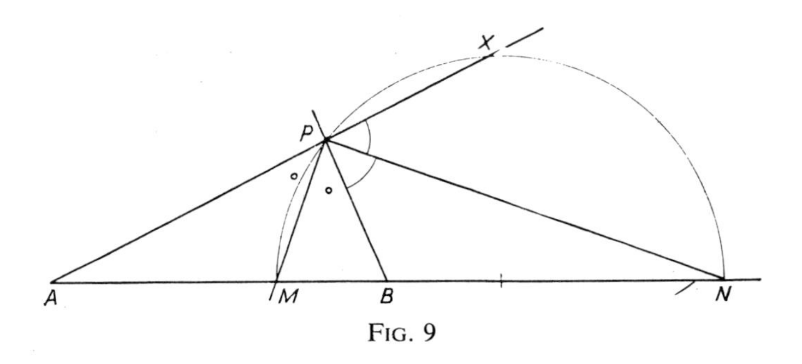

FIG. 9

Two positions for P are actually on the line AB, namely at M and N where AM is 2 in., MB 1 in.; AN 6 in., NB 3 in.

Construction: Mark the two points M, N. Take any point P so that $PA = 2.PB$, and join P to each of the fixed points A, B, M, N.

Proof: $\dfrac{PA}{PB} = \dfrac{AM}{MB}$

$\therefore$ PM bisects $A\hat{P}B$.

Likewise PN bisects the exterior angle, $B\hat{P}X$.

$M\hat{P}N$ is half $A\hat{P}X$, i.e. it is a right-angle.

$\therefore$ The locus of P is a circle with diameter MN.

EXERCISE 6D

1. In Fig. 9, if AB is 4 in., and $\dfrac{AP}{PB} = \dfrac{5}{3}$, find the points M, N, and the distance MN.

2. AB is a fixed length, and P moves so that $\dfrac{PA}{PB}$ is constant and greater than 1, so that the locus of P is a circle. For a different value of the constant ratio, you get a different circle.

Show that the bigger the ratio, the smaller the circle will be, and that the smaller circles are completely inside the bigger ones.

3. What is the locus of P if $\dfrac{PA}{PB}$ is:

(i) very big; (ii) 1; (iii) less than 1; (iv) zero?

4. Sketch Fig. 9 again, and mark C, the mid-point of AB, and D, the mid-point of MN. Draw circles on diameters AB, MN. Let K be one of the points where these circles cross, and prove that $C\hat{K}D$ is a right-angle.

Two Loci Traced by Marking Poin s

(1) Mark AB 2 in. apart, and mark a number of points P so that $AP + PB = 4$ in. each time. All these points make a dotted curve; sometimes this is the only way to "describe" a curve. Some books even say that a locus is nothing more than a set of points; but as no one can possibly mark an infinite number of points, it is better to think of a locus as the path of a point which moves, and which can be traced out complete, usually, by some simple "mechanism."

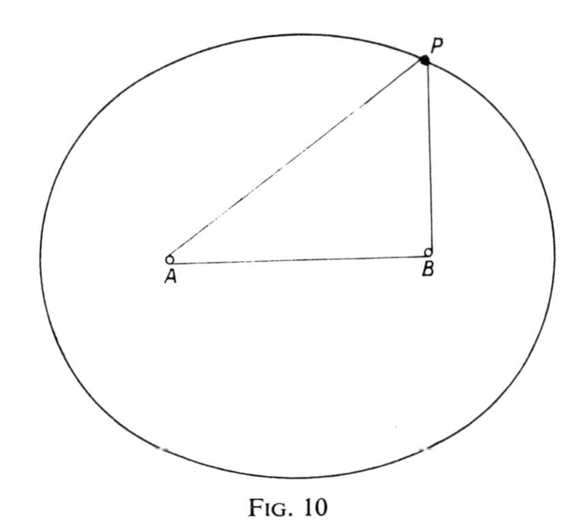

FIG. 10

For this curve, the gardener's method is effective, with two pegs and a loop of string. To imitate it, lay the paper on a board, stick two pins in firmly, 2 in. apart, and make a loop of thin string or strong thread 6 in. long (Fig. 10). P is the point of a pencil, holding the string taut, so that

$$AP + PB = 4 \text{ in.}$$

Move the pencil as far as the string allows, and it traces out the locus of P, an oval curve (an ellipse).

Ellipses are not, like circles, all the same shape. The shadow of a circular disc, cast on a wall, is usually an ellipse. By holding the disc at various angles, you make shadow-ellipses of different widths, from a mere straight line up to a full circle.

(2) Whenever you draw a graph, you are drawing a locus, and you do this by marking as many points as you need, and then drawing the smoothest curve you can, through the points.

The graph for $8y = x^2$, marked out point by point, is a good example. It is the same curve as the curve in Fig. 2.

Two Points Again

In Fig. 11, $AM = 5$ in., $MB = 2$ in. and $MP \perp AB$. Then

$$PA^2 = PM^2 + 25 \text{ (Pythagoras' Theorem)}$$
$$PB^2 = PM^2 + 4$$
$$PA^2 - PB^2 = 21$$

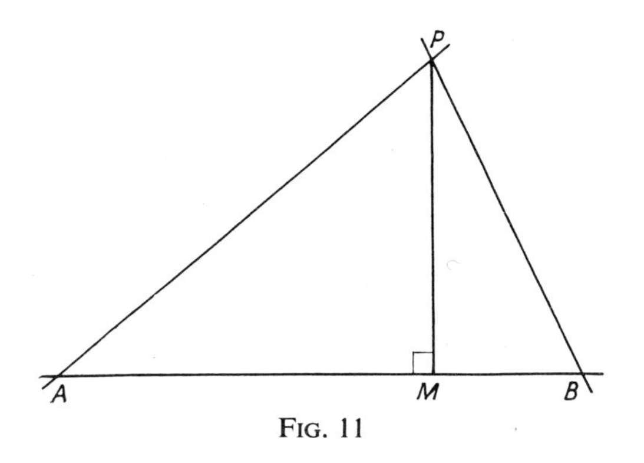

FIG. 11

Does it follow that, given $PA^2 - PB^2 = 21$

$$AB = 7$$

then the locus of P is a straight line perpendicular to AB?

Theorem III

. . . is easier to read if we say it with numbers.

Given: $PA^2 - PB^2 = 21$ (sq. in.), $AB = 7$ (in.).

Prove: The locus of P is a straight line perpendicular to AB at M, where $AM = 5$ in.

Construction: Take one correct position of P; draw $PM \perp AB$.

Proof: (We have to show that M is a fixed point.)

$$AM^2 + PM^2 = PA^2 \text{ (right-angled } \triangle AMP)$$
$$MB^2 + PM^2 = PB^2$$

Subtract: $AM^2 - MB^2 = PA^2 - PB^2 = 21$ (given)

$$AM + MB = AB = 7$$

Divide: $AM - MB = 3$

AM is 5 in., and M is a fixed point.

Therefore P cannot be anywhere, except on this one perpendicular.

Things are quite different if $PA^2 + PB^2 = 50$, and $AB = 6$. Even numbers are used here to save calculation; sketch the figure, and you find three positions for P easily: (i) $PA = 5, PB = 5$; (ii) $PA = 7, PB = 1$; (iii) $PA = 1$, $PB = 7$. Is the path of P an oval curve?

No, it is a circle, and its centre is the mid-point of AB.

Theorem IV

Given: $\triangle ABP$, C the mid-point of AB.

Prove: $PA^2 + PB^2 = 2.PC^2 + 2.CB^2$

Construction: Draw $PX \perp AB$ (Fig. 12).

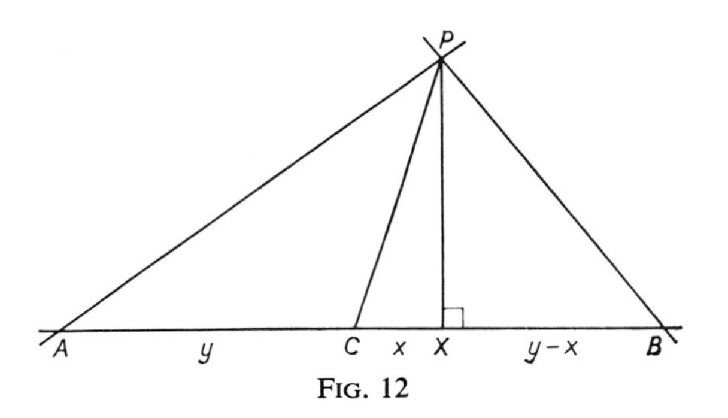

FIG. 12

Proof: Let $AC = y = CB$, and $CX = x$.
There are three right-angled triangles:

$$PA^2 = AX^2 + PX^2 \,(\triangle APX)$$
$$PB^2 = XB^2 + PX^2 \,(\triangle BPX)$$

Since $AX = y + x$, and $XB = y - x$:

$$\begin{aligned} PA^2 + PB^2 &= y^2 + 2yx + x^2 + PX^2 \\ &\quad + y^2 - 2yx + x^2 + PX^2 \\ &= 2.y^2 + 2.(x^2 + PX^2) \\ &= 2.CB^2 + 2.PC^2 \end{aligned}$$

because $\triangle CPX$ is right-angled.

EXERCISE 6E

1. If $PA^2 + PB^2 = 50$, and $AB = 6$, calculate PC.
(Notice that $2.y^2$, or $2.CB^2$, does not equal AB^2, but $= \frac{1}{2}.AB^2$.)

Carried Points

In almost every machine, there are things going to and fro, and things going round. A simple movement is that of a straight bar which turns round on a pivot; every point on the bar moves round a circle, with the pivot for centre. To draw this is hardly necessary; but the next movement here is a little different. A straight bar turns round O, and a point P on the bar is made to move round a circle through O.

In Fig. 13, O is marked on a circle, P moves round the circle. On the line OP, OQ is half OP, and OR is twice OP. How do Q and R move? When you mark a few positions, it looks as though each point moves round a circle of its own. Draw the (fixed) diameter OA; C is the centre. Then:

$$CQ \parallel AP$$
$$\therefore O\hat{Q}C = O\hat{P}A, \text{ which is a right-angle}$$
$$Q \text{ moves on a circle with diameter } OC.$$

In other words, its locus is a circle with centre at the mid-point of OC, and radius half that of the first circle.

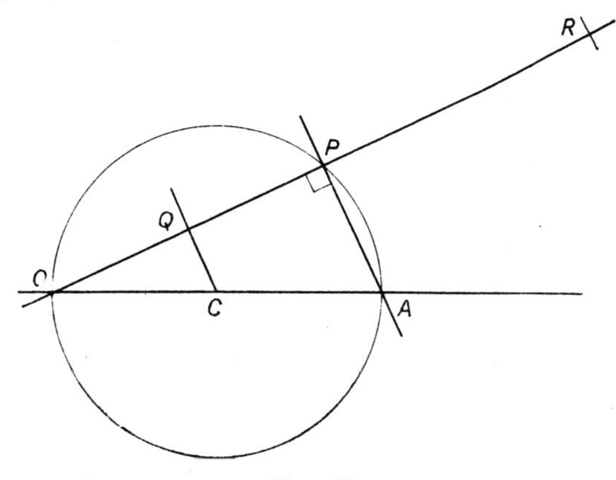

FIG. 13

EXERCISE 6F

1. In Fig. 13, draw $RS \parallel PC$ to meet the line OA at S. Prove that the locus of R is a circle with diameter OS.

2. P moves on a circle, centre C; O is a fixed point, *not* on the circle; show that the mid-point of OP moves on a circle, and state the radius and the position of the centre.

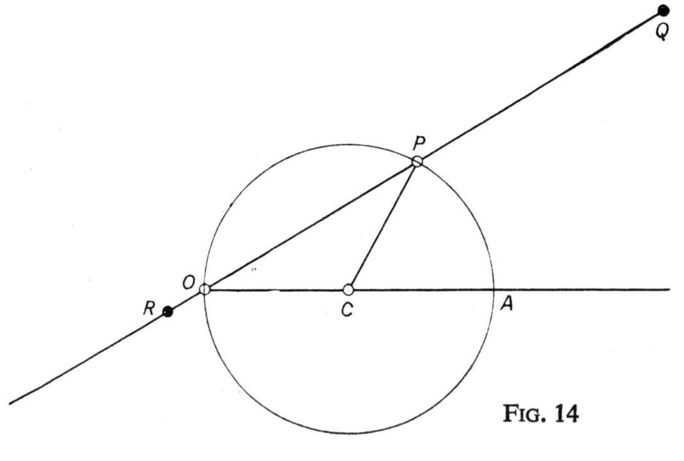

FIG. 14

Fig. 14 shows a method for drawing the locus of another carried point; OA is the diameter of a circle, CP is a bar hinged at C, so that P is kept to the circle. QR is hinged at P, and can slip through a guide at O.

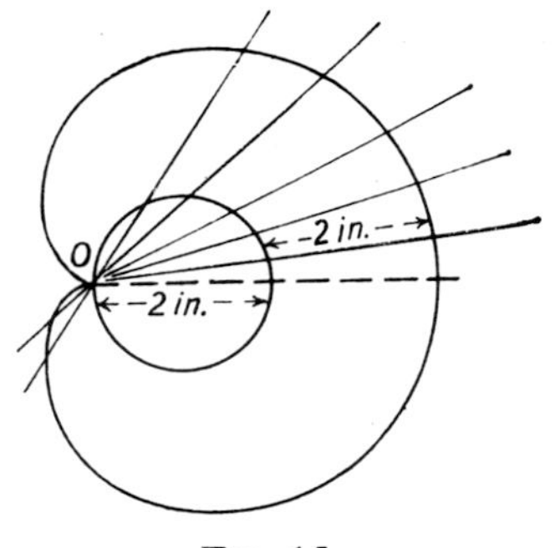

FIG. 15

PQ and PR each equal OA in length. The points Q, R both move on the same curve; it is the shape of one of the "cam wheels" used in machines. To draw it with ruler and compasses you must mark a number of points and draw the curve freehand through them, as in Fig. 15.

EXERCISE 6G

Drawing Exercises

1. A point P is marked on the rim of a circle, and the circle rolls along a straight line. Sketch the locus of P.

2. The same circle rolls round inside another circle, always touching it. Sketch the locus of P when the ratio of the two radii is (i) $\frac{1}{3}$, (ii) $\frac{1}{4}$, (iii) $\frac{1}{2}$.

3. Fasten one point on a fairly long string to a point on the surface of a cylinder, such as a round pencil, and wind the string round the cylinder. What is the locus of the end of the string?

Uses of Geometry in Machine Design

Geometry does not stop short at circles and straight lines; the curves just drawn, and many others, have simple geometrical properties, and for that very reason they are needed in machine design. A wheel shaped like the curve in Fig. 15 is used to wind thread on a reel. To draw the curve, with the mechanism used in Fig. 14, make $PQ = PR$ but a little longer than OA. This smooths out the "kink" at O.

The cam made this way rotates about O, and presses against a reel (Fig. 16), pushing it out about 4 in. and allowing it to move back. A spring keeps the reel up against the cam, and the same machine drives both the moving parts, so that the reel turns steadily and picks up thread evenly.

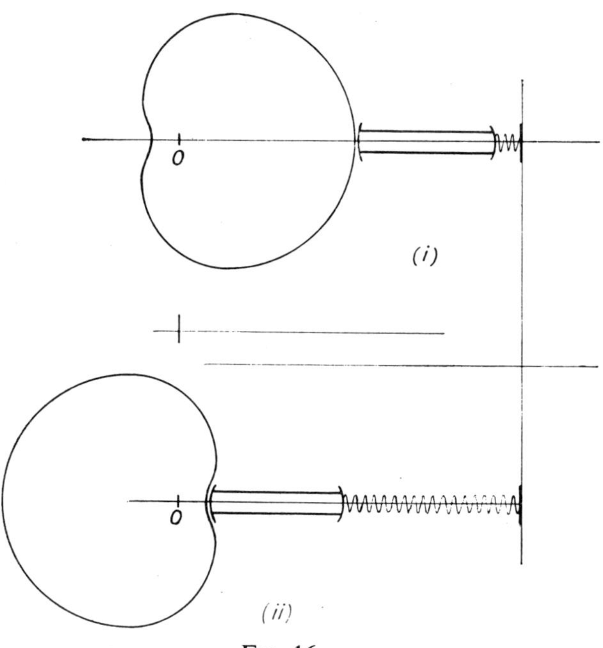

FIG. 16

Movement in a Straight Line (*Valve Gears*)*:* The first practical method of moving a solid object to and fro in a straight line was the three-link motion discovered by James Watt. In this outline sketch, X is the middle point of the short link. The links are hinged, and the long outer links can rotate round their outer ends A, B, which do not move. The point X moves almost in a

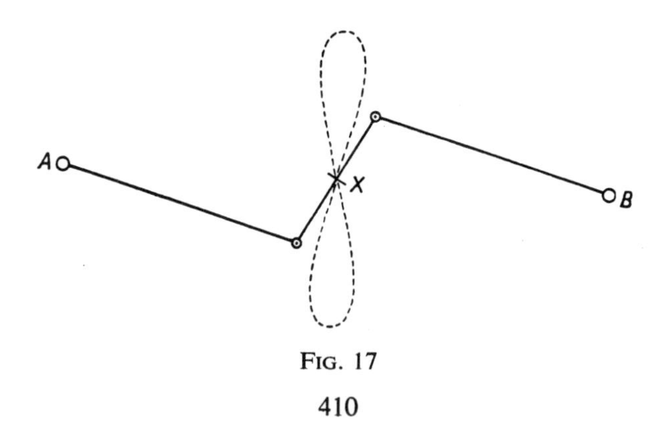

FIG. 17

straight line, near enough to carry a slide-valve. If you sketch the locus with the help of linked strips, it turns out to be a narrow figure-eight (Fig. 17).

Is there a machine that will "draw" an exact straight line? There are several, used for instance in valve gears. Here are two which are quite practical.

First consider the geometry of Fig. 18.

Here $OA.OB = OP.OQ$, and $O\hat{P}A$ is a right-angle. It follows that the triangles OAP, OQB are similar (S A S).

$$\therefore\ O\hat{B}Q = \hat{P}, \text{ a right-angle.}$$

If O, A, B are fixed, P can move round a circle whose diameter is OA, and Q will also move, but $O\hat{B}Q$ will still be a right-angle.

Q moves along a straight line perpendicular to OB.

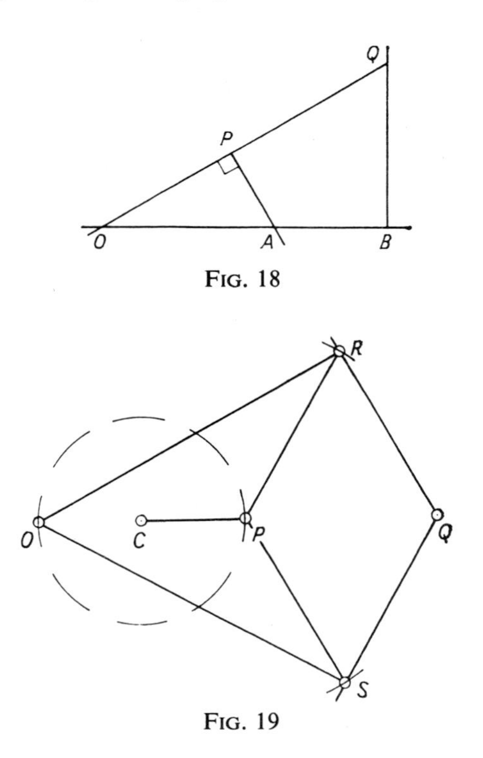

FIG. 18

FIG. 19

The mechanism sketched in Fig. 19 is made of four equal links with smooth pivots at P, Q, R, S and two longer links OR, OS. A pivot at O is fixed.

(1) However P is made to move, say in a curve, Q will move in a different curve; when P moves nearer to O, Q moves further away.

(2) O, P, Q will always be in a straight line (why?).

(3) $OP.OQ$ is constant. For, if M is the mid-point of PQ, $RM \perp PQ$ ($PSQR$ is a rhombus).

$$OR^2 - PR^2 = OM^2 - MP^2 \text{ (Theorem III)}$$
$$= (OM - MP)(OM + MQ) = OP.OQ$$

In use, P is made to move round a circle, through O—an extra link will do this ($CP = CO$); then, as in Fig. 18, Q will move to and fro exactly in a straight line.

Another gear uses two wheels; one is fixed, and the other, of half its radius, is made to roll inside the first one, keeping in contact with it. On the small wheel there is a pin at P; in Fig. 20, P starts at the point A. Later on, the small wheel is touching the bigger one at B, its centre is at C, and the pin is now at P'. O is the centre of the large wheel.

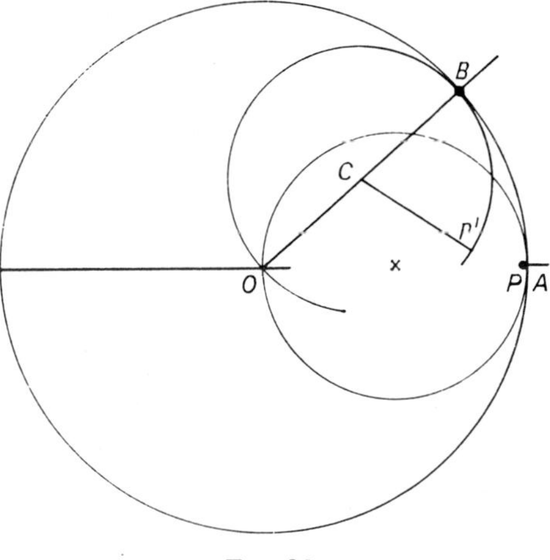

FIG. 20

The last proof: interesting, quite simple, but just a little different. The arcs AB and $P'B$ must be the same length; one has unrolled from the other. The lengths of the arcs are proportional to the radii, *and* to the angles at O, C, the respective centres.

Therefore, $B\hat{C}P'$ is twice $B\hat{O}A$.

But the same angle $B\hat{C}P'$ is twice $B\hat{O}P'$ ("angle at centre is twice angle at circumference").

Therefore, P' is on the line AO, and P moves only along the diameter of the outer circle.

REVISION SUMMARY

GEOMETRY

(**A** = *Syllabus A*; **B** = *Syllabus B*)

SIMILAR FIGURES

Page

(A & B) ***Similar Figures* are exactly the same shape; this means that corresponding angles in each are equal, and corresponding lengths are in the same ratio.**

A triangle is the simplest figure.

1. From what key theorem do you start? 303
2. A drawing is made of straight lines only; what is a simple way to draw a similar figure, with lengths altered in the ratio 3 : 2? 302
3. The figures in No. 2 are in perspective; use the idea of perspective to fit inside a triangle
   (i) a square with its base along one side; 306, Q. 17
   (ii) a triangle with given angles. 308, Q. 21

(A & B) ***Ratios.***

4. A, B, C are three points in a straight line, and $AB : BC = h : k$. Write down the ratio of $AC : AB$. 304, Q. 1
5. AXB, AYC are two straight lines which meet at A. If $AX : XB = AY : YC$, write down five other pairs of equal ratios. XY is parallel to BC; why? 305, Q. 7-9

(A & B) ***Similar Triangles.* If two triangles are equiangular, their corresponding lengths (sides) are in proportion. This fact is important, since it does not hold good for any other figures: all questions of similarity must be answered by "building the figures up in triangles."**

6. Sketch two quadrilaterals which have equal angles, but are not similar. 343
7. Two triangles are proved to be similar by using one of three theorems: state the facts given in each of these theorems. 308/313
8. The three theorems are all proved in the same way; what is the construction, and how do congruent triangles come in? 314

Page

(A & B) ***Bisector of an Angle.*** **PQR is a triangle; PX bisects the angle QPR, and meets QR at X; then $QX : XR = QP : PR$.**

9. How is this proved? 315

10. QP is produced to S; QY bisects the exterior angle RPS, and meets the line QR at Y. What follows? 315

11. Are the converse theorems both true? State them and prove them. 316

(A & B) ***Areas of Similar Figures.*** **When two figures are similar, the ratio of their areas is equal to the *square* of the ratio of corresponding lengths.**

12. Prove this for two similar triangles. 317

(A & B) ***Chords of a Circle.***

AB, CD are two chords of a circle and meet at X. $\triangle$s AXC, BXD are similar (reasons?).

13. Show that $AX.XB = CX.XD$

(i) if X is inside the circle;

(ii) if X is outside. 310, Q. 4

14. O is the centre, and r the radius; show that $AX.XB$ is equal to the difference between r^2 and $(OX)^2$. 310, Q. 5

Page

(A & B) ANGLES AND TANGENTS

***The Key Theorem*: Angles in the same segment of a circle are equal.**

1. What is meant by "the angle subtended by . . . at . . ." and "The angle in the alternate segment"? 322

2. Use this theorem to prove that the exterior angle of a cyclic quadrilateral is equal to . . . (complete the statement). 323

The tangent at A is perpendicular to the radius AO.

3. This includes a theorem and its converse; give one proof for each. 324-5

When two circles touch (at C), the line joining their centres passes through C, the point of contact.

4. Draw a circle of radius 2 in.; mark a point A on the circle. Construct another circle to touch the first one at A and to pass through a given point B. Clue: bisect AB at right-angles. 326

The "Alternate Segment Theorem".

5. Give two different proofs of this theorem. 323/328

TA touches a circle at A; TBC cuts the circle at B, C; then $TA^2 = TB.TC$

6. Can this theorem be proved by adapting Fig. 16 on page 331? 331

7. The converse theorem is important; state it exactly. 331

Constructions.

8. Construct a tangent *from* a point *to* a circle. 332

9. Construct the common tangents to two circles. 333-5

***Example of a Locus.* Two circles cut at A, B. If X is any point on the line AB (but not between A and B), the tangents from X to the two circles are of equal length.**

10. . . . and if X is not on this line, the tangents are not equal. 330

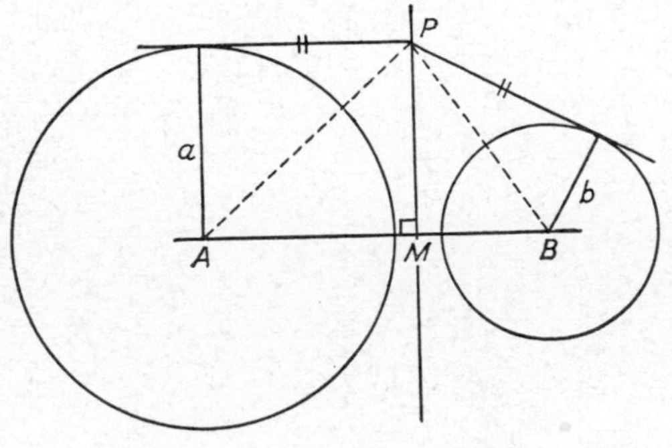

11. Does this locus exist for circles which do not cut? Use this figure, and see Fig. 11 on page 406. 406

. . . radii a, b. $a^2 - b^2 = AM^2 - MB^2 = PA^2 - PB^2$.

Page

(A & B) METHODS OF CONSTRUCTION

***Two simple methods*, on which all the others rest.**

The method used for making equal lengths, or angles.

Drawing two equal circles, with radii large enough for them to cross: used for bisecting a straight line, an arc, or an angle; for making a right angle at a given point. This construction is found in almost every figure, in Chap. 3.

The facts proved in theorems are the clue to all but the very simplest drawings:

***On areas :* Triangles on the same base and between parallels are of equal area.**

***On circles:* The perpendicular bisector of a chord passes through the centre.**

The tangent . . . is perpendicular to the radius.

A circle will *touch* another circle at a point on the line which joins their centres.

"$TA^2 = TB.TC$" (page 329, Th. XI).

For certain angles, and for regular polygons:

(A & B) RIDERS

Riders are exercises in discovery. It is good practice to examine every drawing you meet, to see if there is more to be found in it besides what was put there. See page 368, Fig. 12, and the two figures below.

When attempting a new rider, it will help to use the clues at the end of the chapter. But first make your own list of clues for the nine items on page 363 and try them out.

Work out as many examples as you can from examination papers and text books; make a note as you go on to keep on record *which pieces of evidence are most often useful.*

What else can you prove in these two figures?

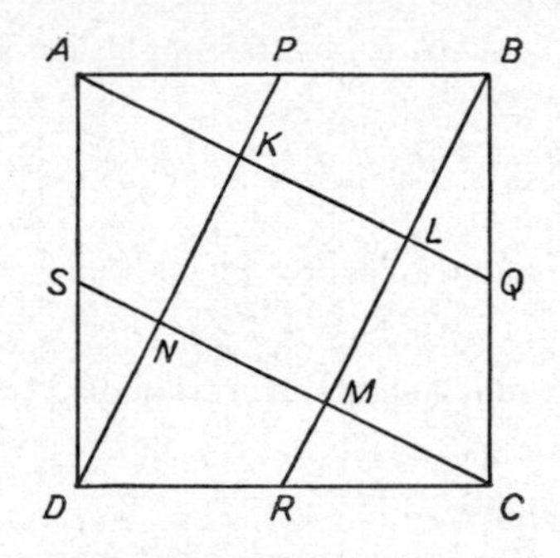

1. A square; P, Q, R, S mid-points.

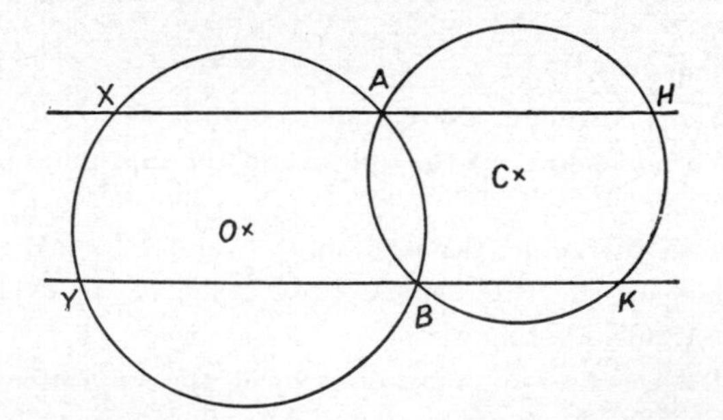

2. Two circles, not equal; XH, YK are parallel. (Draw other lines.)

Page

TRIANGLES AND CIRCLES

(A) The most important fact about any and every triangle is that the sum of any two sides is greater than the third side.

Three steps **in comparing two quantities.**

(A & B) 1. Are they equal? For $\triangle ABC$, if $\hat{B} = \hat{C}$, then $AC = AB$.

(A) 2. Which is greater? If $\hat{B} > \hat{C}$, then $AC < AB$.

This is an inequality: give several examples of using an inequality to find a greatest or least value. 378-380

(B) 3. What is the exact ratio of the two quantities?

For $\triangle ABC, \dfrac{AC}{AB} = \dfrac{\sin B}{\sin C}$.

The area of a $\triangle = \frac{1}{2} ab. \sin C = 2R^2. \sin A. \sin B. \sin C$.

(A & B) ***Circle described round a triangle.***

How do you construct it?

R is its radius: $2R. \sin A = a$. 381

(A) ***Altitudes:*** **perpendicular heights of a triangle.**

Prove that they meet in a point:

1. By using equal angles. 382-3
2. From the centre of a circle through X, Y, Z, where $YZ \parallel BC$ through the point A, etc. 386

If the altitudes AP, BQ, CR meet at H, and the line AP meets the circumcircle at K, then $HP = PK$. 383

(A) ***Special Theorems.***

A circle passes through these nine points: P, Q, R, the feet of the altitudes; the mid-points of the sides; and the mid-points of HA, HB, HC. Proof? 384

P is a point on the circle, through A, B, C and PL, PM, PN are perpendiculars on the three sides. Prove that L, M, N lie on a straight line (Simson's Line). 387

AX, BY, CZ meet in a point, and meet the opposite sides of $\triangle ABC$ at X, Y, Z; then $\dfrac{BX}{XC} \cdot \dfrac{CY}{YA} \cdot \dfrac{AZ}{ZB} = 1$ (Ceva's theorem). 392

Also the converse theorem. 394

Circles touching the sides (in- and ex-circles). 388

GEOMETRY

Page

LOCUS: THE PATH OF A MOVING POINT

(A & B) ***Constructions.*** **To find the centre of a circle through three marked points, you have to draw two loci (the perpendicular bisectors of two lines).**

In making any drawing, each condition that has to be fulfilled means constructing a locus.

(A & B) ***Straight line loci*** **for points** ***PPPPP.***

1. At equal distances from two points which are fixed. 399, Q. 3
2. Equidistant from two fixed lines. 400, Q. 9
3. Vertex of a triangle whose base and area are given. 406
4. $PA^2 - PB^2$ constant. 406

(A & B) ***Circle loci*** **for points** ***PPPPP*** **(*O, A, B* fixed).**

1. OP is a given distance.
2. APB is an angle of given size; this locus is not a whole circle, but two equal arcs. 402-3
3. $\dfrac{PA}{PB}$ is a given ratio. (How to find the centre and radius of the circle?) 403-4
4. $PA^2 + PB^2$ is constant; centre, the mid-point of AB. 407

(A) ***Proof of a locus.***

To confirm the locus of a point under given conditions, it is necessary to show:

1. That if the point is on a certain path, the conditions are satisfied.
2. That if it is not on the path, they are not satisfied; or that the path includes more than one line or curve. 399-400

(A) ***Carried points*****; linkages.**

P moves on a circle, O is fixed; locus of the mid-point of OP is a circle. Many loci are neither straight lines nor circles; a point may be carried by simple mechanism, so as to travel along a definite curve. 407-412

TAKING THE EXAMINATION

THERE IS is no doubt that the best way to make sure that you pass the examination is to have mastered everything in the syllabus so thoroughly that the examiners have no way of catching you out! But whatever standard you have reached, you should give yourself the greatest possible chance of success by acting according to the following suggestions, as far as you can. There are plenty of people who will be ready to tell you that they ignored all the advice they were given, and still did well—but they may have been extra lucky, they may have been able to do still better than they did, and they may even be exaggerating—at all events, don't risk spoiling your own performance by an approach which your own common sense tells you is foolish.

Before

1. During the six weeks or so before the examination, revise your weak points. You can find out what these are by attempting questions set in previous years. Working through a few old examination papers also helps to give you the "feel" of the examination. Your own papers will have a familiar appearance and you will be able to find your way about them with confidence. In the examination room, you always find that you know less than you thought you did, but the more gaps you find beforehand, the better! At least, while there's still time to do something about them!

2. For two or three days before the examination, DON'T DO ANY WORK AT ALL. In a mathematics examination, a fresh alert mind is needed. If you are completely worn out by working up to the last minute, you will forget things through sheer exhaustion, fail to think clearly, make many careless mistakes, and do yourself more harm than good.

3. During this period (the last few days) go to bed at a reasonable time. Sleepiness is no help at all. If you stay up until 1 a.m. doing last minute "swotting," you deserve to fail. And if you stay up late for no adequate reason, you obviously don't really want to pass.

4. Physical exhaustion can be as damaging as mental exhaustion. During the last two days, don't play gruelling tennis matches, or wear yourself out by any strenuous physical activity; take it easy. There will be time afterwards to catch up on your cycling, games and so on.

During

1. READ THE INSTRUCTIONS which you will certainly be given. Although, contrary to general belief, the examiners want to help the candidate to give of his best, candidates are often very perverse, and seem to try to do everything in a different way from that set down in the instructions. For example, many examinations ask for a different page to be used for every question. (This does not mean, by the way, that when a question is in three parts, each part should be done on a separate page.) If a candidate insists on ignoring this, and does several questions, or parts of different questions, on the same page, he has only himself to blame if part of his work is overlooked.

It will never be *deliberately* ignored, but sometimes some badly set out work at the foot of a page may be only just recognized in time as an attempt at another, probably unlabelled, question.

2. Read the questions carefully, and always answer the question you have been asked, not something different.

3. Write clearly even for your "rough" work. Show what you are trying to do, so that even if you fail to complete it you can earn some "method" marks.

4. Do not cross out an uncompleted piece of work until you have replaced it by something better. It may well earn you some marks, if you show that you had the right idea—an arithmetical slip, leading to a ridiculous answer, is unlikely to mean a loss of all the marks for that question.

On the other hand, if you *have* replaced a piece of work don't forget to cross it out—in case the wrong version is marked.

5. In some examinations, you are told, for example, "Do ALL questions in Section A, and FOUR only in Section B." In that case, there is no point in dodging about in Section A—work straight through, abandoning each question at the point where you can't make any more progress, remembering, if so instructed, to turn to a fresh page, and start on the next question in order. You may have time to come back and improve on things later.

Some candidates prefer to try the harder questions in Section B first, while they are at their best. This depends on your own judgement of whether you will give a better account of yourself that way—but, if in doubt, do Section A first—not only is it likely to give you confidence as you get "warmed up"—it will please the examiners, who like a nice orderly approach.

6. Don't waste a lot of time on one question. While you are making progress, carry on; but when you realize, because the work is so laborious or so confusing, that you must be on the wrong track, don't lose valuable time that can be spent more profitably on a different question.

7. Don't panic! In the examination you are quite sure not to do as well as you might have. It happens to everybody. But just because the answers won't seem to come out, it doesn't mean that you are doing very badly—provided you show that you do know what to do, you will get quite a lot of marks even with very few correct answers! Due allowance is made for accidental slips—so don't worry. Just carry on quietly doing the best you can. (Many more pass than fail, by the way!) You may have done worse than you hoped, but you will almost certainly find that you did better than you expected!

8. Don't write rubbish in the hope of deceiving the examiner. Not only will you fail to gain any marks for this (for marks are given for sound arguments and correct procedures, not for pages of nonsense), but you run the risk of having the rest of your work, if set down carelessly, less carefully examined for correct material than would be the case of a candidate who showed that he was thinking about what he wrote.

9. Do only the correct number of questions. If you are told to do four from one section, and you try five, be sure to cross out the one you wish to be ignored—otherwise the first four only may be marked, when you perhaps did the fifth best!

10. If you have time to look through your paper, and think you have seen a mistake—don't make an alteration until you have thought carefully about it. Sometimes, *first* thoughts (and calculations) are best—so check carefully before correcting your earlier result—remember you were fresher when you first wrote it! Of course, if the mistake is obvious, the sooner it is altered the better—but it is very easy to decide suddenly that something is wrong, when it is right all the time. (Candidates sometimes completely cross out some entirely correct work, and either replace it by nothing, or by a faulty alternative.)

After

It is too late now to wish you had paid attention to the advice above! But don't worry—you haven't done nearly as badly as you feel you have! Don't for goodness' sake have an "inquest" on the paper—this will probably lead to your losing confidence, quite needlessly, about some of your work. Forget all about it for the time, and make up for all the things you missed beforehand. Don't listen to the boasts of a good performance by others—for some reason, all sorts of people like to pretend they did better than was in fact the case. Wait and see.

In the specimen examination paper that follows, all the questions have been worked out for you (but try them first yourself, of course) some by alternative methods, and the answers do not, for reasons of space, have a page to themselves. Do not forget that in the examination you must NOT do more questions than asked for, and you must NOT do more than one on a page. And, of course, *one* solution to each question is all you need!

SPECIMEN EXAMINATION PAPER

Ordinary Level

MATHEMATICS

(Syllabus B)

Two and a half hours.

All necessary working must be shown.

Answer ALL questions in Section A and FOUR questions in Section B.

SECTION A

1. (i) Find the cost of 8 tons 15 cwt. of coal at £12 8s. 8d. per ton.
(ii) What length of carpet 27 in. wide would be sufficient to cover the floor of a rectangular room measuring 6 yd. by $4\frac{1}{2}$ yd.?

2. (i) Solve the equations
$$3x - 4y = 10,$$
$$5x + 3y = 7.$$
(ii) AB and CD are two chords of a circle. When produced, they meet outside the circle at X. If $AB = BX = 3$ in., and $CD = 7$ in., calculate the length of DX.

3. (i) Calculate without the use of tables the area of a triangle PQR, given that $PQ = 4$ in., $PR = 2\frac{1}{2}$ in., and the angle $P = 60°$.
(ii) L, M and N are three points on a circle with centre O. The chord LM is produced to T, where $MT = MN$. If the angle $MTN = 32°$ and the angle $OMN = 20°$, calculate the angle LNM, assuming that O lies inside the triangle LMN.

4. (i) Solve the equation $3x^2 - 7x = 2$, giving your solution correct to two places of decimals.
(ii) Evaluate $(1\frac{3}{4} - \frac{4}{5}) \div 2\frac{8}{15}$.

5. (i) If eggs are bought at £1 16s. per gross, and sold at 4d. each, calculate the percentage profit on the cost price.
(ii) Factorize $4x^2 - 7x - 2$.

6. (i) Express as a single fraction in its simplest form
$$\frac{3}{x-3} - \frac{2}{x-2}.$$
(ii) The angles B and C of a triangle ABC are 28° and 42° respectively. The altitude AN is 6 in. Calculate the length of BC.

SECTION B

Answer FOUR questions in this section.

7. (i) Calculate the difference in longitude between two points on the circle of latitude 60° N., if the distance between them measured along the circle of latitude is 242 miles.
(Take the radius of the earth as 3,960 miles, and π as $3\frac{1}{7}$.)
(ii) Given that $T = 2\pi\sqrt{\frac{l}{g}}$ and that $l = h + \frac{k^2}{h}$ where k is positive,
(a) express k in terms of T, π, g and h,
(b) calculate k given that $T = \frac{11}{4}$, $\pi = 3\frac{1}{7}$, $g = 32$ and $h = \frac{2l}{3}$.

8. TY is a diameter of a circle. A point A on the tangent at T to the circle is joined to Y, and AY cuts the circle at X. The line YB is drawn perpendicular to YA at Y, to cut AT produced at B.
Prove that (a) the angle XTA = the angle YBT; (b) $AT^3 = AB.AX^2$.

9. A ship starting at a point A sails $7\frac{1}{2}$ miles on a bearing 053°(N.53°E.), and then 12 miles on a bearing 118°(S.62°E.), arriving at a point B. Calculate the distance AB and the bearing of B from A.

10. (i) The distance s ft. that a point P moves along a straight line AB in t seconds from the beginning of its motion is given by the formula $s = 8t^2 - 2t^3$. Calculate
(a) when it again passes through its starting point A,
(b) at what speed it will be moving two seconds after starting,
(c) how far it moves from A before starting to return.
(ii) Find the volume of the solid obtained by rotating about the x-axis that part of the curve $y^2 = x(4 - x)$ between $x = 0$ and $x = 4$.

11. A man drove three cars in succession over distances of 49 miles. He drove the first at x miles per hour, the second 3 miles per hour slower and the third car 4 miles per hour faster than the first. The difference in the times taken by the second and third cars was 21 minutes. Form an equation for x, and solve it. Calculate also the time taken by the fastest car to cover the 49 miles.

12. Three metals A, B and C have densities of 8·9 grams per c.c., 7·1 grams per c.c. and 7·3 grams per c.c., respectively. Calculate
(a) how many grams each of A and of B must be melted together to give a piece of metal of weight 121 grams and volume 14 c.c.,
(b) if the metals are melted together in the proportions (by volume) 3 : 2 : 5 respectively, calculate the weight of 1 c.c. of the resulting alloy.

(*Answers on page* 456.)

ANSWERS TO EXERCISES

ARITHMETIC AND TRIGONOMETRY

Exercise 1A

1. 18s. 11d. **2.** 664 **3.** 208; 62 **4.** 5 ft. 2 in.

Exercise 1B

1. 765 **2.** 27·1 **3.** 13 years 5·6 months

Exercise 1C

1. 60 m.p.h. **2.** 50 m.p.h. **3.** 31 m.p.h.

Exercise 1D

1. 45 lb. per cu. ft.
2. $\frac{1}{12}$ lb.
3. $\frac{1}{12}$ cu. ft.
4. 10·14 gm. per c.c.
5. 10·1 gm. per c.c. approx.

Exercise 1E

1. 3 : 1 **2.** 13 : 5 **3.** 2 : 5, 19 : 30

Exercise 1F

1. (a) 50, 42; (b) 8, 7·5; (c) 15, 14·4
2. 15 m.p.h.
3. 14·4 m.p.h.
4. 4·5 gm. per c.c.; 4 gm. per c.c.

Exercise 1G

1. 18 **2.** 25, 625 **3.** 10 gm.

Exercise 2A

1. 66 cm.
2. 31 yd.
3. 22 in.
4. 38 ft.
5. 14 in.
6. 14 in.
7. 2·9 in.

Exercise 2B

1. 350 sq. cm.
2. 79 sq. yd.
3. 39 sq. in.
4. 110 sq. ft.
5. 14 in.
6. $1\frac{3}{4}$ cm.

Exercise 2C

1. 440 yd.; £870
2. 33 in.; 31 m.p.h.
3. $10\frac{1}{2}$ in.; 45 m.p.h.; 9·5% approx.
4. 96 acres

Exercise 2D

1. 130 sq. cm.
2. 6·3 sq. ft.
3. 15,800 sq. ft.
4. 3·5 cm.
5. 3·1 miles approx.; 1,900 revs.
6. 140 sq. in.

Exercise 2E

1. 2 cm.
2. 1,100 gal.
3. 2,880
4. 220 cu. ft. approx.
5. about 170 minutes

Exercise 2F

1. $1\frac{1}{8}$ cm.
2. 0·69 in.
3. 0·35 in.

Exercise 2G

1. 400 seconds
2. $5\frac{1}{4}$ ft. per second
3. 7 in.

Exercise 3A

1. 110·7 (approx.)
2. 11,070 (approx.)
3. 0·01107 (approx.)
4. 241·1 (approx.)
5. 1·666 (approx.)
6. 10,190 (approx.)
7. 287·9 (approx.)
8. 1·234 (approx.)
9. 1·450 (approx.)
10. 2,560,000

Exercise 3B

1. 2·435 (approx.)
2. 7·702 (approx.)
3. 24·35 (approx.)
4. 8·128 (approx.)
5. 0·8128 (approx.)
6. 2·530 (approx.)
7. 0·2450 (approx.)
8. 0·07738 (approx.)
9. 256·7 (approx.)
10. 2·490 (approx.)

Exercise 4A

1. £16
2. £9
3. £36

Exercise 4B

1. £20; £25; £1
2. 1,200 shares; £300; £18
3. 9s.; at a discount

Exercise 4C

1. 6%
2. 5%
3. 650
4. £37 10s.
5. £3 4s.
6. 3,840 shares; £2 8s. increase

Exercise 4D

1. £300; £12
2. £400 stock; £24
3. £26 13s. 4d.; £3 6s. 8d. per cent
4. 5%

Exercise 4E

1. £350 stock
2. £50
3. £2 5s. increase
4. £16 13s. 4d. increase
5. £1 18s. 9d. less

Exercise 5A

1. (i) 0·4972
(ii) 0·0157
(iii) 0·9003
(iv) 0·6767

2. (i) 1·491
(ii) 8·104
(iii) 2·113
(iv) 3·162

3. (i) 4
(ii) − 3
(iii) 100,000

4. (i) 7·276
(ii) 6·733
(iii) 7·907

5. (i) 1·908
(ii) 2·859
(iii) 5·077

6. 1·6021; it exceeds it by 1; 2·6021

Exercise 5B

1. (i) 1·8010
(ii) 4·2925
(iii) 5·3856
(iv) 2·9921

2. (i) 3,789
(ii) 10·40
(iii) 8,600,000
(iv) 259·9

3. (i) 3,701
(ii) 81,560
(iii) 9·135
(iv) 5·012
(v) 596·7
(vi) 3·808

Exercise 5C

1. (i) $\bar{3}\cdot5243$
(ii) $\bar{1}\cdot9121$
(iii) $\bar{2}\cdot1504$
(iv) $\bar{5}\cdot4362$

2. (i) 0·02306
(ii) 0·00086
(iii) 0·3789
(iv) 0·000004

3. (i) $\bar{1}$
(ii) $\bar{5}$
(iii) $\bar{3}$
(iv) $\bar{7}$
(v) 0
(vi) $\bar{1}\cdot5715$
(vii) 2·7544
(viii) $\bar{3}$

4. (i) 11·93
(ii) 141·5
(iii) 0·1713
(iv) 0·02623
(v) 4·241
(vi) 0·02836

Exercise 5D

1. 701·5 m.p.h.
2. 753·9 acres
3. 1·141 pints
4. 10·01%
5. 50·0 seconds
6. 3·195 c.c.

Exercise 5E

1. (i) 893·0
 (ii) 29,240
 (iii) 3·035
 (iv) 2·066
2. (i) $\bar{2}$·8876
 (ii) $\bar{1}$·4859
 (iii) $\bar{2}$·9084
3. (i) 0·1199
 (ii) 0·0006183
 (iii) 0·7018
 (iv) 0·2545
4. 0·6204 in.

Exercise 6A

1. 127·2 ft.
2. 6,500 ft.
3. About $36\frac{1}{2}°$
4. 10·7 cm., 19·3 cm.
5. About $67\frac{1}{2}°$

Exercise 6B

1. (i) 0·2404
 (ii) 0·5403
 (iii) 1·6765
 (iv) 7·806
2. (i) 4° 38′
 (ii) 25° 46′
 (iii) 55° 27′
 (iv) 73° 45′
3. 16·81 cm.
4. 5·666 miles
5. $A = 35° 32'$, $C = 54° 28'$

Exercise 6C

1. 16·06 ft.
2. 48° 4′ (or 5′)
3. 11·39 ft.-per-sec.
4. 6·598 miles
5. (i) 8·401
 (ii) 3,032
 (iii) 27° 40′ (or 41′)
6. (i) 2·622 in.
 (ii) 2·917 in.
7. 69·63 cm.^{2}

Exercise 6D

1. 19·11 sq. in.
2. 4° 25′
3. 14·87 ft.
4. 97° 32′
5. 47° 10′
6. (i) 7·262 cm.
 (ii) 9·105 cm.
7. 25° 46′ to the horizontal.
8. (i) 5·289 in.
 (ii) 8·559 in.
9. 166 m.p.h.
10. 4·961 miles

Exercise 7A

1. (i) LN
 (ii) $l.\cos N + n.\cos L$
 (iii) $m.\sin N$ (or $n.\sin M$)
2. (i) 0·2874
 (ii) − 0·6399
 (iii) − 6·314
 (iv) 158° 8′
 (v) 126° 19′
3. (i) 2·719 in.
 (ii) 4·145 in.
 (iii) 4·396 in.

Exercise 7B

1. 38° 13′, 60° and 81° 47′

2. 12·39 miles

3. 8·579 cm.

4. (i) 29° 47′
(ii) 33′ 4 in.

5. (i) 77° 37′
(ii) 5·490 in.

Exercise 7C

1. 5·846 ft. and 5·738 ft.

2. (i) 42° 32′
(ii) 59° 36′ or 120° 24′
(iii) 82° 3′

3. 7·642 miles

4. S. 67° 45′ E.

Exercise 7D

1. 102·2 sq. in.

2. 46° 21′ and 133° 39′

3. (i) $\hat{A} = 31° 23'$, $b = 247{\cdot}7$ yd., $c = 171{\cdot}6$ yd.
(ii) $\hat{P} = 40° 4'$, $\hat{R} = 79° 56'$, $r = 12{\cdot}39$ in.
(iii) $\hat{X} = 21° 48'$, $\hat{Y} = 38° 12'$, $\hat{Z} = 120°$

Exercise 7E

1. 19° 27′, 36° 52′ and 123° 41′

2. 46·28 ft.

3. 45° 23′

4. 383 sq. yd.

5. 5·501 miles

6. 17·82 cm.

7. 3° 38′, 26·1 ft.

8. 17·78 knots in a direction S. 73° E.

9. (i) $\dfrac{\sin 140}{\sin 20}$
(ii) $2.\sin 70$

10. 9·241 in.

11. (i) 20·57 ft.
(ii) 136·2 sq. ft.

12. 3 ft. 5·7 in.

13. $BX = 18{\cdot}0$ cm., $CX = 13{\cdot}5$ cm.

14. 408·5 yd. and 200° 51°
(= S. 20° 51′ W.)

15. N. 52° 29′ E., and it will take 22·92 min.

Exercise 8A

1. 17° 48′

2. (i) 24° 37′
(ii) 17° 8′

3. (i) 106° 47′ (or 73° 13′)
(ii) 47° 52′

4. 3·274 cm.

5. 192 cu. in.

6. (i) S. 55° 28′ W.
(ii) 45° 32′

7. $XP = XQ = 18{\cdot}14$ in.;
XY 17·80 in.

8. AB 9° 36′, AC 30°, BC 19° 28′

9. 59°

10. 109° 26′

Exercise 8B

1. 3·5 in., $25\frac{1}{2}°$

2. 2·82 in., 76°

3. 3·5 in., 37°

4. $VA = 2·14$ in., $VC = 2·61$ in.

5. $92\frac{3}{4}°$

(Answers here are given to constructable accuracy.)

Exercise 9A

1. (i) 190·8 cu. in.
(ii) 190·8 sq. in.

2. 17,100 m.p.h.

3. 51 miles

4. 5·455 cm.

5. 33° 34′ N., or 33° 34′ S.

6. 354·7 miles

7. (i) 2,070 miles
(ii) 1,980 miles

8. (i) 34° 0′ S., 58° 37′ W.
(ii) 34° 50′ S., 57° 36′ W.

9. (i) 10,800 miles
(ii) 8,300 miles
(iii) 6,900 miles

10. 215 m.p.h.

ALGEBRA AND THE CALCULUS

Exercise 1A

1. $a^2 + 5a + 6$
2. $b^2 + 2b - 24$
3. $c^2 - 6c - 16$
4. $d^2 - 8d + 15$
5. $2e^2 + e - 6$
6. $3f^2 + 14f - 24$
7. $2g^2 - 11g - 21$
8. $3h^2 - 7h + 2$
9. $6k^2 - 5k - 6$
10. $8m^2 + 6m - 9$
11. $15n^2 - 19n - 10$
12. $6p^2 - 35p + 36$

Exercise 1B

1. $(2a + 1)(a + 3)$
2. $(2a + 3)(a + 1)$
3. $(2a - 3)(a - 1)$
4. $(2a + 1)(a - 3)$
5. $(2a - 1)(a + 3)$
6. $(b + 2)(b + 3)$
7. $(c - 4)(c - 1)$
8. $(d - 4)(d + 1)$
9. $(3e + 2)(e - 1)$
10. $(2f + 1)(f - 4)$
11. $(3g - 2)(g - 4)$
12. $(5h + 3)(h + 2)$
13. $(3k - 2)(2k + 1)$
14. $(4m - 3)(m + 2)$
15. $(3n - 4)(2n + 5)$
16. $(4p + 3)(3p - 4)$

Exercise 1C

1. $(2x - y)(x - 2y)$
2. $(5 - b)(2 + b)$
3. $(x - y)^2$
4. $(4 + c)(2 - c)$

Exercise 1D

1. $2(c - 5)(c + 1)$
2. $2(a - 3)(x - y)$
3. $(b + 5)(b - 5)(b + 1)(b - 1)$

Exercise 1E

1. $x = 0$
2. Either $a = 0$ or $b = 0$ or both a *and* $b = 0$
3. Either $p = 0$ or $q = -4$ or both $p = 0$ and $q = -4$
4. Either $y = 0$ or $y = 3$
5. Either $x = 3$ or $x = -4$
6. Either $x = 1\frac{1}{2}$ or $x = -2$
7. a must be 2, or 3, or -5

Exercise 1F

1. 2, 3
2. 1, − 3
3. 0, − 3
4. 0, 4
5. 2, − 2
6. 5, − 5
7. 0, − $1\frac{1}{2}$
8. 2, $\frac{1}{2}$
9. 3, − $\frac{1}{2}$
10. $\frac{1}{2}$, − 2
11. $\frac{1}{4}$, − $1\frac{1}{3}$
12. 0, 1, 2
13. 2

Exercise 1G

1. 4, − 1
2. 4·2, − 1·2
3. 3·3, − 0·3
4. 2·6, 0·4
5. No roots in this range of x

Exercise 1H

1. 6 or − 2
2. 13, 15
3. 15 ft., 8 ft.
4. 15 in. × 10 in. × 7 in.
5. 21
6. 8 in., 15 in., 17 in.

Exercise 2A

1. $\dfrac{1}{a+1}$
2. $b-2$
3. $\dfrac{1}{c-2}$
4. $\dfrac{2(d+1)}{d-1}$
5. $\dfrac{e-4}{2f-3}$
6. $\frac{2}{3}$
7. $\frac{3}{4}$
8. 2
9. $\frac{1}{3}$

Exercise 2B

1. $\dfrac{6}{(a-4)(a-5)}$
2. $\dfrac{4(b-6)}{3(b+2)}$
3. $\dfrac{2(c+1)}{c+2}$
4. $\frac{4}{5}$
5. 2
6. $\frac{3}{4}$

Exercise 2C

1. $\dfrac{5a+12}{(a+2)(a+3)}$
2. $\dfrac{17-b}{(b-1)(b+3)}$
3. $\dfrac{5-4c}{5(2c+5)}$
4. $\dfrac{2(3x-y)}{(x+y)(x-y)}$
5. $\dfrac{x^2-8x+18}{(x-3)(x-2)}$
6. $\dfrac{6(3x+10)}{x(x+6)}$
7. $\dfrac{3(y+2)}{(y-2)(y+4)}$
8. $\dfrac{2(d+4)}{(d+3)(d+2)}$

Exercise 2D

1. 2
2. $8\frac{1}{6}$
3. $1\frac{5}{8}$
4. 5, -3
5. 5, $\frac{1}{3}$
6. 2
7. 1, $\frac{6}{7}$
8. 8, $\frac{75}{61}$
9. 6, $-6\frac{2}{3}$

Exercise 2E

1. 40 m.p.h.
2. 24 m.p.h.
3. 40 m.p.h.
4. 50 m.p.h.

Exercise 2F

1. 3d.
2. 1s.
3. 20
4. 10

Exercise 2G

1. $x^2 - 7x + 24$, rem. -79
2. $y^2 - y - 6$
3. $(x^2 - 3y^2)$ rem. $7y^3$

Exercise 3A

1. 1
2. $\frac{1}{5}$
3. $\frac{1}{1000}$
4. $\frac{1}{81}$
5. 7
6. 4
7. 3
8. 10
9. 27
10. 343
11. 1000
12. 32
13. 25
14. 16
15. 81
16. 8
17. 32
18. 81
19. 9
20. 32
21. $\frac{1}{10}$
22. $\frac{1}{2}$
23. 4
24. $\frac{27}{8}$ or $3\frac{3}{8}$
25. $\frac{3}{4}$
26. $\frac{2}{5}$
27. 3
28. $\frac{4}{3}$ or $1\frac{1}{3}$
29. $\frac{5}{2}$ or $2\frac{1}{2}$
30. $\frac{27}{125}$

Exercise 3B

1. (i) $\dfrac{\sqrt{a}}{(\sqrt{b})^3}$
(ii) b^2/a^2
(iii) $\dfrac{(\sqrt[3]{b})^2}{(\sqrt[5]{a})^2}$

2. (i) $x^{\frac{1}{5}}$
(ii) $x^{\frac{3}{4}}$
(iii) $x^{-\frac{2}{3}}$
(iv) x^0

3. (i) 10^{-3}
(ii) 10^4
(iii) $10^{-\frac{1}{2}}$
(iv) 10^{-6}

4. (i) ·01
(ii) ·0000353
(iii) $\sqrt{1000}$
(iv) $\sqrt[5]{\cdot 01}$

5. (i) $x^{2\frac{1}{2}}$
(ii) $\dfrac{b^2}{a}$
(iii) a^5
(iv) $\dfrac{x^3}{y^2} + 1$

Exercise 3C

1. (i) 2
(ii) $\frac{1}{3}$
(iii) -3 or $\bar{3}$
(iv) 5
(v) 0

2. (i) 10,000
(ii) $\sqrt{10} = 3{\cdot}162$
(iii) ·01
(iv) 1

3. (i) 1·43136
(ii) 1·17609
(iii) 1·87506
(iv) ·58805
(v) ·30103
(vi) $\bar{1}{\cdot}25527$ or $-{\cdot}74473$

4. (i) 4
(ii) 2
(iii) 1
(iv) 0

5. (i) $10^{1\cdot 7275}$
(ii) $10^{\bar{2}\cdot 7642}$ or $10^{-1\cdot 2358}$

6. (i) 2·52
(ii) ·919
(iii) ·579

7. 1·20

8. 1·13

Exercise 3D

1. $7{\cdot}5 \times 10^{14}$ cycles/sec.

3. $1{\cdot}22 \times 10^{6}$

4. $8\frac{1}{2}$ years

5. 9×10^{18}

6. ·057 cm.

7. $4{\cdot}69 \times 10^{13}$ cm./sec.

8. 316

Exercise 4A

1. All parallel, gradient 3.

2. All through (0, 3).

3. (i) -11.
(ii) 17; $(-2, -11)$, $(5, 17)$; $(0, -3)$, $(\frac{3}{4}, 0)$.

4. (i) 11.
(ii) -10; $(-2, 11)$, $(5, -10)$; $(0, 5)$, $(1\frac{2}{3}, 0)$.

6. 32; 100;
(i) 140.
(ii) 36·9 approx.

Exercise 4B

1. $(-2, -4)$.

2. $6x - x^2 - 7$; $(3, 2)$; $x = 3$.

3. $(\frac{1}{4}, -3\frac{1}{8})$, min.

4. (i) $(1, 9)$, max.
(ii) $(2\frac{1}{2}, 6\frac{1}{4})$, max.

5. $M = -450$, when $x = 15$.

Exercise 6A

1. (i) $2x - 2$
(ii) $(5, 0)$, $(-3, 0)$, $(0, -15)$.
(iii) $8, -8, -2$.
(iv) $(1, -16)$, min.

2. (i) $3 - 2x$
(ii) $(0, 0)$, $(3, 0)$.
(iii) $3, -3$.
(iv) $(1\frac{1}{2}, 2\frac{1}{4})$, max.

Exercise 6B

1. $4x + 4$
2. $-10 - 16x$
3. $6 - 3x^2$
4. $x^2 + x + 1$
5. $18x^2 - 1 - \frac{1}{x^2}$
6. $\frac{1}{2}x - \frac{2}{x^3}$
7. $6x^2 - 10x + 7$
8. $-3 + \frac{4}{x^3}$
9. $4 - \frac{x^2}{2}$
10. $\frac{1}{3x^2} - \frac{6}{x^3}$

Exercise 7A

1. Min. $-6\frac{1}{4}$
2. Min. 1
3. Max. 0 (when $x = 1$)
4. Max. $6\frac{1}{4}$ (when $x = 2\frac{1}{2}$)
5. Max. -3 (when $x = 2$)
6. Min. $-5\frac{1}{3}$ (when $x = -1\frac{1}{3}$)
7. Min. 2 (when $x = 0$); Max. $6\frac{1}{2}$ (when $x = 3$).
8. Max. 7 (when $x = -1$); Min. -20 (when $x = 2$).
9. Max. 16 (when $x = -2$); Min. -16 (when $x = 2$).

Exercise 7B

1. 100
2. 12
3. 2,500 sq. ft.
4. 20 in.
5. 18 cu. in.
6. 2 cu. ft.
7. 2 ft. × 2 ft. × 1 ft.
8. $\frac{1}{2}$ sq. in.

Exercise 8A

1. $-10{\cdot}6$, $-2{\cdot}71$.
2. $-1{\cdot}86$, ${\cdot}68$, $3{\cdot}16$.
4. (ii) $(-3, 0)$
   (iii) $(1, 4)$
   (iv) $(-2, 4)$

Exercise 8B

1. 1

Exercise 9A

1. $\frac{3}{2}x^2 + x + c$
2. $4x^3 + 6x^2 - 8x + c$
3. $\frac{x^3}{3} - 2x^2 + 4x + c$
4. $5x - \frac{4}{3}x^3 + c$
5. $\frac{1}{3}x^3 - 2x - \frac{1}{x} + c$
6. $5x - \frac{1}{x^2} + c$
7. $\frac{1}{4}x^2 - \frac{2}{15}x^3 + c$
8. $-\frac{1}{2x} + \frac{1}{3x^2} + c$
9. $y = x^2 - 2x - 3$
10. (i) $y = 2x^3 + 3x - 2$
    (ii) 20
11. $y = 4x + 3x^2 - x^3 - 18$
12. (i) 9
    (ii) $y = 9x - x^3$
    (iii) $(\pm 3, 0)$

OCL / M2—2E

Exercise 10A

1. (i) 0, 75 ft.
(ii) 15 ft./sec.
(iii) 0, 6, 12, 18, 24, 30 ft./sec.

2. (i) 12 ft. from 0
(ii) After 3 sec.
(iii) 3 ft.
(iv) 6 ft./sec.; 12 ft. from 0.

3. (i) $64 - 32t$ ft./sec.
(ii) 2 sec., 64 ft.
(iii) After 4 sec.; 64 ft./sec. ($v = -64$).

4. (i) 0, 3.
(ii) $3(t-1)(t-3)$.
When $t = 1$, $s = 4$; or $t = 3$, $s = 0$.

Exercise 10B

1. (i) 8 ft./sec.
(ii) $2t - 5$ ft./sec.^{2}
(iii) -5 ft./sec.^{2}, velocity decreases.
(iv) After $2\frac{1}{2}$ sec.; $1\frac{3}{4}$ ft./sec.
(v) 8 ft./sec., 5 ft./sec.^{2}

2. $15 - 6t$ ft./sec., -6 ft./sec.^{2}

3. $v = 4t - 6$, $a = 4$ ft./sec.^{2}; $-6, -2, 2, 6$ ft./sec.; after $1\frac{1}{2}$ sec., 6 in. from 0.

4. 16 ft.; -24 ft./sec.; -12 ft./sec.^{2}

Exercise 10C

1. $100 - 32t$ ft./sec.; $100t - 16t^2$ ft.; $3\frac{1}{8}$ sec.; $156\frac{1}{4}$ ft.; after $6\frac{1}{4}$ sec.

2. -2 ft./sec.^{2}; $8t - t^2$ ft.

3. $v = \frac{1}{4}t^2 - 1$, $s = \frac{1}{12}t^3 - t + 5$; 2 sec.; $3\frac{2}{3}$ ft.

4. (i) 4, 6, 6, 4, 0 ft./sec.
(ii) After $2\frac{1}{2}$ sec.; $6\frac{1}{4}$ ft./sec.
(iii) $s = \frac{5}{2}t^2 - \frac{1}{3}t^3 + 2$
(iv) Negative; $22\frac{5}{6}$.

Exercise 11A

1. $21\frac{1}{3}$
2. $-5\frac{1}{3}$
3. $4\frac{1}{2}$
4. $-20\frac{5}{6}$
5. (i) $\frac{2}{3}$ (ii) $1\frac{1}{3}$
6. $10\frac{2}{3}$
7. 32
8. $3\frac{2}{3}$

Exercise 11B

1. $48{\cdot}6\pi$
2. $1\frac{1}{15}\pi$
3. $3\frac{3}{4}\pi$
4. $6\frac{2}{5}\pi$
6. 509 cu. in.

Exercise 12A

1. ·65, − 4·65
2. 3·45, − 1·45
3. ·16, − 12·16
4. 4·41, 1·59
5. − ·15, − 6·85
6. 20·16, − ·16

Exercise 12B

1. $-\cdot 38, -2\cdot 62$
2. $\cdot 54, -1\cdot 87$
3. $\frac{1}{2}, 2$
4. $2\cdot 27, -1\cdot 77$
5. $2\frac{2}{5}, -1$
6. $1\cdot 64, \cdot 61$
7. $-\cdot 35, -5\cdot 65$
8. $\frac{5}{6}, -1$
9. $3\cdot 23, \cdot 10$
10. $3\cdot 68, -\cdot 68$
11. $4, 0$
12. $\pm 1\cdot 5$

Exercise 12C

1. (i) $-1\cdot 6, -\cdot 36, 1\cdot 9$.
(ii) $-2, 1$.
(iii) $1\cdot 63$
2. (i) -1 to 3
(ii) $-1\cdot 10$ to $2\cdot 43$
(iii) $-1\cdot 10, 2\cdot 43$
3. $1\cdot 35, -1\cdot 85$.
4. $\cdot 38$ to $2\cdot 62$; $\cdot 38, 2\cdot 62$.
5. (i) $-1\cdot 26$
(ii) 1
(iii) 2
(iv) 3. $x = -1\cdot 21, 1, 3\cdot 21$.
6. (i) $3\cdot 75$ (put $x = 1\cdot 2$)
(ii) $5\cdot 35$ (put $x = 2\cdot 3$, take $y - 1$)
(iii) $2\cdot 65$ (put $y = 8$)
(iv) $1\cdot 55$

Exercise 12D

1. $x = 3, y = 5$
or $x = -5, y = -3$.
2. $\frac{1}{2}, 2\frac{1}{2}$ or $-2, 0$.
3. $1, 1$ or $-11, 7$.
4. $-1, -8$ or $\frac{6}{5}, -\frac{7}{5}$.
5. $4, 2$ or $-4, -2$.
6. $-2, 3$ or $2, -3$.
7. $4, -8$ or $\frac{4}{7}, \frac{4}{7}$.
8. $(2, 1)$ or $-\frac{2}{3}, -\frac{7}{9}$.

Exercise 12E

1. $\pm\sqrt{pq}$
2. $\dfrac{c+d}{a-b}$
3. $\dfrac{2ab}{b-a}$
4. $12a$
5. $\dfrac{a^2+b^2}{ab}$
6. $2a$
7. $a + b$
8. $\dfrac{d-c}{a+b}$
9. $x = 2a, y = 3a$
10. a, b
11. $a^2 + b^2, a - b$
12. $\dfrac{a}{b}, \dfrac{b}{a}$
13. $x = -c$ or $-d$
14. p or $-q$
15. $\pm\sqrt{a^2 - ab + b^2}$
16. $2a$ or $2b$

Exercise 12F

1. $h = \dfrac{V}{\pi r^2}$
2. $r = \sqrt[3]{\dfrac{3V}{4\pi}}$
3. (i) $I = \dfrac{T^2C}{4\pi^2}$
(ii) $C = \dfrac{4\pi^2 I}{T^2}$
4. $C = \dfrac{L}{Q^2R^2}$
5. $f = \dfrac{v-u}{t}$

Exercise 12F

6. (i) $u = \sqrt{v^2 - 2fs}$
   (ii) $s = \dfrac{v^2 - u^2}{2f}$

7. $R = \sqrt{\dfrac{V^2}{I^2} - X^2}$

8. $R_3 = \dfrac{VR_1}{E_1 - V}$

9. $I_1 = \dfrac{E^2 I_2}{I - E^2}$

10. $r = \sqrt{4Rh - R^2}$

11. (i) $K = \dfrac{EN}{3(3N - E)}$
    (ii) $N = \dfrac{3EK}{9K - E}$

12. (i) $R = \dfrac{r(21i_2 - 2I)}{I - i_2}$
    (ii) $r = \dfrac{R(I - i_2)}{21i_2 - 2I}$

Exercise 12G

1. (i) Never true
   (ii) Identity
   (iii) Equation, $x = 3$ or -4.
2. $a = 3, b = -2$.
3. $p = 4, q = -1$.
4. $c = d = e = 1$
5. $a = -1, b = 1$; min. 1.
6. $a = 2, b = 3, c = 9$.

Exercise 13A

1. (i) 48
   (ii) 6
2. $y = \dfrac{20}{x^2}$; 80.
3. 27 shillings.
4. 31
5. (i) 10
   (ii) 32
6. $d = \dfrac{3\sqrt{h}}{\sqrt{6}} = \sqrt{\dfrac{3h}{2}}$; 12 miles.

Exercise 13B

1. Multiplies volume by factor 18. 462 cu. in.
2. 162
3. 64 ft.-lb. wt.
4. $P = \frac{1}{10}W + 25$; 400 lb.
5. 33
6. 300·08

Exercise 14A

1. $\dfrac{t+2}{t}$
2. $x + 1$
3. $x(x - 5)$
4. $\dfrac{-x-1}{3x(2+x)}$
5. $\dfrac{2x - y}{3x + y}$
6. $\dfrac{3x - 1}{2x + 3}$
7. $\dfrac{x + 8}{(x-1)(x+2)}$
8. $\dfrac{1}{(x-3)(x-2)}$
9. $\dfrac{5}{2x(2x-5)}$
10. $\dfrac{7x^2 + 2x - 7}{(4x-3)(3x+4)}$
11. $\dfrac{x^2 + y^2}{x^2 - y^2}$
12. $\dfrac{x^2 + y^2}{x^2 - y^2}$
13. $\dfrac{3}{2x - 1}$
14. $\dfrac{x(x+y)}{y(x-y)}$
15. $\dfrac{1}{3x + 2}$
16. 1
17. $\dfrac{1}{x^2 - a^2}$
18. $\dfrac{x+1}{x-2}$
19. $\dfrac{8}{(x+2)(x-1)}$
20. $x - y$

Exercise 14B

1. $(x + 1)(x - 2)(x + 2)$
2. $(2x + 3)(2x - 1)(2x + 1)$
3. $(x - 1)^2(x + 1)$
4. $(x + 3)^2(x - 3)$
5. $(3x - 4y)(3x - 4y - 5)$
6. $(2x - y)(2x - y + 2)$
7. $(p + q)(p + q + 2)$
8. $(x + y)(x - y + 2)$
9. $(3m - 7n)(3m + 7n - 4)$
10. $(x - 2)(2x - 3)(2x + 3)$
11. $(x - 2)(x + 2)(x - 3)(x + 3)$
12. $(x - 1)(x + 1)(x^2 + 1)$
13. $(2a - 5b - 5c)(2a + 5b + 5c)$
14. $(4p + q)(4p + 7q)$
15. $-(x + 3y)(3x + y)$
16. $-3(x + 4y)(3x + 4y)$

Exercise 14C

1. (i) $(x - 1)(x^2 + 2x - 1)$
   (ii) $(x + 1)(x - 2)(2x - 1)$
   (iii) $(x - 3)(2x + 1)(3x - 1)$
2. $k = -4$; $(x + 2)(x - 2)(x + 1)$
3. $p = -17$; $x + 3$, $4x - 1$
4. $a = -5$, $b = 2$; $x + 2$.
5. $c = 8$, $d = -15$; $x - 1$.
6. $\frac{3}{4}$, $-\frac{4}{3}$.
7. $p = 3$; ± 1.
8. $(x - 2)^2(x + 1)^2$; $x^2 - x - 2$.
9. (i) $(2x - 1)(4x^2 + 2x + 1)$
   (ii) $(4y + 5z)(16y^2 - 20yz + 25z^2)$
   (iii) $(x^2 + y^2)(x^4 - x^2y^2 + y^4)$
10. $x = p^2 + pq + q^2$

Exercise 15A

1. (i) -110
   (ii) 260
   (iii) 284
2. $n = 12$, $d = 2$.
3. $a = 6$, $d = 1\frac{1}{2}$.
4. 125250
5. 25
6. 7, 12, 17, 22, 27.
7. 3 or -8
8. 3; 11; 19; $8n - 5$.

Exercise 15B

1. (i) $T_8 = 320$, $S_8 = 637\frac{1}{2}$.
   (ii) -2187; -1640
   (iii) $\frac{512}{243}$; $\frac{25220}{243}$.
2. $\frac{2}{3}$, 2, 6.
3. $-\frac{9}{8}$, $-\frac{133}{216}$.
4. $\frac{3}{4}$; 32; 18, $13\frac{1}{2}$.
5. $a = \pm\frac{16}{27}$, $r = \pm\frac{3}{2}$; $\frac{26}{27}$.
6. $9\frac{13}{16}$.
7. $x = 3$; sum $170\frac{1}{2}$.

GEOMETRY

Exercise 1A

1. $\frac{3}{5}, \frac{2}{5}, \frac{2}{3}. \quad \frac{h}{h+k}, \quad \frac{k}{h+k}, \quad \frac{k}{h}.$

2. $\frac{AB}{AC} = \frac{XY}{XZ}. \quad \frac{AC}{BC} = \frac{XZ}{YZ}.$ Three more by inverting the fractions.

3.

A P B Q

4. Write $OA = OB = a$; $OP = x$; $OQ = y$. Then $\frac{a+x}{a-x} = \frac{y+a}{y-a}.$

Hence easily $\frac{a}{x} = \frac{y}{a}$ $\therefore$ $a^2 = xy$, i.e. $OA^2 = OP.OQ$.

5. (i) $ay = (bR).y, \; bx = b(Ry)$.

(ii) $\frac{a+b}{a-b} = \frac{bR+b}{bR-b} = \frac{R+1}{R-1}$ and $\frac{x+y}{x-y} = \frac{yR+y}{yR-y}$; this also $= \frac{R+1}{R-1}.$

(iii) $\frac{a+x}{b+y} = \frac{bR+yR}{b+y} = R.$

6. $\left\{\begin{matrix} OP + OA = AP \\ OB - OP = BP \end{matrix}\right\}$ *Subtract:* since $OA = OB$ $\therefore$ $AP - BP = 2.OP$

Likewise $OA + OQ = AQ$, $OQ - OB = BQ$. Add these.

The other two answers are: OA, OB (these are equal).

7. In each of the three figures, join BX first, then join AY. Show that the areas of $\triangle OBX$, $\triangle OAY$ are equal, and that

$$\frac{OA}{OX} = \frac{\triangle OAB}{\triangle OBX}, \quad \frac{OB}{OY} = \frac{\triangle OAB}{\triangle OAY}$$

For the other two results, go back to the Theorem.

8. In Fig. 5, make OA 3 units, AX 5 units, then OX is 8 units.

$$\frac{\triangle OAB}{\triangle OBX} = \frac{OA}{OX}, \quad \frac{\triangle OBX}{\triangle OXY} = \frac{OB}{OY}$$

9. Prove by using areas. There is another way: draw $AC \parallel XY$, to cut OY at C. Then by Theorem I, $\frac{OC}{OY} = \frac{OA}{OX}$ which $= \frac{OB}{OY}$ (given)

$\therefore$ B is the same point as C.

11. $OB = 7\frac{1}{2}$ in.

12. $YX = 7\frac{1}{2}$ in.; $CX = 4\frac{1}{2}$ in.

13. (Pythagoras' Theorem) $BC = 5$ cm. $OX = 15$ cm.

14. $YC = \frac{1}{2}CX$.

15. In the first or third figure, $XY = 2AB \therefore AB = 3$ in.

16. First figure, $\frac{OB}{OY} = \frac{8}{12}$, $OB = 2BY = 30$ in.

Third figure, $\frac{OB}{BY} = \frac{2}{5}$, $OB = 6$ in.

Nos. 17, 21, 22 are examples of perspective; the method is to draw a figure of the right shape and reduce it to fit. (Compare Fig. 3.)

17. Draw a square on the base BC, and below it. Join its corners to A; this gives X, Y, and the small square is found by drawing parallels. For the semicircle; draw a semicircle on BC as diameter; join its centre and its lowest point to A. The latter join cuts BC at D, and $DE \perp BC$ gives the centre of the required semicircle.

18. $MNBP$ is a parallelogram (why?); then use Theorem 1.

20. Produce OM to N, with $MN = 2.OM$. Draw $NY \parallel AO$, to cut OB at Y. Draw the line through YM, to meet OA at X. Then $\frac{XM}{MY} = \frac{OM}{MN} = \frac{1}{2}$.

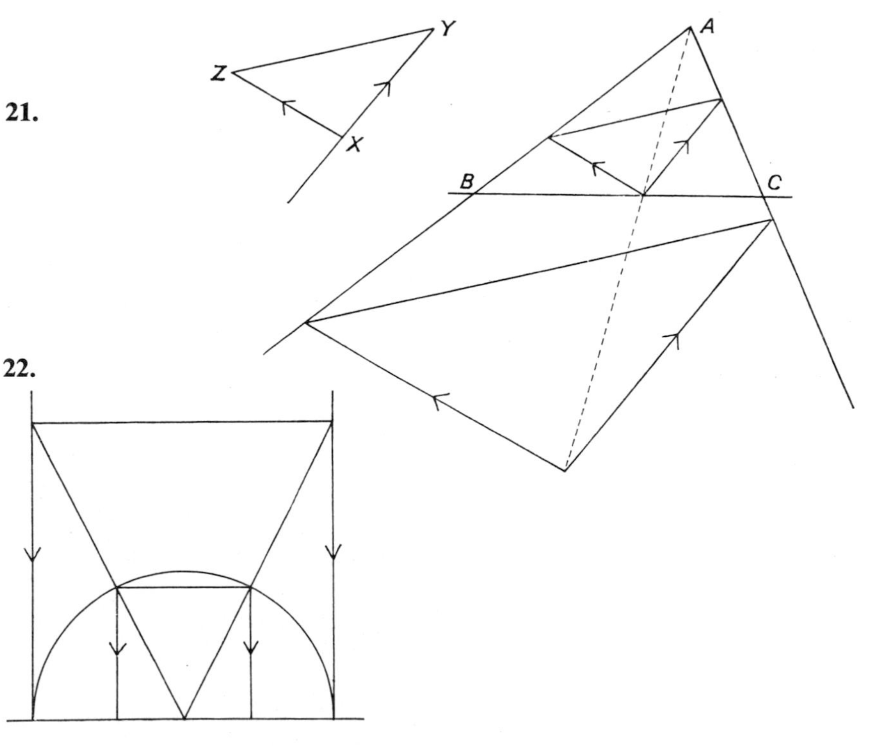

Exercise 1B

2. $\triangle ADB$, $\triangle CDA$ are similar; because $D\hat{A}C = 90° - B\hat{A}D = D\hat{B}A$
$\therefore \dfrac{AD}{CD} = \dfrac{DB}{DA}$

3. If X is inside the circle, the angles at B, C are in the same segment, therefore equal; so are the angles A, D. If X is outside, $BADC$ is a cyclic quadrilateral; $X\hat{B}D$, exterior to this, equals $\hat{C}$; likewise $X\hat{D}B = A$.

6. Is proved by No. 5.

7. To compare with No. 2, notice that $B\hat{A}C$ is a right-angle.

8. Another way to say the same thing is: $\dfrac{CD}{DZ} = \cos \hat{D}$; $\dfrac{DZ}{BD} = \cos \hat{D}$.

Exercise 1C

1. If any pair of parallel radii are drawn in the same sense, their ends are in line with S.
Then $\dfrac{HS}{KS} = \dfrac{H'S}{K'S}$ $\therefore HH' \parallel KK'$. Also $\dfrac{HH'}{KK'} = \dfrac{HS}{KS} = \dfrac{a}{b}$

3. (i) $HK \parallel AB$; there is no S (or "S is at infinity").
S' is the mid-point of AB.
(ii) No point S'.
(iii) S' is the point where the circles touch.
(iv) No S, but S' exists, and is inside both circles.
(v) No S; S' is the common centre.

4. See Chapter 2, Fig. 19 (ii), page 335.

Exercise 1D

1. $\triangle OAB$, $\triangle OHK$ are similar, $O\hat{B}A = O\hat{K}H$, and $ABHK$ is cyclic.

2. $\dfrac{OP}{OX} = \dfrac{OX}{OQ}$. Given $OP.OQ = r^2$ $\therefore$ $\dfrac{OP}{r} = \dfrac{r}{OQ}$ and $OX = r$.
Since $\hat{O}$ is in both $\triangle OPX$ and $\triangle OXQ$, they are similar, and $\dfrac{PX}{XQ} = \dfrac{OP}{OX} = \dfrac{OP}{r}$, wherever X may be on the circle.

3. $\triangle OAB \;|||\; \triangle OBC$ (Theorem IV) $\therefore$ $\dfrac{OA}{OB}$ and $\dfrac{OB}{OC}$ each $= \dfrac{AB}{BC}$.
Multiply these together.

4. If the four points did lie on a circle, $\hat{A} + \hat{C}$ would equal 180°. But $\hat{C} = A\hat{B}O$, so that $\hat{A} + A\hat{B}O$ would have to equal 180°.
This cannot happen unless $A\hat{O}B$ is zero; and then O, A, B and also C would be in a straight line, not on a circle.
A ridiculous figure is possible, in which A, B, C are all at the same place (call it A); then any number of circles can be drawn through O and A.

Exercise 1E

1. In Fig. 24; instead of CZ, draw $KM \perp$ on AC, $KN \perp$ on AB.
Then $KM = KN$.

$$\left.\begin{array}{l}\triangle ABK = \frac{1}{2}.AB.KN \\ \triangle ACK = \frac{1}{2}.AC.KM\end{array}\right\} \text{their ratio} = \frac{AB}{AC}, \text{ but also} = \frac{BK}{CK}.$$

2. In Fig. 25, prove $HP = HQ$, by areas ($HP.AB = BH$.Altitude); or else draw $HL \parallel CA$, to meet AB at L, and prove $LH = LA$ by Theorem I.

3. In Fig. 26, $\hat{D} = \hat{C}$, in the same segment;
$D\hat{B}X = D\hat{A}C$, in the same segment;

$\triangle AXC \ ||| \ \triangle BXD$:

$$\therefore \frac{AX}{BX} = \frac{XC}{XD}$$

$\triangle AXC$, $\triangle ABD$ also have two pairs of equal angles: $\dfrac{AX}{AB} = \dfrac{AC}{AD}$

4. By No. 3, $\left.\begin{array}{l}AB.AC = AX.AD \\ BX.XC = AX.XD\end{array}\right\}$ also $AX = AD - XD$.

Subtract: $AB.AC - BX.XC = AX.(AD - XD)$
$= AX^2$.

Also $\dfrac{BX}{XC} = \dfrac{AB}{AC}$ (by Theorem V).

Hence (i) $\dfrac{BX}{9} = \dfrac{XC}{4}$, and their sum is 39; $BX = 27$, $XC = 12$.

$AX^2 = 45.20 - 27.12$
$= 900 - 324 = 576$, $AX = 24$ in.

(ii) $\dfrac{BX}{4} = \dfrac{XC}{2}$, $BX + XC = 3$; $BX = 2$, $XC = 1$.

$AX^2 = 4.2 - 2.1 = 6$, $AX = \sqrt{6}$ in.

Exercise 1F

2. First make a rectangle on the same base as the triangle, and half the perpendicular height; then construct a square as in Fig. 16.

3. Really the same method as in Fig. 16. Notice how the perpendicular is drawn: AO, BO are made equal, and with centre O a circle is drawn through A, B. AL is a diameter, $A\hat{B}L$ is the angle in a semicircle.

4. There are two semicircles here: $OB^2 = 1 \times 3$
$OY^2 = 1 \times 5$

$\dfrac{XY}{AB} = \dfrac{OY}{OB}$ by parallels. $\therefore \dfrac{XY^2}{AB^2} = \dfrac{5}{3}$

Exercise 2A

1. If $O\hat{A}B$ is obtuse, and C is on the line BA beyond A, then $O\hat{A}C$ is acute; then use Theorem VIII.

2. Construct at A a line $\perp OA$.

3. $\triangle OPB \equiv \triangle OQB$, because $OP = OQ$ radii;
OB is common.
$\hat{P} = \hat{Q}$ right-angles. $\therefore$ $BP = BQ$.

4. Join PQ, to cut OB at C. By No. 3, $C\hat{O}P = C\hat{O}Q$.
$\therefore$ $\triangle OCP \equiv \triangle OCQ$ (S A S); angles at C are equal and are therefore right-angles.

5. Each triangle has a right-angle and each has the same angle at O.

Exercise 2B

2. If C is not on AB, then $AB + BC > AC$.
Also $BY = BC$, so that $AY > AC$. But Y is inside the large circle, so $AY < AX$ which $= AC$.
AY can't be both greater and less, so C *is* on AB.

3. A is on the line through the centres; the distance is 7 in.

4. Draw OCD to cut the outer circle at D. This line is perpendicular to AB (Why?); then $OC = 3 - x$, $BC = 1\frac{1}{2} + x$, and $\triangle OBC$ has a right-angle at O. $OC^2 + OB^2 = BC^2$.

$$\therefore (3 - x)^2 + (1\tfrac{1}{2})^2 = (x + 1\tfrac{1}{2})^2$$
$$x^2 - 6x + 9 = x^2 + 3x$$
$$9x = 9; \text{ the radius is 1 in.}$$

5. $A\hat{O}C$ is 45°, notice two perpendicular lines, each 2 in. $EC = EA = x$. Hence the two lines marked $(x - 2)$, sides of a right-angled triangle whose hypotenuse is $(x + 2)$.

$$2(x - 2)^2 = (x + 2)^2,\ 2x^2 - 8x + 8 = x^2 + 4x + 4$$
$$x^2 - 12x + 4 = 0,\ (x - 6)^2 = 32,\ x = 6 \pm \sqrt{32}.$$

There are two possible circles, radii about 11·66 and 0·34 in. The smaller circle is not shown.

6. Let the tangents at B, C meet at O; $OB = OC$, tangents to the same circle; $OB = OA$ for the same reason, and $OC = OA$.

7. Draw a sketch: a square $ABCD$: two circles must have centres on the diagonal AC (P nearer A), and the other two have centres X (nearer B) and Y both on the line BD. Draw circles P, X.
Mark Q on AC, so that $XQ = XP$, and show that $AP = QC$. You had already sketched two circles, centres X, P, touching each other and

"jammed" in two corners of the square. Now a circle with centre Q to touch CD, CB will be equal to the circle round P ($AP = QC$) and will touch the X-circle. Likewise $XB = YD$ etc.

Exercise 2C

1. $V\hat{A}B = 90° + C\hat{A}B$ $\quad\quad A\hat{D}B = 180° - A\hat{C}B$
   $= 180° - A\hat{C}B$ $\quad\quad$ (in opposite segment)

   A better proof is:
   Join DA, DB. $A\hat{D}C$ is a right-angle (in semicircle)
   $\therefore\ A\hat{D}B =$ right-angle $+ B\hat{D}C$
   $=$ right-angle $+ B\hat{A}C$ (in same segment)
   $= V\hat{A}B$
   Proofs which use 180° are clumsy; see Chapter 4.

2. By Theorem X, the tangent does make an angle with AB, equal to $\hat{C}$: but there is a second line through A which does so . . .

3. . . . on the other side of AB; this line cuts the circle again at Z. $B\hat{A}Z = B\hat{C}A$, so arc $BZ =$ arc BA; $\triangle ABZ$ is isosceles.

4. Construct at A a perpendicular to the radius; this is a tangent. With a protractor draw the marked angles, 60° and 40°. The angles in the alternate segments must be 60° (left) and 40°; the third angle is 80°.

5. Draw a sketch; draw the common tangent at X, RXS; make R, Q on the same side of the line MN. $P\hat{M}N = P\hat{X}S$ (Theorem X)
   $= Q\hat{X}R$ (vert. opp.)
   $= Q\hat{N}X$ (Theorem X)

   $\therefore\ MP \parallel NQ$ (equal alternate angles).

6. For each of the angles $A\hat{B}C$, $A\hat{C}B$ equals the angle between the tangent and AB, by Theorem X and by parallels.

7. First prove $LN = NM$; then $T\hat{M}N = N\hat{L}M$ (alt. segt.)
   $= N\hat{M}L$ ($LN = NM$).

Exercise 2D

1. $TB.TC = TA^2$, so $4.TC = 36$. $TC = 9$ in.

2. Let TB be x in. $x(x + 6) = 16$,
   $\therefore\ (x + 3)^2 = 25$.
   $x + 3 = 5$, $x = 2$. Of course, not $x + 3 = -5$.

3. $TM^2 - MB^2 = (TM - MB)(TM + MB)$
   $= (TM - MB)(TM + MC)$ the perpendicular bisects BC
   $= TB.TC = TA^2$

4. The square of each tangent $= XH.XK$.

Exercise 4A

1. $BP = PQ$ ($PY \parallel QC$). $PQ = QD$ ($QX \parallel AP$). $\therefore$ BD is "trisected."

2, 3. Mid-point Theorem. In each figure two lines are parallel to one diagonal AC, the other two are parallel to BD.

Exercise 4B

1. Of course, you didn't draw the circle to go through B and C. Look at the pairs of equal tangents (Fig. 1):

$$AX = AY, \quad CY = CY',$$
$$BX = BX', \quad ZX' = ZY'$$

and, since $AB = AC$, $BX = CY$.

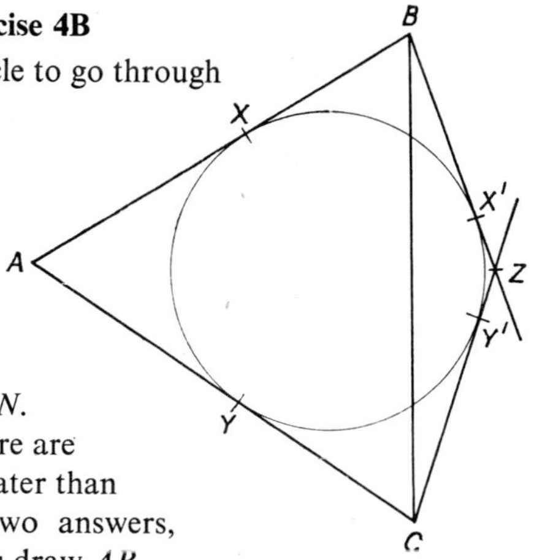

FIG. 1

2. Let P be the point of contact, for the tangent AB.
AO bisects $M\hat{O}P$, BO bisects $P\hat{O}N$.
So, $A\hat{O}B$ is half $M\hat{O}N$, but . . . there are two angles $M\hat{O}N$, one of them greater than two right-angles. So there are two answers, according to which side of MN you draw AB.

3. The area $= AB$ times the average perpendicular height

$$= \tfrac{1}{2}AB.(AP + QB)$$

and $AP + QB = PQ$ (each equals one bit of PQ).
Draw the figure on page 372.

4. Draw $CM \perp$ on AB, to cut PQ at M. CM is a tangent to both circles. $MP = MC = MQ$. M is the centre of a semicircle through P, C, Q.
This circle touches AB at C.
$P\hat{C}R$ is a right-angle, and the line QR passes through C.
The figures $APMC$, $MQBC$ are similar. $A\hat{M}B$ is a right-angle.
The circle through A, M, B touches PQ.
$CM^2 = \ldots$ (you'd never guess?)

Exercise 4C

1. $C\hat{X}O$, $C\hat{Y}O$ are both right-angles, $\therefore$ CO is a diameter of the small circle.

2. Then

$$\begin{aligned} L\hat{X}O &= L\hat{O}X \ldots (LX = LO) \\ &= C\hat{Y}X \ldots \text{same segment} \\ &= X\hat{B}A, \text{ since } XYAB \text{ is cyclic.} \end{aligned}$$

Exercise 5A

1. Join MP; $\triangle OMP$ has $MO + OP > MP$, also $OP = OA$ radii, so $MA = MO + OP > MP$.
2. P is "any other point," so MA is the longest line. $\triangle OMP$ gives $MP + MO > OP$, $\therefore > OB$, which $= MB + MO$, etc.
3. AB the longer side; the diagonals cross at O. Then $OA + OB > AB$. But these are halves of the diagonals, $\therefore$ sum of the diagonals $> 2.AB$.
4. AP the perpendicular on a, AQ any other join. Since $\triangle APQ$ has a right-angle at P, the angle Q is smaller; by Theorem I, $AQ > AP$.
5. PX divides the figure into two triangles, PXQ, PXR; the angles at X are exterior to these two triangles, so one angle at $X > \hat{P}$, the other $> \hat{Q}$, and since angles $\hat{P}$, $\hat{Q}$ are equal, $P\hat{X}Q > Q$; therefore $PQ > PX$, Theorem I. Or, draw the circle centre P, radius PQ; every point on the chord QR is inside this circle.

Exercise 5B

1. Must be a square, and its area is 8 sq. in.
2. Two positions can always be found where the areas of the rectangles are equal. In Fig. 2, $AP = CQ$, and $\triangle AHP \equiv \triangle QYC$ (S A A). So, easily, the rectangles $BHPK$, $BXQY$ are equal in area. Starting with P at A and Q at C, you have two zero rectangles; the area increases as you move P, Q towards the mid-point of AC, and when they reach this point you have the greatest possible area, half that of $\triangle ABC$.

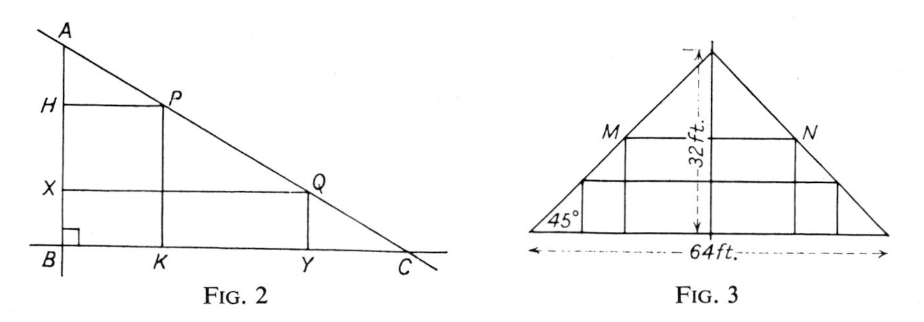

FIG. 2 FIG. 3

3. All possible rectangles are "inscribed" as shown in Fig. 3, in a triangle whose base 64 ft. is along the wall. For the maximum area, the corners are the mid-points M, N, and the area is

$$32 \times 16 = 512 \text{ sq. ft.}$$

4. Since the base is fixed, the triangle will be greatest if its perpendicular height is greatest. Its vertex is A, the mid-point of the larger arc BC (sketch this).

5. Begin with an equilateral triangle ABC. Refer to No. 4; if A is moved along the circumference, this makes the perpendicular height less; so any alteration from the equilateral triangle makes the area less.

6. Take 6 in. as base; the perpendicular height cannot be more than 5 in.; so, make AB 6 in., B a right-angle and BC 5 in. The maximum area is 15 sq. in.

7. Make the diagonals cross at right-angles. One of them is 10 in., the other is cut in two pieces x in., $8 - x$ in., and the total area is $\frac{1}{2}.10x + \frac{1}{2}.10(8 - x)$ sq. in.

Exercise 5C

1. (1) Is proved by $OB = OC$ radii, angles at L are equal (right-angles), and $\hat{B} = \hat{C}$.

(2) By (S S S), hence the adjacent angles at mid-point M are equal.

(3) MP bisects BC at M, at right-angles.

If P is any point on the line (MP), then $PB = PC$. This is not enough to prove that MP passes through the centre of the circle, although OB does equal OC. You must prove that if O is not on the line, then OB cannot equal OC. In Fig. 4, Z is not on MP; left or right makes no difference, but it is shown on the left; then ZC cuts the perpendicular bisector at P.

$ZC = ZP + PC = ZP + PB > ZB$

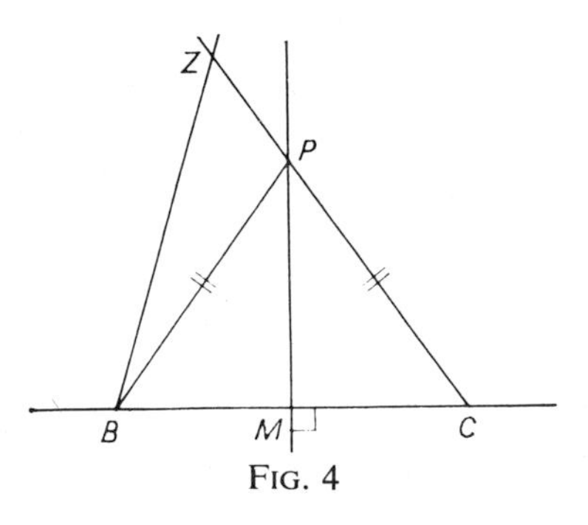

FIG. 4

Exercise 5D

1. E is the centre of a circle through $A\ Q\ H$,

$$\therefore\ E\hat{Q}A = E\hat{A}Q.$$

X is the centre of a circle $B\ Q\ C$,

$$\therefore\ X\hat{Q}C = \hat{C}.$$

The sum of these two angles is a right-angle.

$\therefore\ X\hat{Q}E$ is a right-angle.

2. EY, joining two mid-points, is parallel to CH, likewise $XY \parallel AB$, and CH, AB are at right-angles.

3. $E\hat{P}X$ is a given right-angle; by the same proofs as in No. 1 and 2, EX subtends a right-angle at each of the remaining "nine points."

Exercise 5E

1. $A\hat{K}D$ is a right-angle (in semicircle) $= A\hat{P}B$.

2. $K\hat{A}C = K\hat{B}C$ (same segment)
   $= B\hat{K}D$ ($KD \parallel BC$)
   $= B\hat{A}D$ (same segment), and each $= 90° - \hat{C} = 27°$.
   $\hat{A} = 180° - 103° = 77°$
   Then $D\hat{A}K = (77 - \text{twice } 27)° = 23°$.

3. Another way; equal arcs subtend equal angles at the circle, and also the lengths of arcs are actually proportional to the angles which they subtend at the circle. $K\hat{B}C = B\hat{K}D$ by parallels, so arc KC = arc BD. $DKCA$ and DBA are semicircles, therefore
   arc DK + arc AC = arc BA.
   $\therefore\ D\hat{A}K + \hat{B} = \hat{C}$.
   Finally, $DK = AD.\sin(\hat{C} - \hat{B})$.

4. In Fig. 5, $DE \perp BC$.
   $\triangle DEB \equiv \triangle KPC$, $BE = PC$.
   $BP = EP + PC = DK + PC$.
   Show that
   $$BP^2 - PC^2 = c^2 - b^2$$
   $$BP + PC = a$$
   Then $DK = BP - PC = \dfrac{c^2 - b^2}{a}$

5. This follows because
   $DK = 2R.\sin(\hat{C} - \hat{B})$
   and $a = 2R.\sin\hat{A}$.
   Therefore $\dfrac{c^2 - b^2}{a^2} = \dfrac{DK}{a}$

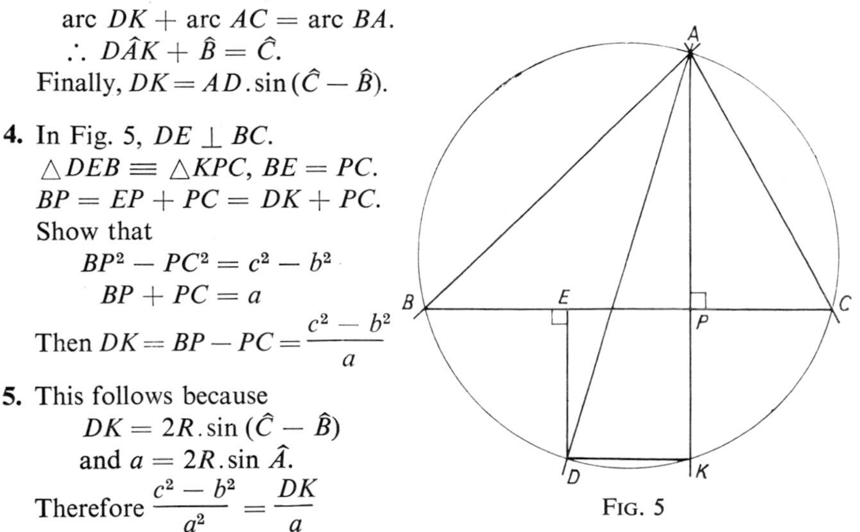

Fig. 5

Exercise 5F

1. $\triangle HBC$, $\triangle KBC$ have BC common
   $B\hat{C}H = B\hat{A}H$ (circle through $A\ C\ P\ S$)
   $= B\hat{C}K$ (same segment)
   likewise $C\hat{B}H = C\hat{B}K$
   So the circle through $B\ H\ C$ = the circle through $B\ K\ C$, which is in fact the circle $A\ B\ C$.

2. $Q\ C\ P\ H$ lie on a circle $\therefore\ Q\hat{P}H = Q\hat{C}H$
   $Q\ C\ B\ S$ also $\quad Q\hat{C}H = Q\hat{B}S$
   and $P\ H\ S\ B$ $\quad Q\hat{B}S = H\hat{P}S$, so HP bisects $Q\hat{P}S$.

Exercise 5G

2. Produce PX to Y. $A\hat{X}Y = A\hat{B}P$ (exterior angle theorem)
$= N\hat{L}X$

Exercise 5H

1. $I\hat{B}L$, $I\hat{C}L$ are right-angles, so a circle can be drawn through $IBLC$. Then $I\hat{L}B = I\hat{C}B = \frac{1}{2}\hat{C}$.

2. $AX = AY$ (tangents from A),
i.e. $AB + BX = AC + CY$.
If the circle touches BC at Z, $BX = BZ$ and $CY = CZ$.
This gives $AB + BZ = AC + CZ$; add these together,

$$AX + AY = AB + BZ + CZ + AC$$
$$= c + a + b$$
$$\triangle = \triangle LBA + \triangle LCA - \triangle LBC$$
$$= \tfrac{1}{2}r_1\,(c + b - a)$$
$$= r_1\,(s - a)$$

3. Angles $M\hat{A}C$, $N\hat{A}B$ are equal, $90° - \frac{1}{2}\hat{A}$.
If $MN \parallel BC$, $M\hat{A}C = \hat{C}$, $N\hat{A}B = \hat{B}$, therefore $\hat{B} = \hat{C}$.

Exercise 5J

1. As in Fig. 18, $x^2 - y^2 = 7^2 - 5^2$
$= 24$
$x + y = 8$ $\qquad \cos\hat{C} = \frac{1}{2}$, $\hat{C} = 60°$
$x - y = 3$ $\qquad \cos\hat{B} = \frac{11}{14}$, $\hat{B} = 38°\ 13'$

2. $x^2 - y^2 = 65^2 - 56^2$
$= 121 \times 9 = 33^2$
Here $x = 33$, $y = 0$; $\hat{C}$ is a right-angle; $\hat{B}$ is almost $60°$; $\cos\hat{B} = \cdot 5077$, and $\hat{B} = 59°\ 30'$.

3. $x^2 - y^2 = 13^2 - 7^2$ $\qquad \cos\hat{B}\ \ \dfrac{12\cdot 03}{13}$ $\qquad \begin{array}{r} 1\cdot 0803 \\ 1\cdot 1139 \\ \hline \bar{1}\cdot 9664 \end{array}$ $\qquad \cos\hat{C}\ \ \dfrac{4\cdot 971}{7}$ $\qquad \begin{array}{r} 0\cdot 6965 \\ 0\cdot 8451 \\ \hline \bar{1}\cdot 8514 \end{array}$
$= 120$
$x + y = 17$ $\qquad \hat{B} = 22°\ 15'$ $\qquad \hat{C} = 44°\ 45'$
$x - y = 7\cdot 058$ $\qquad \hat{A} = 113°$
This calculation avoided the negative sign.

Exercise 6A

5. In No. 3, a plane through MN; at right-angles to AB.
In No. 4, the surface of a cylinder; AB is the axis, and the radius of a cross-section is 2 in.

7. P can move on the perpendicular bisector—and also on the line AB, from A to B only; for then $P\hat{A}B$, $P\hat{B}A$ are both zero. If P is beyond A, $P\hat{A}B = 180°$, $P\hat{B}A = 0$.

8. (1) The perpendicular bisector (Fig. 6).

(2) On the line BC but either beyond B, when $A\hat{P}C$ is the same angle as $A\hat{P}B$.

(3) Or, likewise, beyond C.

(4) Draw the circle through A, B, C; AB, AC are equal chords, therefore they subtend equal angles at every point on the arc opposite A.

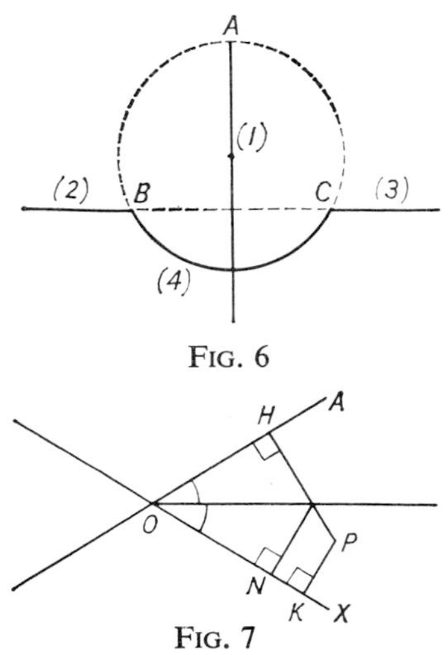

FIG. 6

FIG. 7

9. Nowhere else. If P is "on the X-side"
$PH^2 = OP^2 - OH^2$
$PK^2 = OP^2 - OK^2$
and $OK > ON$, which $= OH$
$\therefore OK > OH$ and $PH > PK$.

Exercise 6B

2. A square. One side AB is drawn first, 2 in. long. C lies on

(1) the perpendicular to AB at B;
(2) the circle, centre B, radius 2 in.

Then D lies on

(1) the circle, centre C, radius 2 in.
(2) the circle, centre A, radius 2 in.

3. Four positions. Two lines parallel to AB, 2 in. distant from AB, cross the circle, centre A, radius 3 in., in four points.

4. Make PQR equilateral, and draw the circle through P, Q with centre R. The angle at R is 60°, and for every point X on the larger arc, $P\hat{X}Q$ is 30°. On the smaller arc, 150°; this arc is out of bounds. The complete locus is two larger arcs, which are images in PQ.

5. P lies (1) on the bisector of $B\hat{A}C$;
(2) on the perpendicular bisector of BC.

Draw the circle through A, B, C. (1) bisects the arc opposite to A. (2) passes through the centre of the circle and also through the mid-point of this arc. The two lines cross at one point only, P, which is on the circle and is the mid-point of this arc.

Exercise 6C

1. Two semicircles, *i.e.* the complete circle on diameter AB.

2.

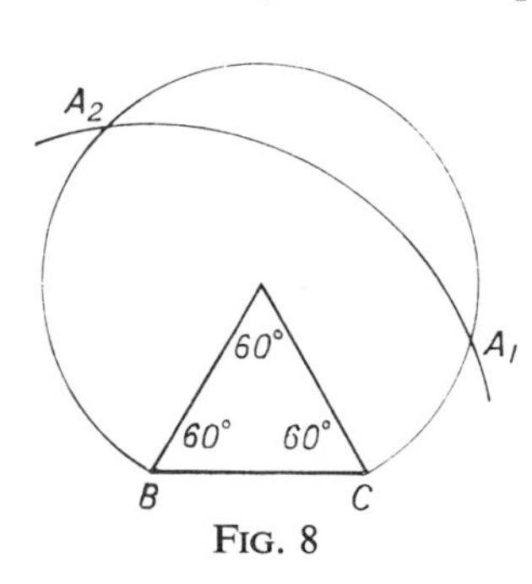

FIG. 8

3.

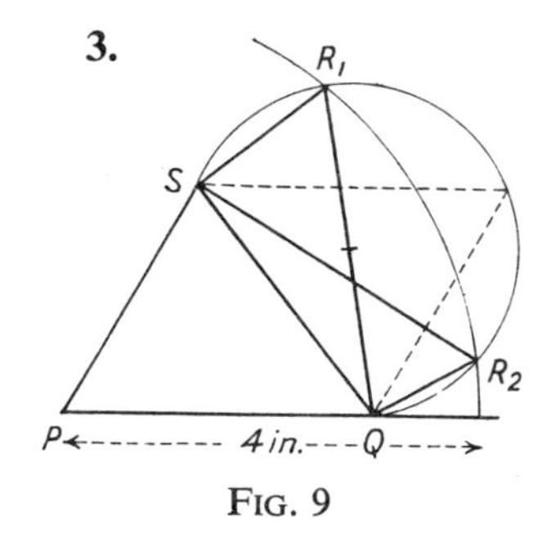

FIG. 9

Exercise 6D

1. AM is $\frac{5}{8}$ of $AB = 2\frac{1}{2}$ in.
AN is $\frac{5}{2}$ of $AB = 10$ in.
$\therefore$ MN is $7\frac{1}{2}$ in.

2. In general if $\dfrac{PA}{PB} = k$

(1) $\begin{cases} AM = \dfrac{k}{k+1}.AB \\ AN = \dfrac{k}{k-1}.AB \end{cases}$ $\quad \therefore MN = AB\left(\dfrac{k}{k-1} - \dfrac{k}{k+1}\right) = AB.\dfrac{2k}{k^2-1}$

when k is greater, AM is greater, but AN is less.

(2) Also MN, the diameter, is smaller. (1) is enough by itself to prove the result.

3. (i) The point B only;
(ii) The perpendicular bisector of AB;
(iii) A circle whose centre is beyond A, instead of beyond B;
(iv) The point A.

4. From the measurements given:

$$CK = CB = 1\tfrac{1}{2} \text{ in.}$$
$$CM.CN = \tfrac{1}{2}.4\tfrac{1}{2} = 2\tfrac{1}{4} \text{ sq. in.} \therefore CK^2 = CM.CN^*$$

(*This is true whatever the given ratio may be.)

Then $\triangle CMK$, $\triangle CKN$ are similar (S A S).

Since $\dfrac{CM}{CK} = \dfrac{CK}{CN}$ and the triangles have the same angle at C.

$\therefore$ $C\hat{K}M = C\hat{N}K$, and CK is a tangent to the circle MKN (alternate segment theorem).

Exercise 6E

1. $CB = 3$; $2(PC^2 + CB^2) = 50$
$$PC^2 = 25 - 9 = 16, \therefore PC \text{ is } 4 \text{ in.}$$

Exercise 6F

1. Sketch the figure; $AC = CS$ (Mid-point Theorem)
and $AP = \frac{1}{2}SR$
Radius of the R-circle is $2CP$.

2. Mark Q, mid-point of OP. Draw $QM \parallel PC$, to cut OC at M. M is the mid-point of OC and $MQ = \frac{1}{2}CP$.
Q moves on a circle; radius one-half that of the given circle, and centre the mid-point of OC.

Exercise 6G

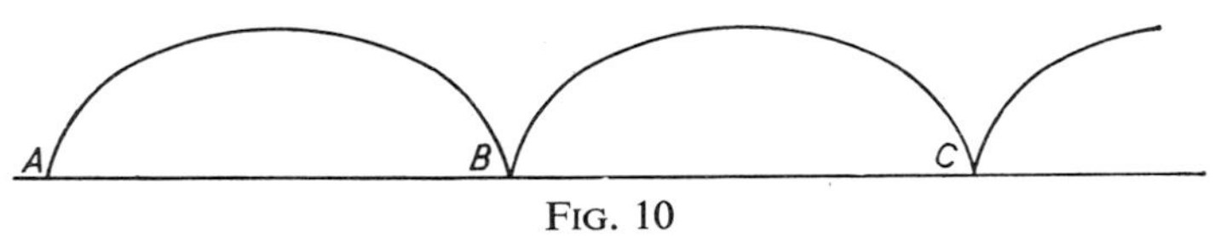

FIG. 10

1. A series of loops. AB = circumference of the circle = BC etc. The area inside each loop is 3 times the area of the circle. The length of the arc from A to B is 4 times the diameter of the circle (a cycloid).

2. For proof see Fig. 19 on page 411.

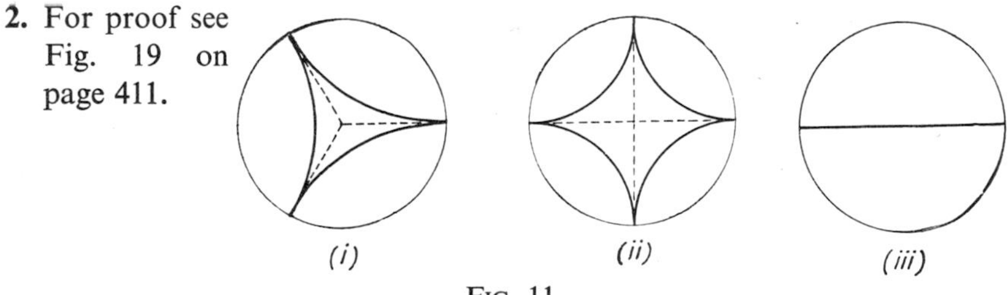

FIG. 11

3. A spiral curve. If the string is first wrapped round the pencil and then unwound, its length in the positions shown (Fig. 12) is roughly 3, 6, 9, times the diameter.

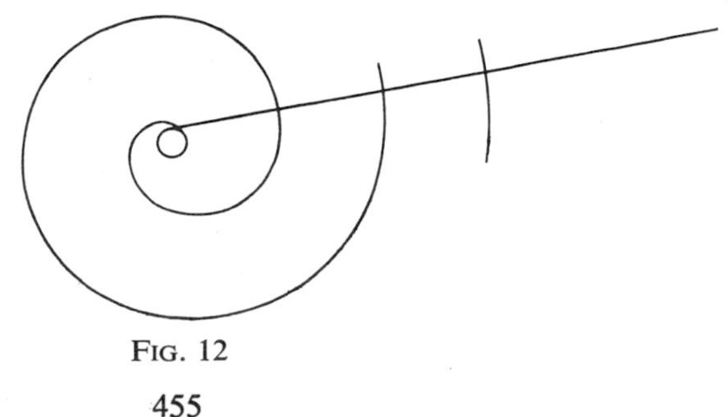

FIG. 12

ANSWERS TO SPECIMEN EXAMINATION PAPER

1. (i) $8\frac{3}{4} \times$ £12 8s. 8d.

	£	s.	d.
	12	8	8
			8
8 tons cost	99	9	4
10 cwt. cost	6	4	4
5 cwt. cost	3	2	2
	£108	15	10

Ans. £108 15s. 10d.

Or $(9 - \frac{1}{4}) \times$ £12 8s. 8d.
= £111 18s. 0d. − £3 2s. 2d.
= £108 15s. 10d. Ans.

(ii) Area of floor $= 6 \times 4\frac{1}{2}$ sq. yd.
$= 27$ sq. yd.
Length of carpet $= 27 \div \frac{3}{4}$ yd.

$$= \frac{\overset{9}{\cancel{27}}}{1} \times \frac{4}{\underset{1}{\cancel{3}}}$$

$= 36$ yd. Ans. 36 yd.

Or $4\frac{1}{2}$ yd. = 162 in.
∴ Width of 27 in. is contained in this 6 times.
∴ Length required is 6×6 yd. = 36 yd. Ans.

2. (i)
$$3x - 4y = 10 \quad (1) \times 3$$
$$5x + 3y = 7 \quad (2) \times 4$$

(1) × 3, $9x - 12y = 30$ (3)
(2) × 4, $20x + 12y = 28$ (4)

(3) + (4), $29x = 58$
$x = 2$

Subst. in (2) $10 + 3y = 7$
$3y = -3$
$y = -1$

Ans. $x = 2, y = -1$

(Check in (1). L.H.S. $= 6 - 4(-1) = 6 + 4 = 10 =$ R.H.S.)

(ii)

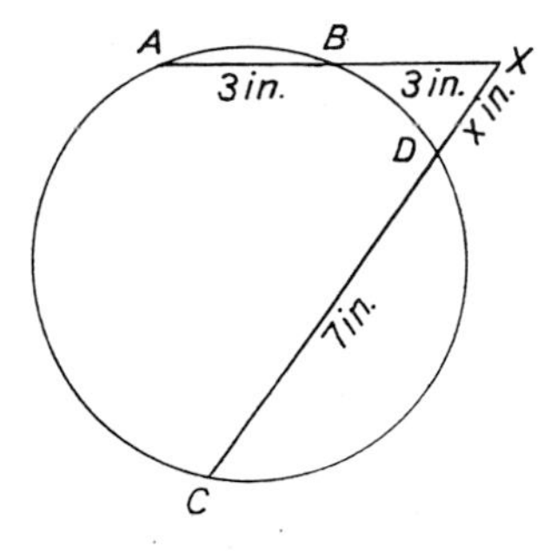

Let DX be x in.

$XB.XA = XD.XC$ (secant theorem)

i.e. $3 \cdot 6 = x(x + 7)$

$18 = x^2 + 7x$

$0 = x^2 + 7x - 18$

Factorize: $(x - 2)(x + 9) = 0$

$\therefore x = 2$ or -9. But -9 is impossible

$\therefore x = 2$

Ans. 2 in.

3. (i)

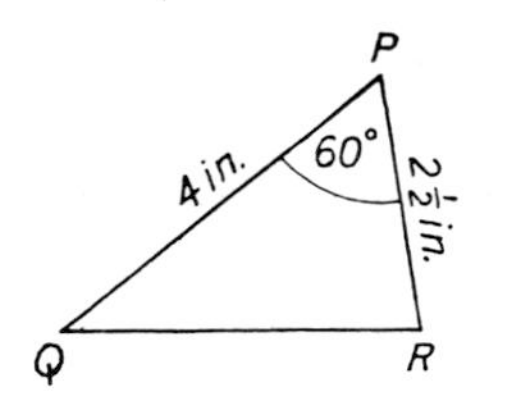

$$\text{Area} = \tfrac{1}{2}\, PQ.PR \sin P$$

$$= \frac{1}{2} \times \frac{4}{1} \times \frac{5}{2} \times \frac{\sqrt{3}}{2}$$

$$= \frac{5\sqrt{3}}{2} \text{ sq. in. Ans.}$$

Note: If the area were wanted correct to, say, one decimal place, you could continue

$$\frac{5 \times 1 \cdot 732}{2} = \frac{17 \cdot 32}{4} = 4 \cdot 33 \quad \text{Ans. } 4 \cdot 3 \text{ sq. in.}$$

(ii)

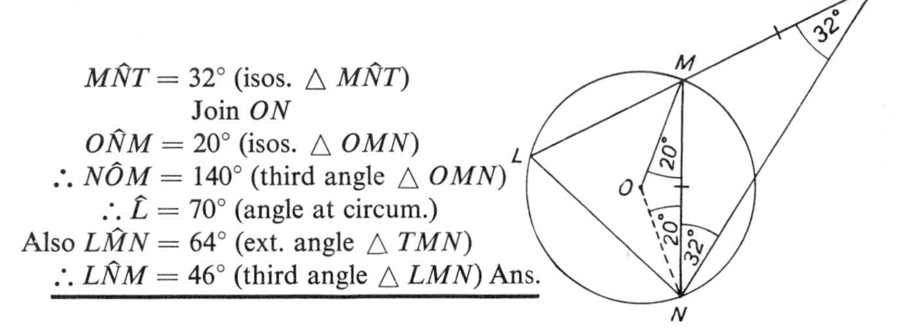

$M\hat{N}T = 32°$ (isos. $\triangle M\hat{N}T$)
Join ON
$O\hat{N}M = 20°$ (isos. $\triangle OMN$)
$\therefore N\hat{O}M = 140°$ (third angle $\triangle OMN$)
$\therefore \hat{L} = 70°$ (angle at circum.)
Also $L\hat{M}N = 64°$ (ext. angle $\triangle TMN$)
$\therefore L\hat{N}M = 46°$ (third angle $\triangle LMN$) Ans.

Note: There are several other methods. For example, you could use the angle sum of $\triangle LTN$. Or you could find $L\hat{M}O\ (= 44°)$ then $L\hat{O}M\ (= 92°)$, then $L\hat{N}M$.

4. (i) $3x^2 - 7x - 2 = 0$

$$x = \frac{-b \pm \sqrt{b^2 - 4ac}}{2a} \text{ where } a = 3,\ b = -7,\ c = -2$$

$$= \frac{+7 \pm \sqrt{49 - 4 \cdot 3(-2)}}{6}$$

$$= \frac{7 \pm \sqrt{49 + 24}}{6}$$

$$= \frac{7 \pm \sqrt{73}}{6}$$

$$= \frac{7 \pm 8 \cdot 544}{6}$$

$$= \frac{15 \cdot 544}{6} \text{ or } \frac{-1 \cdot 544}{6}$$

$$= 2 \cdot 590 \text{ or } -0 \cdot 256$$

Ans. $2 \cdot 59,\ -0 \cdot 26$

Or $x^2 - \frac{7x}{3} = \frac{2}{3}$

$(x - \frac{7}{6})^2 = \frac{49}{36} + \frac{2}{3} = \frac{49 + 24}{36} = \frac{73}{36}$

$\therefore x - \frac{7}{6} = \pm \frac{\sqrt{73}}{6},\ x = \frac{7 \pm \sqrt{73}}{6}$ etc.

(ii) $(1\frac{3}{4} - \frac{4}{5}) \div 2\frac{8}{15} = 1\frac{15-16}{20} \div \frac{38}{15}$

$= \frac{\overset{1}{\cancel{19}}}{\underset{4}{\cancel{20}}} \times \frac{\overset{3}{\cancel{15}}}{\underset{2}{\cancel{38}}}$

$= \frac{3}{8}$ Ans.

5. (i) S.P. of 144 $= 144 \times \frac{1}{3}$s. $= 48$s.
C.P. of 144 $= 36$s.
$\therefore$ Profit $= 12$s. (on C.P. of 36s.)

$\therefore$ % profit $= \frac{\overset{1}{\cancel{12}}}{\underset{3}{\cancel{36}}} \times \frac{100}{1} = 33\frac{1}{3}\%$ Ans.

(ii) $4x^2 - 7x - 2 = (4x + 1)(x - 2)$ Ans.

$\frac{2}{2} \times \frac{2}{1}$

$\frac{4}{1} \times \frac{1}{2}$

6. (i) $\frac{3}{x-3} - \frac{2}{x-2}$

$= \frac{3(x-2) - 2(x-3)}{(x-3)(x-2)}$

$= \frac{3x - 6 - 2x + 6}{(x-3)(x-2)}$

$\frac{x}{(x-3)(x-2)}$ Ans.

(ii)

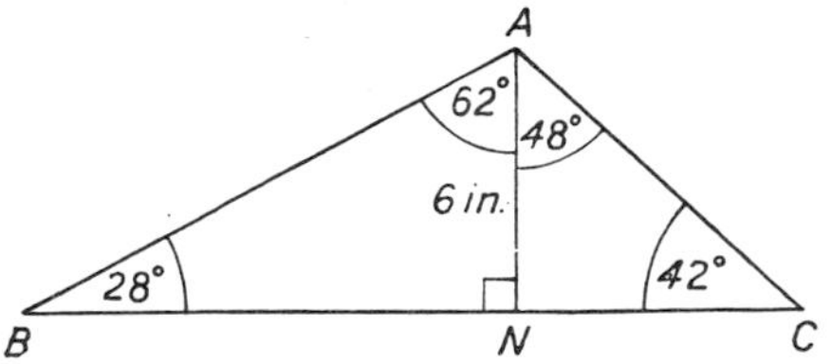

$BC = BN + NC$
$= 6 \tan 62° + 6 \tan 48°$
$= 6(1{\cdot}8807 + 1{\cdot}1106)$
$= 6 \times 2{\cdot}9913$
$= 17{\cdot}9478$ in. Ans.

Or $\frac{BC}{AB} = \frac{\sin 110°}{\sin 42°} = \frac{\sin 70°}{\sin 42°}$ and $\frac{6}{AB} = \sin 28°$

$\therefore BC = \frac{6}{\sin 28°} \times \frac{\sin 70°}{\sin 42°}$
$= 17{\cdot}95$ in. Ans.

No.	*Log*
6	·7782
sin 70	$\bar{1}$·9730
	·7512
1·2541	$\bar{1}$·4971
sin 28	$\bar{1}$·6716
sin 42	$\bar{1}$·8255

7. (i) Circumference of circle of latitude 60° N.

$= 2\pi R \cos 60°$

$= \frac{2}{1} \times \frac{22}{7} \times \frac{3960}{1} \times \frac{1}{2}$

$\therefore \dfrac{242}{\frac{22}{7} \times \frac{3960}{1}} = \dfrac{\text{diff. longitude}}{360°}$

$\therefore$ difference in longitude

$= \frac{242}{3960} \times \frac{7}{22} \times \frac{360°}{1}$

$= 7°$ Ans.

R

60°

(ii) (a) $l = h + \frac{k^2}{h}$ $\quad \therefore lh = h^2 + k^2$

$\therefore k^2 = lh - h^2$

But $T = 2\pi\sqrt{\frac{l}{g}}$

squaring, $T^2 = \frac{4\pi^2 l}{g}$, and $l = \frac{gT^2}{4\pi^2}$ ②

Substitute in ① and take square root.

$$k = \sqrt{\frac{gT^2h}{4\pi^2} - h^2} \text{ Ans. (a)}$$

(b) From ②, $l = \frac{32}{1} \times \frac{121}{16} \times \frac{1}{4} \times \frac{49}{22 \times 22} = \frac{49}{8}$

$\therefore h = \frac{2l}{3} = \frac{49}{12}$

$\therefore k^2 = \frac{49}{8} \times \frac{49}{12} - \frac{49^2}{12^2} = \frac{49^2}{12}\left(\frac{1}{8} - \frac{1}{12}\right) = \frac{49^2}{12} \cdot \frac{1}{24}$

$= \frac{49^2}{24^2} \times \frac{2}{1}$ $\quad \therefore k = \frac{49\sqrt{2}}{24}$ Ans.

8.

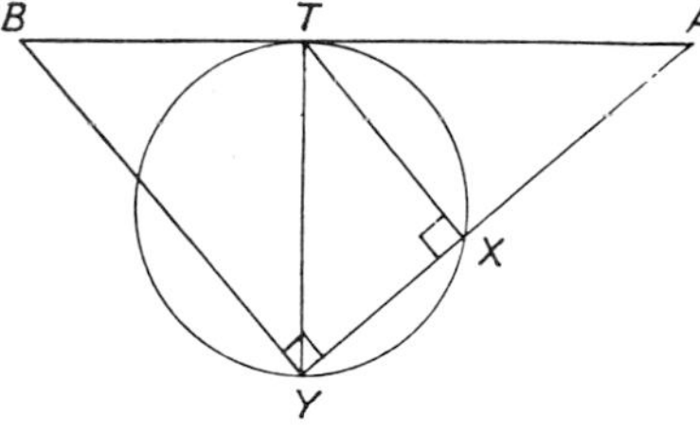

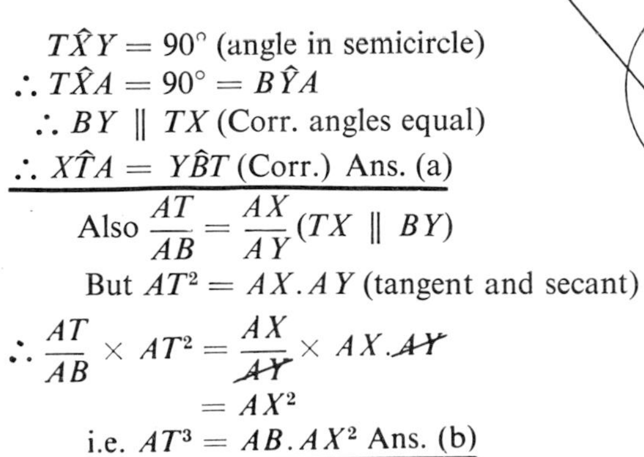

$T\hat{X}Y = 90^\circ$ (angle in semicircle)

$\therefore T\hat{X}A = 90^\circ = B\hat{Y}A$

$\therefore BY \parallel TX$ (Corr. angles equal)

$\therefore X\hat{T}A = Y\hat{B}T$ (Corr.) Ans. (a)

Also $\dfrac{AT}{AB} = \dfrac{AX}{AY} (TX \parallel BY)$

But $AT^2 = AX.AY$ (tangent and secant)

$\therefore \dfrac{AT}{AB} \times AT^2 = \dfrac{AX}{\cancel{AY}} \times AX.\cancel{AY}$

$= AX^2$

i.e. $AT^3 = AB.AX^2$ Ans. (b)

9.

Method 1

$$AB^2 = AX^2 + BX^2 - 2AX.BX \cos AXB$$
$$= (\tfrac{15}{2})^2 + 12^2 - 2.\tfrac{15}{2}.12 \cos 115^\circ$$
$$= \tfrac{225}{4} + 144 - 180(-\cos 65^\circ)$$
$$= 56\tfrac{1}{4} + 144 + 180 \times \cos 65^\circ$$
$$= 200{\cdot}25 + 76{\cdot}07$$
$$= 276{\cdot}32$$
$$AB = 16{\cdot}62 \text{ miles}$$

2·2553
$\bar{1}$·6259
1·8812

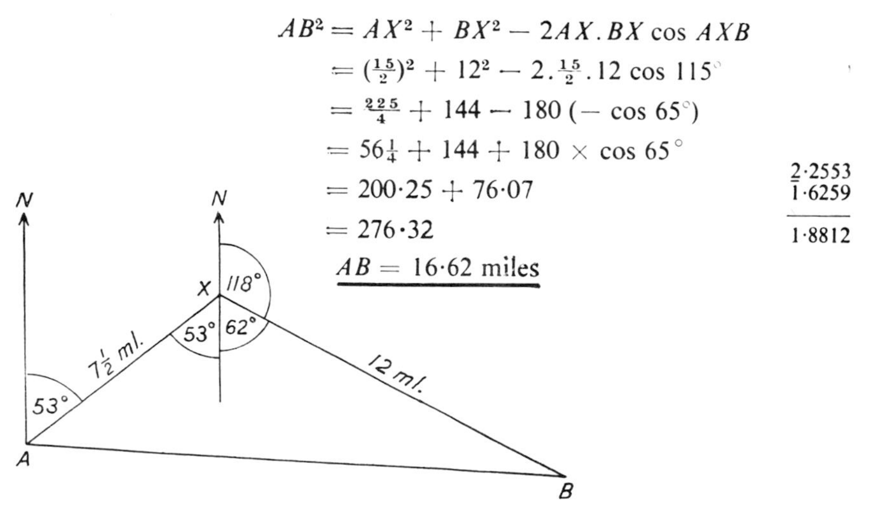

Also $\dfrac{AB}{\sin 115^\circ} = \dfrac{XB}{\sin X\hat{A}B}$, so $\sin X\hat{A}B = \dfrac{12 \sin 65^\circ}{16{\cdot}62}$

$\therefore X\hat{A}B = 40^\circ\ 49'$

$\therefore$ Bearing of B from A

$= 53^\circ + 40^\circ\ 53'$

$= 093^\circ\ 53'$ (or, S.86° 07′E.) Ans.

1·0792
$\bar{1}$·9573
1·0365
1·2206
$\bar{1}$·8159

Method 2 (*same diagram*)

Difference Easting $= 7\frac{1}{2} \sin 53° + 12 \sin 62°$
$= 7\frac{1}{2} \times \cdot 7986 + 12 \times \cdot 8829$
$= 16\cdot 5843$ miles

Difference Northing $= 7\frac{1}{2} \cos 53 - 12 \cos 62°$
$= 7\frac{1}{2} \times \cdot 6018 - 12 \times \cdot 4695$
$= -1\cdot 1205$

Tan (Bearing) $= \dfrac{16\cdot 5843}{-1\cdot 1205}$

$\therefore$ Bearing $= 180° - 86° 08'$
$= \underline{93° 52'}$

$AB^2 = 16\cdot 58^2 + (1\cdot 1205)^2$
$= 274\cdot 9 + 1\cdot 25(5)$
$= 276\cdot 155$

$\underline{AB = 16\cdot 62 \text{ miles Ans.}}$

5·5902
0·3993
8·8290
1·7658
16·5843

4·2126
0·3009
4·5135
− 5·6340
− 1·1205

1·2196
0·049(3)
1·1703

10. (i) $s = 8t^2 - 2t^3$.

(a) When $s = 0$, $8t^2 - 2t^3 = 0$
$2t^2(4 - t) = 0$
$t = 0$ or 4
Ans. (a): 4 sec. after starting.

(b) $\dfrac{ds}{dt} = v = 16t - 6t^2$
$\therefore$ speed after 2 sec. $= 32 - 24 = 8$ ft./sec.
Ans. (b): 8 ft./sec.

(c) When $v = 0$, $2t(8 - 3t) = 0$
$\therefore$ it travels for $2\frac{2}{3}$ secs. before returning
$\therefore s$ max. $= 8 . \frac{64}{9} - 2 . \frac{512}{27}$
$= \frac{512}{27}(3 - 2) = 18\frac{26}{27}$
Ans. (c): $18\frac{26}{27}$ ft.

$$27 \overline{)512} \quad 18; \quad 27,\ 242,\ 216,\ 26$$

(ii) $\dfrac{dV}{dx} = \pi y^2 = \pi(4x - x^2)$

$$\therefore V = \pi\left[2x^2 - \frac{x^3}{3}\right]_0^4$$

$$= \pi\left(32 - \frac{64}{3}\right)$$

$$= \pi \frac{32}{3}$$

$= \underline{10\frac{2}{3}\pi \text{ Ans.}}$

11. Time $= \dfrac{\text{Dist.}}{\text{Speed}}$. Time for second car $= \dfrac{49}{x-3}$ hr.

Time for third car $= \dfrac{49}{x+4}$ hr.

$$\therefore \quad \frac{49}{x-3} - \frac{49}{x+4} = \tfrac{21}{60} \text{ Mult. by } 60(x-3)(x+4)$$

$$49(x+4)60 - 49(x-3)60 = 21(x-3)(x+4). \text{ Div. by 7.}$$
$$7\cdot 60(x+4) - 7\cdot 60(x-3) = 3(x^2+x-12). \text{ Div. by 3.}$$
$$140(x+4) - 140(x-3) = x^2+x-12. \text{ Remove brackets.}$$
$$\cancel{140x} + 560 - \cancel{140x} + 420 = x^2+x-12$$
$$980 = x^2+x-12$$
$$x^2+x-992 = 0$$
$$(x-31)(x+32) = 0$$
$$\therefore x = 31 \text{ (other soln. inadmissible)}$$

$$\begin{array}{r} 31 \\ \underline{32} \\ 93 \\ \underline{62} \\ 992 \end{array}$$

Check: Time for second car $= \frac{49}{28} = \frac{7}{4}$ hr.
Time for third car $= \frac{49}{35} = \frac{7}{5}$ hr. $=$ 1 hr. 24 min.

Difference $= \dfrac{35-28}{20} = \frac{7}{20}$ hr. $= 21$ min.

Ans. $x = 31$ (or -32, inadmissible)
Time for fastest car $=$ 1 hr. 24 min.

12. *Method* 1

(a) Each c.c. of mixture weighs $\frac{121}{14} = 8\frac{9}{14}$ grams
Each c.c. of A weighs $8\frac{9}{10}$ grams
Each c.c. of B weighs $7\frac{1}{10}$ grams
$\therefore$ Each c.c. of A is $(\frac{9}{10} - \frac{9}{14})$ grams too heavy

i.e. $\dfrac{63-45}{70} = \frac{18}{70}$
$= \frac{9}{35}$ grams too heavy

Each c.c. of B is $(1\frac{9}{14} - \frac{1}{10})$ grams too light.
Hence proportions by *volume* must be
$A : B = 1\frac{19}{35} : \frac{9}{35}$, to balance
i.e. $\dfrac{A}{B} = \frac{54}{9} = \frac{6}{1}$

Thus we must mix 6 c.c. of A with each 1 of B. But we need 14 c.c.
$\therefore$ we take 12 c.c. of A and 2 c.c. of B.
Hence weights required are A, $12 \times 8\cdot 9 =$ 106·8 gm.
B, $2 \times 7\cdot 1 =$ 14·2 gm.

Ans. (a): 106·8 gm. of A, 14·2 gm. of B.

(b) $3 \times 8{\cdot}9 + 2 \times 7{\cdot}1 + 5 \times 7{\cdot}3$ gm. is weight of

$$3 + 2 + 5 = 10 \text{ c.c.}$$

i.e. 10 c.c. weigh 77·4 gm.

$\therefore$ weight of 1 c.c. is 7·74 gm.

<u>Ans. (b): 7·74 gm.</u>

$$\begin{array}{r} 26{\cdot}7 \\ 14{\cdot}2 \\ 36{\cdot}5 \\ \hline 77{\cdot}4 \end{array}$$

Method 2

(a) Let there be x gm. of A and $(121 - x)$ gm. of B in the alloy.

Then vol. of A present is $\dfrac{x}{8{\cdot}9}$ c.c., and vol. of B, $\dfrac{121 - x}{7{\cdot}1}$ c.c.

$\therefore \dfrac{x}{8{\cdot}9} + \dfrac{121 - x}{7{\cdot}1} = 14$. Clear of fractions.

$$\begin{aligned} 7{\cdot}1x + 8{\cdot}9(121 - x) &= 14 \times 8{\cdot}9 \times 7{\cdot}1 \\ 7{\cdot}1x + 8{\cdot}9 \times 121 - 8{\cdot}9x &= 14 \times 8{\cdot}9 \times 7{\cdot}1 \\ 8{\cdot}9 \times 121 - 8{\cdot}9 \times 14 \times 7{\cdot}1 &= 8{\cdot}9x - 7{\cdot}1x = 1{\cdot}8x \\ \therefore x &= \frac{8{\cdot}9(121 - 14 \times 7{\cdot}1)}{1{\cdot}8} \\ &= \frac{8{\cdot}9(121 - 99{\cdot}4)}{1{\cdot}8} \\ &= \frac{89 \times 21{\cdot}6}{18} \\ &= 89 \times 1{\cdot}2 \\ &= 106{\cdot}8 \text{ gm.} \\ \therefore \text{Wt. of } B &= 121 - 106{\cdot}8 \\ &= 14{\cdot}2 \text{ gm.} \end{aligned}$$

<u>Ans. (a): 106·8 gm. of A, 14·2 gm. of B.</u>

(b) As in Method 1.

MATHEMATICAL TABLES
(Four-Figure)

(From "Four-Figure Tables" by Godfrey and Siddons, by courtesy of Cambridge University Press.)

LOGARITHMS

	0	1	2	3	4	5	6	7	8	9	1	2	3	4	5	6	7	8	9
10	·0000	0043	0086	0128	0170	0212	0253	0294	0334	0374	4	8	12	17	21	25	29	33	37
11	·0414	0453	0492	0531	0569	0607	0645	0682	0719	0755	4	8	11	15	19	23	26	30	34
12	·0792	0828	0864	0899	0934	0969	1004	1038	1072	1106	3	7	10	14	17	21	24	28	31
13	·1139	1173	1206	1239	1271	1303	1335	1367	1399	1430	3	6	10	13	16	19	23	26	29
14	·1461	1492	1523	1553	1584	1614	1644	1673	1703	1732	3	6	9	12	15	18	21	24	27
15	·1761	1790	1818	1847	1875	1903	1931	1959	1987	2014	3	6	8	11	14	17	20	22	25
16	·2041	2068	2095	2122	2148	2175	2201	2227	2253	2279	3	5	8	11	13	16	18	21	24
17	·2304	2330	2355	2380	2405	2430	2455	2480	2504	2529	2	5	7	10	12	15	17	20	22
18	·2553	2577	2601	2625	2648	2672	2695	2718	2742	2765	2	5	7	9	12	14	16	19	21
19	·2788	2810	2833	2856	2878	2900	2923	2945	2967	2989	2	4	7	9	11	13	16	18	20
20	·3010	3032	3054	3075	3096	3118	3139	3160	3181	3201	2	4	6	8	11	13	15	17	19
21	·3222	3243	3263	3284	3304	3324	3345	3365	3385	3404	2	4	6	8	10	12	14	16	18
22	·3424	3444	3464	3483	3502	3522	3541	3560	3579	3598	2	4	6	8	10	12	14	15	17
23	·3617	3636	3655	3674	3692	3711	3729	3747	3766	3784	2	4	6	7	9	11	13	15	17
24	·3802	3820	3838	3856	3874	3892	3909	3927	3945	3962	2	4	5	7	9	11	12	14	16
25	·3979	3997	4014	4031	4048	4065	4082	4099	4116	4133	2	3	5	7	9	10	12	14	15
26	·4150	4166	4183	4200	4216	4232	4249	4265	4281	4298	2	3	5	7	8	10	11	13	15
27	·4314	4330	4346	4362	4378	4393	4409	4425	4440	4456	2	3	5	6	8	9	11	13	14
28	·4472	4487	4502	4518	4533	4548	4564	4579	4594	4609	2	3	5	6	8	9	11	12	14
29	·4624	4639	4654	4669	4683	4698	4713	4728	4742	4757	1	3	4	6	7	9	10	12	13
30	·4771	4786	4800	4814	4829	4843	4857	4871	4886	4900	1	3	4	6	7	9	10	11	13
31	·4914	4928	4942	4955	4969	4983	4997	5011	5024	5038	1	3	4	6	7	8	10	11	12
32	·5051	5065	5079	5092	5105	5119	5132	5145	5159	5172	1	3	4	5	7	8	9	11	12
33	·5185	5198	5211	5224	5237	5250	5263	5276	5289	5302	1	3	4	5	6	8	9	10	12
34	·5315	5328	5340	5353	5366	5378	5391	5403	5416	5428	1	3	4	5	6	8	9	10	11
35	·5441	5453	5465	5478	5490	5502	5514	5527	5539	5551	1	2	4	5	6	7	9	10	11
36	·5563	5575	5587	5599	5611	5623	5635	5647	5658	5670	1	2	4	5	6	7	8	10	11
37	·5682	5694	5705	5717	5729	5740	5752	5763	5775	5786	1	2	3	5	6	7	8	9	10
38	·5798	5809	5821	5832	5843	5855	5866	5877	5888	5899	1	2	3	5	6	7	8	9	10
39	·5911	5922	5933	5944	5955	5966	5977	5988	5999	6010	1	2	3	4	5	7	8	9	10
40	·6021	6031	6042	6053	6064	6075	6085	6096	6107	6117	1	2	3	4	5	6	8	9	10
41	·6128	6138	6149	6160	6170	6180	6191	6201	6212	6222	1	2	3	4	5	6	7	8	9
42	·6232	6243	6253	6263	6274	6284	6294	6304	6314	6325	1	2	3	4	5	6	7	8	9
43	·6335	6345	6355	6365	6375	6385	6395	6405	6415	6425	1	2	3	4	5	6	7	8	9
44	·6435	6444	6454	6464	6474	6484	6493	6503	6513	6522	1	2	3	4	5	6	7	8	9
45	·6532	6542	6551	6561	6571	6580	6590	6599	6609	6618	1	2	3	4	5	6	7	8	9
46	·6628	6637	6646	6656	6665	6675	6684	6693	6702	6712	1	2	3	4	5	6	7	7	8
47	·6721	6730	6739	6749	6758	6767	6776	6785	6794	6803	1	2	3	4	5	5	6	7	8
48	·6812	6821	6830	6839	6848	6857	6866	6875	6884	6893	1	2	3	4	4	5	6	7	8
49	·6902	6911	6920	6928	6937	6946	6955	6964	6972	6981	1	2	3	4	4	5	6	7	8
50	·6990	6998	7007	7016	7024	7033	7042	7050	7059	7067	1	2	3	3	4	5	6	7	8
51	·7076	7084	7093	7101	7110	7118	7126	7135	7143	7152	1	2	3	3	4	5	6	7	8
52	·7160	7168	7177	7185	7193	7202	7210	7218	7226	7235	1	2	2	3	4	5	6	7	7
53	·7243	7251	7259	7267	7275	7284	7292	7300	7308	7316	1	2	2	3	4	5	6	6	7
54	·7324	7332	7340	7348	7356	7364	7372	7380	7388	7396	1	2	2	3	4	5	6	6	7
	0	1	2	3	4	5	6	7	8	9	1	2	3	4	5	6	7	8	9

LOGARITHMS

	0	1	2	3	4	5	6	7	8	9	1	2	3	4	5	6	7	8	9
55	·7404	7412	7419	7427	7435	7443	7451	7459	7466	7474	1	2	2	3	4	5	5	6	7
56	·7482	7490	7497	7505	7513	7520	7528	7536	7543	7551	1	2	2	3	4	5	5	6	7
57	·7559	7566	7574	7582	7589	7597	7604	7612	7619	7627	1	2	2	3	4	5	5	6	7
58	·7634	7642	7649	7657	7664	7672	7679	7686	7694	7701	1	1	2	3	4	4	5	6	7
59	·7709	7716	7723	7731	7738	7745	7752	7760	7767	7774	1	1	2	3	4	4	5	6	7
60	·7782	7789	7796	7803	7810	7818	7825	7832	7839	7846	1	1	2	3	4	4	5	6	6
61	·7853	7860	7868	7875	7882	7889	7896	7903	7910	7917	1	1	2	3	4	4	5	6	6
62	·7924	7931	7938	7945	7952	7959	7966	7973	7980	7987	1	1	2	3	3	4	5	6	6
63	·7993	8000	8007	8014	8021	8028	8035	8041	8048	8055	1	1	2	3	3	4	5	5	6
64	·8062	8069	8075	8082	8089	8096	8102	8109	8116	8122	1	1	2	3	3	4	5	5	6
65	·8129	8136	8142	8149	8156	8162	8169	8176	8182	8189	1	1	2	3	3	4	5	5	6
66	·8195	8202	8209	8215	8222	8228	8235	8241	8248	8254	1	1	2	3	3	4	5	5	6
67	·8261	8267	8274	8280	8287	8293	8299	8306	8312	8319	1	1	2	3	3	4	5	5	6
68	·8325	8331	8338	8344	8351	8357	8363	8370	8376	8382	1	1	2	3	3	4	4	5	6
69	·8388	8395	8401	8407	8414	8420	8426	8432	8439	8445	1	1	2	2	3	4	4	5	6
70	·8451	8457	8463	8470	8476	8482	8488	8494	8500	8506	1	1	2	2	3	4	4	5	6
71	·8513	8519	8525	8531	8537	8543	8549	8555	8561	8567	1	1	2	2	3	4	4	5	5
72	·8573	8579	8585	8591	8597	8603	8609	8615	8621	8627	1	1	2	2	3	4	4	5	5
73	·8633	8639	8645	8651	8657	8663	8669	8675	8681	8686	1	1	2	2	3	4	4	5	5
74	·8692	8698	8704	8710	8716	8722	8727	8733	8739	8745	1	1	2	2	3	4	4	5	5
75	·8751	8756	8762	8768	8774	8779	8785	8791	8797	8802	1	1	2	2	3	3	4	5	5
76	·8808	8814	8820	8825	8831	8837	8842	8848	8854	8859	1	1	2	2	3	3	4	5	5
77	·8865	8871	8876	8882	8887	8893	8899	8904	8910	8915	1	1	2	2	3	3	4	4	5
78	·8921	8927	8932	8938	8943	8949	8954	8960	8965	8971	1	1	2	2	3	3	4	4	5
79	·8976	8982	8987	8993	8998	9004	9009	9015	9020	9025	1	1	2	2	3	3	4	4	5
80	·9031	9036	9042	9047	9053	9058	9063	9069	9074	9079	1	1	2	2	3	3	4	4	5
81	·9085	9090	9096	9101	9106	9112	9117	9122	9128	9133	1	1	2	2	3	3	4	4	5
82	·9138	9143	9149	9154	9159	9165	9170	9175	9180	9186	1	1	2	2	3	3	4	4	5
83	·9191	9196	9201	9206	9212	9217	9222	9227	9232	9238	1	1	2	2	3	3	4	4	5
84	·9243	9248	9253	9258	9263	9269	9274	9279	9284	9289	1	1	2	2	3	3	4	4	5
85	·9294	9299	9304	9309	9315	9320	9325	9330	9335	9340	1	1	2	2	3	3	4	4	5
86	·9345	9350	9355	9360	9365	9370	9375	9380	9385	9390	1	1	1	2	3	3	4	4	5
87	·9395	9400	9405	9410	9415	9420	9425	9430	9435	9440	0	1	1	2	2	3	3	4	4
88	·9445	9450	9455	9460	9465	9469	9474	9479	9484	9489	0	1	1	2	2	3	3	4	4
89	·9494	9499	9504	9509	9513	9518	9523	9528	9533	9538	0	1	1	2	2	3	3	4	4
90	·9542	9547	9552	9557	9562	9566	9571	9576	9581	9586	0	1	1	2	2	3	3	4	4
91	·9590	9595	9600	9605	9609	9614	9619	9624	9628	9633	0	1	1	2	2	3	3	4	4
92	·9638	9643	9647	9652	9657	9661	9666	9671	9675	9680	0	1	1	2	2	3	3	4	4
93	·9685	9689	9694	9699	9703	9708	9713	9717	9722	9727	0	1	1	2	2	3	3	4	4
94	·9731	9736	9741	9745	9750	9754	9759	9763	9768	9773	0	1	1	2	2	3	3	4	4
95	·9777	9782	9786	9791	9795	9800	9805	9809	9814	9818	0	1	1	2	2	3	3	4	4
96	·9823	9827	9832	9836	9841	9845	9850	9854	9859	9863	0	1	1	2	2	3	3	4	4
97	·9868	9872	9877	9881	9886	9890	9894	9899	9903	9908	0	1	1	2	2	3	3	4	4
98	·9912	9917	9921	9926	9930	9934	9939	9943	9948	9952	0	1	1	2	2	3	3	4	4
99	·9956	9961	9965	9969	9974	9978	9983	9987	9991	9996	0	1	1	2	2	3	3	3	4
	0	1	2	3	4	5	6	7	8	9	1	2	3	4	5	6	7	8	9

ANTI-LOGARITHMS

	0	1	2	3	4	5	6	7	8	9	1	2	3	4	5	6	7	8	9
·00	1000	1002	1005	1007	1009	1012	1014	1016	1019	1021	0	0	1	1	1	1	2	2	2
·01	1023	1026	1028	1030	1033	1035	1038	1040	1042	1045	0	0	1	1	1	1	2	2	2
·02	1047	1050	1052	1054	1057	1059	1062	1064	1067	1069	0	0	1	1	1	1	2	2	2
·03	1072	1074	1076	1079	1081	1084	1086	1089	1091	1094	0	0	1	1	1	1	2	2	2
·04	1096	1099	1102	1104	1107	1109	1112	1114	1117	1119	0	1	1	1	1	2	2	2	2
·05	1122	1125	1127	1130	1132	1135	1138	1140	1143	1146	0	1	1	1	1	2	2	2	2
·06	1148	1151	1153	1156	1159	1161	1164	1167	1169	1172	0	1	1	1	1	2	2	2	2
·07	1175	1178	1180	1183	1186	1189	1191	1194	1197	1199	0	1	1	1	1	2	2	2	2
·08	1202	1205	1208	1211	1213	1216	1219	1222	1225	1227	0	1	1	1	1	2	2	2	3
·09	1230	1233	1236	1239	1242	1245	1247	1250	1253	1256	0	1	1	1	1	2	2	2	3
·10	1259	1262	1265	1268	1271	1274	1276	1279	1282	1285	0	1	1	1	1	2	2	2	3
·11	1288	1291	1294	1297	1300	1303	1306	1309	1312	1315	0	1	1	1	2	2	2	2	3
·12	1318	1321	1324	1327	1330	1334	1337	1340	1343	1346	0	1	1	1	2	2	2	2	3
·13	1349	1352	1355	1358	1361	1365	1368	1371	1374	1377	0	1	1	1	2	2	2	3	3
·14	1380	1384	1387	1390	1393	1396	1400	1403	1406	1409	0	1	1	1	2	2	2	3	3
·15	1413	1416	1419	1422	1426	1429	1432	1435	1439	1442	0	1	1	1	2	2	2	3	3
·16	1445	1449	1452	1455	1459	1462	1466	1469	1472	1476	0	1	1	1	2	2	2	3	3
·17	1479	1483	1486	1489	1493	1496	1500	1503	1507	1510	0	1	1	1	2	2	2	3	3
·18	1514	1517	1521	1524	1528	1531	1535	1538	1542	1545	0	1	1	1	2	2	2	3	3
·19	1549	1552	1556	1560	1563	1567	1570	1574	1578	1581	0	1	1	1	2	2	3	3	3
·20	1585	1589	1592	1596	1600	1603	1607	1611	1614	1618	0	1	1	1	2	2	3	3	3
·21	1622	1626	1629	1633	1637	1641	1644	1648	1652	1656	0	1	1	2	2	2	3	3	3
·22	1660	1663	1667	1671	1675	1679	1683	1687	1690	1694	0	1	1	2	2	2	3	3	3
·23	1698	1702	1706	1710	1714	1718	1722	1726	1730	1734	0	1	1	2	2	2	3	3	4
·24	1738	1742	1746	1750	1754	1758	1762	1766	1770	1774	0	1	1	2	2	2	3	3	4
·25	1778	1782	1786	1791	1795	1799	1803	1807	1811	1816	0	1	1	2	2	2	3	3	4
·26	1820	1824	1828	1832	1837	1841	1845	1849	1854	1858	0	1	1	2	2	3	3	3	4
·27	1862	1866	1871	1875	1879	1884	1888	1892	1897	1901	0	1	1	2	2	3	3	3	4
·28	1905	1910	1914	1919	1923	1928	1932	1936	1941	1945	0	1	1	2	2	3	3	4	4
·29	1950	1954	1959	1963	1968	1972	1977	1982	1986	1991	0	1	1	2	2	3	3	4	4
·30	1995	2000	2004	2009	2014	2018	2023	2028	2032	2037	0	1	1	2	2	3	3	4	4
·31	2042	2046	2051	2056	2061	2065	2070	2075	2080	2084	0	1	1	2	2	3	3	4	4
·32	2089	2094	2099	2104	2109	2113	2118	2123	2128	2133	0	1	1	2	2	3	3	4	4
·33	2138	2143	2148	2153	2158	2163	2168	2173	2178	2183	0	1	1	2	2	3	3	4	4
·34	2188	2193	2198	2203	2208	2213	2218	2223	2228	2234	1	1	2	2	3	3	4	4	5
·35	2239	2244	2249	2254	2259	2265	2270	2275	2280	2286	1	1	2	2	3	3	4	4	5
·36	2291	2296	2301	2307	2312	2317	2323	2328	2333	2339	1	1	2	2	3	3	4	4	5
·37	2344	2350	2355	2360	2366	2371	2377	2382	2388	2393	1	1	2	2	3	3	4	4	5
·38	2399	2404	2410	2415	2421	2427	2432	2438	2443	2449	1	1	2	2	3	3	4	4	5
·39	2455	2460	2466	2472	2477	2483	2489	2495	2500	2506	1	1	2	2	3	3	4	5	5
·40	2512	2518	2523	2529	2535	2541	2547	2553	2559	2564	1	1	2	2	3	4	4	5	5
·41	2570	2576	2582	2588	2594	2600	2606	2612	2618	2624	1	1	2	2	3	4	4	5	5
·42	2630	2636	2642	2649	2655	2661	2667	2673	2679	2685	1	1	2	2	3	4	4	5	6
·43	2692	2698	2704	2710	2716	2723	2729	2735	2742	2748	1	1	2	3	3	4	4	5	6
·44	2754	2761	2767	2773	2780	2786	2793	2799	2805	2812	1	1	2	3	3	4	4	5	6
·45	2818	2825	2831	2838	2844	2851	2858	2864	2871	2877	1	1	2	3	3	4	5	5	6
·46	2884	2891	2897	2904	2911	2917	2924	2931	2938	2944	1	1	2	3	3	4	5	5	6
·47	2951	2958	2965	2972	2979	2985	2992	2999	3006	3013	1	1	2	3	3	4	5	5	6
·48	3020	3027	3034	3041	3048	3055	3062	3069	3076	3083	1	1	2	3	4	4	5	6	6
·49	3090	3097	3105	3112	3119	3126	3133	3141	3148	3155	1	1	2	3	4	4	5	6	6
	0	1	2	3	4	5	6	7	8	9	1	2	3	4	5	6	7	8	9

ANTI-LOGARITHMS

	0	1	2	3	4	5	6	7	8	9	1	2	3	4	5	6	7	8	9
·50	3162	3170	3177	3184	3192	3199	3206	3214	3221	3228	1	1	2	3	4	4	5	6	7
·51	3236	3243	3251	3258	3266	3273	3281	3289	3296	3304	1	2	2	3	4	5	5	6	7
·52	3311	3319	3327	3334	3342	3350	3357	3365	3373	3381	1	2	2	3	4	5	5	6	7
·53	3388	3396	3404	3412	3420	3428	3436	3443	3451	3459	1	2	2	3	4	5	6	6	7
·54	3467	3475	3483	3491	3499	3508	3516	3524	3532	3540	1	2	2	3	4	5	6	6	7
·55	3548	3556	3565	3573	3581	3589	3597	3606	3614	3622	1	2	2	3	4	5	6	7	7
·56	3631	3639	3648	3656	3664	3673	3681	3690	3698	3707	1	2	3	3	4	5	6	7	8
·57	3715	3724	3733	3741	3750	3758	3767	3776	3784	3793	1	2	3	3	4	5	6	7	8
·58	3802	3811	3819	3828	3837	3846	3855	3864	3873	3882	1	2	3	4	4	5	6	7	8
·59	3890	3899	3908	3917	3926	3936	3945	3954	3963	3972	1	2	3	4	5	5	6	7	8
·60	3981	3990	3999	4009	4018	4027	4036	4046	4055	4064	1	2	3	4	5	6	6	7	8
·61	4074	4083	4093	4102	4111	4121	4130	4140	4150	4159	1	2	3	4	5	6	7	8	9
·62	4169	4178	4188	4198	4207	4217	4227	4236	4246	4256	1	2	3	4	5	6	7	8	9
·63	4266	4276	4285	4295	4305	4315	4325	4335	4345	4355	1	2	3	4	5	6	7	8	9
·64	4365	4375	4385	4395	4406	4416	4426	4436	4446	4457	1	2	3	4	5	6	7	8	9
·65	4467	4477	4487	4498	4508	4519	4529	4539	4550	4560	1	2	3	4	5	6	7	8	9
·66	4571	4581	4592	4603	4613	4624	4634	4645	4656	4667	1	2	3	4	5	6	7	9	10
·67	4677	4688	4699	4710	4721	4732	4742	4753	4764	4775	1	2	3	4	5	7	8	9	10
·68	4786	4797	4808	4819	4831	4842	4853	4864	4875	4887	1	2	3	4	6	7	8	9	10
·69	4898	4909	4920	4932	4943	4955	4966	4977	4989	5000	1	2	3	5	6	7	8	9	10
·70	5012	5023	5035	5047	5058	5070	5082	5093	5105	5117	1	2	4	5	6	7	8	9	11
·71	5129	5140	5152	5164	5176	5188	5200	5212	5224	5236	1	2	4	5	6	7	8	10	11
·72	5248	5260	5272	5284	5297	5309	5321	5333	5346	5358	1	2	4	5	6	7	9	10	11
·73	5370	5383	5395	5408	5420	5433	5445	5458	5470	5483	1	3	4	5	6	8	9	10	11
·74	5495	5508	5521	5534	5546	5559	5572	5585	5598	5610	1	3	4	5	6	8	9	10	12
·75	5623	5636	5649	5662	5675	5689	5702	5715	5728	5741	1	3	4	5	7	8	9	10	12
·76	5754	5768	5781	5794	5808	5821	5834	5848	5861	5875	1	3	4	5	7	8	9	11	12
·77	5888	5902	5916	5929	5943	5957	5970	5984	5998	6012	1	3	4	5	7	8	10	11	12
·78	6026	6039	6053	6067	6081	6095	6109	6124	6138	6152	1	3	4	6	7	8	10	11	13
·79	6166	6180	6194	6209	6223	6237	6252	6266	6281	6295	1	3	4	6	7	9	10	11	13
·80	6310	6324	6339	6353	6368	6383	6397	6412	6427	6442	1	3	4	6	7	9	10	12	13
·81	6457	6471	6486	6501	6516	6531	6546	6561	6577	6592	2	3	5	6	8	9	11	12	14
·82	6607	6622	6637	6653	6668	6683	6699	6714	6730	6745	2	3	5	6	8	9	11	12	14
·83	6761	6776	6792	6808	6823	6839	6855	6871	6887	6902	2	3	5	6	8	9	11	13	14
·84	6918	6934	6950	6966	6982	6998	7015	7031	7047	7063	2	3	5	6	8	10	11	13	15
·85	7079	7096	7112	7129	7145	7161	7178	7194	7211	7228	2	3	5	7	8	10	12	13	15
·86	7244	7261	7278	7295	7311	7328	7345	7362	7379	7396	2	3	5	7	8	10	12	13	15
·87	7413	7430	7447	7464	7482	7499	7516	7534	7551	7568	2	3	5	7	9	10	12	14	16
·88	7586	7603	7621	7638	7656	7674	7691	7709	7727	7745	2	4	5	7	9	11	12	14	16
·89	7762	7780	7798	7816	7834	7852	7870	7889	7907	7925	2	4	5	7	9	11	13	14	16
·90	7943	7962	7980	7998	8017	8035	8054	8072	8091	8110	2	4	6	7	9	11	13	15	17
·91	8128	8147	8166	8185	8204	8222	8241	8260	8279	8299	2	4	6	8	9	11	13	15	17
·92	8318	8337	8356	8375	8395	8414	8433	8453	8472	8492	2	4	6	8	10	12	14	15	17
·93	8511	8531	8551	8570	8590	8610	8630	8650	8670	8690	2	4	6	8	10	12	14	16	18
·94	8710	8730	8750	8770	8790	8810	8831	8851	8872	8892	2	4	6	8	10	12	14	16	18
·95	8913	8933	8954	8974	8995	9016	9036	9057	9078	9099	2	4	6	8	10	12	15	17	19
·96	9120	9141	9162	9183	9204	9226	9247	9268	9290	9311	2	4	6	8	11	13	15	17	19
·97	9333	9354	9376	9397	9419	9441	9462	9484	9506	9528	2	4	7	9	11	13	15	17	20
·98	9550	9572	9594	9616	9638	9661	9683	9705	9727	9750	2	4	7	9	11	13	16	18	20
·99	9772	9795	9817	9840	9863	9886	9908	9931	9954	9977	2	5	7	9	11	14	16	18	20
	0	1	2	3	4	5	6	7	8	9	1	2	3	4	5	6	7	8	9

LOG. SINES

	0′	6′	12′	18′	24′	30′	36′	42′	48′	54′	1′	2′	3′	4′	5′
0°	−∞	$\bar{3}$·242	$\bar{3}$·543	$\bar{3}$·719	$\bar{3}$·844	$\bar{3}$·941	$\bar{2}$·020	$\bar{2}$·087	$\bar{2}$·145	$\bar{2}$·196					
1	$\bar{2}$·2419	2832	3210	3558	3880	4179	4459	4723	4971	5206					
2	$\bar{2}$·5428	5640	5842	6035	6220	6397	6567	6731	6889	7041					
3	$\bar{2}$·7188	7330	7468	7602	7731	7857	7979	8098	8213	8326	21	41	62	83	103
4	$\bar{2}$·8436	8543	8647	8749	8849	8946	9042	9135	9226	9315	16	32	48	64	80
5	$\bar{2}$·9403	9489	9573	9655	9736	9816	9894	9970	**0046**	**0120**	13	26	39	52	66
6	$\bar{1}$·0192	0264	0334	0403	0472	0539	0605	0670	0734	0797	11	22	33	44	55
7	$\bar{1}$·0859	0920	0981	1040	1099	1157	1214	1271	1326	1381	10	19	29	38	48
8	$\bar{1}$·1436	1489	1542	1594	1646	1697	1747	1797	1847	1895	8	17	25	34	43
9	$\bar{1}$·1943	1991	2038	2085	2131	2176	2221	2266	2310	2353	8	15	23	30	38
10	$\bar{1}$·2397	2439	2482	2524	2565	2606	2647	2687	2727	2767	7	14	20	27	34
11	$\bar{1}$·2806	2845	2883	2921	2959	2997	3034	3070	3107	3143	6	12	19	25	31
12	$\bar{1}$·3179	3214	3250	3284	3319	3353	3387	3421	3455	3488	6	11	17	23	28
13	$\bar{1}$·3521	3554	3586	3618	3650	3682	3713	3745	3775	3806	5	11	16	21	26
14	$\bar{1}$·3837	3867	3897	3927	3957	3986	4015	4044	4073	4102	5	10	15	20	24
15	$\bar{1}$·4130	4158	4186	4214	4242	4269	4296	4323	4350	4377	5	9	14	18	23
16	$\bar{1}$·4403	4430	4456	4482	4508	4533	4559	4584	4609	4634	4	9	13	17	21
17	$\bar{1}$·4659	4684	4709	4733	4757	4781	4805	4829	4853	4876	4	8	12	16	20
18	$\bar{1}$·4900	4923	4946	4969	4992	5015	5037	5060	5082	5104	4	8	11	15	19
19	$\bar{1}$·5126	5148	5170	5192	5213	5235	5256	5278	5299	5320	4	7	11	14	18
20	$\bar{1}$·5341	5361	5382	5402	5423	5443	5463	5484	5504	5523	3	7	10	14	17
21	$\bar{1}$·5543	5563	5583	5602	5621	5641	5660	5679	5698	5717	3	6	10	13	16
22	$\bar{1}$·5736	5754	5773	5792	5810	5828	5847	5865	5883	5901	3	6	9	12	15
23	$\bar{1}$·5919	5937	5954	5972	5990	6007	6024	6042	6059	6076	3	6	9	12	15
24	$\bar{1}$·6093	6110	6127	6144	6161	6177	6194	6210	6227	6243	3	6	8	11	14
25	$\bar{1}$·6259	6276	6292	6308	6324	6340	6356	6371	6387	6403	3	5	8	11	13
26	$\bar{1}$·6418	6434	6449	6465	6480	6495	6510	6526	6541	6556	3	5	8	10	13
27	$\bar{1}$·6570	6585	6600	6615	6629	6644	6659	6673	6687	6702	2	5	7	10	12
28	$\bar{1}$·6716	6730	6744	6759	6773	6787	6801	6814	6828	6842	2	5	7	9	12
29	$\bar{1}$·6856	6869	6883	6896	6910	6923	6937	6950	6963	6977	2	4	7	9	11
30	$\bar{1}$·6990	7003	7016	7029	7042	7055	7068	7080	7093	7106	2	4	6	9	11
31	$\bar{1}$·7118	7131	7144	7156	7168	7181	7193	7205	7218	7230	2	4	6	8	10
32	$\bar{1}$·7242	7254	7266	7278	7290	7302	7314	7326	7338	7349	2	4	6	8	10
33	$\bar{1}$·7361	7373	7384	7396	7407	7419	7430	7442	7453	7464	2	4	6	8	10
34	$\bar{1}$·7476	7487	7498	7509	7520	7531	7542	7553	7564	7575	2	4	6	7	9
35	$\bar{1}$·7586	7597	7607	7618	7629	7640	7650	7661	7671	7682	2	4	5	7	9
36	$\bar{1}$·7692	7703	7713	7723	7734	7744	7754	7764	7774	7785	2	3	5	7	9
37	$\bar{1}$·7795	7805	7815	7825	7835	7844	7854	7864	7874	7884	2	3	5	7	8
38	$\bar{1}$·7893	7903	7913	7922	7932	7941	7951	7960	7970	7979	2	3	5	6	8
39	$\bar{1}$·7989	7998	8007	8017	8026	8035	8044	8053	8063	8072	2	3	5	6	8
40	$\bar{1}$·8081	8090	8099	8108	8117	8125	8134	8143	8152	8161	1	3	4	6	7
41	$\bar{1}$·8169	8178	8187	8195	8204	8213	8221	8230	8238	8247	1	3	4	6	7
42	$\bar{1}$·8255	8264	8272	8280	8289	8297	8305	8313	8322	8330	1	3	4	6	7
43	$\bar{1}$·8338	8346	8354	8362	8370	8378	8386	8394	8402	8410	1	3	4	5	7
44	$\bar{1}$·8418	8426	8433	8441	8449	8457	8464	8472	8480	8487	1	3	4	5	6
	0′	6′	12′	18′	24′	30′	36′	42′	48′	54′	1′	2′	3′	4′	5′

The black type indicates that the integer changes.

LOG. SINES

	0′	6′	12′	18′	24′	30′	36′	42′	48′	54′	1′	2′	3′	4′	5′
45°	$\bar{1}$·8495	8502	8510	8517	8525	8532	8540	8547	8555	8562	1	2	4	5	6
46	$\bar{1}$·8569	8577	8584	8591	8598	8606	8613	8620	8627	8634	1	2	4	5	6
47	$\bar{1}$·8641	8648	8655	8662	8669	8676	8683	8690	8697	8704	1	2	3	5	6
48	$\bar{1}$·8711	8718	8724	8731	8738	8745	8751	8758	8765	8771	1	2	3	4	6
49	$\bar{1}$·8778	8784	8791	8797	8804	8810	8817	8823	8830	8836	1	2	3	4	5
50	$\bar{1}$·8843	8849	8855	8862	8868	8874	8880	8887	8893	8899	1	2	3	4	5
51	$\bar{1}$·8905	8911	8917	8923	8929	8935	8941	8947	8953	8959	1	2	3	4	5
52	$\bar{1}$·8965	8971	8977	8983	8989	8995	9000	9006	9012	9018	1	2	3	4	5
53	$\bar{1}$·9023	9029	9035	9041	9046	9052	9057	9063	9069	9074	1	2	3	4	5
54	$\bar{1}$·9080	9085	9091	9096	9101	9107	9112	9118	9123	9128	1	2	3	4	5
55	$\bar{1}$·9134	9139	9144	9149	9155	9160	9165	9170	9175	9181	1	2	3	3	4
56	$\bar{1}$·9186	9191	9196	9201	9206	9211	9216	9221	9226	9231	1	2	3	3	4
57	$\bar{1}$·9236	9241	9246	9251	9255	9260	9265	9270	9275	9279	1	2	2	3	4
58	$\bar{1}$·9284	9289	9294	9298	9303	9308	9312	9317	9322	9326	1	2	2	3	4
59	$\bar{1}$·9331	9335	9340	9344	9349	9353	9358	9362	9367	9371	1	1	2	3	4
60	$\bar{1}$·9375	9380	9384	9388	9393	9397	9401	9406	9410	9414	1	1	2	3	4
61	$\bar{1}$·9418	9422	9427	9431	9435	9439	9443	9447	9451	9455	1	1	2	3	3
62	$\bar{1}$·9459	9463	9467	9471	9475	9479	9483	9487	9491	9495	1	1	2	3	3
63	$\bar{1}$·9499	9503	9506	9510	9514	9518	9522	9525	9529	9533	1	1	2	3	3
64	$\bar{1}$·9537	9540	9544	9548	9551	9555	9558	9562	9566	9569	1	1	2	2	3
65	$\bar{1}$·9573	9576	9580	9583	9587	9590	9594	9597	9601	9604	1	1	2	2	3
66	$\bar{1}$·9607	9611	9614	9617	9621	9624	9627	9631	9634	9637	1	1	2	2	3
67	$\bar{1}$·9640	9643	9647	9650	9653	9656	9659	9662	9666	9669	1	1	2	2	3
68	$\bar{1}$·9672	9675	9678	9681	9684	9687	9690	9693	9696	9699	0	1	1	2	2
69	$\bar{1}$·9702	9704	9707	9710	9713	9716	9719	9722	9724	9727	0	1	1	2	2
70	$\bar{1}$·9730	9733	9735	9738	9741	9743	9746	9749	9751	9754	0	1	1	2	2
71	$\bar{1}$·9757	9759	9762	9764	9767	9770	9772	9775	9777	9780	0	1	1	2	2
72	$\bar{1}$·9782	9785	9787	9789	9792	9794	9797	9799	9801	9804	0	1	1	2	2
73	$\bar{1}$·9806	9808	9811	9813	9815	9817	9820	9822	9824	9826	0	1	1	1	2
74	$\bar{1}$·9828	9831	9833	9835	9837	9839	9841	9843	9845	9847	0	1	1	1	2
75	$\bar{1}$·9849	9851	9853	9855	9857	9859	9861	9863	9865	9867	0	1	1	1	2
76	$\bar{1}$·9869	9871	9873	9875	9876	9878	9880	9882	9884	9885	0	1	1	1	2
77	$\bar{1}$·9887	9889	9891	9892	9894	9896	9897	9899	9901	9902	0	1	1	1	1
78	$\bar{1}$·9904	9906	9907	9909	9910	9912	9913	9915	9916	9918	0	1	1	1	1
79	$\bar{1}$·9919	9921	9922	9924	9925	9927	9928	9929	9931	9932	0	0	1	1	1
80	$\bar{1}$·9934	9935	9936	9937	9939	9940	9941	9943	9944	9945	0	0	1	1	1
81	$\bar{1}$·9946	9947	9949	9950	9951	9952	9953	9954	9955	9956	0	0	1	1	1
82	$\bar{1}$·9958	9959	9960	9961	9962	9963	9964	9965	9966	9967	0	0	0	1	1
83	$\bar{1}$·9968	9968	9969	9970	9971	9972	9973	9974	9975	9975					
84	$\bar{1}$·9976	9977	9978	9978	9979	9980	9981	9981	9982	9983					
85	$\bar{1}$·9983	9984	9985	9985	9986	9987	9987	9988	9988	9989					
86	$\bar{1}$·9989	9990	9990	9991	9991	9992	9992	9993	9993	9994					
87	$\bar{1}$·9994	9994	9995	9995	9996	9996	9996	9996	9997	9997					
88	$\bar{1}$·9997	9998	9998	9998	9998	9999	9999	9999	9999	9999					
89	$\bar{1}$·9999	9999	**0000**	**0000**	**0000**	**0000**	**0000**	**0000**	**0000**	**0000**					
	0′	6′	12′	18′	24′	30′	36′	42′	48′	54′	1′	2′	3′	4′	5′

The black type indicates that the integer changes.

	0′	6′	12′	18′	24′	30′	36′	42′	48′	54′	1′	2′	3′	4′	5′
0°	0·0000	0000	0000	0000	0000	0000	0000	0000	0000	**9999**					
1	$\bar{1}$·9999	9999	9999	9999	9999	9999	9998	9998	9998	9998					
2	$\bar{1}$·9997	9997	9997	9996	9996	9996	9996	9995	9995	9994					
3	$\bar{1}$·9994	9994	9993	9993	9992	9992	9991	9991	9990	9990					
4	$\bar{1}$·9989	9989	9988	9988	9987	9987	9986	9985	9985	9984					
5	$\bar{1}$·9983	9983	9982	9981	9981	9980	9979	9978	9978	9977					
6	$\bar{1}$·9976	9975	9975	9974	9973	9972	9971	9970	9969	9968					
7	$\bar{1}$·9968	9967	9966	9965	9964	9963	9962	9961	9960	9959	0	0	0	1	1
8	$\bar{1}$·9958	9956	9955	9954	9953	9952	9951	9950	9949	9947	0	0	1	1	1
9	$\bar{1}$·9946	9945	9944	9943	9941	9940	9939	9937	9936	9935	0	0	1	1	1
10	$\bar{1}$·9934	9932	9931	9929	9928	9927	9925	9924	9922	9921	0	0	1	1	1
11	$\bar{1}$·9919	9918	9916	9915	9913	9912	9910	9909	9907	9906	0	1	1	1	1
12	$\bar{1}$·9904	9902	9901	9899	9897	9896	9894	9892	9891	9889	0	1	1	1	1
13	$\bar{1}$·9887	9885	9884	9882	9880	9878	9876	9875	9873	9871	0	1	1	1	2
14	$\bar{1}$·9869	9867	9865	9863	9861	9859	9857	9855	9853	9851	0	1	1	1	2
15	$\bar{1}$·9849	9847	9845	9843	9841	9839	9837	9835	9833	9831	0	1	1	1	2
16	$\bar{1}$·9828	9826	9824	9822	9820	9817	9815	9813	9811	9808	0	1	1	1	2
17	$\bar{1}$·9806	9804	9801	9799	9797	9794	9792	9789	9787	9785	0	1	1	2	2
18	$\bar{1}$·9782	9780	9777	9775	9772	9770	9767	9764	9762	9759	0	1	1	2	2
19	$\bar{1}$·9757	9754	9751	9749	9746	9743	9741	9738	9735	9733	0	1	1	2	2
20	$\bar{1}$·9730	9727	9724	9722	9719	9716	9713	9710	9707	9704	0	1	1	2	2
21	$\bar{1}$·9702	9699	9696	9693	9690	9687	9684	9681	9678	9675	0	1	1	2	2
22	$\bar{1}$·9672	9669	9666	9662	9659	9656	9653	9650	9647	9643	1	1	2	2	3
23	$\bar{1}$·9640	9637	9634	9631	9627	9624	9621	9617	9614	9611	1	1	2	2	3
24	$\bar{1}$·9607	9604	9601	9597	9594	9590	9587	9583	9580	9576	1	1	2	2	3
25	$\bar{1}$·9573	9569	9566	9562	9558	9555	9551	9548	9544	9540	1	1	2	2	3
26	$\bar{1}$·9537	9533	9529	9525	9522	9518	9514	9510	9506	9503	1	1	2	3	3
27	$\bar{1}$·9499	9495	9491	9487	9483	9479	9475	9471	9467	9463	1	1	2	3	3
28	$\bar{1}$·9459	9455	9451	9447	9443	9439	9435	9431	9427	9422	1	1	2	3	3
29	$\bar{1}$·9418	9414	9410	9406	9401	9397	9393	9388	9384	9380	1	1	2	3	4
30	$\bar{1}$·9375	9371	9367	9362	9358	9353	9349	9344	9340	9335	1	1	2	3	4
31	$\bar{1}$·9331	9326	9322	9317	9312	9308	9303	9298	9294	9289	1	2	2	3	4
32	$\bar{1}$·9284	9279	9275	9270	9265	9260	9255	9251	9246	9241	1	2	2	3	4
33	$\bar{1}$·9236	9231	9226	9221	9216	9211	9206	9201	9196	9191	1	2	3	3	4
34	$\bar{1}$·9186	9181	9175	9170	9165	9160	9155	9149	9144	9139	1	2	3	3	4
35	$\bar{1}$·9134	9128	9123	9118	9112	9107	9101	9096	9091	9085	1	2	3	4	5
36	$\bar{1}$·9080	9074	9069	9063	9057	9052	9046	9041	9035	9029	1	2	3	4	5
37	$\bar{1}$·9023	9018	9012	9006	9000	8995	8989	8983	8977	8971	1	2	3	4	5
38	$\bar{1}$·8965	8959	8953	8947	8941	8935	8929	8923	8917	8911	1	2	3	4	5
39	$\bar{1}$·8905	8899	8893	8887	8880	8874	8868	8862	8855	8849	1	2	3	4	5
40	$\bar{1}$·8843	8836	8830	8823	8817	8810	8804	8797	8791	8784	1	2	3	4	5
41	$\bar{1}$·8778	8771	8765	8758	8751	8745	8738	8731	8724	8718	1	2	3	4	6
42	$\bar{1}$·8711	8704	8697	8690	8683	8676	8669	8662	8655	8648	1	2	3	5	6
43	$\bar{1}$·8641	8634	8627	8620	8613	8606	8598	8591	8584	8577	1	2	4	5	6
44	$\bar{1}$·8569	8562	8555	8547	8540	8532	8525	8517	8510	8502	1	2	4	5	6
	0′	6′	12′	18′	24′	30′	36′	42′	48′	54′	1′	2′	3′	4′	5′

The black type indicates that the integer changes.

LOG. COSINES

SUBTRACT

	0′	6′	12′	18′	24′	30′	36′	42′	48′	54′	1′	2′	3′	4′	5′
45°	$\bar{1}$·8495	8487	8480	8472	8464	8457	8449	8441	8433	8426	1	3	4	5	6
46	$\bar{1}$·8418	8410	8402	8394	8386	8378	8370	8362	8354	8346	1	3	4	5	7
47	$\bar{1}$·8338	8330	8322	8313	8305	8297	8289	8280	8272	8264	1	3	4	6	7
48	$\bar{1}$·8255	8247	8238	8230	8221	8213	8204	8195	8187	8178	1	3	4	6	7
49	$\bar{1}$·8169	8161	8152	8143	8134	8125	8117	8108	8099	8090	1	3	4	6	7
50	$\bar{1}$·8081	8072	8063	8053	8044	8035	8026	8017	8007	7998	2	3	5	6	8
51	$\bar{1}$·7989	7979	7970	7960	7951	7941	7932	7922	7913	7903	2	3	5	6	8
52	$\bar{1}$·7893	7884	7874	7864	7854	7844	7835	7825	7815	7805	2	3	5	7	8
53	$\bar{1}$·7795	7785	7774	7764	7754	7744	7734	7723	7713	7703	2	3	5	7	9
54	$\bar{1}$·7692	7682	7671	7661	7650	7640	7629	7618	7607	7597	2	4	5	7	9
55	$\bar{1}$·7586	7575	7564	7553	7542	7531	7520	7509	7498	7487	2	4	6	7	9
56	$\bar{1}$·7476	7464	7453	7442	7430	7419	7407	7396	7384	7373	2	4	6	8	10
57	$\bar{1}$·7361	7349	7338	7326	7314	7302	7290	7278	7266	7254	2	4	6	8	10
58	$\bar{1}$·7242	7230	7218	7205	7193	7181	7168	7156	7144	7131	2	4	6	8	10
59	$\bar{1}$·7118	7106	7093	7080	7068	7055	7042	7029	7016	7003	2	4	6	9	11
60	$\bar{1}$·6990	6977	6963	6950	6937	6923	6910	6896	6883	6869	2	4	7	9	11
61	$\bar{1}$·6856	6842	6828	6814	6801	6787	6773	6759	6744	6730	2	5	7	9	12
62	$\bar{1}$·6716	6702	6687	6673	6659	6644	6629	6615	6600	6585	2	5	7	10	12
63	$\bar{1}$·6570	6556	6541	6526	6510	6495	6480	6465	6449	6434	3	5	8	10	13
64	$\bar{1}$·6418	6403	6387	6371	6356	6340	6324	6308	6292	6276	3	5	8	11	13
65	$\bar{1}$·6259	6243	6227	6210	6194	6177	6161	6144	6127	6110	3	6	8	11	14
66	$\bar{1}$·6093	6076	6059	6042	6024	6007	5990	5972	5954	5937	3	6	9	12	15
67	$\bar{1}$·5919	5901	5883	5865	5847	5828	5810	5792	5773	5754	3	6	9	12	15
68	$\bar{1}$·5736	5717	5698	5679	5660	5641	5621	5602	5583	5563	3	6	10	13	16
69	$\bar{1}$·5543	5523	5504	5484	5463	5443	5423	5402	5382	5361	3	7	10	14	17
70	$\bar{1}$·5341	5320	5299	5278	5256	5235	5213	5192	5170	5148	4	7	11	14	18
71	$\bar{1}$·5126	5104	5082	5060	5037	5015	4992	4969	4946	4923	4	8	11	15	19
72	$\bar{1}$·4900	4876	4853	4829	4805	4781	4757	4733	4709	4684	4	8	12	16	20
73	$\bar{1}$·4659	4634	4609	4584	4559	4533	4508	4482	4456	4430	4	9	13	17	21
74	$\bar{1}$·4403	4377	4350	4323	4296	4269	4242	4214	4186	4158	5	9	14	18	23
75	$\bar{1}$·4130	4102	4073	4044	4015	3986	3957	3927	3897	3867	5	10	15	20	24
76	$\bar{1}$·3837	3806	3775	3745	3713	3682	3650	3618	3586	3554	5	11	16	21	26
77	$\bar{1}$·3521	3488	3455	3421	3387	3353	3319	3284	3250	3214	6	11	17	23	28
78	$\bar{1}$·3179	3143	3107	3070	3034	2997	2959	2921	2883	2845	6	12	19	25	31
79	$\bar{1}$·2806	2767	2727	2687	2647	2606	2565	2524	2482	2439	7	14	20	27	34
80	$\bar{1}$·2397	2353	2310	2266	2221	2176	2131	2085	2038	1991	8	15	23	30	38
81	$\bar{1}$·1943	1895	1847	1797	1747	1697	1646	1594	1542	1489	8	17	25	34	43
82	$\bar{1}$·1436	1381	1326	1271	1214	1157	1099	1040	0981	0920	10	19	29	38	48
83	$\bar{1}$·0859	0797	0734	0670	0605	0539	0472	0403	0334	0264	11	22	33	44	55
84	$\bar{1}$·0192	0120	0046	**9970**	**9894**	**9816**	**9736**	**9655**	**9573**	**9489**	13	26	39	52	66
85	$\bar{2}$·9403	9315	9226	9135	9042	8946	8849	8749	8647	8543	16	32	48	64	80
86	$\bar{2}$·8436	8326	8213	8098	7979	7857	7731	7602	7468	7330	21	41	62	83	103
87	$\bar{2}$·7188	7041	6889	6731	6567	6397	6220	6035	5842	5640	Differences untrustworthy here				
88	$\bar{2}$·5428	5206	4971	4723	4459	4179	3880	3558	3210	2832					
89	$\bar{2}$·242	$\bar{2}$·196	$\bar{2}$·145	$\bar{2}$·087	$\bar{2}$·020	$\bar{3}$·941	$\bar{3}$·844	$\bar{3}$·719	$\bar{3}$·543	$\bar{3}$·242					
	0′	6′	12′	18′	24′	30′	36′	42′	48′	54′	1′	2′	3′	4′	5′

The black type indicates that the integer changes.

LOG. TANGENTS

	0′	6′	12′	18′	24′	30′	36′	42′	48′	54′	1′	2′	3′	4′	5′
0°	−∞	$\bar{3}$·242	$\bar{3}$·543	$\bar{3}$·719	$\bar{3}$·844	$\bar{3}$·941	$\bar{2}$·020	$\bar{2}$·087	$\bar{2}$·145	$\bar{2}$·196					
1	$\bar{2}$·2419	2833	3211	3559	3881	4181	4461	4725	4973	5208					
2	$\bar{2}$·5431	5643	5845	6038	6223	6401	6571	6736	6894	7046					
3	$\bar{2}$·7194	7337	7475	7609	7739	7865	7988	8107	8223	8336	20	41	62	83	104
4	$\bar{2}$·8446	8554	8659	8762	8862	8960	9056	9150	9241	9331	16	32	48	65	81
5	$\bar{2}$·9420	9506	9591	9674	9756	9836	9915	9992	**0068**	**0143**	13	26	40	53	66
6	$\bar{1}$·0216	0289	0360	0430	0499	0567	0633	0699	0764	0828	11	22	34	45	56
7	$\bar{1}$·0891	0954	1015	1076	1135	1194	1252	1310	1367	1423	10	20	29	39	49
8	$\bar{1}$·1478	1533	1587	1640	1693	1745	1797	1848	1898	1948	9	17	26	35	43
9	$\bar{1}$·1997	2046	2094	2142	2189	2236	2282	2328	2374	2419	8	16	23	31	39
10	$\bar{1}$·2463	2507	2551	2594	2637	2680	2722	2764	2805	2846	7	14	21	28	35
11	$\bar{1}$·2887	2927	2967	3006	3046	3085	3123	3162	3200	3237	6	13	19	26	32
12	$\bar{1}$·3275	3312	3349	3385	3422	3458	3493	3529	3564	3599	6	12	18	24	30
13	$\bar{1}$·3634	3668	3702	3736	3770	3804	3837	3870	3903	3935	6	11	17	22	28
14	$\bar{1}$·3968	4000	4032	4064	4095	4127	4158	4189	4220	4250	5	10	16	21	26
15	$\bar{1}$·4281	4311	4341	4371	4400	4430	4459	4488	4517	4546	5	10	15	20	25
16	$\bar{1}$·4575	4603	4632	4660	4688	4716	4744	4771	4799	4826	5	9	14	19	23
17	$\bar{1}$·4853	4880	4907	4934	4961	4987	5014	5040	5066	5092	4	9	13	18	22
18	$\bar{1}$·5118	5143	5169	5195	5220	5245	5270	5295	5320	5345	4	8	13	17	21
19	$\bar{1}$·5370	5394	5419	5443	5467	5491	5516	5539	5563	5587	4	8	12	16	20
20	$\bar{1}$·5611	5634	5658	5681	5704	5727	5750	5773	5796	5819	4	8	12	15	19
21	$\bar{1}$·5842	5864	5887	5909	5932	5954	5976	5998	6020	6042	4	7	11	15	19
22	$\bar{1}$·6064	6086	6108	6129	6151	6172	6194	6215	6236	6257	4	7	11	14	18
23	$\bar{1}$·6279	6300	6321	6341	6362	6383	6404	6424	6445	6465	3	7	10	14	17
24	$\bar{1}$·6486	6506	6527	6547	6567	6587	6607	6627	6647	6667	3	7	10	13	17
25	$\bar{1}$·6687	6706	6726	6746	6765	6785	6804	6824	6843	6863	3	7	10	13	16
26	$\bar{1}$·6882	6901	6920	6939	6958	6977	6996	7015	7034	7053	3	6	9	13	16
27	$\bar{1}$·7072	7090	7109	7128	7146	7165	7183	7202	7220	7238	3	6	9	12	15
28	$\bar{1}$·7257	7275	7293	7311	7330	7348	7366	7384	7402	7420	3	6	9	12	15
29	$\bar{1}$·7438	7455	7473	7491	7509	7526	7544	7562	7579	7597	3	6	9	12	15
30	$\bar{1}$·7614	7632	7649	7667	7684	7701	7719	7736	7753	7771	3	6	9	12	14
31	$\bar{1}$·7788	7805	7822	7839	7856	7873	7890	7907	7924	7941	3	6	9	11	14
32	$\bar{1}$·7958	7975	7992	8008	8025	8042	8059	8075	8092	8109	3	6	8	11	14
33	$\bar{1}$·8125	8142	8158	8175	8191	8208	8224	8241	8257	8274	3	5	8	11	14
34	$\bar{1}$·8290	8306	8323	8339	8355	8371	8388	8404	8420	8436	3	5	8	11	14
35	$\bar{1}$·8452	8468	8484	8501	8517	8533	8549	8565	8581	8597	3	5	8	11	13
36	$\bar{1}$·8613	8629	8644	8660	8676	8692	8708	8724	8740	8755	3	5	8	11	13
37	$\bar{1}$·8771	8787	8803	8818	8834	8850	8865	8881	8897	8912	3	5	8	10	13
38	$\bar{1}$·8928	8944	8959	8975	8990	9006	9022	9037	9053	9068	3	5	8	10	13
39	$\bar{1}$·9084	9099	9115	9130	9146	9161	9176	9192	9207	9223	3	5	8	10	13
40	$\bar{1}$·9238	9254	9269	9284	9300	9315	9330	9346	9361	9376	3	5	8	10	13
41	$\bar{1}$·9392	9407	9422	9438	9453	9468	9483	9499	9514	9529	3	5	8	10	13
42	$\bar{1}$·9544	9560	9575	9590	9605	9621	9636	9651	9666	9681	3	5	8	10	13
43	$\bar{1}$·9697	9712	9727	9742	9757	9772	9788	9803	9818	9833	3	5	8	10	13
44	$\bar{1}$·9848	9864	9879	9894	9909	9924	9939	9955	9970	9985	3	5	8	10	13
	0′	6′	12′	18′	24′	30′	36′	42′	48′	54′	1′	2′	3′	4′	5′

The black type indicates that the integer changes.

LOG. TANGENTS

	0′	6′	12′	18′	24′	30′	36′	42′	48′	54′	1′	2′	3′	4′	5′
45°	0·0000	0015	0030	0045	0061	0076	0091	0106	0121	0136	3	5	8	10	13
46	0·0152	0167	0182	0197	0212	0228	0243	0258	0273	0288	3	5	8	10	13
47	0·0303	0319	0334	0349	0364	0379	0395	0410	0425	0440	3	5	8	10	13
48	0·0456	0471	0486	0501	0517	0532	0547	0562	0578	0593	3	5	8	10	13
49	0·0608	0624	0639	0654	0670	0685	0700	0716	0731	0746	3	5	8	10	13
50	0·0762	0777	0793	0808	0824	0839	0854	0870	0885	0901	3	5	8	10	13
51	0·0916	0932	0947	0963	0978	0994	1010	1025	1041	1056	3	5	8	10	13
52	0·1072	1088	1103	1119	1135	1150	1166	1182	1197	1213	3	5	8	10	13
53	0·1229	1245	1260	1276	1292	1308	1324	1340	1356	1371	3	5	8	11	13
54	0·1387	1403	1419	1435	1451	1467	1483	1499	1516	1532	3	5	8	11	13
55	0·1548	1564	1580	1596	1612	1629	1645	1661	1677	1694	3	5	8	11	14
56	0·1710	1726	1743	1759	1776	1792	1809	1825	1842	1858	3	5	8	11	14
57	0·1875	1891	1908	1925	1941	1958	1975	1992	2008	2025	3	6	8	11	14
58	0·2042	2059	2076	2093	2110	2127	2144	2161	2178	2195	3	6	9	11	14
59	0·2212	2229	2247	2264	2281	2299	2316	2333	2351	2368	3	6	9	12	14
60	0·2386	2403	2421	2438	2456	2474	2491	2509	2527	2545	3	6	9	12	15
61	0·2562	2580	2598	2616	2634	2652	2670	2689	2707	2725	3	6	9	12	15
62	0·2743	2762	2780	2798	2817	2835	2854	2872	2891	2910	3	6	9	12	15
63	0·2928	2947	2966	2985	3004	3023	3042	3061	3080	3099	3	6	9	13	16
64	0·3118	3137	3157	3176	3196	3215	3235	3254	3274	3294	3	7	10	13	16
65	0·3313	3333	3353	3373	3393	3413	3433	3453	3473	3494	3	7	10	13	17
66	0·3514	3535	3555	3576	3596	3617	3638	3659	3679	3700	3	7	10	14	17
67	0·3721	3743	3764	3785	3806	3828	3849	3871	3892	3914	4	7	11	14	18
68	0·3936	3958	3980	4002	4024	4046	4068	4091	4113	4136	4	7	11	15	19
69	0·4158	4181	4204	4227	4250	4273	4296	4319	4342	4366	4	8	12	15	19
70	0·4389	4413	4437	4461	4484	4509	4533	4557	4581	4606	4	8	12	16	20
71	0·4630	4655	4680	4705	4730	4755	4780	4805	4831	4857	4	8	13	17	21
72	0·4882	4908	4934	4960	4986	5013	5039	5066	5093	5120	4	9	13	18	22
73	0·5147	5174	5201	5229	5256	5284	5312	5340	5368	5397	5	9	14	19	23
74	0·5425	5454	5483	5512	5541	5570	5600	5629	5659	5689	5	10	15	20	25
75	0·5719	5750	5780	5811	5842	5873	5905	5936	5968	6000	5	10	16	21	26
76	0·6032	6065	6097	6130	6163	6196	6230	6264	6298	6332	6	11	17	22	28
77	0·6366	6401	6436	6471	6507	6542	6578	6615	6651	6688	6	12	18	24	30
78	0·6725	6763	6800	6838	6877	6915	6954	6994	7033	7073	6	13	19	26	32
79	0·7113	7154	7195	7236	7278	7320	7363	7406	7449	7493	7	14	21	28	35
80	0·7537	7581	7626	7672	7718	7764	7811	7858	7906	7954	8	16	23	31	39
81	0·8003	8052	8102	8152	8203	8255	8307	8360	8413	8467	9	17	26	35	43
82	0·8522	8577	8633	8690	8748	8806	8865	8924	8985	9046	10	20	29	39	49
83	0·9109	9172	9236	9301	9367	9433	9501	9570	9640	9711	11	22	34	45	56
84	0·9784	9857	9932	**0008**	**0085**	**0164**	**0244**	**0326**	**0409**	**0494**	13	26	40	53	66
85	1·0580	0669	0759	0850	0944	1040	1138	1238	1341	1446	16	32	48	65	81
86	1·1554	1664	1777	1893	2012	2135	2261	2391	2525	2663	20	41	62	83	104
87	1·2806	2954	3106	3264	3429	3599	3777	3962	4155	4357	Differences untrustworthy here				
88	1·4569	4792	5027	5275	5539	5819	6119	6441	6789	7167					
89	1·758	1·804	1·855	1·913	1·980	2·059	2·156	2·281	2·457	2·758					
	0′	6′	12′	18′	24′	30′	36′	42′	48′	54′	1′	2′	3′	4′	5′

The black type indicates that the integer changes.

NATURAL SINES

	0′	6′	12′	18′	24′	30′	36′	42′	48′	54′	1′	2′	3′	4′	5′
0°	·0000	0017	0035	0052	0070	0087	0105	0122	0140	0157	3	6	9	12	15
1	·0175	0192	0209	0227	0244	0262	0279	0297	0314	0332	3	6	9	12	15
2	·0349	0366	0384	0401	0419	0436	0454	0471	0488	0506	3	6	9	12	15
3	·0523	0541	0558	0576	0593	0610	0628	0645	0663	0680	3	6	9	12	15
4	·0698	0715	0732	0750	0767	0785	0802	0819	0837	0854	3	6	9	12	14
5	·0872	0889	0906	0924	0941	0958	0976	0993	1011	1028	3	6	9	12	14
6	·1045	1063	1080	1097	1115	1132	1149	1167	1184	1201	3	6	9	12	14
7	·1219	1236	1253	1271	1288	1305	1323	1340	1357	1374	3	6	9	12	14
8	·1392	1409	1426	1444	1461	1478	1495	1513	1530	1547	3	6	9	12	14
9	·1564	1582	1599	1616	1633	1650	1668	1685	1702	1719	3	6	9	11	14
10	·1736	1754	1771	1788	1805	1822	1840	1857	1874	1891	3	6	9	11	14
11	·1908	1925	1942	1959	1977	1994	2011	2028	2045	2062	3	6	9	11	14
12	·2079	2096	2113	2130	2147	2164	2181	2198	2215	2233	3	6	9	11	14
13	·2250	2267	2284	2300	2317	2334	2351	2368	2385	2402	3	6	8	11	14
14	·2419	2436	2453	2470	2487	2504	2521	2538	2554	2571	3	6	8	11	14
15	·2588	2605	2622	2639	2656	2672	2689	2706	2723	2740	3	6	8	11	14
16	·2756	2773	2790	2807	2823	2840	2857	2874	2890	2907	3	6	8	11	14
17	·2924	2940	2957	2974	2990	3007	3024	3040	3057	3074	3	6	8	11	14
18	·3090	3107	3123	3140	3156	3173	3190	3206	3223	3239	3	6	8	11	14
19	·3256	3272	3289	3305	3322	3338	3355	3371	3387	3404	3	5	8	11	14
20	·3420	3437	3453	3469	3486	3502	3518	3535	3551	3567	3	5	8	11	14
21	·3584	3600	3616	3633	3649	3665	3681	3697	3714	3730	3	5	8	11	14
22	·3746	3762	3778	3795	3811	3827	3843	3859	3875	3891	3	5	8	11	13
23	·3907	3923	3939	3955	3971	3987	4003	4019	4035	4051	3	5	8	11	13
24	·4067	4083	4099	4115	4131	4147	4163	4179	4195	4210	3	5	8	11	13
25	·4226	4242	4258	4274	4289	4305	4321	4337	4352	4368	3	5	8	11	13
26	·4384	4399	4415	4431	4446	4462	4478	4493	4509	4524	3	5	8	10	13
27	·4540	4555	4571	4586	4602	4617	4633	4648	4664	4679	3	5	8	10	13
28	·4695	4710	4726	4741	4756	4772	4787	4802	4818	4833	3	5	8	10	13
29	·4848	4863	4879	4894	4909	4924	4939	4955	4970	4985	3	5	8	10	13
30	·5000	5015	5030	5045	5060	5075	5090	5105	5120	5135	3	5	8	10	13
31	·5150	5165	5180	5195	5210	5225	5240	5255	5270	5284	2	5	7	10	12
32	·5299	5314	5329	5344	5358	5373	5388	5402	5417	5432	2	5	7	10	12
33	·5446	5461	5476	5490	5505	5519	5534	5548	5563	5577	2	5	7	10	12
34	·5592	5606	5621	5635	5650	5664	5678	5693	5707	5721	2	5	7	10	12
35	·5736	5750	5764	5779	5793	5807	5821	5835	5850	5864	2	5	7	9	12
36	·5878	5892	5906	5920	5934	5948	5962	5976	5990	6004	2	5	7	9	12
37	·6018	6032	6046	6060	6074	6088	6101	6115	6129	6143	2	5	7	9	12
38	·6157	6170	6184	6198	6211	6225	6239	6252	6266	6280	2	5	7	9	11
39	·6293	6307	6320	6334	6347	6361	6374	6388	6401	6414	2	4	7	9	11
40	·6428	6441	6455	6468	6481	6494	6508	6521	6534	6547	2	4	7	9	11
41	·6561	6574	6587	6600	6613	6626	6639	6652	6665	6678	2	4	7	9	11
42	·6691	6704	6717	6730	6743	6756	6769	6782	6794	6807	2	4	6	9	11
43	·6820	6833	6845	6858	6871	6884	6896	6909	6921	6934	2	4	6	8	11
44	·6947	6959	6972	6984	6997	7009	7022	7034	7046	7059	2	4	6	8	10
	0′	6′	12′	18′	24′	30′	36′	42′	48′	54′	1′	2′	3′	4′	5′

NATURAL SINES

	0′	6′	12′	18′	24′	30′	36′	42′	48′	54′	1′	2′	3′	4′	5′
45°	·7071	7083	7096	7108	7120	7133	7145	7157	7169	7181	2	4	6	8	10
46	·7193	7206	7218	7230	7242	7254	7266	7278	7290	7302	2	4	6	8	10
47	·7314	7325	7337	7349	7361	7373	7385	7396	7408	7420	2	4	6	8	10
48	·7431	7443	7455	7466	7478	7490	7501	7513	7524	7536	2	4	6	8	10
49	·7547	7559	7570	7581	7593	7604	7615	7627	7638	7649	2	4	6	8	9
50	·7660	7672	7683	7694	7705	7716	7727	7738	7749	7760	2	4	6	7	9
51	·7771	7782	7793	7804	7815	7826	7837	7848	7859	7869	2	4	5	7	9
52	·7880	7891	7902	7912	7923	7934	7944	7955	7965	7976	2	4	5	7	9
53	·7986	7997	8007	8018	8028	8039	8049	8059	8070	8080	2	3	5	7	9
54	·8090	8100	8111	8121	8131	8141	8151	8161	8171	8181	2	3	5	7	8
55	·8192	8202	8211	8221	8231	8241	8251	8261	8271	8281	2	3	5	7	8
56	·8290	8300	8310	8320	8329	8339	8348	8358	8368	8377	2	3	5	6	8
57	·8387	8396	8406	8415	8425	8434	8443	8453	8462	8471	2	3	5	6	8
58	·8480	8490	8499	8508	8517	8526	8536	8545	8554	8563	2	3	5	6	8
59	·8572	8581	8590	8599	8607	8616	8625	8634	8643	8652	1	3	4	6	7
60	·8660	8669	8678	8686	8695	8704	8712	8721	8729	8738	1	3	4	6	7
61	·8746	8755	8763	8771	8780	8788	8796	8805	8813	8821	1	3	4	6	7
62	·8829	8838	8846	8854	8862	8870	8878	8886	8894	8902	1	3	4	5	7
63	·8910	8918	8926	8934	8942	8949	8957	8965	8973	8980	1	3	4	5	6
64	·8988	8996	9003	9011	9018	9026	9033	9041	9048	9056	1	3	4	5	6
65	·9063	9070	9078	9085	9092	9100	9107	9114	9121	9128	1	2	4	5	6
66	·9135	9143	9150	9157	9164	9171	9178	9184	9191	9198	1	2	3	5	6
67	·9205	9212	9219	9225	9232	9239	9245	9252	9259	9265	1	2	3	4	6
68	·9272	9278	9285	9291	9298	9304	9311	9317	9323	9330	1	2	3	4	5
69	·9336	9342	9348	9354	9361	9367	9373	9379	9385	9391	1	2	3	4	5
70	·9397	9403	9409	9415	9421	9426	9432	9438	9444	9449	1	2	3	4	5
71	·9455	9461	9466	9472	9478	9483	9489	9494	9500	9505	1	2	3	4	5
72	·9511	9516	9521	9527	9532	9537	9542	9548	9553	9558	1	2	3	4	4
73	·9563	9568	9573	9578	9583	9588	9593	9598	9603	9608	1	2	2	3	4
74	·9613	9617	9622	9627	9632	9636	9641	9646	9650	9655	1	2	2	3	4
75	·9659	9664	9668	9673	9677	9681	9686	9690	9694	9699	1	1	2	3	4
76	·9703	9707	9711	9715	9720	9724	9728	9732	9736	9740	1	1	2	3	3
77	·9744	9748	9751	9755	9759	9763	9767	9770	9774	9778	1	1	2	3	3
78	·9781	9785	9789	9792	9796	9799	9803	9806	9810	9813	1	1	2	2	3
79	·9816	9820	9823	9826	9829	9833	9836	9839	9842	9845	1	1	2	2	3
80	·9848	9851	9854	9857	9860	9863	9866	9869	9871	9874	0	1	1	2	2
81	·9877	9880	9882	9885	9888	9890	9893	9895	9898	9900	0	1	1	2	2
82	·9903	9905	9907	9910	9912	9914	9917	9919	9921	9923	0	1	1	2	2
83	·9925	9928	9930	9932	9934	9936	9938	9940	9942	9943	0	1	1	1	2
84	·9945	9947	9949	9951	9952	9954	9956	9957	9959	9960	0	1	1	1	1
85	·9962	9963	9965	9966	9968	9969	9971	9972	9973	9974	0	0	1	1	1
86	·9976	9977	9978	9979	9980	9981	9982	9983	9984	9985	0	0	1	1	1
87	·9986	9987	9988	9989	9990	9990	9991	9992	9993	9993					
88	·9994	9995	9995	9996	9996	9997	9997	9997	9998	9998					
89	·9998	9999	9999	9999	9999	1·000	1·000	1·000	1·000	1·000					
	0′	6′	12′	18′	24′	30′	36′	42′	48′	54′	1′	2′	3′	4′	5′

OCL/M2—2H

NATURAL COSINES

SUBTRACT

°	0′	6′	12′	18′	24′	30′	36′	42′	48′	54′	1′	2′	3′	4′	5′
0	1·0000	1·000	1·000	1·000	1·000	1·000	**9999**	**9999**	**9999**	**9999**					
1	·9998	9998	9998	9997	9997	9997	9996	9996	9995	9995					
2	·9994	9993	9993	9992	9991	9990	9990	9989	9988	9987	0	0	0	0	1
3	·9986	9985	9984	9983	9982	9981	9980	9979	9978	9977	0	0	1	1	1
4	·9976	9974	9973	9972	9971	9969	9968	9966	9965	9963	0	0	1	1	1
5	·9962	9960	9959	9957	9956	9954	9952	9951	9949	9947	0	1	1	1	1
6	·9945	9943	9942	9940	9938	9936	9934	9932	9930	9928	0	1	1	1	2
7	·9925	9923	9921	9919	9917	9914	9912	9910	9907	9905	0	1	1	2	2
8	·9903	9900	9898	9895	9893	9890	9888	9885	9882	9880	0	1	1	2	2
9	·9877	9874	9871	9869	9866	9863	9860	9857	9854	9851	0	1	1	2	2
10	·9848	9845	9842	9839	9836	9833	9829	9826	9823	9820	1	1	2	2	3
11	·9816	9813	9810	9806	9803	9799	9796	9792	9789	9785	1	1	2	2	3
12	·9781	9778	9774	9770	9767	9763	9759	9755	9751	9748	1	1	2	3	3
13	·9744	9740	9736	9732	9728	9724	9720	9715	9711	9707	1	1	2	3	3
14	·9703	9699	9694	9690	9686	9681	9677	9673	9668	9664	1	1	2	3	4
15	·9659	9655	9650	9646	9641	9636	9632	9627	9622	9617	1	2	2	3	4
16	·9613	9608	9603	9598	9593	9588	9583	9578	9573	9568	1	2	2	3	4
17	·9563	9558	9553	9548	9542	9537	9532	9527	9521	9516	1	2	3	4	4
18	·9511	9505	9500	9494	9489	9483	9478	9472	9466	9461	1	2	3	4	5
19	·9455	9449	9444	9438	9432	9426	9421	9415	9409	9403	1	2	3	4	5
20	·9397	9391	9385	9379	9373	9367	9361	9354	9348	9342	1	2	3	4	5
21	·9336	9330	9323	9317	9311	9304	9298	9291	9285	9278	1	2	3	4	5
22	·9272	9265	9259	9252	9245	9239	9232	9225	9219	9212	1	2	3	4	6
23	·9205	9198	9191	9184	9178	9171	9164	9157	9150	9143	1	2	3	5	6
24	·9135	9128	9121	9114	9107	9100	9092	9085	9078	9070	1	2	4	5	6
25	·9063	9056	9048	9041	9033	9026	9018	9011	9003	8996	1	3	4	5	6
26	·8988	8980	8973	8965	8957	8949	8942	8934	8926	8918	1	3	4	5	6
27	·8910	8902	8894	8886	8878	8870	8862	8854	8846	8838	1	3	4	5	7
28	·8829	8821	8813	8805	8796	8788	8780	8771	8763	8755	1	[illegible]	4	6	7
29	·8746	8738	8729	8721	8712	8704	8695	8686	8678	8669	1	3	4	6	7
30	·8660	8652	8643	8634	8625	8616	8607	8599	8590	8581	1	3	4	6	7
31	·8572	8563	8554	8545	8536	8526	8517	8508	8499	8490	2	3	5	6	8
32	·8480	8471	8462	8453	8443	8434	8425	8415	8406	8396	2	3	5	6	8
33	·8387	8377	8368	8358	8348	8339	8329	8320	8310	8300	2	3	5	6	8
34	·8290	8281	8271	8261	8251	8241	8231	8221	8211	8202	2	3	5	7	8
35	·8192	8181	8171	8161	8151	8141	8131	8121	8111	8100	2	3	5	7	8
36	·8090	8080	8070	8059	8049	8039	8028	8018	8007	7997	2	3	5	7	9
37	·7986	7976	7965	7955	7944	7934	7923	7912	7902	7891	2	4	5	7	9
38	·7880	7869	7859	7848	7837	7826	7815	7804	7793	7782	2	4	5	7	9
39	·7771	7760	7749	7738	7727	7716	7705	7694	7683	7672	2	4	6	7	9
40	·7660	7649	7638	7627	7615	7604	7593	7581	7570	7559	2	4	6	8	9
41	·7547	7536	7524	7513	7501	7490	7478	7466	7455	7443	2	4	6	8	10
42	·7431	7420	7408	7396	7385	7373	7361	7349	7337	7325	2	4	6	8	10
43	·7314	7302	7290	7278	7266	7254	7242	7230	7218	7206	2	4	6	8	10
44	·7193	7181	7169	7157	7145	7133	7120	7108	7096	7083	2	4	6	8	10
	0′	6′	12′	18′	24′	30′	36′	42′	48′	54′	1′	2′	3′	4′	5′

The black type indicates that the integer changes.

NATURAL COSINES

SUBTRACT

	0′	6′	12′	18′	24′	30′	36′	42′	48′	54′	1′	2′	3′	4′	5′
45°	·7071	7059	7046	7034	7022	7009	6997	6984	6972	6959	2	4	6	8	10
46	·6947	6934	6921	6909	6896	6884	6871	6858	6845	6833	2	4	6	8	11
47	·6820	6807	6794	6782	6769	6756	6743	6730	6717	6704	2	4	6	9	11
48	·6691	6678	6665	6652	6639	6626	6613	6600	6587	6574	2	4	7	9	11
49	·6561	6547	6534	6521	6508	6494	6481	6468	6455	6441	2	4	7	9	11
50	·6428	6414	6401	6388	6374	6361	6347	6334	6320	6307	2	4	7	9	11
51	·6293	6280	6266	6252	6239	6225	6211	6198	6184	6170	2	5	7	9	11
52	·6157	6143	6129	6115	6101	6088	6074	6060	6046	6032	2	5	7	9	12
53	·6018	6004	5990	5976	5962	5948	5934	5920	5906	5892	2	5	7	9	12
54	·5878	5864	5850	5835	5821	5807	5793	5779	5764	5750	2	5	7	9	12
55	·5736	5721	5707	5693	5678	5664	5650	5635	5621	5606	2	5	7	10	12
56	·5592	5577	5563	5548	5534	5519	5505	5490	5476	5461	2	5	7	10	12
57	·5446	5432	5417	5402	5388	5373	5358	5344	5329	5314	2	5	7	10	12
58	·5299	5284	5270	5255	5240	5225	5210	5195	5180	5165	2	5	7	10	12
59	·5150	5135	5120	5105	5090	5075	5060	5045	5030	5015	3	5	8	10	13
60	·5000	4985	4970	4955	4939	4924	4909	4894	4879	4863	3	5	8	10	13
61	·4848	4833	4818	4802	4787	4772	4756	4741	4726	4710	3	5	8	10	13
62	·4695	4679	4664	4648	4633	4617	4602	4586	4571	4555	3	5	8	10	13
63	·4540	4524	4509	4493	4478	4462	4446	4431	4415	4399	3	5	8	10	13
64	·4384	4368	4352	4337	4321	4305	4289	4274	4258	4242	3	5	8	11	13
65	·4226	4210	4195	4179	4163	4147	4131	4115	4099	4083	3	5	8	11	13
66	·4067	4051	4035	4019	4003	3987	3971	3955	3939	3923	3	5	8	11	13
67	·3907	3891	3875	3859	3843	3827	3811	3795	3778	3762	3	5	8	11	13
68	·3746	3730	3714	3697	3681	3665	3649	3633	3616	3600	3	5	8	11	14
69	·3584	3567	3551	3535	3518	3502	3486	3469	3453	3437	3	5	8	11	14
70	·3420	3404	3387	3371	3355	3338	3322	3305	3289	3272	3	5	8	11	14
71	·3256	3239	3223	3206	3190	3173	3156	3140	3123	3107	3	6	8	11	14
72	·3090	3074	3057	3040	3024	3007	2990	2974	2957	2940	3	6	8	11	14
73	·2924	2907	2890	2874	2857	2840	2823	2807	2790	2773	3	6	8	11	14
74	·2756	2740	2723	2706	2689	2672	2656	2639	2622	2605	3	6	8	11	14
75	·2588	2571	2554	2538	2521	2504	2487	2470	2453	2436	3	6	8	11	14
76	·2419	2402	2385	2368	2351	2334	2317	2300	2284	2267	3	6	8	11	14
77	·2250	2233	2215	2198	2181	2164	2147	2130	2113	2096	3	6	9	11	14
78	·2079	2062	2045	2028	2011	1994	1977	1959	1942	1925	3	6	9	11	14
79	·1908	1891	1874	1857	1840	1822	1805	1788	1771	1754	3	6	9	11	14
80	·1736	1719	1702	1685	1668	1650	1633	1616	1599	1582	3	6	9	11	14
81	·1564	1547	1530	1513	1495	1478	1461	1444	1426	1409	3	6	9	12	14
82	·1392	1374	1357	1340	1323	1305	1288	1271	1253	1236	3	6	9	12	14
83	·1219	1201	1184	1167	1149	1132	1115	1097	1080	1063	3	6	9	12	14
84	·1045	1028	1011	0993	0976	0958	0941	0924	0906	0889	3	6	9	12	14
85	·0872	0854	0837	0819	0802	0785	0767	0750	0732	0715	3	6	9	12	14
86	·0698	0680	0663	0645	0628	0610	0593	0576	0558	0541	3	6	9	12	15
87	·0523	0506	0488	0471	0454	0436	0419	0401	0384	0366	3	6	9	12	15
88	·0349	0332	0314	0297	0279	0262	0244	0227	0209	0192	3	6	9	12	15
89	·0175	0157	0140	0122	0105	0087	0070	0052	0035	0017	3	6	9	12	15
	0′	6′	12′	18′	24′	30′	36′	42′	48′	54′	1′	2′	3′	4′	5′

NATURAL TANGENTS

	0′	6′	12′	18′	24′	30′	36′	42′	48′	54′	1′	2′	3′	4′	5′
0°	0·0000	0017	0035	0052	0070	0087	0105	0122	0140	0157	3	6	9	12	15
1	0·0175	0192	0209	0227	0244	0262	0279	0297	0314	0332	3	6	9	12	15
2	0·0349	0367	0384	0402	0419	0437	0454	0472	0489	0507	3	6	9	12	15
3	0·0524	0542	0559	0577	0594	0612	0629	0647	0664	0682	3	6	9	12	15
4	0·0699	0717	0734	0752	0769	0787	0805	0822	0840	0857	3	6	9	12	15
5	0·0875	0892	0910	0928	0945	0963	0981	0998	1016	1033	3	6	9	12	15
6	0·1051	1069	1086	1104	1122	1139	1157	1175	1192	1210	3	6	9	12	15
7	0·1228	1246	1263	1281	1299	1317	1334	1352	1370	1388	3	6	9	12	15
8	0·1405	1423	1441	1459	1477	1495	1512	1530	1548	1566	3	6	9	12	15
9	0·1584	1602	1620	1638	1655	1673	1691	1709	1727	1745	3	6	9	12	15
10	0·1763	1781	1799	1817	1835	1853	1871	1890	1908	1926	3	6	9	12	15
11	0·1944	1962	1980	1998	2016	2035	2053	2071	2089	2107	3	6	9	12	15
12	0·2126	2144	2162	2180	2199	2217	2235	2254	2272	2290	3	6	9	12	15
13	0·2309	2327	2345	2364	2382	2401	2419	2438	2456	2475	3	6	9	12	15
14	0·2493	2512	2530	2549	2568	2586	2605	2623	2642	2661	3	6	9	12	16
15	0·2679	2698	2717	2736	2754	2773	2792	2811	2830	2849	3	6	9	13	16
16	0·2867	2886	2905	2924	2943	2962	2981	3000	3019	3038	3	6	9	13	16
17	0·3057	3076	3096	3115	3134	3153	3172	3191	3211	3230	3	6	10	13	16
18	0·3249	3269	3288	3307	3327	3346	3365	3385	3404	3424	3	6	10	13	16
19	0·3443	3463	3482	3502	3522	3541	3561	3581	3600	3620	3	7	10	13	16
20	0·3640	3659	3679	3699	3719	3739	3759	3779	3799	3819	3	7	10	13	17
21	0·3839	3859	3879	3899	3919	3939	3959	3979	4000	4020	3	7	10	13	17
22	0·4040	4061	4081	4101	4122	4142	4163	4183	4204	4224	3	7	10	14	17
23	0·4245	4265	4286	4307	4327	4348	4369	4390	4411	4431	3	7	10	14	17
24	0·4452	4473	4494	4515	4536	4557	4578	4599	4621	4642	4	7	11	14	18
25	0·4663	4684	4706	4727	4748	4770	4791	4813	4834	4856	4	7	11	14	18
26	0·4877	4899	4921	4942	4964	4986	5008	5029	5051	5073	4	7	11	15	18
27	0·5095	5117	5139	5161	5184	5206	5228	5250	5272	5295	4	7	11	15	18
28	0·5317	5340	5362	5384	5407	5430	5452	5475	5498	5520	4	8	11	15	19
29	0·5543	5566	5589	5612	5635	5658	5681	5704	5727	5750	4	8	12	15	19
30	0·5774	5797	5820	5844	5867	5890	5914	5938	5961	5985	4	8	12	16	20
31	0·6009	6032	6056	6080	6104	6128	6152	6176	6200	6224	4	8	12	16	20
32	0·6249	6273	6297	6322	6346	6371	6395	6420	6445	6469	4	8	12	16	20
33	0·6494	6519	6544	6569	6594	6619	6644	6669	6694	6720	4	8	13	17	21
34	0·6745	6771	6796	6822	6847	6873	6899	6924	6950	6976	4	9	13	17	21
35	0·7002	7028	7054	7080	7107	7133	7159	7186	7212	7239	4	9	13	18	22
36	0·7265	7292	7319	7346	7373	7400	7427	7454	7481	7508	5	9	14	18	23
37	0·7536	7563	7590	7618	7646	7673	7701	7729	7757	7785	5	9	14	18	23
38	0·7813	7841	7869	7898	7926	7954	7983	8012	8040	8069	5	9	14	19	24
39	0·8098	8127	8156	8185	8214	8243	8273	8302	8332	8361	5	10	15	20	24
40	0·8391	8421	8451	8481	8511	8541	8571	8601	8632	8662	5	10	15	20	25
41	0·8693	8724	8754	8785	8816	8847	8878	8910	8941	8972	5	10	16	21	26
42	0·9004	9036	9067	9099	9131	9163	9195	9228	9260	9293	5	11	16	21	27
43	0·9325	9358	9391	9424	9457	9490	9523	9556	9590	9623	6	11	17	22	28
44	0·9657	9691	9725	9759	9793	9827	9861	9896	9930	9965	6	11	17	23	29
	0′	6′	12′	18′	24′	30′	36′	42′	48′	54′	1′	2′	3′	4′	5′

NATURAL TANGENTS

	0′	6′	12′	18′	24′	30′	36′	42′	48′	54′	1′	2′	3′	4′	5′
45°	1·0000	0035	0070	0105	0141	0176	0212	0247	0283	0319	6	12	18	24	30
46	1·0355	0392	0428	0464	0501	0538	0575	0612	0649	0686	6	12	18	25	31
47	1·0724	0761	0799	0837	0875	0913	0951	0990	1028	1067	6	13	19	25	32
48	1·1106	1145	1184	1224	1263	1303	1343	1383	1423	1463	7	13	20	26	33
49	1·1504	1544	1585	1626	1667	1708	1750	1792	1833	1875	7	14	21	28	34
50	1·1918	1960	2002	2045	2088	2131	2174	2218	2261	2305	7	14	22	29	36
51	1·2349	2393	2437	2482	2527	2572	2617	2662	2708	2753	8	15	23	30	38
52	1·2799	2846	2892	2938	2985	3032	3079	3127	3175	3222	8	16	24	31	39
53	1·3270	3319	3367	3416	3465	3514	3564	3613	3663	3713	8	16	25	33	41
54	1·3764	3814	3865	3916	3968	4019	4071	4124	4176	4229	9	17	26	34	43
55	1·4281	4335	4388	4442	4496	4550	4605	4659	4715	4770	9	18	27	36	45
56	1·4826	4882	4938	4994	5051	5108	5166	5224	5282	5340	10	19	29	38	48
57	1·5399	5458	5517	5577	5637	5697	5757	5818	5880	5941	10	20	30	40	50
58	1·6003	6066	6128	6191	6255	6319	6383	6447	6512	6577	11	21	32	43	53
59	1·6643	6709	6775	6842	6909	6977	7045	7113	7182	7251	11	23	34	45	56
60	1·7321	7391	7461	7532	7603	7675	7747	7820	7893	7966	12	24	36	48	60
61	1·8040	8115	8190	8265	8341	8418	8495	8572	8650	8728	13	26	38	51	64
62	1·8807	8887	8967	9047	9128	9210	9292	9375	9458	9542	14	27	41	55	68
63	1·9626	9711	9797	9883	9970	**0057**	**0145**	**0233**	**0323**	**0413**	15	29	44	58	73
64	2·0503	0594	0686	0778	0872	0965	1060	1155	1251	1348	16	31	47	63	78
65	2·1445	1543	1642	1742	1842	1943	2045	2148	2251	2355	17	34	51	68	85
66	2·2460	2566	2673	2781	2889	2998	3109	3220	3332	3445	18	37	55	73	91
67	2·3559	3673	3789	3906	4023	4142	4262	4383	4504	4627	20	40	60	79	99
68	2·4751	4876	5002	5129	5257	5386	5517	5649	5782	5916	22	43	65	87	108
69	2·6051	6187	6325	6464	6605	6746	6889	7034	7179	7326	24	47	71	95	119
70	2·7475	7625	7776	7929	8083	8239	8397	8556	8716	8878	26	52	78	104	130
71	2·9042	9208	9375	9544	9714	9887	**0061**	**0237**	**0415**	**0595**	29	58	87	116	144
72	3·0777	0961	1146	1334	1524	1716	1910	2106	2305	2506	32	64	97	129	161
73	3·2709	2914	3122	3332	3544	3759	3977	4197	4420	4646	36	72	108	144	180
74	3·4874	5105	5339	5576	5816	6059	6305	6554	6806	7062	41	81	122	163	203
75	3·7321	7583	7848	8118	8391	8667	8947	9232	9520	9812	46	93	139	186	232
76	4·0108	0408	0713	1022	1335	1653	1976	2303	2635	2972	53	107	160	214	267
77	4·3315	3662	4015	4373	4737	5107	5483	5864	6252	6646	62	124	186	248	310
78	4·7046	7453	7867	8288	8716	9152	9594	**0045**	**0504**	**0970**	73	146	220	293	366
79	5·1446	1929	2422	2924	3435	3955	4486	5026	5578	6140	87	175	263	350	438
80	5·671	5·730	5·789	5·850	5·912	5·976	6·041	6·107	6·174	6·243					
81	6·314	6·386	6·460	6·535	6·612	6·691	6·772	6·855	6·940	7·026					
82	7·115	7·207	7·300	7·396	7·495	7·596	7·700	7·806	7·916	8·028					
83	8·144	8·264	8·386	8·513	8·643	8·777	8·915	9·058	9·205	9·357					
84	9·51	9·68	9·84	10·02	10·20	10·39	10·58	10·78	10·99	11·20					
85	11·43	11·66	11·91	12·16	12·43	12·71	13·00	13·30	13·62	13·95					
86	14·30	14·67	15·06	15·46	15·89	16·35	16·83	17·34	17·89	18·46					
87	19·08	19·74	20·45	21·20	22·02	22·90	23·86	24·90	26·03	27·27					
88	28·64	30·14	31·82	33·69	35·80	38·19	40·92	44·07	47·74	52·08					
89	57·29	63·66	71·62	81·85	95·49	114·6	143·2	191·0	286·5	573·0					
	0′	6′	12′	18′	24′	30′	36′	42′	48′	54′	1′	2′	3′	4′	5′

Differences untrustworthy here

The black type indicates that the integer changes.

	0	1	2	3	4	5	6	7	8	9	1	2	3	4	5	6	7	8	9
10	1000	1020	1040	1061	1082	1103	1124	1145	1166	1188	2	4	6	8	10	13	15	17	19
11	1210	1232	1254	1277	1300	1323	1346	1369	1392	1416	2	5	7	9	11	14	16	18	21
12	1440	1464	1488	1513	1538	1563	1588	1613	1638	1664	2	5	7	10	12	15	17	20	22
13	1690	1716	1742	1769	1796	1823	1850	1877	1904	1932	3	5	8	11	13	16	19	22	24
14	1960	1988	2016	2045	2074	2103	2132	2161	2190	2220	3	6	9	12	14	17	20	23	26
15	2250	2280	2310	2341	2372	2403	2434	2465	2496	2528	3	6	9	12	15	19	22	25	28
16	2560	2592	2624	2657	2690	2723	2756	2789	2822	2856	3	7	10	13	16	20	23	26	30
17	2890	2924	2958	2993	3028	3063	3098	3133	3168	3204	3	7	10	14	17	21	24	28	31
18	3240	3276	3312	3349	3386	3423	3460	3497	3534	3572	4	7	11	15	18	22	26	30	33
19	3610	3648	3686	3725	3764	3803	3842	3881	3920	3960	4	8	12	16	19	23	27	31	35
20	4000	4040	4080	4121	4162	4203	4244	4285	4326	4368	4	8	12	16	20	25	29	33	37
21	4410	4452	4494	4537	4580	4623	4666	4709	4752	4796	4	9	13	17	21	26	30	34	39
22	4840	4884	4928	4973	5018	5063	5108	5153	5198	5244	4	9	13	18	22	27	31	36	40
23	5290	5336	5382	5429	5476	5523	5570	5617	5664	5712	5	9	14	19	23	28	33	38	42
24	5760	5808	5856	5905	5954	6003	6052	6101	6150	6200	5	10	15	20	24	29	34	39	44
25	6250	6300	6350	6401	6452	6503	6554	6605	6656	6708	5	10	15	20	25	31	36	41	46
26	6760	6812	6864	6917	6970	7023	7076	7129	7182	7236	5	11	16	21	26	32	37	42	48
27	7290	7344	7398	7453	7508	7563	7618	7673	7728	7784	5	11	16	22	28	33	38	44	49
28	7840	7896	7952	8009	8066	8123	8180	8237	8294	8352	6	11	17	23	28	34	40	46	51
29	8410	8468	8526	8585	8644	8703	8762	8821	8880	8940	6	12	18	24	30	35	41	47	53
30	9000	9060	9120	9181	9242	9303	9364	9425	9486	9548	6	12	18	24	31	37	43	49	55
31	9610	9672	9734	9797	9860	9923	9986				6	13	19	25	31	38	44	50	56
31								1005	1011	1018	1	1	2	3	3	4	5	5	6
32	1024	1030	1037	1043	1050	1056	1063	1069	1076	1082	1	1	2	3	3	4	5	5	6
33	1089	1096	1102	1109	1116	1122	1129	1136	1142	1149	1	1	2	3	3	4	5	5	6
34	1156	1163	1170	1176	1183	1190	1197	1204	1211	1218	1	1	2	3	3	4	5	6	6
35	1225	1232	1239	1246	1253	1260	1267	1274	1282	1289	1	1	2	3	4	4	5	6	6
36	1296	1303	1310	1318	1325	1332	1340	1347	1354	1362	1	1	2	3	4	4	5	6	7
37	1369	1376	1384	1391	1399	1406	1414	1421	1429	1436	1	2	2	3	4	5	5	6	7
38	1444	1452	1459	1467	1475	1482	1490	1498	1505	1513	1	2	2	3	4	5	5	6	7
39	1521	1529	1537	1544	1552	1560	1568	1576	1584	1592	1	2	2	3	4	5	6	6	7
40	1600	1608	1616	1624	1632	1640	1648	1656	1665	1673	1	2	2	3	4	5	6	6	7
41	1681	1689	1697	1706	1714	1722	1731	1739	1747	1756	1	2	2	3	4	5	6	7	7
42	1764	1772	1781	1789	1798	1806	1815	1823	1832	1840	1	2	3	3	4	5	6	7	8
43	1849	1858	1866	1875	1884	1892	1901	1910	1918	1927	1	2	3	3	4	5	6	7	8
44	1936	1945	1954	1962	1971	1980	1989	1998	2007	2016	1	2	3	4	5	5	6	7	8
45	2025	2034	2043	2052	2061	2070	2079	2088	2098	2107	1	2	3	4	5	5	6	7	8
46	2116	2125	2134	2144	2153	2162	2172	2181	2190	2200	1	2	3	4	5	6	7	7	8
47	2209	2218	2228	2237	2247	2256	2266	2275	2285	2294	1	2	3	4	5	6	7	8	9
48	2304	2314	2323	2333	2343	2352	2362	2372	2381	2391	1	2	3	4	5	6	7	8	9
49	2401	2411	2421	2430	2440	2450	2460	2470	2480	2490	1	2	3	4	5	6	7	8	9
50	2500	2510	2520	2530	2540	2550	2560	2570	2581	2591	1	2	3	4	5	6	7	8	9
51	2601	2611	2621	2632	2642	2652	2663	2673	2683	2694	1	2	3	4	5	6	7	8	9
52	2704	2714	2725	2735	2746	2756	2767	2777	2788	2798	1	2	3	4	5	6	7	8	9
53	2809	2820	2830	2841	2852	2862	2873	2884	2894	2905	1	2	3	4	5	6	7	9	10
54	2916	2927	2938	2948	2959	2970	2981	2992	3003	3014	1	2	3	4	6	7	8	9	10
	0	1	2	3	4	5	6	7	8	9	1	2	3	4	5	6	7	8	9

The position of the decimal point must be determined by inspection.

SQUARES

	0	1	2	3	4	5	6	7	8	9	1	2	3	4	5	6	7	8	9
55	3025	3036	3047	3058	3069	3080	3091	3102	3114	3125	1	2	3	4	6	7	8	9	10
56	3136	3147	3158	3170	3181	3192	3204	3215	3226	3238	1	2	3	5	6	7	8	9	10
57	3249	3260	3272	3283	3295	3306	3318	3329	3341	3352	1	2	3	5	6	7	8	9	10
58	3364	3376	3387	3399	3411	3422	3434	3446	3457	3469	1	2	4	5	6	7	8	9	11
59	3481	3493	3505	3516	3528	3540	3552	3564	3576	3588	1	2	4	5	6	7	8	10	11
60	3600	3612	3624	3636	3648	3660	3672	3684	3697	3709	1	2	4	5	6	7	8	10	11
61	3721	3733	3745	3758	3770	3782	3795	3807	3819	3832	1	2	4	5	6	7	9	10	11
62	3844	3856	3869	3881	3894	3906	3919	3931	3944	3956	1	3	4	5	6	8	9	10	11
63	3969	3982	3994	4007	4020	4032	4045	4058	4070	4083	1	3	4	5	6	8	9	10	11
64	4096	4109	4122	4134	4147	4160	4173	4186	4199	4212	1	3	4	5	6	8	9	10	12
65	4225	4238	4251	4264	4277	4290	4303	4316	4330	4343	1	3	4	5	7	8	9	10	12
66	4356	4369	4382	4396	4409	4422	4436	4449	4462	4476	1	3	4	5	7	8	9	11	12
67	4489	4502	4516	4529	4543	4556	4570	4583	4597	4610	1	3	4	5	7	8	9	11	12
68	4624	4638	4651	4665	4679	4692	4706	4720	4733	4747	1	3	4	5	7	8	10	11	12
69	4761	4775	4789	4802	4816	4830	4844	4858	4872	4886	1	3	4	6	7	8	10	11	13
70	4900	4914	4928	4942	4956	4970	4984	4998	5013	5027	1	3	4	6	7	8	10	11	13
71	5041	5055	5069	5084	5098	5112	5127	5141	5155	5170	1	3	4	6	7	9	10	11	13
72	5184	5198	5213	5227	5242	5256	5271	5285	5300	5314	1	3	4	6	7	9	10	11	13
73	5329	5344	5358	5373	5388	5402	5417	5432	5446	5461	1	3	4	6	7	9	10	12	13
74	5476	5491	5506	5520	5535	5550	5565	5580	5595	5610	1	3	4	6	7	9	10	12	13
75	5625	5640	5655	5670	5685	5700	5715	5730	5746	5761	2	3	5	6	8	9	11	12	14
76	5776	5791	5806	5822	5837	5852	5868	5883	5898	5914	2	3	5	6	8	9	11	12	14
77	5929	5944	5960	5975	5991	6006	6022	6037	6053	6068	2	3	5	6	8	9	11	12	14
78	6084	6100	6115	6131	6147	6162	6178	6194	6209	6225	2	3	5	6	8	9	11	13	14
79	6241	6257	6273	6288	6304	6320	6336	6352	6368	6384	2	3	5	6	8	10	11	13	14
80	6400	6416	6432	6448	6464	6480	6496	6512	6529	6545	2	3	5	6	8	10	11	13	14
81	6561	6577	6593	6610	6626	6642	6659	6675	6691	6708	2	3	5	7	8	10	11	13	15
82	6724	6740	6757	6773	6790	6806	6823	6839	6856	6872	2	3	5	7	8	10	12	13	15
83	6889	6906	6922	6939	6956	6972	6989	7006	7022	7039	2	3	5	7	8	10	12	13	15
84	7056	7073	7090	7106	7123	7140	7157	7174	7191	7208	2	3	5	7	8	10	12	14	15
85	7225	7242	7259	7276	7293	7310	7327	7344	7362	7379	2	3	5	7	9	10	12	14	15
86	7396	7413	7430	7448	7465	7482	7500	7517	7534	7552	2	3	5	7	9	10	12	14	16
87	7569	7586	7604	7621	7639	7656	7674	7691	7709	7726	2	4	5	7	9	11	12	14	16
88	7744	7762	7779	7797	7815	7832	7850	7868	7885	7903	2	4	5	7	9	11	12	14	16
89	7921	7939	7957	7974	7992	8010	8028	8046	8064	8082	2	4	5	7	9	11	13	14	16
90	8100	8118	8136	8154	8172	8190	8208	8226	8245	8263	2	4	5	7	9	11	13	14	16
91	8281	8299	8317	8336	8354	8372	8391	8409	8427	8446	2	4	5	7	9	11	13	15	16
92	8464	8482	8501	8519	8538	8556	8575	8593	8612	8630	2	4	6	7	9	11	13	15	17
93	8649	8668	8686	8705	8724	8742	8761	8780	8798	8817	2	4	6	7	9	11	13	15	17
94	8836	8855	8874	8892	8911	8930	8949	8968	8987	9006	2	4	6	8	9	11	13	15	17
95	9025	9044	9063	9082	9101	9120	9139	9158	9178	9197	2	4	6	8	10	11	13	15	17
96	9216	9235	9254	9274	9293	9312	9332	9351	9370	9390	2	4	6	8	10	12	14	15	17
97	9409	9428	9448	9467	9487	9506	9526	9545	9565	9584	2	4	6	8	10	12	14	16	18
98	9604	9624	9643	9663	9683	9702	9722	9742	9761	9781	2	4	6	8	10	12	14	16	18
99	9801	9821	9841	9860	9880	9900	9920	9940	9960	9980	2	4	6	8	10	12	14	16	18
	0	1	2	3	4	5	6	7	8	9	1	2	3	4	5	6	7	8	9

The position of the decimal point must be determined by inspection.

SQUARE ROOTS

	0	1	2	3	4	5	6	7	8	9	1	2	3	4	5	6	7	8	9
10	1000	1005	1010	1015	1020	1025	1030	1034	1039	1044	0	1	1	2	2	3	3	4	4
	3162	3178	3194	3209	3225	3240	3256	3271	3286	3302	2	3	5	6	8	9	11	12	14
11	1049	1054	1058	1063	1068	1072	1077	1082	1086	1091	0	1	1	2	2	3	3	4	4
	3317	3332	3347	3362	3376	3391	3406	3421	3435	3450	1	3	4	6	7	9	10	12	13
12	1095	1100	1105	1109	1114	1118	1122	1127	1131	1136	0	1	1	2	2	3	3	4	4
	3464	3479	3493	3507	3521	3536	3550	3564	3578	3592	1	3	4	6	7	8	10	11	13
13	1140	1145	1149	1153	1158	1162	1166	1170	1175	1179	0	1	1	2	2	3	3	3	4
	3606	3619	3633	3647	3661	3674	3688	3701	3715	3728	1	3	4	5	7	8	10	11	12
14	1183	1187	1192	1196	1200	1204	1208	1212	1217	1221	0	1	1	2	2	3	3	3	4
	3742	3755	3768	3782	3795	3808	3821	3834	3847	3860	1	3	4	5	7	8	9	11	12
15	1225	1229	1233	1237	1241	1245	1249	1253	1257	1261	0	1	1	2	2	3	3	3	4
	3873	3886	3899	3912	3924	3937	3950	3962	3975	3987	1	3	4	5	6	8	9	10	11
16	1265	1269	1273	1277	1281	1285	1288	1292	1296	1300	0	1	1	2	2	3	3	3	4
	4000	4012	4025	4037	4050	4062	4074	4087	4099	4111	1	2	4	5	6	7	9	10	11
17	1304	1308	1311	1315	1319	1323	1327	1330	1334	1338	0	1	1	2	2	2	3	3	3
	4123	4135	4147	4159	4171	4183	4195	4207	4219	4231	1	2	4	5	6	7	8	10	11
18	1342	1345	1349	1353	1356	1360	1364	1367	1371	1375	0	1	1	1	2	2	3	3	3
	4243	4254	4266	4278	4290	4301	4313	4324	4336	4347	1	2	3	5	6	7	8	9	10
19	1378	1382	1386	1389	1393	1396	1400	1404	1407	1411	0	1	1	1	2	2	3	3	3
	4359	4370	4382	4393	4405	4416	4427	4438	4450	4461	1	2	3	5	6	7	8	9	10
20	1414	1418	1421	1425	1428	1432	1435	1439	1442	1446	0	1	1	1	2	2	2	3	3
	4472	4483	4494	4506	4517	4528	4539	4550	4561	4572	1	2	3	4	5	7	8	9	10
21	1449	1453	1456	1459	1463	1466	1470	1473	1476	1480	0	1	1	1	2	2	2	3	3
	4583	4593	4604	4615	4626	4637	4648	4658	4669	4680	1	2	3	4	5	6	8	9	10
22	1483	1487	1490	1493	1497	1500	1503	1507	1510	1513	0	1	1	1	2	2	2	3	3
	4690	4701	4712	4722	4733	4743	4754	4764	4775	4785	1	2	3	4	5	6	7	8	9
23	1517	1520	1523	1526	1530	1533	1536	1539	1543	1546	0	1	1	1	2	2	2	3	3
	4796	4806	4817	4827	4837	4848	4858	4868	4879	4889	1	2	3	4	5	6	7	8	9
24	1549	1552	1556	1559	1562	1565	1568	1572	1575	1578	0	1	1	1	2	2	2	3	3
	4899	4909	4919	4930	4940	4950	4960	4970	4980	4990	1	2	3	4	5	6	7	8	9
25	1581	1584	1587	1591	1594	1597	1600	1603	1606	1609	0	1	1	1	2	2	2	3	3
	5000	5010	5020	5030	5040	5050	5060	5070	5079	5089	1	2	3	4	5	6	7	8	9
26	1612	1616	1619	1622	1625	1628	1631	1634	1637	1640	0	1	1	1	2	2	2	2	3
	5099	5109	5119	5128	5138	5148	5158	5167	5177	5187	1	2	3	4	5	6	7	8	9
27	1643	1646	1649	1652	1655	1658	1661	1664	1667	1670	0	1	1	1	2	2	2	2	3
	5196	5206	5215	5225	5235	5244	5254	5263	5273	5282	1	2	3	4	5	6	7	8	9
28	1673	1676	1679	1682	1685	1688	1691	1694	1697	1700	0	1	1	1	1	2	2	2	3
	5292	5301	5310	5320	5329	5339	5348	5357	5367	5376	1	2	3	4	5	6	7	7	8
29	1703	1706	1709	1712	1715	1718	1720	1723	1726	1729	0	1	1	1	1	2	2	2	3
	5385	5394	5404	5413	5422	5431	5441	5450	5459	5468	1	2	3	4	5	5	6	7	8
30	1732	1735	1738	1741	1744	1746	1749	1752	1755	1758	0	1	1	1	1	2	2	2	3
	5477	5486	5495	5505	5514	5523	5532	5541	5550	5559	1	2	3	4	4	5	6	7	8
31	1761	1764	1766	1769	1772	1775	1778	1780	1783	1786	0	1	1	1	1	2	2	2	3
	5568	5577	5586	5595	5604	5612	5621	5630	5639	5648	1	2	3	3	4	5	6	7	8
32	1789	1792	1794	1797	1800	1803	1806	1808	1811	1814	0	1	1	1	1	2	2	2	2
	5657	5666	5675	5683	5692	5701	5710	5718	5727	5736	1	2	3	3	4	5	6	7	8
	0	1	2	3	4	5	6	7	8	9	1	2	3	4	5	6	7	8	9

The first significant figure and the position of the decimal point must be determined by inspection.

SQUARE ROOTS

	0	1	2	3	4	5	6	7	8	9	1	2	3	4	5	6	7	8	9
33	1817	1819	1822	1825	1828	1830	1833	1836	1838	1841	0	1	1	1	1	2	2	2	2
	5745	5753	5762	5771	5779	5788	5797	5805	5814	5822	1	2	3	3	4	5	6	7	8
34	1844	1847	1849	1852	1855	1857	1860	1863	1865	1868	0	1	1	1	1	2	2	2	2
	5831	5840	5848	5857	5865	5874	5882	5891	5899	5908	1	2	3	3	4	5	6	7	8
35	1871	1873	1876	1879	1881	1884	1887	1889	1892	1895	0	1	1	1	1	2	2	2	2
	5916	5925	5933	5941	5950	5958	5967	5975	5983	5992	1	2	2	3	4	5	6	7	8
36	1897	1900	1903	1905	1908	1910	1913	1916	1918	1921	0	1	1	1	1	2	2	2	2
	6000	6008	6017	6025	6033	6042	6050	6058	6066	6075	1	2	2	3	4	5	6	7	7
37	1924	1926	1929	1931	1934	1936	1939	1942	1944	1947	0	1	1	1	1	2	2	2	2
	6083	6091	6099	6107	6116	6124	6132	6140	6148	6156	1	2	2	3	4	5	6	7	7
38	1949	1952	1954	1957	1960	1962	1965	1967	1970	1972	0	1	1	1	1	2	2	2	2
	6164	6173	6181	6189	6197	6205	6213	6221	6229	6237	1	2	2	3	4	5	6	6	7
39	1975	1977	1980	1982	1985	1987	1990	1992	1995	1997	0	1	1	1	1	2	2	2	2
	6245	6253	6261	6269	6277	6285	6293	6301	6309	6317	1	2	2	3	4	5	6	6	7
40	2000	2002	2005	2007	2010	2012	2015	2017	2020	2022	0	0	1	1	1	1	2	2	2
	6325	6332	6340	6348	6356	6364	6372	6380	6387	6395	1	2	2	3	4	5	6	6	7
41	2025	2027	2030	2032	2035	2037	2040	2042	2045	2047	0	0	1	1	1	1	2	2	2
	6403	6411	6419	6427	6434	6442	6450	6458	6465	6473	1	2	2	3	4	5	5	6	7
42	2049	2052	2054	2057	2059	2062	2064	2066	2069	2071	0	0	1	1	1	1	2	2	2
	6481	6488	6496	6504	6512	6519	6527	6535	6542	6550	1	2	2	3	4	5	5	6	7
43	2074	2076	2078	2081	2083	2086	2088	2090	2093	2095	0	0	1	1	1	1	2	2	2
	6557	6565	6573	6580	6588	6595	6603	6611	6618	6626	1	2	2	3	4	5	5	6	7
44	2098	2100	2102	2105	2107	2110	2112	2114	2117	2119	0	0	1	1	1	1	2	2	2
	6633	6641	6648	6656	6663	6671	6678	6686	6693	6701	1	2	2	3	4	4	5	6	7
45	2121	2124	2126	2128	2131	2133	2135	2138	2140	2142	0	0	1	1	1	1	2	2	2
	6708	6716	6723	6731	6738	6745	6753	6760	6768	6775	1	1	2	3	4	4	5	6	7
46	2145	2147	2149	2152	2154	2156	2159	2161	2163	2166	0	0	1	1	1	1	2	2	2
	6782	6790	6797	6804	6812	6819	6826	6834	6841	6848	1	1	2	3	4	4	5	6	7
47	2168	2170	2173	2175	2177	2179	2182	2184	2186	2189	0	0	1	1	1	1	2	2	2
	6856	6863	6870	6877	6885	6892	6899	6907	6914	6921	1	1	2	3	4	4	5	6	7
48	2191	2193	2195	2198	2200	2202	2205	2207	2209	2211	0	0	1	1	1	1	2	2	2
	6928	6935	6943	6950	6957	6964	6971	6979	6986	6993	1	1	2	3	4	4	5	6	6
49	2214	2216	2218	2220	2223	2225	2227	2229	2232	2234	0	0	1	1	1	1	2	2	2
	7000	7007	7014	7021	7029	7036	7043	7050	7057	7064	1	1	2	3	4	4	5	6	6
50	2236	2238	2241	2243	2245	2247	2249	2252	2254	2256	0	0	1	1	1	1	2	2	2
	7071	7078	7085	7092	7099	7106	7113	7120	7127	7134	1	1	2	3	4	4	5	6	6
51	2258	2261	2263	2265	2267	2269	2272	2274	2276	2278	0	0	1	1	1	1	2	2	2
	7141	7148	7155	7162	7169	7176	7183	7190	7197	7204	1	1	2	3	4	4	5	6	6
52	2280	2283	2285	2287	2289	2291	2293	2296	2298	2300	0	0	1	1	1	1	2	2	2
	7211	7218	7225	7232	7239	7246	7253	7259	7266	7273	1	1	2	3	3	4	5	6	6
53	2302	2304	2307	2309	2311	2313	2315	2317	2319	2322	0	0	1	1	1	1	2	2	2
	7280	7287	7294	7301	7308	7314	7321	7328	7335	7342	1	1	2	3	3	4	5	5	6
54	2324	2326	2328	2330	2332	2335	2337	2339	2341	2343	0	0	1	1	1	1	1	2	2
	7348	7355	7362	7369	7376	7382	7389	7396	7403	7409	1	1	2	3	3	4	5	5	6
	0	1	2	3	4	5	6	7	8	9	1	2	3	4	5	6	7	8	9

The first significant figure and the position of the decimal point must be determined by inspection.

SQUARE ROOTS

	0	1	2	3	4	5	6	7	8	9	1	2	3	4	5	6	7	8	9
55	2345	2347	2349	2352	2354	2356	2358	2360	2362	2364	0	0	1	1	1	1	1	2	2
	7416	7423	7430	7436	7443	7450	7457	7463	7470	7477	1	1	2	3	3	4	5	5	6
56	2366	2369	2371	2373	2375	2377	2379	2381	2383	2385	0	0	1	1	1	1	1	2	2
	7483	7490	7497	7503	7510	7517	7523	7530	7537	7543	1	1	2	3	3	4	5	5	6
57	2387	2390	2392	2394	2396	2398	2400	2402	2404	2406	0	0	1	1	1	1	1	2	2
	7550	7556	7563	7570	7576	7583	7589	7596	7603	7609	1	1	2	3	3	4	5	5	6
58	2408	2410	2412	2415	2417	2419	2421	2423	2425	2427	0	0	1	1	1	1	1	2	2
	7616	7622	7629	7635	7642	7649	7655	7662	7668	7675	1	1	2	3	3	4	5	5	6
59	2429	2431	2433	2435	2437	2439	2441	2443	2445	2447	0	0	1	1	1	1	1	2	2
	7681	7688	7694	7701	7707	7714	7720	7727	7733	7740	1	1	2	3	3	4	5	5	6
60	2449	2452	2454	2456	2458	2460	2462	2464	2466	2468	0	0	1	1	1	1	1	2	2
	7746	7752	7759	7765	7772	7778	7785	7791	7797	7804	1	1	2	3	3	4	4	5	6
61	2470	2472	2474	2476	2478	2480	2482	2484	2486	2488	0	0	1	1	1	1	1	2	2
	7810	7817	7823	7829	7836	7842	7849	7855	7861	7868	1	1	2	3	3	4	4	5	6
62	2490	2492	2494	2496	2498	2500	2502	2504	2506	2508	0	0	1	1	1	1	1	2	2
	7874	7880	7887	7893	7899	7906	7912	7918	7925	7931	1	1	2	3	3	4	4	5	6
63	2510	2512	2514	2516	2518	2520	2522	2524	2526	2528	0	0	1	1	1	1	1	2	2
	7937	7944	7950	7956	7962	7969	7975	7981	7987	7994	1	1	2	3	3	4	4	5	6
64	2530	2532	2534	2536	2538	2540	2542	2544	2546	2548	0	0	1	1	1	1	1	2	2
	8000	8006	8012	8019	8025	8031	8037	8044	8050	8056	1	1	2	2	3	4	4	5	6
65	2550	2551	2553	2555	2557	2559	2561	2563	2565	2567	0	0	1	1	1	1	1	2	2
	8062	8068	8075	8081	8087	8093	8099	8106	8112	8118	1	1	2	2	3	4	4	5	5
66	2569	2571	2573	2575	2577	2579	2581	2583	2585	2587	0	0	1	1	1	1	1	2	2
	8124	8130	8136	8142	8149	8155	8161	8167	8173	8179	1	1	2	2	3	4	4	5	5
67	2588	2590	2592	2594	2596	2598	2600	2602	2604	2606	0	0	1	1	1	1	1	2	2
	8185	8191	8198	8204	8210	8216	8222	8228	8234	8240	1	1	2	2	3	4	4	5	5
68	2608	2610	2612	2613	2615	2617	2619	2621	2623	2625	0	0	1	1	1	1	1	2	2
	8246	8252	8258	8264	8270	8276	8283	8289	8295	8301	1	1	2	2	3	4	4	5	5
69	2627	2629	2631	2632	2634	2636	2638	2640	2642	2644	0	0	1	1	1	1	1	2	2
	8307	8313	8319	8325	8331	8337	8343	8349	8355	8361	1	1	2	2	3	4	4	5	5
70	2646	2648	2650	2651	2653	2655	2657	2659	2661	2663	0	0	1	1	1	1	1	2	2
	8367	8373	8379	8385	8390	8396	8402	8408	8414	8420	1	1	2	2	3	4	4	5	5
71	2665	2666	2668	2670	2672	2674	2676	2678	2680	2681	0	0	1	1	1	1	1	1	2
	8426	8432	8438	8444	8450	8456	8462	8468	8473	8479	1	1	2	2	3	3	4	5	5
72	2683	2685	2687	2689	2691	2693	2694	2696	2698	2700	0	0	1	1	1	1	1	1	2
	8485	8491	8497	8503	8509	8515	8521	8526	8532	8538	1	1	2	2	3	3	4	5	5
73	2702	2704	2706	2707	2709	2711	2713	2715	2717	2718	0	0	1	1	1	1	1	1	2
	8544	8550	8556	8562	8567	8573	8579	8585	8591	8597	1	1	2	2	3	3	4	5	5
74	2720	2722	2724	2726	2728	2729	2731	2733	2735	2737	0	0	1	1	1	1	1	1	2
	8602	8608	8614	8620	8626	8631	8637	8643	8649	8654	1	1	2	2	3	3	4	5	5
75	2739	2740	2742	2744	2746	2748	2750	2751	2753	2755	0	0	1	1	1	1	1	1	2
	8660	8666	8672	8678	8683	8689	8695	8701	8706	8712	1	1	2	2	3	3	4	5	5
76	2757	2759	2760	2762	2764	2766	2768	2769	2771	2773	0	0	1	1	1	1	1	1	2
	8718	8724	8729	8735	8741	8746	8752	8758	8764	8769	1	1	2	2	3	3	4	5	5
77	2775	2777	2778	2780	2782	2784	2786	2787	2789	2791	0	0	1	1	1	1	1	1	2
	8775	8781	8786	8792	8798	8803	8809	8815	8820	8826	1	1	2	2	3	3	4	4	5
	0	1	2	3	4	5	6	7	8	9	1	2	3	4	5	6	7	8	9

The first significant figure and the position of the decimal point must be determined by inspection.

SQUARE ROOTS

	0	1	2	3	4	5	6	7	8	9	1	2	3	4	5	6	7	8	9
78	2793	2795	2796	2798	2800	2802	2804	2805	2807	2809	0	0	1	1	1	1	1	1	2
	8832	8837	8843	8849	8854	8860	8866	8871	8877	8883	1	1	2	2	3	3	4	4	5
79	2811	2812	2814	2816	2818	2820	2821	2823	2825	2827	0	0	1	1	1	1	1	1	2
	8888	8894	8899	8905	8911	8916	8922	8927	8933	8939	1	1	2	2	3	3	4	4	5
80	2828	2830	2832	2834	2835	2837	2839	2841	2843	2844	0	0	1	1	1	1	1	1	2
	8944	8950	8955	8961	8967	8972	8978	8983	8989	8994	1	1	2	2	3	3	4	4	5
81	2846	2848	2850	2851	2853	2855	2857	2858	2860	2862	0	0	1	1	1	1	1	1	2
	9000	9006	9011	9017	9022	9028	9033	9039	9044	9050	1	1	2	2	3	3	4	4	5
82	2864	2865	2867	2869	2871	2872	2874	2876	2877	2879	0	0	1	1	1	1	1	1	2
	9055	9061	9066	9072	9077	9083	9088	9094	9099	9105	1	1	2	2	3	3	4	4	5
83	2881	2883	2884	2886	2888	2890	2891	2893	2895	2897	0	0	1	1	1	1	1	1	2
	9110	9116	9121	9127	9132	9138	9143	9149	9154	9160	1	1	2	2	3	3	4	4	5
84	2898	2900	2902	2903	2905	2907	2909	2910	2912	2914	0	0	1	1	1	1	1	1	2
	9165	9171	9176	9182	9187	9192	9198	9203	9209	9214	1	1	2	2	3	3	4	4	5
85	2915	2917	2919	2921	2922	2924	2926	2927	2929	2931	0	0	1	1	1	1	1	1	2
	9220	9225	9230	9236	9241	9247	9252	9257	9263	9268	1	1	2	2	3	3	4	4	5
86	2933	2934	2936	2938	2939	2941	2943	2944	2946	2948	0	0	1	1	1	1	1	1	2
	9274	9279	9284	9290	9295	9301	9306	9311	9317	9322	1	1	2	2	3	3	4	4	5
87	2950	2951	2953	2955	2956	2958	2960	2961	2963	2965	0	0	1	1	1	1	1	1	2
	9327	9333	9338	9343	9349	9354	9359	9365	9370	9375	1	1	2	2	3	3	4	4	5
88	2966	2968	2970	2972	2973	2975	2977	2978	2980	2982	0	0	1	1	1	1	1	1	2
	9381	9386	9391	9397	9402	9407	9413	9418	9423	9429	1	1	2	2	3	3	4	4	5
89	2983	2985	2987	2988	2990	2992	2993	2995	2997	2998	0	0	1	1	1	1	1	1	2
	9434	9439	9445	9450	9455	9460	9466	9471	9476	9482	1	1	2	2	3	3	4	4	5
90	3000	3002	3003	3005	3007	3008	3010	3012	3013	3015	0	0	0	1	1	1	1	1	1
	9487	9492	9497	9503	9508	9513	9518	9524	9529	9534	1	1	2	2	3	3	4	4	5
91	3017	3018	3020	3022	3023	3025	3027	3028	3030	3032	0	0	0	1	1	1	1	1	1
	9539	9545	9550	9555	9560	9566	9571	9576	9581	9586	1	1	2	2	3	3	4	4	5
92	3033	3035	3036	3038	3040	3041	3043	3045	3046	3048	0	0	0	1	1	1	1	1	1
	9592	9597	9602	9607	9612	9618	9623	9628	9633	9638	1	1	2	2	3	3	4	4	5
93	3050	3051	3053	3055	3056	3058	3059	3061	3063	3064	0	0	0	1	1	1	1	1	1
	9644	9649	9654	9659	9664	9670	9675	9680	9685	9690	1	1	2	2	3	3	4	4	5
94	3066	3068	3069	3071	3072	3074	3076	3077	3079	3081	0	0	0	1	1	1	1	1	1
	9695	9701	9706	9711	9716	9721	9726	9731	9737	9742	1	1	2	2	3	3	4	4	5
95	3082	3084	3085	3087	3089	3090	3092	3094	3095	3097	0	0	0	1	1	1	1	1	1
	9747	9752	9757	9762	9767	9772	9778	9783	9788	9793	1	1	2	2	3	3	4	4	5
96	3098	3100	3102	3103	3105	3106	3108	3110	3111	3113	0	0	0	1	1	1	1	1	1
	9798	9803	9808	9813	9818	9823	9829	9834	9839	9844	1	1	2	2	3	3	4	4	5
97	3114	3116	3118	3119	3121	3122	3124	3126	3127	3129	0	0	0	1	1	1	1	1	1
	9849	9854	9859	9864	9869	9874	9879	9884	9889	9894	1	1	2	2	3	3	4	4	5
98	3130	3132	3134	3135	3137	3138	3140	3142	3143	3145	0	0	0	1	1	1	1	1	1
	9899	9905	9910	9915	9920	9925	9930	9935	9940	9945	0	1	1	2	2	3	3	4	4
99	3146	3148	3150	3151	3153	3154	3156	3158	3159	3161	0	0	0	1	1	1	1	1	1
	9950	9955	9960	9965	9970	9975	9980	9985	9990	9995	0	1	1	2	2	3	3	4	4
	0	1	2	3	4	5	6	7	8	9	1	2	3	4	5	6	7	8	9

The first significant figure and the position of the decimal point must be determined by inspection.

RECIPROCALS

SUBTRACT

	0	1	2	3	4	5	6	7	8	9	1	2	3	4	5	6	7	8	9
1.0	1.0000	.9901	.9804	.9709	.9615	.9524	.9434	.9346	.9259	.9174	9	18	27	36	45	55	64	73	82
1.1	.9091	.9009	.8929	.8850	.8772	.8696	.8621	.8547	.8475	.8403	8	15	23	30	38	45	53	61	68
1.2	.8333	.8264	.8197	.8130	.8065	.8000	.7937	.7874	.7813	.7752	6	13	19	26	32	38	45	51	58
1.3	.7692	.7634	.7576	.7519	.7463	.7407	.7353	.7299	.7246	.7194	5	11	16	22	27	33	38	44	49
1.4	.7143	.7092	.7042	.6993	.6944	.6897	.6849	.6803	.6757	.6711	5	10	14	19	24	29	33	38	43
1.5	.6667	.6623	.6579	.6536	.6494	.6452	.6410	.6369	.6329	.6289	4	8	13	17	21	25	29	33	38
1.6	.6250	.6211	.6173	.6135	.6098	.6061	.6024	.5988	.5952	.5917	4	7	11	15	18	22	26	29	33
1.7	.5882	.5848	.5814	.5780	.5747	.5714	.5682	.5650	.5618	.5587	3	7	10	13	16	20	23	26	30
1.8	.5556	.5525	.5495	.5464	.5435	.5405	.5376	.5348	.5319	.5291	3	6	9	12	15	18	20	23	26
1.9	.5263	.5236	.5208	.5181	.5155	.5128	.5102	.5076	.5051	.5025	3	5	8	11	13	16	18	21	24
2.0	.5000	.4975	.4950	.4926	.4902	.4878	.4854	.4831	.4808	.4785	2	5	7	10	12	14	17	19	21
2.1	.4762	.4739	.4717	.4695	.4673	.4651	.4630	.4608	.4587	.4566	2	4	7	9	11	13	15	17	20
2.2	.4545	.4525	.4505	.4484	.4464	.4444	.4425	.4405	.4386	.4367	2	4	6	8	10	12	14	16	18
2.3	.4348	.4329	.4310	.4292	.4274	.4255	.4237	.4219	.4202	.4184	2	4	5	7	9	11	13	14	16
2.4	.4167	.4149	.4132	.4115	.4098	.4082	.4065	.4049	.4032	.4016	2	3	5	7	8	10	12	13	15
2.5	.4000	.3984	.3968	.3953	.3937	.3922	.3906	.3891	.3876	.3861	2	3	5	6	8	9	11	12	14
2.6	.3846	.3831	.3817	.3802	.3788	.3774	.3759	.3745	.3731	.3717	1	3	4	6	7	8	10	11	13
2.7	.3704	.3690	.3676	.3663	.3650	.3636	.3623	.3610	.3597	.3584	1	3	4	5	7	8	9	11	12
2.8	.3571	.3559	.3546	.3534	.3521	.3509	.3497	.3484	.3472	.3460	1	2	4	5	6	7	9	10	11
2.9	.3448	.3436	.3425	.3413	.3401	.3390	.3378	.3367	.3356	.3344	1	2	3	5	6	7	8	9	10
3.0	.3333	.3322	.3311	.3300	.3289	.3279	.3268	.3257	.3247	.3236	1	2	3	4	5	6	7	9	10
3.1	.3226	.3215	.3205	.3195	.3185	.3175	.3165	.3155	.3145	.3135	1	2	3	4	5	6	7	8	9
3.2	.3125	.3115	.3106	.3096	.3086	.3077	.3067	.3058	.3049	.3040	1	2	3	4	5	6	7	8	9
3.3	.3030	.3021	.3012	.3003	.2994	.2985	.2976	.2967	.2959	.2950	1	2	3	4	4	5	6	7	8
3.4	.2941	.2933	.2924	.2915	.2907	.2899	.2890	.2882	.2874	.2865	1	2	3	3	4	5	6	7	8
3.5	.2857	.2849	.2841	.2833	.2825	.2817	.2809	.2801	.2793	.2786	1	2	2	3	4	5	6	6	7
3.6	.2778	.2770	.2762	.2755	.2747	.2740	.2732	.2725	.2717	.2710	1	2	2	3	4	5	5	6	7
3.7	.2703	.2695	.2688	.2681	.2674	.2667	.2660	.2653	.2646	.2639	1	1	2	3	4	4	5	6	6
3.8	.2632	.2625	.2618	.2611	.2604	.2597	.2591	.2584	.2577	.2571	1	1	2	3	3	4	5	5	6
3.9	.2564	.2558	.2551	.2545	.2538	.2532	.2525	.2519	.2513	.2506	1	1	2	3	3	4	4	5	6
4.0	.2500	.2494	.2488	.2481	.2475	.2469	.2463	.2457	.2451	.2445	1	1	2	2	3	4	4	5	5
4.1	.2439	.2433	.2427	.2421	.2415	.2410	.2404	.2398	.2392	.2387	1	1	2	2	3	3	4	5	5
4.2	.2381	.2375	.2370	.2364	.2358	.2353	.2347	.2342	.2336	.2331	1	1	2	2	3	3	4	4	5
4.3	.2326	.2320	.2315	.2309	.2304	.2299	.2294	.2288	.2283	.2278	1	1	2	2	3	3	4	4	5
4.4	.2273	.2268	.2262	.2257	.2252	.2247	.2242	.2237	.2232	.2227	1	1	2	2	3	3	4	4	5
4.5	.2222	.2217	.2212	.2208	.2203	.2198	.2193	.2188	.2183	.2179	0	1	1	2	2	3	3	4	4
4.6	.2174	.2169	.2165	.2160	.2155	.2151	.2146	.2141	.2137	.2132	0	1	1	2	2	3	3	4	4
4.7	.2128	.2123	.2119	.2114	.2110	.2105	.2101	.2096	.2092	.2088	0	1	1	2	2	3	3	4	4
4.8	.2083	.2079	.2075	.2070	.2066	.2062	.2058	.2053	.2049	.2045	0	1	1	2	2	3	3	3	4
4.9	.2041	.2037	.2033	.2028	.2024	.2020	.2016	.2012	.2008	.2004	0	1	1	2	2	2	3	3	4
5.0	.2000	.1996	.1992	.1988	.1984	.1980	.1976	.1972	.1969	.1965	0	1	1	2	2	2	3	3	4
5.1	.1961	.1957	.1953	.1949	.1946	.1942	.1938	.1934	.1931	.1927	0	1	1	2	2	2	3	3	3
5.2	.1923	.1919	.1916	.1912	.1908	.1905	.1901	.1898	.1894	.1890	0	1	1	1	2	2	3	3	3
5.3	.1887	.1883	.1880	.1876	.1873	.1869	.1866	.1862	.1859	.1855	0	1	1	1	2	2	3	3	3
5.4	.1852	.1848	.1845	.1842	.1838	.1835	.1832	.1828	.1825	.1821	0	1	1	1	2	2	2	3	3

RECIPROCALS

SUBTRACT

	0	1	2	3	4	5	6	7	8	9	1	2	3	4	5	6	7	8	9
5·5	·1818	·1815	·1812	·1808	·1805	·1802	·1799	·1795	·1792	·1789	0	1	1	1	2	2	2	3	3
5·6	·1786	·1783	·1779	·1776	·1773	·1770	·1767	·1764	·1761	·1757	0	1	1	1	2	2	2	3	3
5·7	·1754	·1751	·1748	·1745	·1742	·1739	·1736	·1733	·1730	·1727	0	1	1	1	2	2	2	2	3
5·8	·1724	·1721	·1718	·1715	·1712	·1709	·1706	·1704	·1701	·1698	0	1	1	1	1	2	2	2	3
5·9	·1695	·1692	·1689	·1686	·1684	·1681	·1678	·1675	·1672	·1669	0	1	1	1	1	2	2	2	3
6·0	·1667	·1664	·1661	·1658	·1656	·1653	·1650	·1647	·1645	·1642	0	1	1	1	1	2	2	2	3
6·1	·1639	·1637	·1634	·1631	·1629	·1626	·1623	·1621	·1618	·1616	0	1	1	1	1	2	2	2	2
6·2	·1613	·1610	·1608	·1605	·1603	·1600	·1597	·1595	·1592	·1590	0	1	1	1	1	2	2	2	2
6·3	·1587	·1585	·1582	·1580	·1577	·1575	·1572	·1570	·1567	·1565	0	0	1	1	1	1	2	2	2
6·4	·1563	·1560	·1558	·1555	·1553	·1550	·1548	·1546	·1543	·1541	0	0	1	1	1	1	2	2	2
6·5	·1538	·1536	·1534	·1531	·1529	·1527	·1524	·1522	·1520	·1517	0	0	1	1	1	1	2	2	2
6·6	·1515	·1513	·1511	·1508	·1506	·1504	·1502	·1499	·1497	·1495	0	0	1	1	1	1	2	2	2
6·7	·1493	·1490	·1488	·1486	·1484	·1481	·1479	·1477	·1475	·1473	0	0	1	1	1	1	2	2	2
6·8	·1471	·1468	·1466	·1464	·1462	·1460	·1458	·1456	·1453	·1451	0	0	1	1	1	1	2	2	2
6·9	·1449	·1447	·1445	·1443	·1441	·1439	·1437	·1435	·1433	·1431	0	0	1	1	1	1	1	2	2
7·0	·1429	·1427	·1425	·1422	·1420	·1418	·1416	·1414	·1412	·1410	0	0	1	1	1	1	1	2	2
7·1	·1408	·1406	·1404	·1403	·1401	·1399	·1397	·1395	·1393	·1391	0	0	1	1	1	1	1	2	2
7·2	·1389	·1387	·1385	·1383	·1381	·1379	·1377	·1376	·1374	·1372	0	0	1	1	1	1	1	2	2
7·3	·1370	·1368	·1366	·1364	·1362	·1361	·1359	·1357	·1355	·1353	0	0	1	1	1	1	1	2	2
7·4	·1351	·1350	·1348	·1346	·1344	·1342	·1340	·1339	·1337	·1335	0	0	1	1	1	1	1	1	2
7·5	·1333	·1332	·1330	·1328	·1326	·1325	·1323	·1321	·1319	·1318	0	0	1	1	1	1	1	1	2
7·6	·1316	·1314	·1312	·1311	·1309	·1307	·1305	·1304	·1302	·1300	0	0	1	1	1	1	1	1	2
7·7	·1299	·1297	·1295	·1294	·1292	·1290	·1289	·1287	·1285	·1284	0	0	0	1	1	1	1	1	1
7·8	·1282	·1280	·1279	·1277	·1276	·1274	·1272	·1271	·1269	·1267	0	0	0	1	1	1	1	1	1
7·9	·1266	·1264	·1263	·1261	·1259	·1258	·1256	·1255	·1253	·1252	0	0	0	1	1	1	1	1	1
8·0	·1250	·1248	·1247	·1245	·1244	·1242	·1241	·1239	·1238	·1236	0	0	0	1	1	1	1	1	1
8·1	·1235	·1233	·1232	·1230	·1229	·1227	·1225	·1224	·1222	·1221	0	0	0	1	1	1	1	1	1
8·2	·1220	·1218	·1217	·1215	·1214	·1212	·1211	·1209	·1208	·1206	0	0	0	1	1	1	1	1	1
8·3	·1205	·1203	·1202	·1200	·1199	·1198	·1196	·1195	·1193	·1192	0	0	0	1	1	1	1	1	1
8·4	·1190	·1189	·1188	·1186	·1185	·1183	·1182	·1181	·1179	·1178	0	0	0	1	1	1	1	1	1
8·5	·1176	·1175	·1174	·1172	·1171	·1170	·1168	·1167	·1166	·1164	0	0	0	1	1	1	1	1	1
8·6	·1163	·1161	·1160	·1159	·1157	·1156	·1155	·1153	·1152	·1151	0	0	0	1	1	1	1	1	1
8·7	·1149	·1148	·1147	·1145	·1144	·1143	·1142	·1140	·1139	·1138	0	0	0	1	1	1	1	1	1
8·8	·1136	·1135	·1134	·1133	·1131	·1130	·1129	·1127	·1126	·1125	0	0	0	1	1	1	1	1	1
8·9	·1124	·1122	·1121	·1120	·1119	·1117	·1116	·1115	·1114	·1112	0	0	0	1	1	1	1	1	1
9·0	·1111	·1110	·1109	·1107	·1106	·1105	·1104	·1103	·1101	·1100	0	0	0	1	1	1	1	1	1
9·1	·1099	·1098	·1096	·1095	·1094	·1093	·1092	·1091	·1089	·1088	0	0	0	0	1	1	1	1	1
9·2	·1087	·1086	·1085	·1083	·1082	·1081	·1080	·1079	·1078	·1076	0	0	0	0	1	1	1	1	1
9·3	·1075	·1074	·1073	·1072	·1071	·1070	·1068	·1067	·1066	·1065	0	0	0	0	1	1	1	1	1
9·4	·1064	·1063	·1062	·1060	·1059	·1058	·1057	·1056	·1055	·1054	0	0	0	0	1	1	1	1	1
9·5	·1053	·1052	·1050	·1049	·1048	·1047	·1046	·1045	·1044	·1043	0	0	0	0	1	1	1	1	1
9·6	·1042	·1041	·1040	·1038	·1037	·1036	·1035	·1034	·1033	·1032	0	0	0	0	1	1	1	1	1
9·7	·1031	·1030	·1029	·1028	·1027	·1026	·1025	·1024	·1022	·1021	0	0	0	0	1	1	1	1	1
9·8	·1020	·1019	·1018	·1017	·1016	·1015	·1014	·1013	·1012	·1011	0	0	0	0	1	1	1	1	1
9·9	·1010	·1009	·1008	·1007	·1006	·1005	·1004	·1003	·1002	·1001	0	0	0	0	0	1	1	1	1
	0	1	2	3	4	5	6	7	8	9	1	2	3	4	5	6	7	8	9

RADIANS AND DEGREES

°	Rad.	°	Rad.	°	Rad.	′	Rad.	′	Rad.
0	0·0000	**30**	0·5236	**60**	1·0472	**0**	·0000	**30**	·0087
1	0·0175	31	0·5411	61	1·0647	1	·0003	31	·0090
2	0·0349	32	0·5585	62	1·0821	2	·0006	32	·0093
3	0·0524	33	0·5760	63	1·0996	3	·0009	33	·0096
4	0·0698	34	0·5934	64	1·1170	4	·0012	34	·0099
5	0·0873	35	0·6109	65	1·1345	5	·0015	35	·0102
6	0·1047	36	0·6283	66	1·1519	6	·0017	36	·0105
7	0·1222	37	0·6458	67	1·1694	7	·0020	37	·0108
8	0·1396	38	0·6632	68	1·1868	8	·0023	38	·0111
9	0·1571	39	0·6807	69	1·2043	9	·0026	39	·0113
10	0·1745	**40**	0·6981	**70**	1·2217	**10**	·0029	**40**	·0116
11	0·1920	41	0·7156	71	1·2392	11	·0032	41	·0119
12	0·2094	42	0·7330	72	1·2566	12	·0035	42	·0122
13	0·2269	43	0·7505	73	1·2741	13	·0038	43	·0125
14	0·2443	44	0·7679	74	1·2915	14	·0041	44	·0128
15	0·2618	45	0·7854	75	1·3090	15	·0044	45	·0131
16	0·2793	46	0·8029	76	1·3265	16	·0047	46	·0134
17	0·2967	47	0·8203	77	1·3439	17	·0049	47	·0137
18	0·3142	48	0·8378	78	1·3614	18	·0052	48	·0140
19	0·3316	49	0·8552	79	1·3788	19	·0055	49	·0143
20	0·3491	**50**	0·8727	**80**	1·3963	**20**	·0058	**50**	·0145
21	0·3665	51	0·8901	81	1·4137	21	·0061	51	·0148
22	0·3840	52	0·9076	82	1·4312	22	·0064	52	·0151
23	0·4014	53	0·9250	83	1·4486	23	·0067	53	·0154
24	0·4189	54	0·9425	84	1·4661	24	·0070	54	·0157
25	0·4363	55	0·9599	85	1·4835	25	·0073	55	·0160
26	0·4538	56	0·9774	86	1·5010	26	·0076	56	·0163
27	0·4712	57	0·9948	87	1·5184	27	·0079	57	·0166
28	0·4887	58	1·0123	88	1·5359	28	·0081	58	·0169
29	0·5061	59	1·0297	89	1·5533	29	·0084	59	·0172
30	0·5236	**60**	1·0472	**90**	1·5708	**30**	·0087	**60**	·0175

Rad.	Degrees
0·001	0·06
0·002	0·11
0·003	0·17
0·004	0·23
0·005	0·29
0·006	0·34
0·007	0·40
0·008	0·46
0·009	0·52
0·01	0·57
0·02	1·15
0·03	1·72
0·04	2·29
0·05	2·86
0·06	3·44
0·07	4·01
0·08	4·58
0·09	5·16
0·1	5·73
0·2	11·46
0·3	17·19
0·4	22·92
0·5	28·65
0·6	34·38
0·7	40·11
0·8	45·84
0·9	51·57
1	57·30
2	114·59
3	171·89
4	229·18
5	286·48
6	343·77

INDEX